Physical and Chemical Aspects of Adsorbents and Catalysts

PROFESSOR DR. J. H. DE BOER

Physical and Chemical Aspects of Adsorbents and Catalysts

dedicated to J. H. de Boer
on the occasion of his retirement from the
Technological University
Delft, The Netherlands

Edited by B. G. Linsen
Unilever Research Laboratory,
Vlaardingen, The Netherlands

co-editors
J. M. H. Fortuin, C. Okkerse and J. J. Steggerda

1970

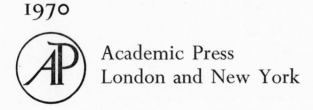

Academic Press
London and New York

ACADEMIC PRESS INC. (LONDON) LTD
Berkeley Square House
Berkeley Square
London, W1X 6BA

U.S. Edition published by
ACADEMIC PRESS INC.
111 Fifth Avenue
New York, New York 10003

Library of Congress Catalog Card Number: 78–92405
SBN: 12–451150–3

CHEMISTRY

PRINTED IN GREAT BRITAIN AT
ABERDEEN UNIVERSITY PRESS

CONTRIBUTORS

J. C. P. BROEKHOFF, Department of Chemical Technology, Technological University of Delft, The Netherlands.

J. W. E. COENEN, Unilever Research Laboratory, Vlaardingen, The Netherlands.

R. H. VAN DONGEN, Department of Chemical Technology, Technological University of Delft, The Netherlands.

J. W. GEUS, Central Laboratory, N.V. Staatsmijnen/DSM, Geleen, The Netherlands.

M. E. A. HERMANS, RCN-KEMA Reactor Development Group, Arnhem, The Netherlands.

S. KRUYER, Central Laboratory, N.V. Staatsmijnen/DSM, Geleen, The Netherlands.

B. G. LINSEN, Unilever Research Laboratory, Vlaardingen, The Netherlands.

B. C. LIPPENS, European Research Center, Texaco Belgium N.V., Ghent, Belgium.

C. OKKERSE, Unilever Research Laboratory, Vlaardingen, The Netherlands.

TH. VAN DER PLAS, RCN-KEMA Reactor Development Group, Arnhem, The Netherlands.

H. TH. RIJNTEN, Department of Chemical Technology, Technological University of Delft, The Netherlands.

J. J. F. SCHOLTEN, Central Laboratory, N.V. Staatsmijnen/DSM, Geleen, The Netherlands.

J. J. STEGGERDA, University of Nijmegen, The Netherlands.

W. F. N. M. DE VLEESSCHAUWER, Department of Chemical Technology, Technological University of Delft, The Netherlands.

*

PREFACE

This book deals with the greater part of the recent research on the physics and chemistry of a number of adsorbents and catalysts; many of the chapters contain detailed surveys and extensive literature references. Thus the book provides a key to a number of sectors in this special field. Many of the investigations discussed relate to the work of the research group of Professor J. H. de Boer at the Technological University of Delft and have been published in a variety of journals and dissertations. For this reason research workers have found it difficult to gain information on these subjects.

We considered the 70th birthday of Professor de Boer and his retirement from the Technological University of Delft an appropriate opportunity to invite several experts—most of them de Boer's pupils —to contribute to a comprehensive work. The fourteen authors have for many years been engaged—either at university or in industry—in the study of adsorbents and catalysts. Each contribution is included as a separate chapter and contains ideas inspired by Professor de Boer; preceding the whole are two brief contributions giving a survey of his scientific activities. The first, by Dr. E. J. W. Verwey, covers the period 1923–40, and the second, written by Professor G. C. A. Schuit, the period 1945–69.

Thus this book has been realized with the co-operation of many scientists who during their study and work have profited by the expert guidance and stimulating influence of Professor J. H. de Boer.

Technological University J. M. H. FORTUIN
Delft B. G. LINSEN
September, 1969 C. OKKERSE
J. J. STEGGERDA

CONTENTS

1 Studies on Pore Systems in Adsorbents and Catalysts

J. C. P. BROEKHOFF AND B. G. LINSEN

2 Mobility and Adsorption on Homogeneous Surfaces. A Theoretical and Experimental Study

J. C. P. BROEKHOFF AND R. H. VAN DONGEN

3 Some Recent Applications of the Calculation of the Entropy of the Adsorbed Phase According to de Boer

J. J. F. SCHOLTEN AND S. KRUYER

4 Active Alumina

B. C. LIPPENS AND J. J. STEGGERDA

5 Porous Silica

C. OKKERSE

6 Active Magnesia

W. F. N. M. DE VLEESSCHAUWER

7 Formation, Preparation and Properties of Hydrous Zirconia

H. TH. RIJNTEN

8 Hydrolytic Phenomena in U(VI)–Precipitation

M. E. A. HERMANS

9 The Texture and the Surface Chemistry of Carbons

TH. VAN DER PLAS

10 Structure and Activity of Silica–Supported Nickel Catalysts

J. W. E. COENEN AND B. G. LINSEN

11 Interaction of Oxygen with Tungsten and Molybdenum Surfaces

J. W. GEUS

J. H. de Boer and the Inorganic and Physical Chemistry
The Period 1923–1940

Most contributions to this book deal with subjects more or less related to surface chemistry, including heterogeneous catalysis and catalysts. Collaborators and pupils of the past 20-odd years have all been associated with Professor de Boer at a time when his interest was chiefly centred upon this area of physical chemistry.

This was the period during which Professor de Boer held a leading research position at the laboratory of the Dutch State Mines (1950–62) and the period of his extraordinary professorship at the Technological University of Delft (1946–69). His interest in surface chemistry had been awakened much earlier, as indicated by the title of his book (1935) "Electron Emission and Adsorption Phenomena", and was further supported when he was called into military service, at the beginning of 1939, in order to become the leader of a laboratory for chemical defence in Leiden and, after May 1940, in London.

However, it would be entirely wrong to infer from this that Professor de Boer can be classified as a specialist in the field of surface chemistry. First of all it can be pointed out that his book mentioned above had an industrial background (viz. mainly vacuum chemistry) entirely different from that of his later work, partly summarized in "The Dynamical Character of Adsorption" (1953, second edition 1968). But even that would deny his dynamic character. His scientific achievements are those of a chemist in the broadest sense. Indeed, he started as an organic chemist, but his work rapidly expanded to comprise many sides of inorganic and physical chemistry.

De Boer was born March 19, 1899. I know little about the very beginning, the work on his doctor's thesis, dealing with the preparation and the physical properties of α-sulpho-butyric acid. This thesis was the first of a long series of dissertations with H. J. Backer at Groningen University on organic sulphur compounds. It shows an interest broader that that of the pure organic chemist. Its impact upon the later work in Backer's laboratory became clear to me when I worked in Jaeger's laboratory in the same building of the Groningen University between 1931–34 and visited occasionally the "organic side" of the chemistry building. Upon questioning one of the researchers about the progress of his work he answered jokingly: "I am at page . . .", meaning the relevant page of de Boer's dissertation.

In June 1923, at the age of 24, de Boer went to the Philips Research Laboratory in Eindhoven, where Holst, the leader of the Natuurkundig Laboratorium of the N. V. Philips' Gloeilampenfabriek, felt that the academic staff (at that time comprising about twenty people) needed an extension in the direction of chemistry in order to meet the various fundamental material problems created by a rapidly expanding electrical industry. One and a half years earlier A. E. van Arkel had started to work there. The presence of these two chemists in the same laboratory (for many years in the same room) has led to a most impressive piece of team-work and co-operation. From the beginning each of them had his own problems, but following an accepted tradition of the National Laboratory, much of the experimental work of the first few years was published jointly. Examples are the work on the separation of zirconium and hafnium, and the preparation of pure titanium, zirconium, hafnium and thorium metal. But also later, when the number of collaborators increased, and their activities diverged more and more, their theoretical team-work continued for several years.

A considerable part of this work is contained in the well-known book "Chemische Binding als Electrostatisch Verschijnsel" (1930), translated into German (1931) and extended in the French translation (1936),[1] an elaborate attempt to order systematically and to explain at least qualitatively the facts of inorganic chemistry on the basis of Kossel's concept of electrostatic valence theory. This line was pursued by van Arkel when he left Eindhoven and went to Leiden University (1934). To me, as a student, the book was a revolution in chemical thought, because it was a vigorous attempt (at a time when quantum chemistry was still in an initial stage) to contrive chemistry in the light of interatomic and intermolecular forces. It was in accordance with one of Holst's basic philosophies: the necessity to bring physics and chemistry together.

It is interesting to consider, after forty years, the present status of this "electrostatic" approximation of the chemical bond, the hypothesis that the chemical interactions in many cases can be treated by considering separately a purely electrostatic interaction between ions or molecules (including dipoles or even multipoles, and also including mutual polarization on a quasi-classical basis), a Born-Mayer repulsion and a van der Waals-London attraction. In certain chapters of physics it had already been shown that such a treatment had a rather sound basis, e.g. in the dynamical lattice theory (Born-Madelung) and

---

[1] D. B. Centen, Amsterdam ("Chemische Bindung als electrostatische Erscheinung") Hirzel Verlag, Stuttgart; (A Valence et l'Electrostatique) Alcan, Paris.

Debye's work on polar molecules. However, one may say in retrospect that this approximation has been immensely fruitful to chemists (van Arkel and de Boer the pioneers) as a guiding principle in the whole field of chemistry, including inorganic chemistry, if limited to inter-molecular forces. One may even be convinced that biochemistry, with its multitude of molecular interactions, it waiting for a second van Arkel and de Boer enterprise.

Recently the conviction has grown that the "limits" of the electro-static approximation are wider than one was inclined to think ten years ago. As an example I mention the compounds which are usually considered as intermediate cases between polar bond and co-valent bond. Recent work by the theoretical chemist L. Jansen, for instance, has shown that the weak point in the approximation is not in the electrostatic part of the interaction, but in the approximations used hitherto for the repulsion forces and the van der Waals-London attraction. By considering the quantum-mechanical basis of these forces Jansen could show that it is imperative to treat them as a multi-body problem, which means that for instance for three atoms or ions, the force depends not only on their mutual distance, but also on the valence angles between them. By taking this into account a quantita-tive description could be given for the lattices of the noble gases, for the pressure-dependent behaviour of the alkali halides, and even for the II-VI and III-V compounds if considered as ionic lattices.

As stated above, de Boer himself with an increasing number of collaborators (chemists and physicists), covered a wide variety of subjects of inorganic and physical chemistry. In all this work his eagerness to discuss the facts of chemistry in terms of qualitative or, if possible, quantitative considerations of atomic or molecular inter-action is always present. I cannot recall a lecture by de Boer from this period in which he did not fill the blackboard with potential curves describing the potential energy of an adsorbed atom on a substrate, or an atom incorporated in a lattice, or the potential energy of an inter-or intra-molecular interaction. It was almost thrilling to see how these potential curves, derived with the aid of semi-quantitative arguments, together formed a picture into which all the facts fitted nicely.

Actually de Boer was the first to describe, at least qualitatively, the behaviour of colloid chemical systems in terms of potential curves for the colloid particle interaction. At that time we were very much interested in the properties of suspensions in connection with de Boer and Hamaker's discovery of the electrophoretic deposition of all sorts of inorganic materials from suspensions in organic media. It induced Hamaker to produce his theory of van der Waals-London interaction of particles embedded in a medium and gave a start to the later work on the stability of colloid systems, now known as the DLVO-theory (Deryagin, Landau, Verwey, Overbeek).

The work to which I am referring here has all been done in an industrial research laboratory, based on the problems suggested by practical applications. The strong tradition of this laboratory, that fundamental and applied research must go hand in hand and reinforce each other, finds in de Boer's work one of its best examples, supported by about 150 publications and an equally long list of patent applications between 1923 and 1939.

Of the scientific publications of this period only a few subjects can be mentioned. Apart from the work mentioned above it comprises, for instance, the well-known preparation of the metals of the titanium group by thermal dissociation of their iodides (with J. D. Fast), chemical and physical properties of alkali-boriumfluorides, adsorption phenomena at surfaces of polar lattices (especially evaporated layers of CaF_2), photo-emission of layers consisting of alkali-atoms adsorbed on various substrated (with M. C. Teves), secondary electronic emission (with H. G. Bruining), reactions of organic molecules with evaporated layers of various salts, optical properties of adsorption layers, etc. (partly with J. F. H. Custers, C. J. Dippel and C. F. Veenemans), photo-effect and rectification with semi-conductors (with W. Ch. van Geel), the adsorption of alkali-atoms on metal surfaces (with C. F. Veenemans), the diffusion of hydrogen through metals and the behaviour of oxygen or nitrogen in zirconium (both with J. D. Fast), the role of van der Waals-London forces in inorganic and organic chemistry, the nature of colour centres in alkali-halides, surface oxide films, molecular energy of binary molecules and various subjects of solid state chemistry and colloid chemistry (partly with E. J. W. Verwey).

It is difficult to characterize de Boer's work in a few words because it does not belong to any established category. I have never met an investigator who found his way so easily between experimental facts and simple theoretical concepts in his attempts to open new roads in science and technology. In the five years that I worked with him I was repeatedly struck by his flexible mind. No discouraging experiment could defeat him; on the contrary, an unexpected result or a new theoretical concept was always immediately incorporated in his arsenal and used successfully. He showed continually that he combined the typical traits of an inventor and of a scientist, a mixture rarely met in such high concentration, in a single person.

As a typical example of his working method I recall the birth of de

Boer's concept of the colour centres in alkali-halides. In "Electron Emission and Adsorption Phenomena"[1] de Boer gave an exhaustive and original survey of the way in which electron emission and optical response of various types of emitters are influenced by a layer of adsorbed atoms (or molecules). Under the impression of Smekal's work on lattice imperfections and internal surfaces he included a few chapters in which he tried to work out the analogy between surface phenomena and the properties of semi-conductors, and insulators with colour centres. The well-known F centre in alkali-halides, for instance, was explained as a metal atom adsorbed at an inner surface. Shortly after the appearance of this book Schottky published his paper on ion vacancies. I told de Boer about this when I met him in the corridor. The following day he came to tell me his new idea about the F centre, which, after the refinement added by Mott, is now generally known as the de Boer-Mott picture of this centre: an electron at a halogen-vacancy. De Boer had not hesitated to sacrifice the whole internal surface story in a single night, as soon as a better basic concept became available.

It may be added that also in this case a new field was opened. The paper on the F centre stands at the very beginning of the development of a new branch of chemistry (now indicated as defect chemistry, cf. "The Chemistry of Imperfect Crystals" by F. A. Kröger (1964).

Collaborators of de Boer from the National Laboratory period consider it a great privilege to have had the opportunity to do research work in his companionship. Among the many things de Boer has taught us, the most precious is perhaps the spirit of scientific endeavour and curiosity, with which he infected everyone around him.

E. J. W. VERWEY

[1] Cambridge University Press, 1935; German translation, Leipzig, J. A. Barth, 1937.

J. H. de Boer and Heterogeneous Catalysis
The Period after 1945

"Electron Emission and Adsorption Phenomena" appeared in 1934: its subject index does not contain the item "catalysis". And indeed, as Dr. Verwey pointed out, de Boer was not particularly concerned with heterogeneous catalysis at the time when he prepared the manuscript. However, this does not mean that the book is not relevant to our understanding of catalysis. It was in fact an astonishingly ambiguous attempt to describe adsorption in terms of a theory of the chemical bond. In other words what de Boer realized at that time was that the forces active in adsorption were completely similar to those encountered in the interaction of atoms and molecules.

The particular theory applied was the electrostatic concept, introduced by Kossel and systematically worked out by van Arkel and de Boer. It uses attractive forces described in terms of interactions between charges and permanent or induced dipoles on the one hand and repulsive forces approximated according to Born on the other hand. Precisely these same elements appear in de Boer's description of adsorption. The important point is not whether the theory is adequate but rather that the two phenomena, formation of the chemical bond and adsorption, are handled from one and the same point of view. Later on, others such as Eley, would make similar attempts, using valence-bond models that were perhaps somewhat better adapted to the problem. But there is no doubt that de Boer was among the very first to attempt a quantitative treatment.

I first read the book when working for my Ph.D. thesis and remember vividly how impressed I was at that time. Now, some 30 years later, I still feel impressed, although for somewhat different reasons. At that time it was fascinating to follow the brilliant construction of a model by the skilful manipulation of a number of factors often working in opposite directions. Verwey has already mentioned the frequent use of potential diagrams in this connection. At present, although still admiring the ingenuity of this manipulation, one is less impressed by this aspect: too much was tried to be explained that in fact would have been better left unexplained at the time. It is now the fundamental and deep insight of a very gifted young scientist that comes to the fore. In the beginning of the thirties quantum chemistry was still in its infancy and completely unmanageable for such an intricate problem as adsorption. The only existing alternative was the electrostatic theory, simple but also naive. That one could go so far as de Boer did at that time seems almost a miracle.

It is difficult to estimate the impact of de Boer's book on the development of theories on catalysis. Initially this impact was probably not very great. The electrostatic theory, thanks to the work of van Arkel and de Boer, was quite popular in The Netherlands but far less so elsewhere. Moreover the book was not written particularly to inform investigators working on catalysis; its audience was occupied with other industrial problems that seemed remote from it. However, gradually the news got through and at later times it must have been a source of constant information also for catalysis students.

It took a war to separate de Boer from his initial fields of scientific interest. But once separated the trends hidden in his book formed the impetus to project him into the centre of catalysis.

It is not surprising then to notice a considerable similarity in de Boer's first attacks on catalysis and the earlier methods he applied. This similarity is particularly noticeable in his paper for the First Symposium on Catalysis in The Netherlands. The potential diagrams are there and also the electrostatic elements. But at that time he was already closely connected with the "massive effort" applied by the investigators of the Central Laboratory of the Dutch State Mines to unravel the mechanism of the ammonia-synthesis. In the paper an attempt is made to explain the superior properties of Fe for this reaction. The method applied shows a definite similarity to that later used by Balandin in his volcano-curves and in a more provocative and explicit manner by Fahrenfort, van Reyen and Sachtler, to explain the sequence of metal reactivities for the formic acid decomposition. Tungsten is not a good catalyst for the ammonia synthesis because the adsorption of N_2 visualized as the heat of formation of a W-nitride is too large. Other metals may have an activation energy for adsorption that is high because the bonding of N_2 to the surface is weak. To translate, "for a well developed catalytic action it is desirable that adsorption is intermediate in its strength". However, there are also signs of a realization that the electrostatic model is after all insufficient as a tool for the intricate phenomena encountered in heterogeneous catalysis. De Boer is now in search of models based on covalent bonding that could guide him in the explanation of surface reactions. The action of the third body in enabling two H-atoms to combine to a molecule H_2 is visualized as an example of catalysis, an amusing idea but at present not considered as entirely relevant. A much better model is the cis-trans conversion of olefins under the influence of atoms such as I. This is even worked out quantitatively and shown to correspond to one of de Boer's favourite axioms: catalysis means a lowering of the activation energy of the reaction. However, although this model is completely relevant and again stresses the fundamental similarity of forces of interaction between surfaces and molecules on the one hand and atoms and molecules on the other hand it is ultimately restricted in its potential possibilities. Although preserved as an example the study of cis-trans conversion is not followed up.

The man whose activities we are now following has evolved very far from the young scientist of the thirties. He is now undoubtedly the central figure in the Dutch catalysis efforts. Both a leader of the State Mines research and an extraordinary professor at the Technological University of Delft he influences a team of mature scientists and at the same time persuades a number of young students to perform scientific research. A leader in the Dutch chemistry field he was President of the Royal Netherlands Chemical Society from 1953 till 1956, Chairman of the organization committees of a number of international congresses (Reactivity in Solids 1960 and 3rd International Congress on Catalysis 1964, both at Amsterdam), and ultimately responsible for directing research on nuclear reactions in an exalted government position.

But we also see that his interests changed as concerns the particular detail of catalysis in which he was primarily interested. In 1953 a new book "The Dynamical Character of Adsorption" proved entirely different from his first. It is an extremely lucid and interesting version of what was essentially a well worked-out concept: the "localized adsorption model" of Langmuir, later discussed in detail by such prominent scientists as Hinshelwood, G. Schwab, H. S. Taylor and Rideal. It does not add significant new features to the theory, but in its stress on the dynamical character of the adsorption it certainly sheds new light on it. Elements such as "residence time" and "hopping frequency" of an adsorbed complex do not really introduce something fundamentally new but succeed in making the subject far more lively.

From here on he proceeded in a somewhat different direction by a further study of the statistical mechanical approach to adsorption equilibria. This method was established by Fowler and Guggenheim but de Boer in collaboration with Kruyer followed it up in all its consequences in a series of papers (6–9). Entropy-differences appeared to interest de Boer far more than energy-differences. Potential energy diagrams are far less frequent in his more recent papers but partition functions occur almost constantly.

Two concepts from this work are of special relevance: mobile adsorption, and endothermic adsorption. Mobile adsorption appears to be a truly legitimate off-shoot from the statistical mechanical analysis of adsorption. It is readily reconciled with our models for physical adsorption and represents the two-dimensional analogy of a three dimensional gas. However, one gets into difficulties if seeking a three-dimensional model for a chemisorptive process *while still adhering to the fundamental similarity of the chemisorptive bond and the valence bond*. Can we find situations in which atoms in, say, unsaturated molecules change places so rapidly that their position is actually an average one? Isomerization in carbonium-ions might be somewhat related to such a mobile adsorption but in the carbonium-ion as a consequence of its electron deficiency the type of bonding is more a cooperative one, as in B_2H_6, than a localized one as in say an olefine. If then we find that mobile adsorption occurs frequently does this mean that chemisorptive bonds are after all different from "normal" valence bonds? The solution of the problem de Boer's concept thus introduces should be regarded with great interest.

Endothermic adsorption follows in de Boer's treatment from mobile adsorption. At first sight it cannot occur since energy and entropy differences of the adsorption are both unfavourable. But de Boer succeeds in finding an ingenious model: suppose that the adsorption is dissociative and the fragments mobile, hence possessing two fully-developed freedoms of movement. Then an entropy-gain occurs during adsorption and even for endothermic adsorption the free energy difference could still be negative. De Boer also finds an experimental case for his model: the adsorption of H_2 on glass. However, some doubts remain: how can one describe the bonding of the hydrogen atoms with the surface atoms so that the frequent change in position becomes understandable?

His interest in adsorption preceding the chemical reaction must have led de Boer to the kinetic analysis of systems of successive and parallel reactions, a subject that he investigated in collaboration with van den Borg. Another impetus in this direction was given by circumstances. The research groups Waterman and de Boer at the Technological University of Delft were situated in the same building and cooperative efforts were not infrequent. Since Waterman was interested at that time in unravelling the kinetics of the catalytic reforming process it is not surprising that de Boer also became interested in the problems typical of this bifunctional catalysis. He developed the analysis in a quite general form however and indeed appears to have aroused new interest: the problem has since been vigorously attacked by Weiss, Prater and their collaborators.

In the last decade de Boer has vigorously followed up his interest in the texture of catalysts. The roots of the work are situated in the investigations at the Dutch State Mines but his Delft group formed the main source. As a number of his past and present collaborators have contributed to the present book the reader can judge their work for himself. However, it seems fit to note that the main activities of his "school"—indeed an appropriate name—are now directed to a somewhat different branch of heterogeneous catalysis, that is, the texture and structure of industrial catalysts. The work of Coenen and Linsen on Ni—SiO_2 and of Lippens on Al_2O_3, among others, furnishes models of the catalysts in terms of assemblies of small particles separated by an intricate system of pores. The surfaces of the solid particles are important since they form the seat of the catalytic reactions, but the pores are the roads that lead to the surfaces and transport barriers such as diffusion may find their origin here. Not surprisingly, de Boer's first interest was in the nature of the solids as determining the properties of the surface; this was his old "metier". But from here he turned to a study of the pore systems by such tools as electron-microscopy. However, his most powerful apparatus for investigating these pore systems again is adsorption. Having studied such things as the adsorption of I_2 on CaF_2 and encountered the useful adsorption of lauric acid on oxides he could easily select the appropriate type of adsorption for the special case investigated. But the most flexible and informative tool was the van der Waals adsorption of gases such as N_2, Xe and the like. Already in the thirties Brunauer, Emmett and Teller had proposed a model to explain the phenomena of van der Waals adsorption on porous substances ranging from monolayer adsorption to capillary condensation. Being rather a naive model in spite of its resounding success in actual application, numerous attempts were made to improve on it. De Boer, who had developed his own approach, originally was rather critical. Later on, however, he adopted it and in his usual manner proceeded to improve it and with considerable success. He even went so far as to reverse the normal procedure, i.e. instead of predicting the adsorption isotherm from the known properties of the pore system, he predicted the properties of the pore system: number, diameter and particularly the form of the pores from analysis of the adsorption isotherm.

Knowing de Boer, one could guess what would happen: from the specific he went back to the general problem and in collaboration with Broekhoff again attacked the phenomenon of van der Waals adsorption on surfaces. And in a way he has retraced his steps to the interesting problem he encountered at the start of his scientific career.

In his introduction Verwey remarked that de Boer is not only a good scientist but also a remarkably able inventor. This is perhaps the most striking characteristic of his theoretical work, the clever construction of his models. They are often somewhat complex but the parts from which they are made are scientifically sound and assembled in a logical manner. Less inventive people may have difficulty in following him; others will disagree as to their reality. But they are always interesting, provocative and illuminating. Which is why Professor J. H. de Boer, certainly one of the top Dutch chemists, is moreover one of the most inventive and dynamic of his generation.

G. C. A. SCHUIT

Chapter 1

STUDIES ON PORE SYSTEMS IN ADSORBENTS AND CATALYSTS

J. C. P. BROEKHOFF

Department of Chemical Technology, Technological University, Delft, The Netherlands

and

B. G. LINSEN

Unilever Research Laboratory, Vlaardingen, The Netherlands

I Introduction

Heterogeneous catalysts have been used in catalytic processes for more than 50 years. During this time the catalyst consumption has increased rapidly. In the United States, for example, the petroleum industry is today spending annually about 70 million dollars on 140,000 tons of heterogeneous catalysts. There is of course a continuous tendency to improve the quality of the catalysts, and an enormous volume of literature describing extensive investigations into catalytic reactions and the catalysts used has been published in the past. Similarly, many patents have been filed, concerning the preparation of catalysts.

The action in heterogeneous catalysis occurs at the interface of two phases. The most important function of a catalyst in chemical catalysis is to lower the activation energy; in other words, catalysts owe their activity to the presence of an extended "catalytically active" surface. In order to achieve the best effect, efforts are therefore made to obtain a larger surface area per unit volume or weight of the catalyst.

Large specific surface areas may be obtained by using a porous system consisting of a solid substance having a network of pores. Such networks have sometimes been idealized in the literature as uniform cylindrical capillaries, all having the same diameter and distributed randomly through the matrix (Wheeler, 1955). Other possible arrangements are a network built up of globules with connecting channels, or a network consisting of plane-parallel plates with spaces in between throughout the crystallite. In all such cases we speak of the *texture* of a catalyst, which is by definition the individual structure and arrangement of the coherent particles with open spaces in between.

In heterogeneous catalysis the reaction process can be resolved into the following steps (de Boer, 1959):

1. Transport of the reactants from the reaction mixture to the external surface of the catalyst particles;
2. Transport of the reactants from the external surface of the catalyst particles to the internal surface;
3. Adsorption of the reactants on the active centres of the catalyst;
4. Reaction between adsorbed reactants;
5. Desorption of the reaction product;

6. Transport of the reaction product from the internal surface of the catalyst particles to the external surface;
7. Transport of the reaction product from the external surface of the catalyst to the reaction mixture.

At first sight a relationship may be expected to exist between the catalytic activity and the magnitude of the catalyst surface, but this will only be the case if transport of the reactants to and from the active centres of the catalyst plays a negligible part. In other words, such a relationship is only found if the reaction rate is determined by the reaction itself. In most studies it is therefore important to know the rate-determining steps during the catalytic reaction, because the slowest step will determine this rate.

It is clear that questions concerning the diffusion into and through the capillary system of the catalyst are important. In studies regarding the mechanism of catalytic reactions—with respect to activity and selectivity—considerable attention must therefore be paid to the size and shape of the pores. One must be aware of the difference between diffusion through capillaries having a more or less cylindrical cross-section and through slit-shaped capillaries that have only one small dimension and two large ones.

From the above one may conclude that the efficiency of a catalyst will be determined mainly by its texture. Various methods for the determination of the specific surface area of a catalyst are described in the literature. Most of them are based on the adsorption of substances on this surface. One of the methods used most frequently at the moment is based on the adsorption of inert gases, such as nitrogen, argon, and krypton, at low temperatures, namely that of liquid nitrogen or oxygen. In the case of the application of metals on carrier catalysts —in which the metal is the active component—chemisorption may form an ideal basis for the determination of the magnitude of the catalytic active surface.

As already mentioned, the specific surface area alone is not sufficient to characterize a catalyst. For a study of the accessibility to the surface, the shape and dimensions of the pores present in the matrix should also be known. Low-temperature adsorption of inert gases may also provide important information on this point.

In the present chapter we shall discuss in detail the adsorption of nitrogen at low temperatures on porous and non-porous solids, and the influence of such adsorption on capillary condensation and evaporation, and shall evaluate the practical application of these concepts to pore size distribution calculations.

II   Surface Area and Pore Structure

A   Macro- and Microporous Substances

The title of this section suggests that porous substances may be divided into at least two sub-groups, macroporous and microporous. Everybody agrees that porous materials such as sponge or pumice can be classified as macroporous, and as long as the pores can be seen with the naked eye there will be no difference of opinion about the classification. Scott Russel (1927), distinguishing between macropores and micropores in building stone, fixed the borderline in that case at a pore diameter of 0·005 mm (5 μ). It is indeed, for practical reasons, useful to agree on a definite pore size as a division line. A more logical division however, is obtained by taking a figure rather different from the one just mentioned, i.e. roughly 500 Å, 100 times smaller than the figure suggested by Scott Russel. This brings paper, fabrics and cloth (wool, cotton, nylon, etc.), building stone, coke, and wood mainly in the group of macroporous materials and catalysts mainly in the group of microporous materials. This does not mean that the first group does not contain micropores or that the second group is devoid of macropores, but rather that the characteristic properties of these materials are mainly determined by macropores in the first case and by micropores in the second.

B   The Surface Area in the Pores

Wicke (1939) examined some samples of charcoal and silica gel. From the adsorption isotherms of benzene on these materials and from the total pore space, found by immersion in benzene, he determined the volumes of the macro- and micropores. The volume of the macropores of his sample varied between 0·35 and 0·60 cm^3/g and that of the micropores between 0·14 and 0·67 cm^3/g. Practically all the micropores had radii smaller than 30 Å, the average being about 10 Å. The smallest macropores had radii of about 0·1 μ (1000 Å) and the average was about 1 μ. Wicke assumed that the surface area within the pores is given by:

$$S = \frac{2 \cdot 5 V_p}{\bar{r}_p} \cdot 10^4 \tag{1}$$

in which S = the specific surface area in m^2/g;

     V_p = the specific pore volume in cm^3/g;

     $\bar{r}_p$ = the mean pore radius in Å.

The factor 2·5 was obviously chosen because Wicke did not know the shape of the pores. If it is assumed that the pores are cylindrical or slit-shaped and do not intersect, the radius $\bar{r}_p$ (or the width $\bar{d}_p$ for slit-shaped pores) is given by:

$$S = \frac{2V_p}{\bar{r}_p} \cdot 10^4 \tag{2}$$

in the case of spherical pores the radius $\bar{r}_p$ is given by:

$$S = \frac{3V_p}{\bar{r}_p} \cdot 10^4. \tag{3}$$

As Wicke presumably had in his sample tubular pores with various widths a factor 2·5 may be justified. Wicke obtained values varying between 0·9 and 1·5 m²/g for the surface area in the macropores and figures between 350 and 1700 m²/g for the surface area in the micropores. The results of this study thus indicated that the surface area available in the macropores is negligible in comparison with that in the micropores. As already mentioned in the introduction, catalysts operate via the adsorption of molecules, and the surface area that is available for this adsorption is of major importance. This surface area is determined by the surface area in the micropores. Nevertheless, macropores play an important role in the operational use of these substances, since the rates of adsorption and the rates of the catalytic reactions depend largely on the rate of diffusion in the pores.

III Origin of Pores

As may be seen from the foregoing, it is necessary to have adsorbents and catalysts with large specific surface areas. A large specific surface area can hardly be obtained by grinding. Even grinding to a size of 1μ results only in raising the specific surface area to about 1 m²/g. As in practice the desired specific areas vary from 10 to over 500 m²/g, other methods have to be used to prepare microporous substances. The most important of these methods are outlined below.

A Precipitation

Precipitates can often be formed as very minute particles which later "flock" together to give a porous mass. The ill-fitting initial particles are relatively loosely cemented together, the pore space being the space between these primary particles. Silica gel can be mentioned as a good example of this method (Chapter 5).

B   Thermal Decomposition

Thermal decomposition of various compounds, such as hydroxides, hydrates or carbonates, may lead to the removal of one of the dissociation products. If the compound formed sinters together completely, the resultant solid decomposition product may be compact. However, very often the sintering is negligible or only partial and a set of capillaries is left behind, sometimes showing very definite pore sizes and also occasionally a very definite orientation with respect to the directions of the original crystals. The outer form of these crystals before decomposition is often retained after decomposition. Such pseudomorphism is frequently found, and it is a most useful property of matter in the preparation of a well-defined set of capillaries. Examples of this method can be found in the decomposition of aluminium hydroxide (gibbsite, bayerite, nordstandite) (Chapter 4) and in the decomposition of magnesium carbonate (nesquehonite, magnesite) (Chapter 6).

C   Leaching of Substances

Chemical removal of selected constituents is a common method of creating porosity. When a nickel-aluminium alloy is leached using potassium hydroxide, a highly porous nickel catalyst (Raney nickel) is left behind. When fused iron oxide in the form of magnetite (Fe_3O_4) is reduced a highly porous form of α-iron is obtained. Careful reduction conserves the outer form of the original crystals (pseudomorphism) (Westrik and Zwietering, 1953).

High-temperature attack by steam and/or oxygen on vegetable structures (wood or coconut shells), on peat, and on coke leads to activated carbons having very large internal surface areas.

D   Sublimation

Sublimation of inorganic salts or metals and condensation of the vapours on a substrate, such as glass or quartz may lead to the formation of lamellar structures possessing a very large specific surface area.

In modern catalytic research use is often made of thin metal films obtained by sublimation of metals in high vacuum on to a carrier. These films are not compact, but have a more or less well-determined pore structure, depending on the temperature at which they were formed. Salts can be sublimed in the same way. De Boer (1935, 1938, 1958a) made an extensive study of the structure and properties of thin films of salts obtained by sublimation in a vacuum. The majority of these experiments were performed with CaF_2. About 1 mg of this salt was applied to a tungsten filament and the filament was placed in a glass bulb, which was then evacuated. The salt was next evaporated by electrical heating of the filament to about 2000°C. The resulting salt film on the inside wall of the bulb was invisible even in ultraviolet light, which made it very suitable for light absorption studies of substances adsorbed on the film. The results of these studies were striking. The specific surface area of the films was of the order of a few hundred square metres per gram.

IV Historical Survey of the Development of Pore Size Distribution Calculations

A Theories of Zsigsmundy, Foster, Kraemer and McBain, Cohan and others

Attempts to obtain detailed information on pore size and pore shape in microporous solids are in the majority of cases made from a detailed interpretation of the complete vapour sorption isotherm, using, e.g. nitrogen as the adsorbate. To this end, extensive use has been made of the laws of capillarity in various modification and formulations.

The behaviour of liquids enclosed in capillary vessels has been studied extensively since the seventeenth century. Careful experiments, e.g. by Hawksbee (1709), Newton (1704) and Jurin (1718) on the capillary rise of water in small glass cylindrical capillaries and between parallel plates, established firmly the connection between the capillary radius and the height of ascent. The capillary action was attributed to interatomic forces of very short range nature (as was concluded from the fact that the thickness of the capillary wall did not seem to influence the phenomena). The theory of capillarity has been given a firm statistical mechanical basis by Laplace (1806) who concluded that there is a pressure difference over a curved interface between two phases, whose magnitude is equal to:

$$\Delta P = K(1/R_1 + 1/R_2) \tag{4}$$

where R_1 and R_2 are the two main radii of curvature of the meniscus and K is nowadays called the surface tension. From a more phenomenological point of view, Young (1805) at the same time also reached this conclusion. This latter author also established the constancy of the contact angle between a solid and a liquid partly wetting the solid (Fig. 1), completely determined by the equilibrium between the three different surface tensions:

$$\gamma_{LV} \cos \theta = \gamma_{SV} - \gamma_{SL} \tag{5}$$

where θ is the contact angle, γ_{LV} the surface tension of the liquid-gas interface, and γ_{SV} and γ_{SL} are those of the solid-gas and solid-liquid interfaces.

Thomson (1871) deduced, from the existence of capillary rise and the fact that in a gaseous atmosphere the pressure varies with altitude, that the vapour pressure above a curved interface must be different

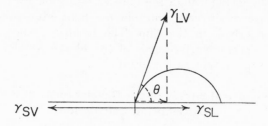

FIG. 1 *Young's* theory of contact angle.

from that above a flat liquid surface. According to his calculations this difference was equal to:

$$p_0 - p = \frac{\gamma \cdot \rho_g}{\rho_L - \rho_g} (1/R_1 + 1/R_2) \qquad (6)$$

where γ is the surface tension, ρ_g the mean gas density, ρ_L the liquid density, p the vapour pressure of the meniscus, and p_0 the saturation pressure of the bulk liquid.

This equation is a simplified version of what is now known as Kelvin's equation (Thomson later became Lord Kelvin). About that time the description of capillary phenomena was put on a rigorous thermodynamic basis by Gibbs (1961a) in his brilliant treatment of phase equilibria. Gibbs occupied himself extensively with the stability of curved interfaces and with the influence of curvature on surface tension and on the state of the adjacent bulk phases.

The application of capillarity to the determination of pore radii in microporous substances is probably due to Zsigsmundy (1911), who seems to have been the first to explain the retention of water by certain silica gels at reduced water vapour pressures by capillary vapour pressure depression in narrow pores. With the aid of Eq. (6) he calculated these pores to be as narrow as 50 Å. Meanwhile, it was realized by thermodynamicists that Eq. (6) is only a crude approximation. A more rigorous derivation was given by Hückel (1928) leading to the expression

$$RT \ln (p_0/p) = \gamma V_L \cdot (1/R_1 + 1/R_2) + V_L(p_0 - p) \qquad (7)$$

where V_L is the molar volume of the liquid phase. If the second term on the right-hand side of Eq. (7) is neglected and the contact angle is introduced (an intuitive step that is not always admitted), we arrive at Kelvin's equation in its usual form:

$$RT \ln (p_0/p) = \gamma V_L \cos (\theta) . (1/R_1 + 1/R_2). \tag{8}$$

Initially, all vapour sorption by solid was attributed by McGavick and Patrick (1928), to the effects of capillary vapour depression. On the other hand, Polanyi's (1916) potential theory of adsorption neglected all capillary effects and attributed vapour sorption solely to gas-solid interactions. Several attempts have been made to reconcile the two theories of physical adsorption, the most important of them being that of Schuchowitzky (1934), which now seems to have been virtually forgotten. Schuchowitzky introduced a "Kelvin potential",

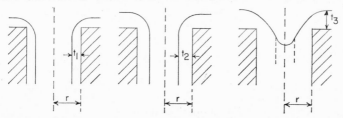

FIG. 2 Filling of pores during adsorption according to *Foster*; $r =$ capillary radius, $t =$ layer thickness.

defined as $RT \ln (p_0/p)$ and determined by Eq. (8), and supposed this potential to be additive to the "adsorption potential" as given by the interaction between the adsorbent and the absorbate. The sum of the two potentials according to this author completely determines the vapour sorption equilibrium, as it must be equal to the vapour phase potential $RT \ln (p_0/p_g)$ where p_g is the vapour pressure. This idea of additive sorption potentials was taken up nearly 25 years later by Foster (1952) in an attempt to explain vapour sorption hysteresis. In 1932, Foster still assumed adsorption and capillary vapour pressure depression to be completely independent and never cooperating jointly. He assumed the pores in solids to be tubular and open at both ends. During adsorption an adsorbed layer is formed, which becomes thicker with increasing pressure until the pore is completely filled, resulting in the formation of a meniscus (Fig. 2). During desorption capillary evaporation takes place whenever the pressure drops below the value given by Eq. (8), where it is assumed that the meniscus in the pore is hemispherical with two equal radii of curvature. The desorption pressure is thus given by:

$$RT \ln (p_0/p_d) = 2\gamma V_L \cos (\theta)/r \tag{9}$$

where r is the radius of the capillary.

2*

In this way a satisfactory explanation is given of vapour sorption hysteresis, provided the pores are really cylinders of uniform radius open at both ends. Jurin (1718) suggested a different explanation of vapour sorption hysteresis and contended that the emptying of capillary vessels of non-uniform radius, once they were completely filled, was controlled by the smallest dimension of the vessel rather than by the mean dimension, whereas once empty, spontaneous filling under the same conditions is not possible. This suggestion seems to have been rediscovered by Kraemer (1931) and was popularized by McBain (1935) under the name of the bottle-neck theory of hysteresis. Consider, for example, a relatively wide spheroidal cavity with a narrow neck of radius r_n (Fig. 3). During adsorption, filling is controlled by the

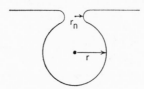

FIG. 3 Spheroidal cavity.

formation of an adsorbed layer on the walls of the wide pore body, but, once the pore is completely filled, emptying is controlled by the small dimension of the neck r_n and only occurs at a relative pressure just below that given by Eq. (9) (with r_n substituted for r). Foster's model of sorption hysteresis was reconsidered by Cohan (1938). According to the latter author during adsorption in a cylinder with radius r, open at both ends, an adsorbed layer of thickness t is formed. Cohan proposed to apply Kelvin's equation to the surface of this cylindrical adsorbed film, one radius of curvature of which is equal to $r-t$ and the other to infinity (Fig. 4). Consequently, Eq. (8) reads:

$$RT \ln (p_0/p_a) = \gamma V_L/(r-t). \tag{10}$$

According to Cohan, capillary condensation should take place whenever the relative pressure during adsorption exceeds that given by Eq. (10). A doubly curved meniscus is present during desorption, and evaporation takes place whenever the pressure falls below the value given by Eq. (9). When the thickness t is neglected in comparison with r and the contact angle is put equal to zero, then clearly p_a is related to p_d by:

$$p_a^2 = p_0 \cdot p_d \tag{11}$$

and hysteresis results. Independently, Coelingh (1939) reached exactly the same conclusions in interpreting sorption hysteresis on silica.

Later Cohan (1944) applied an analogue of Eq. (10), to the adsorption branch for ink-bottle pores; if the bodies of these pores consist of spheroidal cavities of radius r (see Fig. 3), the relative pressure of capillary condensation during adsorption is given by:

$$RT \ln (p_0/p_a) = 2\gamma V_L/(r-t). \qquad (12)$$

We now know Cohan's equation to be incorrect, as application of Kelvin's equation to the adsorbed layer is equivalent to neglecting

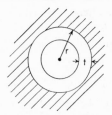

FIG. 4 *Cohan's* picture of the adsorbed film in a cylindrical pore.

the differences between the bulk liquid and the adsorbed layer. It is easy to realize that a cylindrical film of liquid with bulk properties is never stable and that Kelvin's equation may not be applied to this situation (see Section VI). An alternative procedure is to adopt Schuchowitzky's point of view on the additivity of the "Kelvin potential" and the sorption potential. It was Foster (1952) who showed that this additivity could lead to the concept of a restricted stability of the adsorbed layer, resulting in capillary condensation at a certain relative pressure, depending on pore radius. This concept was further worked out to some extent by Everett (1958), who investigated the influence of pore shape on capillary condensation. The application of Kelvin's equation requires the supposition of bulk liquid in relatively narrow pores. Not only does this lead to serious difficulties in describing capillary condensation during adsorption, but also the influence of sorption forces has to be taken into account during desorption. Wheeler (1945–46) proposed to subtract from the pore radius the thickness of the adsorbed layer in order to obtain an effective radius. In that case, the equation for the desorption branch would read

$$RT \ln (p_0/p_a) = 2\gamma V_L/(r-t). \qquad (13)$$

Already in 1940 a theory of capillary evaporation, was formulated making use of the concept of disjoining pressure which properly took into account the influence of sorption on the process of capillary evaporation (Deryagin, 1940). The difficulties connected with the last-mentioned concept and the external circumstances were not favourable to a widespread distribution of Deryagin's ideas. Later on, he published a new version of his theory, adapted to the model of slit-shaped pores (Deryagin, 1967). He showed, that for such pores the capillary evaporation pressure is related to the pore diameter (d) by:

$$d = 2\gamma V_L / RT \ln (p_0/p_d) + \frac{2V_L}{RT \ln (p_0/p_d)} \int_{p_d}^{p_0} \frac{N_s}{S} . RT \, d \ln (p) \qquad (14)$$

where N_s/S denotes the number of moles adsorbed per unit surface area on a completely flat surface of the same material as a function of the relative pressure. This formula should be compared with the classical one, which would follow from Eq. (8) after subtraction of the thickness of the adsorbed layer:

$$d = 2\gamma V_L / RT \ln (p_0/p_d) + 2t. \qquad (15)$$

It seems that until recently Deryagin's formula has not found systematic practical application, although the integral on the right-hand side of Eq. (14) can be evaluated with the aid of the t-curve of multimolecular adsorption (see Section V) (Broekhoff and de Boer, 1968d).

A different approach to the capillary evaporation phenomenon is due to Kiselev (1958). This author maintains that, at a relative pressure at which capillary evaporation takes place, the change in thermodynamic potential on evaporation of the capillary condensed phase is equal to the change in free energy of the system owing to the creation of the liquid-vapour interface connected with the adsorbed layer, i.e.:

$$\gamma \, dA = \Delta\mu \, dN \qquad (16)$$

where γ is the surface tension, dA is the magnitude of the created surface, dN the number of moles desorbed from the pore, and $\Delta\mu$ the difference in thermodynamic potential between the capillary condensed phase and the vapour phase. It has been assumed (Brunauer et al., 1967) that the thermodynamic potential of the capillary condensed phase is equal to that of the bulk liquid phase, in which case for cylindrical pores Eq. (16) is equivalent to Eq. (13) and for slits to Eq. (15). It has been shown recently (Broekhoff and de Boer, 1967a) that this assumption is incompatible with the existence of multilayer adsorption at relative pressures below saturation. For slits, integration of Eq. (16) while taking into account the dependence of the thermodynamic potential of the adsorbed layer on the distance of the pore wall, leads to an equation similar to Eq. (14) (Broekhoff and de Boer, 1968d) (see also Section VI B).

As may be apparent from the foregoing discussion, a more rigorous correction of Kelvin's equation for the influence of multilayer adsorption is necessary, and Eqs (9), (10), (12), (13) and (15) may only be regarded as first approximations, often leading to serious quantitative errors as well as fundamental inconsistencies. A general theory of capillary condensation and evaporation for different pore shapes will be given in Section VI.

B   Application of the Foregoing Theories to Pore Size Distribution

Since the second world war calculation of detailed distribution functions for microporous substances from sorption isotherms, preferably those of nitrogen, has become a subject of great interest to those occupied with the characterization of heterogeneous catalysts. Apart from some pre-war attempts, e.g. by Foster (1932), Wheeler (1945–46) seems to have been the first to have aimed at the calculation of complete pore size distributions. Initially a Gaussian distribution of pore sizes was postulated assuming cylindrical pores, and the mean pore radius and the width of the distribution were adjusted to obtain an optimum fit between calculated and measured adsorption isotherms. The application of this method was demonstrated by Shull (1948). For a non-Gaussian distribution, Wheeler (1955) formulated the fundamental equations in terms of the total pore length $L(r)$ of pores with radius r, as follows:

$$V_a = V_t + V_c \tag{17a}$$

where V_a is the total volume adsorbed, V_t the volume of the multilayer absorbed in other wise emptied pores, and V_c the volume of the capillary condensate held by the pores. In terms of $L(r)$, V_t is equal to:

$$V_t = t \int_{r_c}^{\infty} 2\pi r L(r)\, \mathrm{d}r - t^2 \int_{r_c}^{\infty} \pi L(r)\, \mathrm{d}r \tag{17b}$$

and

$$V_c(<r_c) = \int_0^{r_c} \pi r^2 L(r)\, \mathrm{d}r \tag{17c}$$

whereas

$$S_c(>r_c) = \int_{r_c}^{\infty} 2\pi r L(r)\, \mathrm{d}r \tag{17d}$$

where S_c is the total surface area present in pores with radii greater than r_c. Moreover, if the total pore volume is denoted by V_p, then:

$$V_p - V_a = \int_{r_c}^{\infty} \pi(r-t)^2 L(r)\, \mathrm{d}r. \tag{17e}$$

Here r_c denotes the radius of the pore just filled with capillary condensate at a certain relative pressure, as given by Eq. (13). If t is also known as a function of relative pressure, then all quantities of interest are fixed by Eqs (17a) to (17e) through the distribution function $L(r)$, and this function is in principle uniquely defined. Actual calculation of $L(r)$ from a given set of values of V_a as a function of pressure is, however, rather difficult. Wheeler (1955) has shown, how with certain simplifying assumptions, $S_c(>r_c)$ may be calculated from the sorption isotherm by graphical integration of a differential equation from Eqs (17a–e). In practice, several approximate numerical methods have been developed, one of the most well known being that of Barrett et al. (1951a). According to these authors, the isotherm is divided into a number of intervals. Over the kth interval the decrease in the amount adsorbed, ΔV_k^a, is attributed to:

1. Emptying of pores with mean radius r_k, as given by Eq. (13), and differential pore volume V_k, except for an adsorbed layer of thickness t_k;
2. Decrease of the thickness of the adsorbed layer present in pores already emptied in the previous $k-1$ intervals with total surface area $\sum_{i=1}^{k-1} S_i$, from t_{k-1} to t_k.

Equating these two contributions to ΔV_k^a and solving for V_k we find:

$$V_k = R_k \left\{ (\Delta V_k^a) - (t_{k-1} - t_k) \sum_{i=1}^{k-1} c_i S_i \right\} \tag{18}$$

where $R_k \equiv \{r_k/(r_k - t_k)\}^2$ and $c_i \equiv (r_i - t_k)/r_i$.

To simplify the calculational procedure, Barrett et al. (1951a) proposed to approximate c_i by a constant mean value, dependent on the estimated mean pore radius of the system under consideration. Eq. (18) then reduces to:

$$V_k = R_k \left\{ (\Delta V_k^a) - (t_{k-1} - t_k) \cdot c \cdot \sum_{i=1}^{k-1} S_i \right\}. \tag{19}$$

Since then, the use of Eq. (18) has been revived by a number of authors, occasionally in a somewhat different notation (Montarnal, 1953; Clement et al., 1962; Emig and Hofmann, 1967). Cranston and Inkley (1957) noted—for a wide number of non-porous inorganic adsorbents and using nitrogen as an adsorbate—that plotting of the amount adsorbed per m² of surface area resulted in a common reduced isotherm, from which the thickness of the adsorbed layer could be calculated (see Section V). These authors came to the conclusion that in many cases the cumulative surface area resulting from the pore distribution calculation was approximately equal to the BET surface area, provided the adsorption branch of the isotherm was used instead of the desorption branch. They thus preferred to adopt the use of the adsorption branch only. As will be shown in Section IV C, from the work of de Boer (1958b), it appears that the choice of the adsorption or the desorption branch is not free but is determined by the most probable pore shape which may be inferred from the shape and width of the hysteresis loop.

A method of calculating the pore distribution specially adapted to the model of slit-shaped pores was developed independently by Innes (1957) and by Steggerda (1955). Their method is analogous to that of Barrett et al. (1951a). Again the isotherm is divided into a number of intervals and the change in volume adsorbed over the kth interval, ΔV_k^a, is related to the pore volume of the group of pores with mean pore width d_k, pore volume V_k, and surface area S_k, by:

$$V_k = R_k \left\{ \Delta V_k^a - (t_{k-1} - t_k) \cdot \sum_{i=1}^{k-1} S_i \right\} \qquad (20)$$

where $R_k \equiv d_k/(d_k - 2t_k)$ and t_k is the thickness of the adsorbed layer at the end of the kth interval. The mean pore diameter d_k over the kth interval is estimated from the mean relative pressure over this interval by means of Eq. (15). A number of recent publications on the calculational technique of pore distribution (Vishnawathan and Sastri, 1967; John and Bohra, 1967), is occupied by mere changes in algebraic formulation or by the introduction of approximations while sacrificing accuracy. In view of the advent of modern high-speed computers the importance of the introduction of such changes and approximations seems questionable: the accuracy of the application of Eqs (19) or (20) may be increased at will merely by decreasing the size of the intervals, and there really seems to be no point in saving calculation time at the expense of accuracy. The most laborious step in determining the pore size distributions is still the accurate measurement of the adsorption isotherm.

C Classification of Pore Shapes by Barrer and de Boer, types of Hysteresis Loops

Barrer et al. (1956), investigated the shape of the isotherm and of the hysteresis loop to be expected theoretically for different pore shapes, as calculated by means of Eq. (8) for different shapes of the meniscus. Following the reverse procedure, de Boer (1958b) showed that in practical cases the shape of the hysteresis loop may lead to a more or less detailed picture of the shape of the pores present in a certain adsorbent. De Boer distinguished five different types of hysteresis loops, three of which have proved of great importance in the interpretation of sorption isotherms. These three are commonly denoted by the types A, B and E (see Fig. 5).

Type A has two very steep branches and can be related in its simplest form to cylindrical pores open at both ends. The classical explanation of hysteresis in this type of pores has been given by Cohan (1938) (see Section IV B), and the width of the hysteresis loop is approximated by Eq. (11).

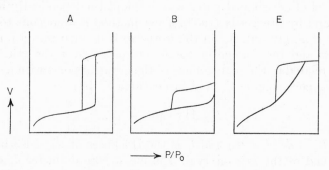

FIG. 5 Three types of hysteresis loop according to *de Boer*'s classification.

For ideal open cylinders, both the adsorption and the desorption branch is stable (although the adsorption branch is metastable relative to the desorption branch). In principle it should be possible to use both branches independently for the calculation of pore distributions (provided the correct formulations for the capillary condensation and evaporation criteria are used), and the resulting cumulative surface areas should be both approximately equal to the total surface area (e.g. the BET area). De Boer has shown that if tubular capillaries contain slightly widened parts (see Fig. 6), then there also results an A-type hysteresis loop, though its width is smaller than that for "ideal" open cylinders. If the wide parts are essentially spheroidal in shape, then the adsorption branch is governed by condensation in these parts, while the narrow necks govern the desorption. If the volume of these narrow necks is negligible, the adsorption branch is the sole stable branch and cumulative distribution functions may be determined from it. In other cases both branches are unstable with respect to some parts of the pores. The same remarks apply for narrow necked ink-bottles with not too wide bodies, also exhibiting A-type behaviour. Here again the adsorption branch is favoured, as the desorption branch is never thermodynamically stable. This prediction was confirmed experimentally by Kington and Smith (1964) by comparison of the measured heat of adsorption over the whole isotherm with the calculated isosteric heats of adsorption from isotherms measured at different temperatures. The shape of their hysteresis loops on porous glass showed non-ideal A-type behaviour, indicating the presence of ink-bottle-like structures, and the adsorption branch proved to be the thermodynamically stable one.

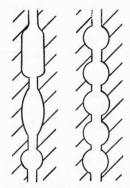

FIG. 6 Tubular pores with widened parts.

For a more detailed review of the different pore shapes consistent with non-ideal A-type hysteresis-loops, the reader is referred to the paper by Linsen and van den Heuvel (1967).

A B-type hysteresis loop is characterized by a vertical adsorption branch near saturation and a steep desorption branch at intermediate relative pressures. This type of hysteresis may be caused by either ink-bottle structures with very wide bodies and narrow necks or by slit-shaped pores open at all sides.

In wide-bodied ink-bottles filling up of the body takes place at very high relative pressures, while during desorption evaporation is hindered by the narrow neck in which the capillary-held liquid has a very low vapour pressure. In slit-shaped pores open at all sides pore filling has to take place through the formation of a multilayer that at a certain moment fills completely the void between the walls of the slit. A meniscus is formed at that moment, controlling the evaporation during desorption. If the B-type behaviour is caused by slits then the desorption branch is stable, which should be used for the calculation of pore distributions. In contrast, for wide-bodied ink-bottles the adsorption branch is the only stable one and pore distribution calculations should be done with the aid of the proper formulation of the condensation criterion, e.g. by assuming either spheroidal or cylindrical cavities.

An E-type hysteresis loop is intermediate between types A and B. While the desorption branch is steep, the adsorption branch is sloping.

This type of hysteresis may be attributed to a distribution of pores with narrow necks of rather uniform diameters, but with wide bodies of different diameters (if the shape of the body is irregular and shows varying diameters, then in principle a single pore may show the same behaviour). For this type of isotherms the adsorption branch is the stable one if the radius of the wide body of an individual pore is sufficiently uniform and the volume of the necks may be neglected. The pore distributions should be calculated from the adsorption branch.

Strict interpretation of the shape of a hysteresis loop is complicated by two factors:

1. The existence of a distribution of in themselves "ideal" pores with different characteristic diameters, or of different types of pore shapes in one and the same adsorbent, may influence the shape of the hysteresis loop. For example, it may be proved that the width of a hysteresis loop resulting from a distribution of open cylinders is smaller than one would expect for a set of pores of the same radius. Moreover, it is not always easy to separate the pores within particles from the irregular voids formed between particles by accidental packing configurations.

2. In small micropores and in sub-micropores (pores with radii smaller than, say, 15 Å), hysteresis with many adsorbates is never observed and the concepts of capillarity definitely seem to break down. For example, with nitrogen as an adsorbate, hysteresis in rigid absorbents is hardly ever observed at relative pressures below 0·40. Although this breakdown of macroscopic thermodynamics in very narrow pores should not be surprising, there is as yet no satisfactory quantitative theory of hysteresis.

V Adsorption of Nitrogen on Non-porous Solids

A Apparatus and Experimental Procedure

The amount of nitrogen adsorbed by a solid substance at −196°C at an increasing or decreasing relative pressure can be determined volumetrically or gravimetrically. Joy (1953) has reviewed all existing techniques. The volumetric technique, especially, is frequently preferred. A detailed description of the conventional apparatus used for this purpose has been given, for example, by Coenen (1958) and by Lippens and Hermans (1961). This conventional BET apparatus has various disadvantages:

(a) The heat of adsorption to be removed tends to be large as a result of the rather large amount of substance used;

(b) The point at which equilibrium is obtained is difficult to determine in connection with the large dead volume present;

(c) The volumes adsorbed are calculated cumulatively;

(d) Leakage during the measurement is difficult to detect;

(e) The measurement is difficult to interrupt.

All these disadvantages have led to the development of a micro BET apparatus (Lippens and Hermans, 1961; Lippens, 1961; Lippens *et al.*,

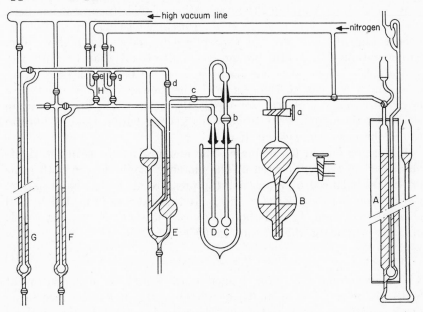

Fig. 7 Adsorption apparatus.

1964) (see Fig. 7). The principal parts of this gas-adsorption apparatus are as follows:

1. Gas burette (A) filled with mercury (capacity 100 ml, graduated in 0·1 ml).

2. Adsorption vessel (C) closed off from the measuring system by means of a small filter plate (b) to prevent contamination of the apparatus by solid material.

3. Mercury pump (B) for the transport of gas from burette (A) to adsorption vessel (C).

4. A capillary differential manometer (E).

5. Vacuum and pressure chamber (H) to equalize the pressures in the left part of the differential manometer (E) and that in the adsorption vessel (C).

6. Manometer (G) indicating the pressure in this left part.
7. Manometer (F) connected to the vessel (D) containing some pure condensed nitrogen, by which changes in the temperature of the liquid nitrogen can be determined in the Dewar vessel placed around the adsorption vessel (C).

High vacuum is obtained by means of an oil pump and a diffusion pump.

A detailed description of the calibration of such apparatus has been given (Lippens, 1961; Lippens et al., 1964). For the calibration of the dead volume (C), the taps c, d, e, and f are opened so that high vacuum can be obtained. When the pressure has fallen to less than 10^{-5} mm Hg, and after the apparatus has been checked for possible leakage, taps d, e, and f are closed. Subsequently the Dewar vessel is filled with liquid nitrogen and placed around (C). By means of the mercury pump (B) a certain amount of nitrogen is transferred from the gas burette (A) to the measuring system (C).

If the pressure in (C) increases, the mercury meniscus in the right-hand part of (E) will decrease. The mercury meniscuses in both arms of (E) are balanced by increasing the pressure in the left-hand part of (E) by opening stop cocks g and h. If the pressure indicated by (G) is equal to p_G mm Hg and the difference between the mercury levels of (E) is p_E mm Hg, the pressure in (C) is:

$$p = p_G - p_E. \tag{21}$$

The dead volume V_d is now defined as the volume of nitrogen (ml at STP) giving a pressure in (C) of 1000 mm Hg under the measuring conditions (room temperature 20°C, temperature of liquid nitrogen -196°C; level of liquid nitrogen in the Dewar vessel adjusted at a fixed point of (C); mercury levels in both arms of (E) balanced). If the volume of gas (ml at STP) introduced from (A) into (C) is equal to V:

$$V = 0 \cdot 001 p(V_d - K \cdot p_E) \tag{22}$$

in which K is a constant given by the diameter of the capillary of (E). The quantities V_d and K can be determined, by varying V as a function of p_E. When measuring the adsorption isotherm, V_d must be diminished by an amount of gas at 1000 mm Hg under the measuring conditions, namely the amount of gas that has been replaced by the volume of the sample to be measured. This amount V_s is given by:

$$V_s = \frac{1000}{760} \times \frac{273}{78} \times V_{sp} \times G \times 1 \cdot 04 = 4 \cdot 78 \times V_{sp} \times G \tag{23}$$

in which V_{sp} is the specific volume of the substance, G the weight in g, and is 1·04 a correction for the ideal gas law.

The adsorption isotherm is now measured in the same way as the dead volume. If the total volume of the gas in (C) is equal to V, the volume V_a adsorbed by 1 g of the substance to be investigated is given by:

$$V_a = \frac{1}{G}\left[V - \frac{p_G - p_E}{1000} \times (V_d - V_s - K \cdot p_E)\right].$$ (24)

The moment at which the pressure in (C) no longer changes faster than 0·1 mm/min is taken as equilibrium. This change will more or less correspond to an adsorbed volume of about 0·001 ml. The maximum equilibrium pressure obtainable measured in (C) is taken as the saturation pressure. The variations in the saturation pressure during the measurement are observed with the aid of the manometer (F).

B Determination of the Specific Surface Area by means of the Method of Brunauer, Emmett and Teller

The method usually applied for the determination of the specific surface area of solid substances is that proposed by Brunauer *et al.* (1938). The surface area is calculated from the reversible part of the isotherm. The equation derived by Brunauer *et al.* is based on the theory of multimolecular adsorption of gases on the surface. This theory assumes that, in the case of a normal adsorption by van der Waals bonds, bi-, tri-, etc., molecular layers can be formed before the surface is completely covered with the first layer. The conclusions arrived at by the above authors on the basis of the equation derived by them have been formulated as follows by de Boer (1953):

the average time of adsorption of a molecule on the surface of a solid substance is independent of the degree of occupation;
the average time of adsorption of a molecule on the layers already adsorbed is independent of the thickness of the adsorbed layer and of the degree of occupation.

The equation obtained by applying these assumptions is then:

$$\frac{p/p_0}{V_a(1 - p/p_0)} = \frac{1}{V_m C} + \frac{C - 1}{V_m C} \cdot p/p_0$$ (25)

in which V_a is the volume of gas adsorbed (ml STP/g substance); V_m is the volume of gas required to cover the whole surface of the solid substance with a unimolecular layer (ml STP/g substance); C is a constant, indicating the ratio between the adsorption time of the molecules in the first layer and the adsorption time of the molecules in the second and following layers, and p/p_0 denotes the relative pressure. Although the assumptions used in the derivation of this equation are very doubtful, practice has shown that the equation derived by Brunauer *et al.* is certainly useful when low relative pressures are concerned. The values obtained in this way for the specific surface area are in good agreement with those obtained by other methods (Harkins and Jura, 1944a; Zwietering, 1956; de Boer *et al.*, 1962). The surface area is obtained by plotting:

$$y = \frac{p/p_0}{V_a(1-p/p_0)} \text{ of equation (25) against } x = p/p_0.$$

In most cases a straight line will be obtained with a sufficient number of measuring points between a relative pressure of 0·05 and 0·25. V_m can be calculated from the slope of this straight line and the intercept on the y-axis.

For the calculation of the specific surface from V_m, the area occupied by a molecule in the unimolecular layer should be known. Emmett and Brunauer (1937) assumed that the density of a physically adsorbed multilayer is equal to the density of the liquid at the same temperature.

If it is assumed that the liquid structure corresponds to the closest packing of spheres with a diameter d, the specific surface area of a molecule is given by

$$s = \tfrac{1}{2}d^2\sqrt{3}$$

and its volume by

$$v = \tfrac{1}{2}d^3\sqrt{2} = \frac{MV_{sp}}{6·022\times10^{23}} \times 10^{24} \text{ Å}^3.$$

From this volume and the surface of a molecule it follows that

$$s = \tfrac{1}{2}\sqrt{3}\times\sqrt[3]{2v^2} = 1·530\sqrt[3]{M^2V_{sp}^2} \text{ Å}^2 \tag{26}$$

in which M is the molecular weight of the adsorbate and V_{sp} the specific volume of the liquid adsorbate in ml/g. In this way a value of 16·27 Å^2 is found for a nitrogen molecule. Using this value, the specific surface area of a solid substance is given by:

$$S_{\text{BET}} = 6·023\times10^{23}\times16·27\times10^{-20}\times\frac{V_m}{22414} \text{ m}^2/\text{g} = 4·371V_m \text{ m}^2/\text{g}. \tag{27}$$

De Boer and Kruyer (1952, 1958) showed that the picture given is not always correct, because especially in the case of very strong adsorption, the nitrogen molecule will lose one of its rotational degrees of freedom and will consequently occupy a different surface area. Experiments carried out by Harkins and Jura (1944b) and by Livingstone (1949) showed indeed that the surface (s) of a nitrogen molecule can vary from 14 to 17 Å^2.

The comparative measurements carried out by Lippens (1961), Meys (1961) and de Boer *et al.* (1962), with adsorption of lauric acid indicate, however, that a value of 16·27 Å^2 can be used very well for the surface determinations carried out with oxides and related substances.

$t = 0.35 \frac{V}{V_{III}}$

C The Common *t*-curve, its Extent and Limitation

Shull (1948) showed that for a number of non-porous solids, the nitrogen adsorption isotherms of which gave no indications of capillary condensation, the ratio between the adsorbed volume V_a and the volume of the unimolecular layer V_m, if plotted as a function of the relative pressure, could be represented approximately by a single curve. With the aid of this function the thickness of the adsorbed layer as a function of the relative pressure could be calculated, if this thickness was known for one point of the curve. Shull supposed that the thickness of a unimolecular layer is equal to the diameter of the nitrogen molecule. Assuming closest packing of spheres, this diameter has a value of 4·3 Å. In Shull's conception, however, the successive layers of the multimolecular adsorption assembly are packed in such a way that each nitrogen molecule of a following layer is situated just on top of a nitrogen molecule of the previous layer. This does not correspond to closest packing, which he assumed for the calculation of the diameter of the nitrogen molecule. For the calculation of the *t*-values we have to assign the same density to the adsorbed layers as to the capillary condensed liquid, which is taken to have the density of normal liquid nitrogen. It is therefore necessary to use in this case a statistical thickness which is defined as:

$$t = (X/S) \cdot 10^4 \text{ Å} = (M \cdot V_{sp}/22414) \cdot (V_a/S) \cdot 10^4 \text{ Å} \qquad (28)$$

where t is the statistical thickness of the adsorbed layer; X is the adsorbed volume in ml of liquid adsorbate; S is the specific surface area in m^2/g of adsorbent; M is the molecular weight of the adsorbate; V_{sp} is the specific volume of the adsorbate in ml/g; and V_a is the adsorbed volume of the adsorbate in ml gas STP/g of adsorbent.

For nitrogen we obtain:

$$t = 15\cdot 47(V_a/S) \text{ Å}. \qquad (29)$$

For S in this equation we take the surface area S_{BET} measured by the method described above in Section V B. We assumed the adsorbate

V_a : ml of absorbed gas per gram of adsorbent

at standard phase

to have a close-packed structure, like liquid nitrogen, so that $16.27 \, \text{Å}^2$ may be taken for the surface area occupied by one molecule. This figure leads us to Eq. (27). Introducing this into Eq. (29), we obtain

$$t = 3.54(V_a/V_m) \, \text{Å}. \tag{30}$$

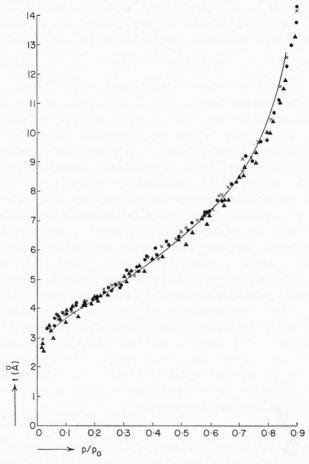

FIG. 8 Calculated t-values as a function of the relative pressure for $BaSO_4$ ($\bullet$) TiO_2 ($\times$), and Al_2O_3 ($\blacktriangle$).

From the latter equation it follows that for a unimolecular layer where $V_a = V_m$, the value of t equals $3.54 \, \text{Å}$. This value differs considerably from the figure of $4.3 \, \text{Å}$ used by Shull.

The t-values of the adsorption branches of several well selected samples of aluminium hydroxide and oxide (Lippens, 1961; Lippens *et al.*, 1964), TiO_2, $BaSO_4$, ZrO_2, MgO, Ni-antigorite, SiO_2 (Aerosil) and three graphitized carbon blacks (de Boer *et al.*, 1965a) were calculated using Eq. (30). Figures 8–10 show that the *t*-curves measured for TiO_2, MgO, ZrO_2, $BaSO_4$, and Ni-antigorite are practically identical

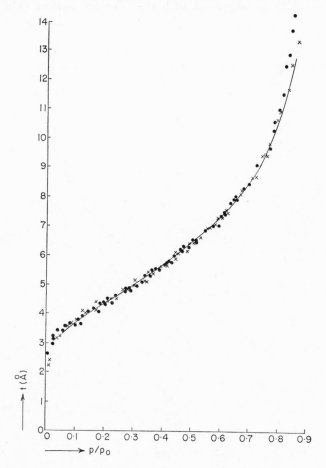

FIG. 9 Calculated *t*-values as a function of the relative pressure for ZrO_2 (●) and MgO (×).

with the curve measured for aluminium hydroxides and oxides (drawn line) up to a relative pressure of 0·75. It is quite understandable that at this relative pressure capillary condensation can start and deviations occur. There is no appreciable influence of the nature of the surface on the thickness of the adsorbed layer, although such an influence might have been expected considering the difference in structure. However, the fact that no difference is observed is not surprising, because many authors have in the past found indications of the same phenomenon (Brunauer, 1943).

In the case of SiO_2 (Aerosil), the t-values calculated for relative pressures <0.15 are identical with the common t-curve (Fig. 10). In

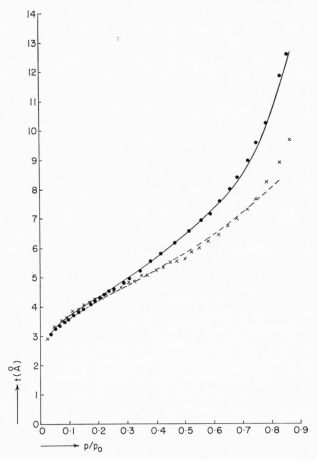

FIG. 10 Calculated t-values as a function of the relative pressure for SiO_2 (Aerosil) ($\times$) and nickel antigorite ($\bullet$).

this case, again, there is no appreciable influence of the nature of the surface on the thickness of the adsorbed layer. Other silica gels show the same pattern (Linsen, 1964). For relative pressures >0.15 the thickness t calculated for SiO_2 greatly deviates from the common t-curve. This can be explained by an influence of the silica (Linsen,

1964; de Boer *et al.*, 1968). The *t*-curves for Al_2O_3, TiO_2, MgO, ZrO_2, $BaSO_4$, and nickel antigorite are derived from adsorption isotherms measured with preparations having slit-shaped pores (Al_2O_3 and nickel antigorite) or with preparations having large elementary particles (Al_2O_3, TiO_2, MgO, ZrO_2 and $BaSO_4$), for which the surface can be assumed to be flat and in or between which no capillary condensation takes place at relative pressures lower than 0·7. Several geometric explanations are possible for the deviations of SiO_2 (Aerosil). A simple explanation, that would also be in agreement with the work of Geus and Kiel (1966), would be that the particles of Aerosil contain narrow pores. The latter authors state that the particles of Aerosil consist of small non-porous particles of about 15 Å, between which narrow pores may be present.

Another explanation would be the open structure of the arrangement of the surface atoms in non-porous silica gel particles (Okkerse, 1961). In that case too high a value may be calculated for the capacity of the unimolecular layer (V_m). As a result of it the calculated value for the thickness is too small, and deviations in the *t*-curve may occur.

A third explanation is based on geometric considerations. The particles of Aerosil are built up of very small non-porous spherical particles. The surface available for adsorption is not constant during adsorption, but is a function of the thickness t and of the average number of particles touching each given particle, which we shall call the coordination number. As a result of this texture, using Eq. (30), a formal thickness t_f of the adsorbed layer (Broekhoff and de Boer, 1967b) will be found and not the actual one (t).

The last explanation is based on the general phenomenon that the curvature of a surface has an influence on the adsorption. The thermodynamic treatment of this phenomenon will be given in Section VI of this chapter, in which it is shown that the thickness of the adsorbed layer of nitrogen on a curved surface is different from that on a flat surface at the same pressure. The last two explanations, which are considered to be the most plausible, will be treated in detail in the same section. The effects exerted on the *t*-values calculated from Eq. (30) by the surface curvature (itself a function of the particle size) and by the coordination number will be shown quantitatively for four different Degussa Aerosils.

Using the V_m-value calculated from the BET equation (25), in equation (30) the *t*-values of the graphitized carbon blacks do not correspond to the common *t*-curve. However, a plot of V_a as a function of the thickness t, measured on alumina and other preparations, gives a straight line passing through the origin and shows that only the points corresponding to lower pressures deviate from this straight line (Fig. 11).

The value of the surface area (S_t) calculated from this V_a/t-plot (Lippens, 1961; Linsen, 1964; Lippens and de Boer, 1965) is larger than the value obtained by means of the BET equation. The ratio

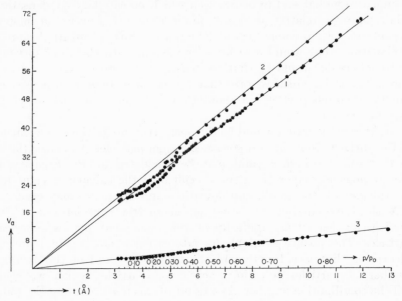

FIG. 11 Total volume adsorbed *vs.* layer thickness of Graphon I (1), Graphon II (2), and Sterling FT (3).

S_t/S_{BET} is constant for the three graphitized carbon blacks (1.10). This difference is already indicated in the literature (Pierce and Ewing, 1962; Pierce and Ewing, 1964). The observed deviations have been discussed in detail by de Boer *et al.* (1967) and may be ascribed to super-critical two-dimensional densification bends. From these discussions one may conclude that the surface area S_t obtained from the V_a/t plot using the common t-curve is a better one than the surface area obtained from the BET equation. When one uses the value S_t in Eq. (29) for the calculation of the t-values, the resulting t-curve is exactly the same as the common t-curve above relative pressures of about 0·35 (Fig. 12).

Comparing the common t-curve—the values of which are given in Table I—with a t-curve drawn by Barrett *et al.* (1951b), derived from data of various other substances (but corrected by multiplying the figures by 3·54/4·3 because of the considerations at the beginning of this section), one finds that the common t-curve lies slightly higher (Lippens, 1961). Cranston and Inkley (1957) published a t-versus p/p_0 curve for substances of very divergent nature; this curve is higher than the other two, especially at low values of p/p_0 (Lippens, 1961).

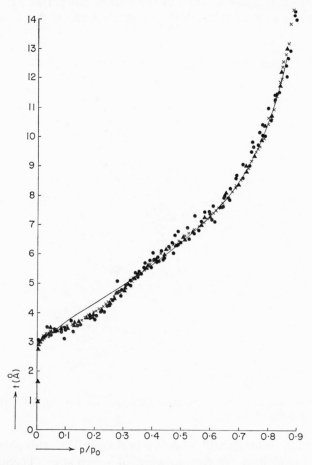

FIG. 12 Calculated t-values as a function of the relative pressure for graphitized carbon blacks (2700°C): (▲) Graphon I, (×) Graphon II, (●) Sterling FT.

Adamson *et al.* (1967) studied the adsorption of nitrogen one ice-powders prepared at 77°K. The adsorption isotherms clearly indicated a fairly uniform and not highly polar surface. Annealing at −70°C led to adsorption behaviour characteristic of non-polar surfaces, and the surface inertness towards nitrogen reached an extreme in the case of snow samples. For some of these samples (1A, 4A, 2A and 3A) the

V_a-values are plotted against the common t-values in Fig. 13. Zettle-moyer (1950) and Graham (1962) studied the adsorption of nitrogen at 78°K on polyethylene and polytetrafluoroethylene. In Fig. 13 the V_a-values for these samples are also plotted against the common t-values (curves B and C). None of the curves plotted in Fig. 13 gives a straight line passing through the origin, but all cut the V_a-axis with

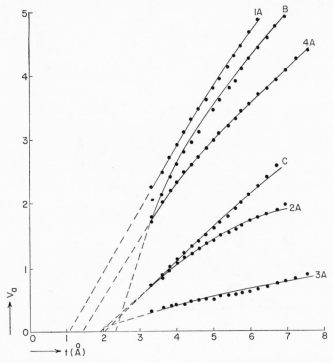

FIG. 13 Total volume adsorbed *vs.* layer thickness for ice (A), polyethylene (B), and polytetrafluoroethylene (C).

a negative intercept. As will be shown in Section V D, this phenomenon cannot be explained by the presence of micropores. Therefore, one must draw the conclusion that the common t-curve does not apply to every solid substance, and that especially non-polar samples with primarily hydrogen atoms exposed on the surface may give rise to difficulties.

One would be tempted to expect that water adsorbed on solid surfaces may cause deviations from the common t-curve. The work of Karasz *et al.* (1956) shows, however, that this expectation is not ful-filled. These authors studied the influence of pre-adsorbed water on anatase on the adsorption of nitrogen at 78°K. Figure 14 shows their V_a-values plotted against the common t-values. From this figure it follows that all samples give straight lines running through the origin below a t-value of about 6 Å. Only the surface area decreases with increasing amount of pre-adsorbed layers of water. The latter phenomenon is probably caused by blocking of micropores. The fact, that

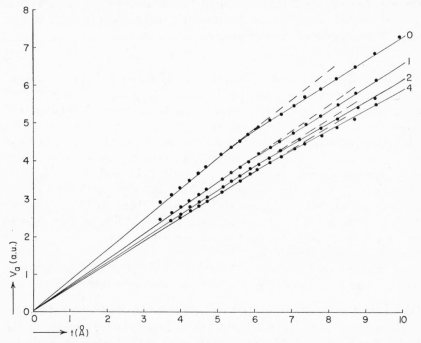

FIG. 14 Total volume adsorbed *vs.* layer thickness for TiO_2 with 0, 1, 2 and 4 layers of water pre-adsorbed.

all the curves bend downwards above a t-value of about 6 Å and then all have nearly the same slope, indicates also the presence of micropores. Despite the presence of rather large amounts of pre-adsorbed water, the common t-curve remains equally useful.

D Application of the t-curve to the Interpretation of Pore Shape and Width

In the previous section it has been shown that for several well selected samples, in which the multimolecular layer of adsorbed nitrogen could be formed freely on all parts of the surface, its statistical thickness $t = 15\cdot47\ V_a/S_{BET}$, practically independently of the nature of the sample. Deviations occur only in a few special cases (carbon, ice, polyethylene, and polytetrafluoroethylene). The experimental values of V_a (the volume of nitrogen adsorbed in cm³ STP/g sample) which are obtained as a function of the relative pressure p/p_0, may be transformed with the aid of Table I into functions of t, as already shown in Figs 11, 13, and 14. By plotting V_a for an unknown sample as a function of the t-value, corresponding to the relative pressures of the experiment, we obtain a straight line as long as the multilayer is formed unhindered. This straight line runs through the origin, and its slope is a measure of the surface area

$$S_t = 15 \cdot 47 V_a/t. \tag{31}$$

This quantity S_t will not always be exactly equal to S_{BET}, as instead of the various C-values in the BET equation (depending on the sample) an average value is used by introducing the t-curve. A further consequence of averaging the C-values is that at lower relative pressures, where the influence of the C-value on the shape of the isotherm is largest, noticeable deviations from the straight line through the origin may sometimes occur. In almost all cases it was found (Lippens, 1961; Lippens et al., 1964; Linsen, 1964; de Boer and Lippens, 1964a, 1964b; de Boer et al., 1965b; Lippens and de Boer, 1965; de Vleesschauwer, 1967) that the first part of such curves is a straight line passing through the origin, from which S_t could be calculated; the values obtained were in good agreement with S_{BET}.

At higher relative pressures (higher t-values) deviations from a straight line may occur (Fig. 15). We may distinguish three cases:

(a) *There is no deviation from the straight line running through the origin*

The surface is freely accessible up to high relative pressures; the multilayer can form unhindered on all parts of the surface; the adsorption branch of the isotherm has entirely the shape of the t-curve; the V_a/t plot is a straight line.

(b) *At a certain relative pressure the curve bends upwards*

At this pressure capillary condensation will occur in pores of certain shapes and dimensions; the material takes up more adsorbate than corresponds to the volume of the multilayer. The adsorption branch lies above the t-curve; the slope of the V_a/t plot increases.

(c) *At a certain relative pressure the curve bends downwards*

In some types of pores capillary condensation is only possible at very high relative pressures (slit-shaped pores or large holes). As long as the multilayer adsorption is unhindered, the V_a/t plot is a straight line. If the pressure increases the free space in the pores becomes

smaller owing to the growth of the adsorbed layer. Large holes will only
be filled by capillary condensation at relative pressures close to unity.
In a slit-shaped pore, however, again no capillary condensation can
occur, but at a certain moment the pore may be completely filled by
the adsorbed layers on both parallel walls. The surface area in such
pores is no longer accessible above a certain relative pressure; the
V_a/t plot will now have a smaller slope, corresponding to the surface
area still accessible.

Striking conclusions concerning the shape and dimensions of pores
can be drawn from V_a/t plots (Lippens, 1961; Lippens *et al.*, 1964;
Linsen, 1964; de Boer and Lippens, 1964a, 1964b; de Boer *et al.*,
1965b; Lippens and de Boer, 1965; de Vleesschauwer, 1967).

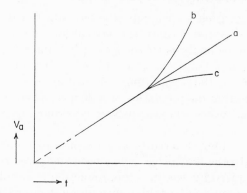

FIG. 15 Three fundamental shapes of a total volume adsorbed *vs.* layer thickness
plot.

TABLE I. Experimental thickness t of the multimolecular layer

p/p_0	t (Å)	p/p_0	t (Å)	p/p_0	t (Å)	p/p_0	t (Å)
0·08	3·51	0·32	5·14	0·56	6·99	0·80	10·57
0·10	3·68	0·34	5·27	0·58	7·17	0·82	11·17
0·12	3·83	0·36	5·41	0·60	7·36	0·84	11·89
0·14	3·97	0·38	5·56	0·62	7·56	0·86	12·75
0·16	4·10	0·40	5·71	0·64	7·77	0·88	13·82
0·18	4·23	0·42	5·86	0·66	8·02	0·90	14·94
0·20	4·36	0·44	6·02	0·68	8·26		
0·22	4·49	0·46	6·18	0·70	8·57		
0·24	4·62	0·48	6·34	0·72	8·91		
0·26	4·75	0·50	6·50	0·74	9·27		
0·28	4·88	0·52	6·66	0·76	9·65		
0·30	5·01	0·54	6·82	0·78	10·07		

3

VI   The Influence of Adsorption on Capillary Condensation and Evaporation

A   Introduction

The analysis of pore shapes and sizes from the vapour sorption iso-therm involves three important steps:

1. Reduction of the actual shape of the pores present in the adsorbent to a restricted number of idealized shapes, i.e. cylindrical, spheroidal, or slit-like shapes.
2. Identification of the sorbed phase with capillary-retained bulk liquid.
3. Application of Kelvin's equation to the (supposedly) bulk liquid present in (supposedly) ideal pore shapes.

Strictly speaking, each step involves severe simplification of physical reality, and we cannot expect the conclusions drawn from a pore size and pore shape analysis to be rigorously valid. Nevertheless, in a number of instances (Lippens, 1961; Linsen, 1964; de Vleesschauwer, 1967; Coenen *et al.*, 1964) the results of such an analysis have yielded valuable information on pore sizes and shapes, fairly consistent with information from other sources such as crystallography and electron microscopy.

A number of attempts have been published to improve the rigour of the method. In the first place, it has been suggested repeatedly that the errors introduced by the first step, reduction to simple pore shapes, may be partly compensated taking into account intersections between non-parallel oriented pores (Steggerda, 1955; Wheeler, 1951; Flood, 1958). All these attempts depend on a definite picture of the pore orientation, whereas in practice this orientation is hardly ever known in advance and may be completely dependent on the mode of prepara-tion of the adsorbent. The corrections involved in the introduction of pore intersections will not be pursued in this chapter.

The identification of the capillary-held adsorbate with bulk liquid (apart from the presence of a meniscus) is an intuitive one. Hardly anything is as yet known about the state of multimolecularly adsorbed and capillary-condensed phases. The multimolecular adsorption of krypton (Chapter 2) suggests that the field of attraction emanating from the pore walls, although falling off roughly in proportion to the cube of the distance, may not be negligible even for the fifth or higher layers. If the density of the adsorbed layer is assumed to be equal to that of the bulk liquid (an assumption contradictory to, e.g. the BET picture of multimolecular adsorption), then the mere existence of multilayer adsorption implies that the adsorbed (and so the capillary-

held) phase is never identical with the bulk liquid at the same temperature. Even if we assume the density and the liquid-vapour surface
tension of the adsorbed phase to be identical with those of the bulk
liquid, we still have to assign to the thermodynamic potential of the
adsorbed layer a value lower than that of the bulk liquid for adsorption
to be possible. This thermodynamic potential will be a function of the
number of moles adsorbed per unit surface area, and thus of the thickness of the adsorbed layer, and for very large thicknesses may be
assumed to converge to the value for the bulk liquid (neglecting the
possibility of enantiotropic or monotropic phase relations between the
adsorbed and the bulk liquid phase (Deryagin, 1967)).

As to the application of Kelvin's equation, there is of course the
question of the validity of applying macroscopic thermodynamics to
the relatively small number of molecules present in one single pore.
This problem has not yet been treated satisfactorily, and no statistical
treatment of sorption in pores has yet been developed. Even if we
accept the methods of macroscopic thermodynamics, we are still faced
with the problems involved in the definition of surface tension for
highly curved interfaces and with the influence of large curvatures on
the value of the surface tension (Gibbs, 1961b; Tolman, 1948; Kirkwood
and Buff, 1949; Buff, 1955; Defay et al., 1966). Both problems have
enjoyed a vivid interest in recent times, but no satisfactory definite
treatment is available. Ignoring all these problems, it still remains
clear from the previous points that we have to apply Kelvin's equation
not to a bulk liquid but to a phase whose properties depend on the
distance from the pore wall. In this section we shall give a detailed
treatment of the liquid-vapour equilibria for adsorbed phases present
in pores, based on the following assumptions:

1. It is permissible to use macroscopic thermodynamic methods for
   pores with radii down to approximately 20 Å.
2. The density of the adsorbed phase and its surface tension do not
   differ significantly from those of the bulk liquid at the same temperature.
3. The thermodynamic potential of the adsorbed phase is determined
   by the distance of the adsorbate/vapour interface from the surface
   of the adsorbent; its dependence on pore geometry is negligible for
   practical purposes.
4. There is a continuous transition from the adsorbed phase to the
   bulk liquid when the thickness of the adsorbed phase is increased.
   Essentially, this means that the bulk liquid wets the surface of
   the adsorbent completely at saturation. The case of contact angle
   has been treated elsewhere (Broekhoff and de Boer, 1968d).

Assumption 3 may be written as:

$$\mu_a = \mu_L - F(t) \tag{32}$$

where μ_a is the thermodynamic potential of the adsorbed phase having thickness t, μ_L is that of the bulk liquid at the same temperature, and $F(t)$ is a function which at each sub-critical temperature may be determined from a t-curve of multimolecular adsorption.

B—Capillary Condensation in Open Cylinders and Spheroidal Cavities

Consider an open cylinder of uniform radius r, in contact with a vapour of relative pressure p/p_0 at some temperature T. The thickness of the adsorbed layer at this pressure may be denoted by t_e. This thickness differs from that measured on a flat surface of the same adsorbent at the same relative pressure, owing to the curvature of the adsorbate/vapour interface. The magnitude of this difference may be estimated as follows.

Considering a transfer of dN moles of vapour to the adsorbed phase at the same pressure and temperature, equilibrium requires that there will be no change in the free enthalpy of the system. The change in the free enthalpy of the system is given by:

$$dG_{p,T} = (\mu_a - \mu_g)\, dN + \gamma\, dA \tag{33}$$

where μ_g is the thermodynamic potential of the gas phase; γ is the adsorbate/vapour surface tension; and dA is the change in absorbate/vapour interface associated with the transfer of dN moles of vapour to the adsorbed phase.

The ratio of dA to dN—completely determined by the curvature of the adsorbate/vapour interface and by the molar volume of the adsorbate—is given by Adam (1930):

$$dA/dN = V_L(1/R_1 + 1/R_2) \tag{34}$$

where V_L is the molar volume, and R_1 and R_2 are the two principal radii of curvature.

For a meniscus that is convex as viewed from the vapour phase, R_1 and R_2 are positive. For the adsorbate/vapour interface in a cylinder open at both sides Eq. (34) reduces to:

$$dA/dN = -V_L/(r-t). \tag{35}$$

Combination of Eqs (32), (33), and (35) and making use of the relations

$$\partial G_{p,T} = 0 \tag{36}$$

for equilibrium, and

$$\mu_L - \mu_g = RT \ln (p_0/p) \tag{37}$$

leads to:

$$RT \ln (p_0/p) - F(t) = \gamma V_L/(r-t) \text{ for } t = t_e. \tag{38}$$

For a given (p/p_0), Eq. (38) may be solved for t. However, as we shall show, there is a restriction on the values of t corresponding to a stable liquid-vapour equilibrium. The requirement for a stable equilibrium is:

$$\eth^2 G_{p,T} \geqslant 0 \tag{39}$$

for every possible infinitesimal change in the state of the system at constant p and T. In the case considered here, condition (39) is equivalent to

$$d^2G/dN^2_{p,T} \geqslant 0. \tag{40}$$

From Eqs (32), (33), (35), and (37), it follows that:

$$-dF(t)/dt - \gamma V_L/(r-t)^2 \geqslant 0 \text{ for } t = t_e. \tag{41}$$

Relation (41) is always satisfied for sufficiently small values of t_e, but there is a value of t_e, which we shall denote by t_{cr}, given by:

$$-\left(\frac{dF(t)}{dt}\right)_{t = t_{cr}} = \gamma V_L/(r-t_{cr})^2 \tag{42}$$

at which the adsorbed phase in a cylindrical pore just becomes unstable. At this point capillary condensation takes place and the pore fills spontaneously. The corresponding critical relative pressure of capillary condensation may be calculated directly from Eq. (38) by inserting this value for t_{cr}. The general behaviour of t as a function of p/p_0 is given in Fig. 16. The thickness of the adsorbed layer is seen to be increased substantially by the effect of curvature, even at moderate relative pressure. The outcome of the present treatment differs considerably from that of Cohan (1938). Evidently, Cohan neglected $F(t)$, implicitly assuming it to be identical with zero. In this case Eq. (38) reduces to

$$RT \ln (p_0/p) = \gamma V_L/(r-t). \tag{43}$$

However, relation (41) is never satisfied, as

$$-\gamma V_L/(r-t)^2 \leqslant 0.$$

This means that a concavely curved ring of bulk liquid is never stable, so that the application of (38) to the adsorbed layer, if $F(t)$ is neglected, is not permitted thermodynamically for any relative pressure or thickness of the adsorbed layer. Thus, we may conclude that Cohan's equation (43) is erroneous, and hence this equation has to be replaced by an equation of the type of Eq. (41). For further details the reader is referred to Broekhoff and de Boer (1967a). The application of the present theory to adsorption in spheroidal cavities (the idealization of type I ink-bottle bodies) (Broekhoff and de Boer, 1968a) is straight-forward. In spheroidal cavities the adsorbate/vapour interface has two equal radii of curvature. Equation (34) reduces to:

$$dA/dN = -2\gamma V_L/(r-t) \qquad (44)$$

where r is the radius of the cavity. As we have assumed $F(t)$ to be independent of the pore shape, the requirement of a minimum free

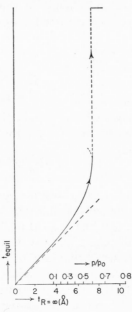

FIG. 16 The equilibrium thickness of the adsorbed nitrogen layer in a cylindrical pore, as a function of pressure, in comparison with the corresponding thickness of the adsorbed layer at a flat surface.

enthalpy of the system for spheroidal cavities leads to an analogue of Eq. (38), namely

$$RT \ln (p_0/p) - F(t) = 2\gamma V_L/(r-t) \text{ for } t = t_e. \qquad (45)$$

The condition for stability is that t_e should be smaller than a critical value of t, which may again be denoted by t_{cr} and which is determined by the relation:

$$-dF(t)/dt - 2\gamma V_L/(r-t)^2 = 0 \text{ for } t = t_{cr}. \qquad (46)$$

Neglecting $F(t)$ in Eq. (45) we obtain:

$$RT \ln (p_0/p) = 2\gamma V_L/(r-t) \qquad (47)$$

an equation already derived by Cohan (1944). This equation is again incompatible with the requirement of thermodynamic stability. Physically, this means that there is an inconsistency in assuming the thermodynamic potential of the condensed phase at a distance t from the pore wall to be equal to that of the bulk phase (an explicit assumption in Cohan's original treatment) and at the same time allowing adsorption to take place at relative pressures lower than unity.

The behaviour of the adsorbed layer in a spheroidal cavity is completely analogous to that in a cylindrical pore open at both ends. It must be realized, however, that over a certain range of relative pressures the adsorbed layer, although stable according to relation (41), is thermodynamically metastable with respect to a completely filled pore. In the present treatment, hysteresis of sorption in open cylinders may be explained along these lines. For details the reader is referred to Broekhoff and de Boer (1967a). For spheroidal cavities with narrow necks, part of the hysteresis may be explained along the lines adopted by Jurin (1718), Kraemer (1931) and McBain (1935), but it must be realized that hysteresis is also caused by the fact that over a certain range of relative pressures the adsorbed film is metastable with respect to the completely filled pore (Broekhoff and de Boer, 1968a).

C   Capillary Evaporation from Slit-shaped Pores

In slit-shaped pores the adsorbate/vapour interface is not curved, and —if we neglect the influence of the opposite wall on the state of the adsorbed layer—the thickness of this layer may be assumed to be equal to that on the surface of a non-porous adsorbent. This greatly simplifies the discussion of the adsorption branch for slit-shaped pores. The growth of the adsorbed layer may lead to pore blocking in sufficiently narrow pores, a phenomenon discussed in Section V, but no capillary condensation may be expected to occur.

Once a pore is completely filled with the capillary condensate, a meniscus is formed and capillary evaporation is controlled by this meniscus. Consider a pore of width d. In the classical theory of capillarity, where μ_a is taken to be equal to μ_L and the correction term $F(t)$ for adsorption is neglected, a hemi-cylindrical meniscus is formed at the edges of the pore. As a result of the pore symmetry one of the two principal radii of curvature of this meniscus will be infinite, assuming the length of the pore to be large in comparison with the width. The other radius of curvature will be completely determined by Kelvin's equation:

$$-R_1 = \gamma V_L / RT \ln (p_0/p). \tag{48}$$

An obvious requirement of physical stability for the meniscus is

$$R_1 \geqslant \tfrac{1}{2}d-t \tag{49}$$

where t is the thickness of the adsorbed layer. This means that evaporation will take place at a pressure just below that given by

$$\tfrac{1}{2}d-t = \gamma V_L/RT \ln (p_0/p). \tag{50}$$

This equation follows immediately from the appropriate analogues of Eqs (33) and (37). Contrary to Cohan's equation, Eq. (50) does not lead to thermodynamic inconsistencies. It is easy to show that Eq. (50) indeed corresponds to the limit of thermodynamic stability for a hemi-cylindrical meniscus. Here the neglect of $F(t)$ does not lead to a fundamental defect but rather to a quantitative error.

Accepting the dependence of the thermodynamic potential μ_a of the adsorbed and capillary-held phase on the distance from the pore wall, involves a meniscus that is no longer hemi-cylindrical. The criterion for capillary evaporation is then no longer as straightforward as Eq. (50) in the classical case (Broekhoff and de Boer, 1968d). Figure 17 shows an axial section through a meniscus in a slit-shaped pore. At a point P, lying at a distance x from the pore centre (a distance $t = x+\tfrac{1}{2}d$ from the nearest pore wall), the thermodynamic potential of the sorbed phase is equal to $\mu_a(t)$. The curvature $1/R_1$ at this point—being negative —may be expressed in coordinates of the line describing the section through the meniscus:

$$-1/R_1 = y''/(1+(y')^2)^{3/2}. \tag{51}$$

This curvature may be expressed more conveniently in terms of the angle (a) between the tangent at P and the positive direction of the abscissa. With the aid of the following substitutions

$$y' = tg(a), \quad y'' = 1/\cos^2 (a) \cdot d(a)/d(x),$$

Eq. (51) is transformed into:

$$-1/R_1 = d\{\sin (a)\}/dx. \tag{52}$$

To obtain the equilibrium condition for the meniscus we may now apply Eqs (33) and (34) to the point P of the meniscus and equate the result to zero. We then obtain:

$$d \sin (a)/dx = 1/\gamma V_L[RT \ln (p_0/p)-F(t)]. \tag{53}$$

This is a very simple differential equation describing completely the shape of the meniscus. The slope of the meniscus at many points may be calculated directly from Eq. (53), making use of the relation:

$$y' = tg(a) = \sin (a)/(1-\sin^2 (a))^{\tfrac{1}{2}}$$

and the complete shape of the meniscus may be found by integration. It is often convenient to transform Eq. (53) (using $t = x + \frac{1}{2}d$) into a function of t:

$$d \sin (a)/dt = 1/(\gamma V_L) \cdot [RT \ln (p_0/p) - F(t)]. \tag{54}$$

Integrating this equation from $d/2$ to t, and making use of the fact that on grounds of symmetry $\sin (a) = 0$ for $t = d/2$, we obtain:

$$\sin (a) = \frac{RT \ln (p_0/p) \cdot (t - d/2) + \int_t^{d/2} F(t) dt.}{\gamma V_L} \tag{55}$$

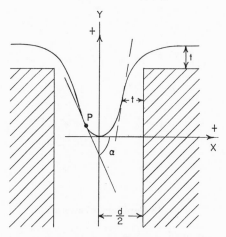

FIG. 17 Axial section through the meniscus in a slit-shaped pore.

At a relative pressure p_d/p_0, the thickness of the adsorbed layer at parts of the pore not covered with a meniscus is equal to t_d. The limiting shape of the meniscus is such that the meniscus just touches this adsorbed layer for $t = t_d$. This means, if p_d is the capillary desorption pressure, that $\sin (a)$ must be equal to -1 for $p = p_d$. The desorption criterion may then be derived from Eq. (55):

$$\frac{1}{2}d - t_d = \frac{\gamma V_L + \int_{t_d}^{d/2} F(t) \, dt}{RT \ln (p_0/p_d)}. \tag{56}$$

As t_d is supposed to be independent of the pore width and thus uniquely defined by the relative pressure, a relative pressure p_d/p_0 for each value of d can be calculated from Eq. (56). More detailed analysis of (55) leads to the conclusion that the meniscus is indeed no longer hemi-cylindrical. At $p = p_d$ the meniscus is infinitely extended, leading to complete emptying of the pore except for the adsorbed layer of thickness

t_d (see Fig. 18). Eq. (56), which resembles the equation given earlier by Deryagin (1957) (Eq. (14), contains an additional correction term for the influence of adsorption on capillary evaporation. This equation may be obtained in different ways by thermodynamic reasoning (Broekhoff, 1969). However, the derivation given here in principle leads to a more detailed insight into the mechanism of capillary evaporation.

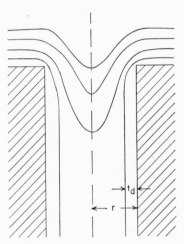

FIG. 18 Capillary evaporation.

D   Desorption from Cylindrical Pores

The treatment of capillary evaporation from cylindrical pores is analogous to that for slit-shaped pores (Broekhoff and de Boer, 1968b), although the meniscus geometry is somewhat more complicated. An axial section through the meniscus is shown in Fig. 19. At a point P of the meniscus the two main radii of curvature of the meniscus are unequal and are both finite. The first principal radius of curvature is equal to the radius of curvature of the line tracing the intersection of the meniscus with a plane passing through the axis of the cylinder. If the intersection line coordinates are denoted by X and Y, the radius of curvature of this line is given by:

$$-1/R_1 = \frac{y''}{(1+(y')^2)^{3/2}} = \frac{d \sin (a)}{dx} \tag{57}$$

where (a) again denotes the angle, between the tangent at P and the positive direction of the abscissa in Fig. 19. The second radius of curvature, R_2, which is perpendicular to R_1, is determined by the same angle (a) and by the distance of P from the pore axis. It may be proved that R_2 is given by:

$$1/R_2 = \frac{-\sin(a)}{x} \tag{58}$$

We now may use Eqs (57) and (58) to derive the local equilibrium condition for the meniscus at the liquid-vapour interface. From Eqs (33), (36), and (37), we obtain the differential equation:

d $\sin(a)/\mathrm{d}x + \sin(a)/x = [\mu_a - \mu_g]/(\gamma V_L)$

$$= [RT \ln(p_0/p) - F(t)]/\gamma V_L \tag{59}$$

As, according to definition, x is equal to $(t-r)$, Eq. (59) may be solved in terms of r and t, leading to

$$-\sin(a) \cdot (r-t) = 1/(\gamma V_L) \int_t^r (r-t) \cdot [RT \ln(p_0/p) - F(t)] \, \mathrm{d}t \tag{60}$$

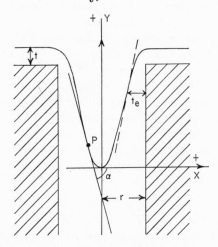

FIG. 19 Axial section through the meniscus in a cylindrical pore.

This equation again describes at each given relative pressure the shape of the meniscus as a function of the pore radius and the distance from the pore wall. The complete equation of the meniscus may again be found from the relation $y' = tg(a)$ by integration. The shape of the meniscus depends on the relative pressure and deviates considerably from the hemispherical shape of the meniscus given by the classical capillarity treatment.

In parts of the pore not filled with capillary condensate, and in particular at the mouth of the pore, there is an adsorbed layer of thickness t_e, dependent on the relative pressure and the pore radius. This thickness t_e is given by Eq. (45). At the relative pressure of capillary evaporation (p_d/p_0) the meniscus just touches this adsorbed layer at a distance t_e from the pore wall. At this relative pressure sin $(a) = -1$ for $p = p_d$ and $t = t_e$. Under these circumstances Eq. (60) reduces to:

$$r - t_e = \frac{2\gamma V_L + 2\int_{te}^{r} (r-t) \cdot F'(t)\, \mathrm{d}t\, (r-te)}{RT \ln (p_0/p_d)} \tag{61}$$

Eq. (61) is the proper desorption criterion for uniform cylindrical pores, when the corrections for adsorption are taken into account. For each relative pressure it contains two parameters, r and t_e. According to Eq. (45), t_e is itself a function of r and p/p_0. For each relative pressure the corresponding r and t_e may be found by solving Eqs (45) and (61) simultaneously.

It may be proved that at the pressure p_d the meniscus is infinitely elongated, so that the pore is completely empty. Below this pressure, only an adsorbed layer remains at the pore walls, the thickness of which is given by Eq. (45). As the pressure p_d may be shown to be always smaller than the pressure p_a corresponding to relation (46), for every pore radius hysteresis is to be expected (Broekhoff and de Boer, 1967a). During adsorption, every state corresponding to pressures between p_d and p_a is metastable with respect to the desorption branch at the same relative pressure. The phenomenon of the inception of hysteresis, frequently observed in practice, may be taken as a sign of a breakdown in the macroscopic description of capillarity in pores below a certain critical radius.

E The Thickness of the Adsorbed Layer on Curved Surfaces

In Section VI B, we have shown how curvature influences the thickness of the adsorbed layer in a cylindrical pore. The general trend was found to be an increase in the thickness of the adsorbed layer up to a certain critical thickness at which the whole adsorbed layer becomes unstable, leading to complete pore filling. On spheroidal particles, exactly the opposite phenomenon may be expected (de Boer et al., 1968). Here we may expect the influence of curvature to result in a decreased thickness of the adsorbed layer with respect to that on a non-curved surface at the same relative pressure. The question that now arises is whether there is a limit to the stability of the adsorbed layer on a spheroidal particle.

Thermodynamic treatment of this situation follows the same lines as that of the adsorbed layer in a cylindrical pore. Consider a sphere of radius r, covered with an adsorbed layer of thickness t. If the adsorbed layer is in equilibrium with the gas phase, then according to Eq. (36), $\delta G_{p,T} = 0$ for a transfer of dN moles of gas to the adsorbed phase. The curvature of the adsorbate/vapour interface of a spherical particle is given by:

$$R_1 = R_2 = r+t$$

so that Eq. (34) reads

$$dA/dN = 2V_L/(r+t). \tag{62}$$

The equilibrium condition of the adsorbed layer from Eq. (33) is then seen to be equivalent to

$$RT \ln (p_0/p) - F(t) = -\gamma V_L/(r+t) \text{ for } t = t_e. \tag{63}$$

Contrary to Eq. (38), this last equation has, for a given value of r, a solution for t if $p/p_0 = 1$; we shall denote this solution by t_s. Thus, at saturation at a single spherical particle a finite number of layers is adsorbed. On the other hand, if $F(t)$ tends to zero for values of t tending to infinity, this last value of t is also a solution of Eq. (63) at $p/p_0 = 1$. The resulting isotherm is schematically represented in Fig. 20. The stability requirement, $\delta^2 G_{p,T} \geqslant 0$, here reduces to

$$-dF(t)/dt - \gamma V_L/(r+t)^2 \geqslant 0. \tag{64}$$

Consequently, there is a value t_m, situated between t_s and $t = \infty$, corresponding to the equality sign of Eq. (64) and to the point on the adsorption isotherm with a vertical slope in Fig. 20. For values of $t > t_m$ the adsorption isotherm is unstable, resulting in bulk condensation. Thus, in principle we may expect a certain degree of supersaturation for adsorption at spherical particles to be possible. It is interesting to compare the situation with that of a drop of bulk liquid in contact with its vapour. For such a drop the vapour pressure is higher than the bulk vapour pressure. However, at a constant temperature and vapour pressure a drop of bulk liquid is never stable, as may be immediately seen from Eq. (64) when $F(t)$ is put equal to zero. At constant vapour pressure a drop of bulk liquid starts to grow, resulting in a bulk mass of liquid. For adsorption at solid spherical particles, the adsorption forces restrict the stability of the adsorbed layer, until a limiting t_m for the thickness of this layer has been reached. This value of t_m corresponds to relative vapour pressures higher than unity. This behaviour is very difficult to verify in practice, as in agglomerates of particles interparticle condensation will occur at relative pressures lower than unity. It will be shown in Section VII that a reduction in the thickness of the adsorbed layer for spherical particles has been found experimentally, using nitrogen as an adsorbate at 77°K.

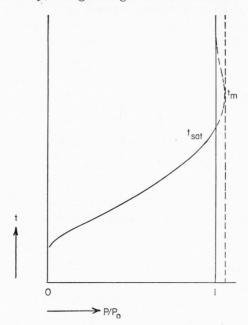

FIG. 20 Schematical representation of the adsorption on a curved surface.

VII   Application to the Calculation of Pore Size Distribution

A   Introduction

The nearly universal use of nitrogen as an adsorbate for the determination of complete sorption isotherms and the existence of a common t-curve on many adsorbents for the adsorption of nitrogen greatly simplifies the application of the concepts of the preceding section to actual pore size analysis. From the common t-curve of multimolecular nitrogen adsorption, we may derive an expression for the dependence of the thermodynamic potential on the thickness of the adsorbed layer (Broekhoff and de Boer, 1967b). Of course, the simplifying assumptions of constant adsorbate density and surface tension still remain. On these assumptions the curve $RT \ln (p_0/p)$ as a function of the thickness of the adsorbed layer expresses the difference between the thermodynamic potential of the adsorbed layer and that of the bulk phase.

If an analytical expression for this difference, which has been denoted by $F(t)$ in the preceding section, is obtained, a numerical application of the formulae derived for the capillary condensation and evaporation from pores becomes quite straightforward.

B Fundamental Numerical Relationships

As has been shown earlier (de Boer *et al.*, 1966), the common t-curve of multimolecular nitrogen adsorption between relative pressures of 0·1 and 0·8 may be described satisfactorily by an expression of the Harkins-Jura (1944a) type, namely

$$\log (p_0/p) = 13\cdot99/t^2 - 0\cdot034. \tag{65}$$

A modified equation has to be used for higher relative pressures, i.e.

$$\log (p_0/p) = 16\cdot11/t^2 - 0\cdot1682 \exp (-0\cdot1137t). \tag{66}$$

This expression describes the common t-curve adequately over the whole range from $p/p_0 = 0\cdot4$ onwards.

Consequently, we may express $F(t)$ as:

$$F(t) = 2\cdot3026 \, RT \, (13\cdot99/t^2 - 0\cdot034) \text{ for } t \text{ smaller than 10 Å} \tag{67a}$$

and

$$F(t) = 2\cdot3026 \, RT \{16\cdot11/t^2 - 0\cdot1682 \exp (-0\cdot1137t)\}$$
$$\text{for } t \text{ larger than 5 Å.} \tag{67b}$$

If we adopt the following values of surface tension and molar volume for liquid nitrogen at its normal boiling point

$$\gamma = 8\cdot72 \text{ dyne/cm}$$
$$V_L = 34\cdot68 \text{ cm}^3/\text{mole}$$

then the following numerical relations may be easily obtained:

(a) According to Eq. (38) the thickness t_e of the adsorbed layer in a cylindrical pore of radius r may be expressed as:

$$\log (p_0/p) - 13\cdot99/t_e^2 + 0\cdot034 = 2\cdot025/(r-t_e) \text{ for } t < 10 \text{ Å} \tag{68a}$$

or:

$$\log (p_0/p) - 16\cdot11/t_e^2 + 0\cdot1682 \exp (-0\cdot1137t_e) = 2\cdot025/(r-t_e) \tag{68b}$$
for $t > 5$ Å

(b) For a spheroidal cavity of radius r, the analogous expressions are:

$$\log (p_0/p) - 13\cdot99/t_e^2 + 0\cdot034 = 4\cdot05/(r-t_e) \tag{69a}$$

and

$$\log (p_0/p) - 16\cdot11/t_e^2 + 0\cdot1682 \exp (-0\cdot1137t_e) = 4\cdot05/(r-t_e) \tag{69b}$$

(c) If the cylinder is open at both ends and has a uniform diameter, then the stability limit during adsorption according to Eq. (42) is given by:

$$27 \cdot 98/t_{cr}^3 = 2 \cdot 025/(r-t_{cr})^2 \qquad (70a)$$

for $t_{cr} < 10$ Å and

$$32 \cdot 22/t_{cr}^3 - 0 \cdot 1682 \times 0 \cdot 1137 \; \exp \; (-0 \cdot 1137 t_{cr}) = 2 \cdot 025/(r-t_{cr})^2 \qquad (70b)$$

for $t > 5$ Å.

(d) The analogous expressions for spheroidal cavities of uniform dimensions are

$$27 \cdot 98/t_{cr}^3 = 4 \cdot 05/(r-t_{cr})^2 \qquad (71a)$$

and

$$32 \cdot 22/t_{cr}^3 - 0 \cdot 1682 \times 0 \cdot 1137 \; \exp \; (-0 \cdot 1137 t_{cr}) = 4 \cdot 05/(r-t_{cr})^2 \qquad (71b)$$

Equations (70) and (71) may be solved for t_{cr}, and p_a/p_0 may be found by substituting t_{cr} in the corresponding Eqs (68) and (69).

(e) According to Eq. (61), the relative pressure of capillary evaporation p_a/p_0 from cylinders of uniform diameter, either open at both ends or closed at one end, is related to t_e and r by (Broekhoff and de Boer, 1968c):

$$r-t_e = \frac{4 \cdot 05}{\log \; (p_0/p_a)} + \frac{27 \cdot 98[r/t_e - 1 - \ln \; (r/t_e)] - 0 \cdot 034(r-t_e)^2}{(r-t_e) \log \; (p_0/p_a)} \qquad (72a)$$

for $t_e < 10$ Å and

$$r-t_e = \frac{4 \cdot 05}{\log \; (p_0/p_a)} + \frac{32 \cdot 22[r/t_e - 1 - \ln \; (r/t_e)]}{(r-t_e) \log \; (p_0/p_a)} -$$

$$\frac{2 \cdot 964 \; \exp \; (-0 \cdot 1137 t_e)[r-t_e - 8 \cdot 795]}{(r-t_e) \log \; (p_0/p_a)} - \frac{26 \cdot 068 \exp(-0 \cdot 1137 r)}{(r-t_e) \log \; (p_0/p_a)} \qquad (72b)$$

for $t_e > 5$ Å.

These equations may be solved for p_a/p_0 when they are combined with the corresponding Eq. (66).

(f) For slit-shaped pores no corrections to the t-values are necessary. At each relative pressure the t-value may be calculated from Eqs (65) and (66) according to Eq. (56). In this case p_a/p_0 is given by the relations

$$\frac{d}{2} - t_a = \frac{2 \cdot 025 + 13 \cdot 99(1/t_a - 2/d) - 0 \cdot 034(d/2 - t_a)}{\log \; (p_0/p_a)} \qquad (73a)$$

for $t_a < 10$ Å and

$$\frac{d}{2} - t_a =$$

$$\frac{2 \cdot 025 + 16 \cdot 11(1/t_a - 2/d) + 1 \cdot 483[\exp(-0 \cdot 05685d) - \exp(-0 \cdot 1137t_a)]}{\log(p_0/p_a)}$$

(73b)

for $t_a > 5$ Å.

(g) According to Eq. (63), for spherical particles of radius r the thickness of the adsorbed layer at each relative pressure may be calculated from de Boer *et al.* (1968):

$$\log(p_0/p) = \frac{13 \cdot 99}{(t_e)^2} + \frac{4 \cdot 05}{(r + t_e)} - 0 \cdot 034.$$

(74)

As said already in Section V C, on a curved surface a formal thickness t_f is found from the relation:

$$t_f = \frac{V_a}{S_{\text{BET}}}$$

(75)

This thickness need not be equal to the thickness measured on flat surfaces. For adsorption on the wall of a cylindrical pore of radius r, the formal thickness is related to the equilibrium thickness (Broekhoff and de Boer, 1967b) t_e by:

$$t_f = t_e(1 - t_e/2r).$$

(76)

The analogue for a spheroidal cavity (Broekhoff and de Boer, 1968a) with radius r is:

$$t_f = t_e(1 - t_e/r + t_e^2/3r^2).$$

(77)

For the adsorption on a spherical particle t_f is given by:

$$t_f = t_e(1 + t_e/r + t_e^2/3r^2).$$

(78)

Deviations from the straight V_a/t plot, other than those due to capillary condensation or blocking of the pores (see Section V D), are due to deviations in t_f as a result of curvature of the surface.

In spite of the strong influence of curvature on t_e, in cylinders with medium pore radii t_f is not greatly different from the thickness measured on a flat surface (Broekhoff and de Boer, 1967b). An appreciable deviation from the straight line in a V_a/t plot is therefore generally caused by capillary condensation or pore blocking. A similar situation occurs in spheroidal cavities (Broekhoff and de Boer, 1968a). For adsorption on small spherical particles, however, t_f may greatly deviate from the thickness measured on a flat surface (de Boer *et al.*,

1968). A further complicating factor in the latter case is the coordination of particles.

In principle, the calculation of pore distributions from the sorption isotherm may be performed along the lines developed in Section IV B. There is, however, a complication due to the fact that, according to Eq. (68), the thickness of the adsorbed layer in cylindrical pores depends not only on the relative pressure but also on the pore radius.

It is possible to divide the whole range of pore diameters into certain groups of specified mean pore diameter and to assign to each group a corrected t-curve, the proper thickness of the adsorbed layer as a function of pressure to be calculated by means of Eq. (68). As the number of data is increasing quickly with the number of groups of pores with specified mean diameter, the method of calculation, although in principle very simple and straightforward, is too laborious to be performed on a desk calculator or a slide rule for routine work. If, however, a high-speed computer is available, no difficulties are encountered, as the calculation method is easy to program and the data of Eq. (68) only need to be calculated once and can be stored for later use.

For cylindrical pores, the equation for the pore size distribution calculation (Broekhoff and de Boer, 1967b) can be derived as follows: When the total length of the pores belonging to the kth pore group, filling or emptying at a relative pressure between x_k and $x_{(k-1)}$, with a corresponding mean pore radius r_k (for the adsorption branch r_k is calculated by means of Eq. (70) and for the desorption branch by Eq. (72)), is denoted by L_k, the total surface area by S_k, and the total pore volume of pores in this group by V_k, then it is immediately clear that the change in volume condensed in the porous system over the kth interval, ΔV_k^c, is given by:

$$\Delta V_k^c = \pi(r_k - t_{rk,xk})^2 L_k + \pi \sum_{i=1}^{k-1} L_i[(r_i - t_{ri,xk})^2 - (r_i - t_{ri,x(k-1)})^2] \quad (79)$$

in which $t_{ri,xk}$ denotes the equilibrium thickness of the adsorbed layer in a pore with radius r_i at a relative pressure x_k. The first part of the right-hand side of (79) corresponds to the change in the adsorbed volume due to pore filling or emptying, and the second part to the change in thickness of the adsorbed layer in the pores not filled with capillary condensate. With the aid of the obvious relations

$$S_k = 2\pi r_k L_k \quad (80)$$

and

$$V_k = \pi r_k^2 L_k \quad (81)$$

after rearranging, Eq. (79) may be written as:

$$S_k = \frac{2r_k}{(r_k-t_{rk,xk})^2}\left\{\Delta V_k^c - \sum_{i=1}^{k-1}\frac{S_i}{2r_i}[(r_i-t_{ri,xk})^2-(r_i-t_{ri,x(k-1)})^2]\right\} =$$

$$\frac{2r_k}{(r_k-t_{rk,xk})^2}\left[\Delta V_k^c - \sum_{i=1}^{k-1}S_i(t_{ri,x(k-1)}-t_{ri,xk}) + \sum_{i=1}^{k-1}\frac{S_i}{2r_i}(t_{ri,x(k-1)}^2-t_{ri,xk}^2)\right]. \qquad (82)$$

Equation (82) may be applied to the desorption as well as to the adsorption branch of the isotherm if the calculation is started in both cases as saturation, when all the pores are filled with capillary condensate. Thus the first interval corresponds, for example, to a pressure range of 1·000 to 0·995 relative pressure. In general, the kth interval is bounded by $x_{(k-1)}$, the upper pressure bound, and x_k, the lower pressure bound.

An analogous equation may be derived for spheroidal cavities (Broekhoff and de Boer, 1968a):

$$S_k = \frac{3r_k^2}{(r_k-t_{rk,xk})^3}\left\{\Delta V_k^c - \sum_{i=1}^{k-1}\frac{S_i}{3r_i^2}[(r_i-t_{ri,xk})^3-(r_i-t_{ri,x(k-1)})^3]\right\} \qquad (83)$$

It is clear that in this case only the adsorption branch of the isotherm applies. r_k is calculated by means of Eq. (71) and $t_{rk,xk}$ by means of Eq. (69).

For slit-shaped pores Eq. (20) may be used. However, the mean pore width d_k in this equation, is now given by Eq. (73).

C Examples of Pore Size Distributions

The proposed methods of calculation have been applied to a number of isotherms already published before for samples of alumina (Lippens, 1961; de Boer and Lippens, 1964a), zirconia (de Boer, 1965), porous glasses (Emmett and Cines, 1947), graphite oxides (van Doorn, 1957) and a nickel-silica catalyst (Linsen, 1964). The results of the calculations were given before (Broekhoff and de Boer, 1967b, 1968a,c,d). Three examples are given in Table II.

The isotherm measured for ZrO_2 was clearly of the A-type, and hence Eq. (82), valid for cylindrical pores, was applied to the adsorption branch as well as to the desorption branch, with the appropriate values for r_k. From Table II and Fig. 21 it is clear that both branches lead to the same results. The agreement between S_{cum} and S_{BET} and also between V_{cum} and V_p is excellent.

Application of the classical methods does not lead to satisfactory results. Cohan's equation (10) in particular gives relatively high values for S_{cum} and V_{cum}.

TABLE II. Cumulative surface areas and pore volumes as calculated from nitrogen sorption isotherms, compared with the results of a classical calculation

	p/p_0		S_{BET} (m²/g)	S_{cum} (m²/g)		S_{cum}-class (m²/g)		V_p ml/g	V_{cum} (ml/g)		V_{cum}-class (ml/g)	
	First deviation from t-plot	Closing point of hysteresis loop		Ads.	Des.	Ads.	Des.		Ads.	Des.	Ads.	Des.
ZrO₂-450 [1]	0·64	0·64	64	67	64	119	85	0·190	0·197	0·190	0·218	0·199
Porous glass No. 4 [2]	0·38	0·42	25·1	21·1	22·0	37·5	32·0	0·0305	0·0287	0·0290	0·0335	0·0315
Pr 21 reduced Ni/SiO₂ catalyst [3]	0·74	0·41	212	—	212	—	302	1·139	—	1·143	—	1·193

[1] Isotherm measured by Rijnten (de Boer, 1965). [2] Emmett and Cines (1947). [3] Isotherm measured by Linsen (1964).

Equation (83), valid for spheroidal cavities, was applied for the same isotherm. In this case also a good agreement between S_{BET} and S_{cum} (64 m^2/g) on the one hand and between V_p and V_{cum} (0·191 ml/g) on the other hand was found using the adsorption branch of the isotherm. Since application of the cylindrical model for the adsorption branch as

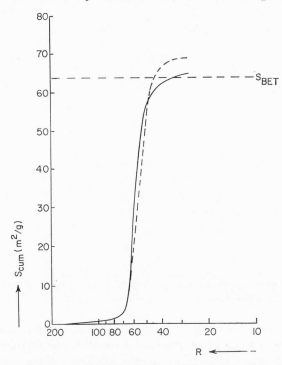

FIG. 21 Distribution curves for ZrO$_2$-450 (——) from desorption branch, (– – –) from adsorption branch.

well as the desorption branch leads to much the same distribution curves (Fig. 21), we must conclude that the sample of ZrO$_2$ clearly contains cylindrical pores.

The isotherm measured on porous glass was of the type E. From Table II it appears that in this case application of Eq. (82) valid for cylindrical pores, also results in values of S_{cum} and V_{cum} agreeing closely with those of S_{BET} and V_p. Using the model of spheroidal cavities for the adsorption branch (Eq. (83)) leads also to a good agreement $(S_{cum} = 21·1$ m^2/g and $V_{cum} = 0·0287$ ml/g). For this sample, however, application of the cylindrical model for the adsorption branch as well as for the desorption branch does not lead to coincident distribution curves (Fig. 22), and it must be concluded that this sample contains spheroidal cavities.

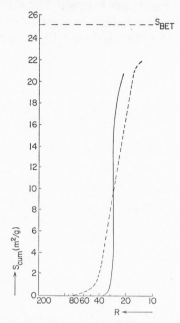

FIG. 22 Distribution curves for porous glass No. 4 (———) from desorption branch, (– – –) from adsorption branch.

The conclusions that the ZrO_2 sample contains cylindrical pores and the sample of porous glass spheroidal cavities are further supported by the shapes and widths of the hysteresis loops of the corresponding isotherms. For an ideal A-type isotherm the theoretical width of the hysteresis loop may be calculated from Eqs (70) and (72). For a distribution of pores the experimental width of the hysteresis loop on the high relative pressure side should be equal to the theoretical one, whereas on the low-pressure side a considerably smaller value will be observed.

From Table III it appears that only for ZrO_2-450 are the experimental and predicted widths equal at the high-pressure side. At the low-pressure side the experimental width is indeed smaller than the predicted one, and again the conclusion must be drawn that ZrO_2 contains cylindrically shaped pores. For the porous glass sample the experimental width differs greatly from the theoretical one at the high pressure side. This difference may be explained either by assuming the occurrence of spheroidal cavities or by assuming the occurrence of slit-shaped pores. From the fact, however, that for this sample the V_a/t plot deviates upwards in the appropriate relative pressure range (Broekhoff and de Boer, 1968d), one may exclude the presence of slit-shaped pores. The conclusion that the porous glass sample contains spheroidal cavities implies that the adsorption branch of the isotherm is the thermodynamically stable one. This conclusion is in agreement with the work of Kington and Smith (1964), who found by comparing calorimetric heats of adsorption with the isosteric ones that for porous glass the adsorption branch of the isotherm must be the stable one, again pointing to spheroidal cavities.

TABLE III. Observed and predicted widths of hysteresis loops

| Sample | p_a/p_0 | $p_a/p_0 - p_d/p_0$ | |
		Experimental	Predicted
ZrO_2-450	0·85	0·05	0·06
	0·81	0·05	0·07
	0·79	0·04	0·08
Porous glass No. 4	0·73	0·20	0·09
	0·67	0·14	0·10
	0·61	0·08	0·11
Pr 21 reduced	0·85	0·19	0·06
	0·73	0·24	0·09
	0·55	0·10	0·11

For the reduced Ni/SiO_2-catalyst "Pr 21" the isotherm was of type B, indicating the presence of slit-shaped pores. The V_a/t plot, also points to slit-shaped pores—no deviation occurred up to a relative pressure of 0·74 (Linsen, 1964). In agreement with the latter, the observed width of the hysteresis loop excludes the presence of cylindrical pores. The occurrence of spheroidal cavities could be excluded by electron-microscopic observations (Chapter 8). Calculation of the pore distribution from the desorption branch of the isotherm using the model of slit-shaped pores and the appropriate values for the mean pore width results in values of S_{cum} and V_{cum} that are in excellent agreement with S_{BET} and V_p. The evidence for the occurrence of slit-shaped pores is therefore quite strong. This conclusion is substantiated by Coenen's work (1958).

D   The Adsorption of Nitrogen on Loosely Packed Spherical Particles

In Section VC we showed that t-curves measured on SiO_2 (Aerosil) for relative pressures $> 0{\cdot}15$ deviate greatly from the common t-curve.

One of the possible explanations was based on geometric considerations. The particles of Aerosil are composed of very small non-porous spherical particles. The surface available for adsorption is not constant during the adsorption process, but is a function of the thickness t and of the average number of particles touching each particle, which is indicated by the "coordination number" a. In Section VII B it was shown that, on thermodynamic grounds, for spherical particles the equilibrium thickness t_e must be expected to be lower than the thickness measured on a flat surface at the same relative pressure (Eq. (74)).

It can be postulated that the BET area (S_{BET}°) of one elementary particle is given by the surface area of a sphere with radius r less the surface area of the segments cut off by other elementary particles touching the elementary particle under consideration:

$$S_{BET}^{\circ} = 2\pi\{2(r^2+2rn)-a(r^2+2rn-r\sqrt{r^2+2rn})\} \qquad (84)$$

The volume V_a° of the adsorbed layer of nitrogen on one elementary particle is given by the volume of a sphere with radius $(r+t_e)$ less the volume of the particle with radius r, the volume of the segments cut off by other elementary particles, and the volume of the space not accessible to nitrogen.

In this way the following equation (Linsen, 1964; de Boer et al., 1968) is obtained:

$$V_a^{\circ} = \frac{4}{3}\pi\left(3r^2t_e+3rt_e^2+t_e^3-\frac{3art_e^2}{4}-\frac{at_e^3}{2}\right)-$$
$$a\pi\left[\frac{r^3n^2(n+2r)}{(r+n)^3}-\frac{r^2n^2(2rn+3r^2)}{3(r+n)^3}-\left\{\frac{r\sqrt{n(n+2r)}}{r+n}-\right.\right.$$
$$\left.\left.\frac{5}{12}n\left(1-\frac{\sqrt{n(n+2r)}}{r+n}\right)\right\}\left(\frac{\pi n^2\theta}{360}-\frac{n^2\sin\theta}{2}\right)\right]. \qquad (85)$$

In these equations n is the radius of the adsorbed molecule, t_e is the equilibrium thickness of the adsorbed layer, and θ is the angle formed between the radii of the adsorbed molecule, drawn through the tangent points with the elementary particles.

The formal thickness t_f is given by the formula:

$$V_a^\circ = t_f \cdot S_{\mathrm{BET}}^\circ. \tag{86}$$

For each relative pressure, t_e may be calculated as a function of r by Eq. (74).

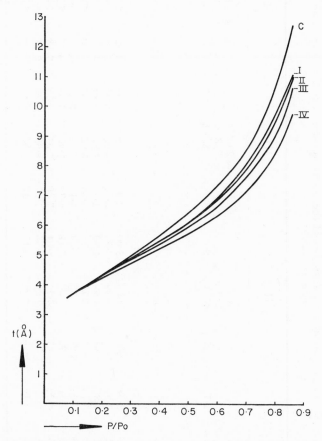

FIG. 23 Comparison between the common t-curve (C) and the curves measured on the Aerosil samples (I–IV).

The t-curves were measured for four different Aerosils (de Boer *et al.*, 1968) (Fig. 23). The deviation from the common t-curve increases with decreasing particle size of the Aerosil. Using the obtained values of t_e for each radius of r, we calculated t_f by means of Eqs (84)–(86) as a function of the relative pressure and hence as a function of the common t. The coordination number a in Eqs (84) and (85) is found by trial and error to obtain the best fit to each of the experimental isotherms

TABLE IV. Comparison between measured and calculated thicknesses of the adsorbed layer, taking the curvature of the surface into account

		I			II			III			IV		
		$r = 80$ Å $S_{BET} = 162$ m²/g $r_{corr} = 79$ Å $a = 2.7$			$r = 46$ Å $S_{BET} = 281$ m²/g $r_{corr} = 45$ Å $a = 2.0$			$r = 39$ Å $S_{BET} = 333$ m²/g $r_{corr} = 38$ Å $a = 2.3$			$r = 33$ Å $S_{BET} = 394$ m²/g $r_{corr} = 33$ Å $a = 3.2$		
p/p_0	Common t	t_e	t_f meas.	t_f calc.	t_e	t_f meas.	t_f calc.	t_e	t_f meas.	t_f calc.	t_e	t_f meas.	t_f calc.
0.032	3	2.99	2.96	2.98	2.94	2.90	3.00	2.93	2.98	2.97	2.92	2.95	2.91
0.146	4	3.90	4.01	3.94	3.83	3.99	3.96	3.91	4.00	3.81	3.78	3.95	3.80
0.300	5	4.81	4.91	4.87	4.68	4.90	4.89	4.63	4.83	4.81	4.58	4.72	4.64
0.440	6	5.65	5.72	5.75	5.45	5.75	5.74	5.38	5.62	5.61	5.30	5.42	5.41
0.562	7	6.50	6.58	6.64	6.21	6.55	6.59	6.10	6.38	6.43	6.00	6.08	6.13
0.660	8	7.32	7.60	7.51	6.92	7.40	7.41	6.78	7.23	7.19	6.63	6.78	6.81
0.725	9	7.97	8.45	8.20	7.47	8.26	8.04	7.30	7.97	7.78	7.13	7.42	7.33
0.778	10	8.60	9.34	8.87	7.98	9.20	8.65	7.78	8.68	8.33	7.58	8.08	7.82
0.818	11	9.15	10.10	9.46	8.43	10.00	9.17	8.19	9.35	8.80	7.96	8.76	8.22

below $p/p_0 = 0.7$. Meanwhile, the radius r compatible with (84) was calculated from a and S_{BET}, and the calculation was again performed with this new value of r. This procedure was repeated until consistent values for r and a were obtained. The results of these calculations are presented in Table IV.

The coordination numbers thus found are all between 2 and 3, in reasonable agreement with those expected from porosity data (de Boer *et al.*, 1968). The correspondence between measured and calculated t_f-values is quite good for p/p_0 below 0.7. Above this relative pressure we may expect capillary condensation in the cavities between the particles to become important, and eventually to predominate.

VIII References

Adam, N. K. (1930). "The Physics and Chemistry of Surfaces", p. 13. Oxford University Press, Oxford.

Adamson, A. W., Dormant, L. M., and Orem, M. (1967). *J. Colloid Sci.* **26**, 206.

Barrer, R. M., McKenzie, N. and Reay, J. S. S. (1956). *J. Colloid Sci.* **11**, 479.

Barrett, E. P., Joyner, L. G. and Halenda, P. P. (1951a). *J. Am. chem. Soc.* **73**, 373.

Barrett, E. P., Joyner, L. G. and Halenda, P. P. (1951b). *ADI-Document* No. 2936.

de Boer, J. H. (1935). "Electron Emission and Adsorption Phenomena". Chapter VIII. Cambridge University Press, Cambridge.

de Boer, J. H. (1938). *Z. Elektrochem.* **44**, 488.

de Boer, J. H. (1953). "The Dynamical Character of Adsorption". Clarendon Press, Oxford.

de Boer, J. H. (1958a). *Angew. Chem.* **70**, 383.

de Boer, J. H. (1958b). *In* "The Structure and Properties of Porous Materials" (D. H. Everett and S. Stone, eds), p. 68. Butterworth, London.

de Boer, J. H. (1959). *Chemy Ind.* 934.

de Boer, J. H. (1965). *Proc. Br. ceram. Soc.* **5**, 5.

de Boer, J. H. and Kruyer, S. (1952). *Koninkl. Ned. Akad. Wetenschap. Proc. Ser.* **B 55**, 451.

de Boer, J. H. and Kruyer, S. (1958). *Trans. Faraday Soc.* **54**, 540.

de Boer, J. H. and Lippens, B. C. (1964a). *J. Catalysis* **3**, 38.

de Boer, J. H. and Lippens, B. C. (1964b). *J. Catalysis* **3**, 44.

de Boer, J. H., Houben, G. M. M., Lippens, B. C., Meys, W. H. and Walrave, W. K. A. (1962). *J. Catalysis* **1**, 1.

de Boer, J. H., Linsen, B. G. and Osinga, Th. J. (1965a). *J. Catalysis* **4**, 643.

de Boer, J. H., Linsen, B. G., van der Plas, Th. and Zondervan, G. J. (1965b). *J. Catalysis* **4**, 649.

de Boer, J. H., Lippens, B. C., Linsen, B. G., Broekhoff, J. C. P., van den Heuvel, A. and Osinga, Th. J. (1966). *J. Colloid Interface Sci.* **21**, 405.

de Boer, J. H., Broekhoff, J. C. P., Linsen, B. G. and Meyer, A. L. (1967). *J. Catalysis* **7**, 135.

de Boer, J. H., Linsen, B. G., Broekhoff, J. C. P. and Osinga, Th. J. (1968). *J. Catalysis* **11**, 46.

Broekhoff, J. C. P. (1969). Thesis, Delft University of Technology, The Netherlands.

Broekhoff, J. C. P. and de Boer, J. H. (1967a). *J. Catalysis* **9**, 9.

Broekhoff, J. C. P. and de Boer, J. H. (1967b). *J. Catalysis* **9**, 15.

Broekhoff, J. C. P. and de Boer, J. H. (1968a). *J. Catalysis* **10**, 153.

Broekhoff, J. C. P. and de Boer, J. H. (1968b). *J. Catalysis* **10**, 368.

Broekhoff, J. C. P. and de Boer, J. H. (1968c). *J. Catalysis* **10**, 377.

Broekhoff, J. C. P. and de Boer, J. H. (1968d). *J. Catalysis* **10**, 391.

Brunauer, S. (1943). "The Adsorption of Gases and Vapor". Chapter X. Oxford University Press, London.

Brunauer, S., Emmett, P. H. and Teller, E. (1938). *J. Am. chem. Soc.* **60**, 309.

Brunauer, S., Mikhail, R. and Bodor, E. E. (1967). *J. Colloid Interface Sci.* **24**, 451.

Buff, F. P. (1955). *J. chem. Phys.* **23**, 419.

Clement, C., Montarnal, R. and Trambouze, P. (1962). *Revue Inst. frc. Pétrole* **17**, 558.

Coelingh, Miss B. (1939). *Kolloidzeitschrift* **87**, 251.

Coenen, J. W. E. (1958). "Technische Nikkelkatalysatoren op Drager". Thesis, Delft University of Technology, The Netherlands.

Coenen, J. W. E., Boerma, H., Linsen, B. G. and de Vries, B. (1964). *Proc. Int. Congr. Catal. 3rd, Amsterdam*, 1387.

Cohan, L. H. (1938). *J. Am. chem. Soc.* **60**, 433.

Cohan, L. H. (1944). *J. Am. chem. Soc.* **66**, 98.

Cranston, R. W. and Inkley, F. A. (1957). *Adv. Catalysis* **9**, 143.

Defay, R., Prigogine, I. and Bellemans, A. (1966). "Surface Tension and Adsorption", p. 256. Longmans, London.

Deryagin, B. V. (1940). *Acta phys. chim. USSR* **12**, 139.

Deryagin, B. V. (1957). *Proc. Int. Congr. Surf. Activ., 2nd*, **II**, 112.

Deryagin, B. V. (1967). *J. Colloid Interface Sci.* **24**, 357.

de Vleesschauwer, W. F. N. M. (1967). "Active Magnesia". Thesis, Delft University of Technology, The Netherlands; see also Chapter 6 of this book.

Emig, G. and Hofmann, H. (1967). *J. Catalysis* **8**, 303.

Emmett, P. H. and Brunauer, S. (1937). *J. Am. chem. Soc.* **59**, 310.

Emmett, P. H. and Cines, M. (1947). *J. phys. Colloid Chem.* **51**, 1260.

Everett, D. H. (1958). *In* "The Structure and Properties of Porous Materials" (D. H. Everett and F. S. Stone, eds), p. 95. Butterworth, London.

Flood, E. A. (1958). *In* "The Structure and Properties of Porous Materials" (D. H. Everett and F. S. Stone, eds), p. 68. Butterworth, London.

Foster, A. G. (1932). *Trans. Faraday Soc.* **28**, 645.

Foster, A. G. (1952). *J. chem. Soc.*, 1806.

Geus, J. W. and Kiel, A. M. (1966). Paper read to the Dutch Society of Electron Microscopy, Utrecht, The Netherlands.

Gibbs, J. W. (1961a). "The Scientific Papers". Vol. I, p. 219, Dover Publications Inc., New York.

Gibbs, J. W. (1961a). "The Scientific Papers". Vol. I, p. 219, Dover Publications Inc., New York.

Graham, D. (1962). *J. phys. Chem.* **66**, 1815.

Harkins, W. D. and Jura, G. (1944a). *J. Am. chem. Soc.* **66**, 1366.

Harkins, W. D. and Jura, G. (1944b). *J. Am. chem. Soc.* **66**, 919, 1362.

Hawksbee, F. (1709). *Proc. R. Soc.* **26**, 27.

Hückel, E. (1928). "Adsorption und Kapillarkondensation". Akademische Verlaggesellschaft, Leipzig.

Innes, W. B. (1957). *Analyt. Chem.* **29**, 1069.

John, P. T. and Bohra, J. N. (1967). *J. phys. Chem.* **71**, 4041.

Joy, A. S. (1953). *Vacuum* **3**, 254.

Jurin, J. (1718). *Phil. Trans. R. Soc.* **30**, 355.

Karasz, F. E., Champion, W. M. and Halsey Jr., G. D. (1956). *J. phys. Chem.* **60**, 376.

Kington, G. L. and Smith, F. S. (1964). *Trans. Faraday Soc.* **60**, 705.

Kirkwood, J. C. and Buff, F. P. (1949). *J. chem. Phys.* **17**, 338.

Kiselev, A. V. (1958). *In* "The Structure and Properties of Porous Materials" (D. H. Everett and F. S. Stone, eds), p. 130. Butterworth, London.

Kraemer, E. O. (1931). *In* "A Treatise on Physical Chemistry" (H. S. Taylor, ed.), p. 1661 Macmillan. New York.

Laplace, P. S. (1806). "Traité de Méchanique Céleste", Supp. livre X. *See:* Oeuvres Complètes VI, p. 349, Paris (1883).

Linsen, B. G. (1964). "The Texture of Nickel-Silica Catalysts". Thesis, Delft University of Technology, The Netherlands.

Linsen, B. G. and van den Heuvel, A. (1967). *In* "The Gas Solid Interface" (E. A. Flood, ed.) Vol. II, p. 185. Marcel Dekker, New York.

Lippens, B. C. (1961). "Structure and Texture of Aluminas". Thesis, Delft University of Technology, The Netherlands.

Lippens, B. C. and Hermans, M. E. A. (1961). *Powder Metall.* **7**, 66.

Lippens, B. C. and de Boer, J. H. (1965). *J. Catalysis* **4**, 319.

Lippens, B. C., Linsen, B. G. and de Boer, J. H. (1964). *J. Catalysis* **3**, 32.

Livingstone, H. K. (1949). *J. Colloid Sci.* **4**, 447.

McBain, J. W. (1935). *J. Am. chem. Soc.* **57**, 699.

McGavick, J. and Patrick, W. A. (1928). *J. Am. chem. Soc.* **42**, 946.

Meys, W. H. (1961). "Alumina Coated Silica". Thesis, Delft University of Technology, The Netherlands.

Montarnal, R. (1953). *J. Phys. Radium, Paris* **14**, 732.

Newton, I. (1704). "Opticks", p. 31.

Okkerse, C. (1961). "Submicroporous and Macroporous Silica". Thesis, Delft University of Technology, The Netherlands.

Pierce, C. and Ewing, B. (1962). *J. Am. chem. Soc.* **84**, 4070.

Pierce, C. and Ewing, B. (1964). *J. phys. Chem.* **68**, 2562.

Polanyi, M. (1916). *Verh. dt. phys. Ges.* **15**, 55.

Schuchowitzky, A. A. (1934). *Kolloidzeitschrift.* **66**, 139.

Scott Russel, A. (1927). "Stone Preservation Committee Report", Appendix I. H.M.S.O., London. See also: Honeyborne, D. B. and Harris, P. B. (1958). *In* "The Structure and Properties of Porous Materials" (D. H. Everett and F. S. Stone, eds). Butterworth, London.

Shull, C. G. (1948). *J. Am. chem. Soc.* **70**, 1405.

Steggerda, J. J. (1955). "De vorming van actief aluminiumoxide." Thesis, Delft University of Technology, The Netherlands, p. 92.

Thomson, W. (1871). *Phil. Mag.* **42**, 448.

Tolman, R. C. (1949). *J. chem. Phys.* **17**, 758.

van Doorn, A. B. C. (1957). "Grafietoxyde", Thesis, Delft University of Technology, The Netherlands.

Vishnawathan, B. and Sastri, M. V. C. (1967). *J. Catalysis* **8**, 312.

Westrik, R. and Zwietering, P. (1953). *Koninkl. Ned. Akad. Wetenschap. Proc. Ser.* **B 56**, 492.

Wheeler, A. (1945–1946). Paper presented at the Gordon Conference on Catalysis; see Wheeler (1955).

Wheeler, A. (1951). *Adv. Catalysis* **3**, 314.

Wheeler, A. (1955). *Catalysis* **2**, 105.

Wicke, E. (1939). *Kolloidzeitschrift.* **86**, 167.

Young, Th. (1805). *Phil. Trans. R. Soc.* **95**, 65.

Zettlemoyer, A. C. (1950). *J. Am. chem. Soc.* **72**, 2752.

Zsigsmundy, R. (1911). *Z. anorg. allg. Chem.* **71**, 356.

Zwietering, P. (1956). *Proc. Int. Symp. React. Solids, 3rd, Madrid.*

Chapter 2

MOBILITY AND ADSORPTION ON HOMOGENEOUS SURFACES

A Theoretical and Experimental Study

J. C. P. BROEKHOFF and R. H. VAN DONGEN

Laboratory of Chemical Technology, Technological University of Delft,
The Netherlands

I Introduction

For many years scientists have been fascinated by the study of two-dimensional phases. It has been known for a long time that certain substances may spread on the surface of liquids to form two-dimensional states capable of phase transitions, such as liquid-gas and solid-liquid transitions. The existence of two-dimensional gases, liquids and solids in monolayers of, for example, fatty acids on the surface of water, is commonly accepted (Harkins, 1952). In the 2-D gaseous and liquid state the mobility of the molecules is immediately apparent from the extremely large velocity of spreading, which may be demonstrated experimentally with the aid of the Langmuir trough, for example.

In the case of spreading on liquids, the two-dimensional pressure may be measured directly and empirical equations of state may be determined (Jura and Harkins, 1943). This leads to an understanding of the two-dimensional state based on the experimental evidence. For 2-D states present at the gas-solid interface, no direct experimental procedure to determine 2-D pressure and surface concentration at once, is available. Experimentally, only the number of moles present at a certain solid-gas interface at a certain temperature as a function of 3-D gas-pressure may be determined. If it were possible to express the number of moles present at the solid-gas interface in terms of surface concentration, then 2-D pressures could be calculated from the Gibbs adsorption equation (Bangham and Farhouky, 1931). Unfortunately, no way of establishing the solid-gas interface area independently and beyond reasonable doubt, has been developed at present. Nearly all interpretations of adsorption data at solids depend on *a priori* assumptions on the 2-D state of the adsorbed molecules. Only in a restricted number of cases, has it been possible to measure the surface area of particular solids by methods such as electron microscopy (Young and Crowell, 1962), chemical reactions restricted to the surface (de Boer, 1937), specific adsorption (Gregg and Sing, 1967a) and immersion calorimetry (Harkins and Jura, 1944) (see Section V C). In the majority of cases, the surface area of the solid has to be evaluated from the physical adsorption data themselves, and this is only possible if specific assumptions are made on the behaviour of the two-dimensional state.

One of the earliest theories of adsorption at the gas-solid interface, that of Langmuir (1918), assumed that a certain molecule hitting a part of the surface not already covered by a molecule, resided in the 2-D state for a certain time. This time is assumed to be only dependent on the interaction energy between the molecule and the solid and the temperature, but independent of the surface concentration. By tradition, Langmuir's assumptions have been interpreted as assuming the adsorbed molecule to be held by definite sites on the surface, which implies that the adsorbed molecule, during its stay at the surface, remains fixed to a certain site (Fowler and Guggenheim, 1939a). This state is referred to as *localized* adsorption and sometimes even as *immobile* adsorption. It has been stressed by de Boer (1953a), that at least in physical adsorption, the picture of an immobile adsorbed molecule is a highly improbable one. In his book "The Dynamical Character of Adsorption" (1953a), de Boer shows how there is an intense migratory movement of the molecules along the surface, even when there exists an energy barrier for the molecules to move from one surface region to another. If this energy barrier is substantial, then the molecule may be pictured to *hop* from one region to the other. If this energy barrier is negligibly small, then, at least in dilute surface films, the molecules may be pictured to translate freely along the surface (de Boer and Kruyer, 1953, 1954). For higher surface concentrations, this translational freedom becomes restricted and the density of the *2-D* state becomes comparable to that of a *3-D* liquid (de Boer and Broekhoff 1967a). At still higher surface concentrations, there possibly is a transition to a *2-D* solid state with even further restriction of the *2-D* translational degrees of freedom (Alder and Wainwright, 1962). In most cases we may then expect multilayer adsorption to set in, resulting in a transition to a *3-D* adsorbed layer. Thus, for *2-D* phases, we may expect mobility to be rule rather than exception. If the surface of the solid under investigation is relatively homogeneous and if the variations of the adsorption energy along the surface are relatively small, then it is even impossible to speak any longer of surface sites. Adsorption on such surfaces is commonly referred to as *mobile* adsorption as contrasted to *localized* adsorption. The term *immobile* adsorption should be reserved to those exceptional cases, where the molecules are strongly bound to specific sites for a relative long time. Such states might possibly occur at parts of the surface of highly heterogeneous solids, and are of restricted interest. In many cases, although the adsorbed molecule may be strongly adsorbed at the solid surface, leading to long times of residence at the surface, the molecules are more or less free to move along the surface. Whether a molecule may be described as mobile adsorbed or rather as localized adsorbed, depends on the contribution of the movement of the molecules along the surface to the entropy of the adsorbed state, as was pointed out by de Boer and Kruyer (1953, 1954) and Kruyer (1955a). In *localized* adsorption, although a molecule is certainly not fixed to a specific site, its statistical preference for certain sites leads to a vanishing small contribution of translational degrees of freedom to the entropy of the adsorbed layer. As a consequence of the preference for certain sites, in localized adsorption the *2-D* state is influenced by the geometry of the surface, whereas in mobile adsorption the *2-D* state is primarily determined by the *2-D*

4

concentration. As is described elsewhere in this volume, whether adsorption is mobile or localized may be inferred from entropy of adsorption data. It may already be mentioned here, that from the work of de Boer and Kruyer (1953, 1954) and Kruyer (1955a) on physical adsorption at carbon surfaces it is apparent that in the majority of cases adsorption essentially is mobile. It is all the more surprising that many other authors, in trying to give a theoretical description of the 2-D state, picture the adsorption to be localized.

De Boer (1953a), in stressing the mobility of physical adsorbed molecules, showed how on relatively homogeneous surfaces mobile gaseous films may condense to 2-D liquids or densify to 2-D super-critical phases. At that time (1953), no homogeneous adsorbents were known, and de Boer's predictions could not be tested experimentally. Shortly afterwards, 2-D condensation of krypton on a homogeneous carbon surface at 77°K was established experimentally (Halsey and Singleton, 1954). Since that time, many other examples of 2-D condensation on homogeneous adsorbents have been found. Although 2-D condensation may theoretically also occur in localized systems, as was demonstrated by Fowler (Fowler and Guggenheim, 1939b), in the majority of cases, the 2-D condensation phenomena found experimentally may be satisfactorily described by assuming mobile rather than localized adsorption, as will be shown in this chapter. Recently, a rather extensive review of the current state in the theory of adsorption of gases on solids has been given by Steele (1967). From this review it is apparent that neither the study of 2-D condensation phenomena nor the role of mobility in adsorption has received the attention it certainly deserves. Rather than to try to review all present theories of physical adsorption (which has been done excellently by Steele) or to try to summarize all of de Boer's previous work of adsorption, including, apart from his monograph "The Dynamical Character of Adsorption", many sorption studies during his pre-war research period at Philips' laboratories in Eindhoven, we will give an account of the work done under his direction at the Delft University of Technology, on two-dimensional condensation phenomena, the mobility of the adsorbed layer and the determination of surface areas from physical adsorption data.

II The Two-Dimensional State

A General Characteristics

In the present discussion we will restrict ourselves to the physical adsorption of vapours on inert adsorbents. For an inert adsorbent it is assumed that the state of the adsorbent is not changed by the act of physical adsorption. Unless explicitly stated, we will restrict ourselves to uni-molecular adsorption. The adsorbed layer will be treated as a strictly two-dimensional phase, perfectly distinguishable both from the adsorbent and from the gas phase. We will assume the gas phase to be sufficiently dilute to be treated as ideal, its pressure being denoted by p. The 2-D phase will be characterized by a two-dimensional pressure F and area A. By definition *the molar area in a completely close-packed monolayer*, A_0, *is the area for* N_a *molecules for an infinite 2-D pressure* F. The common temperature of adsorbent, adsorbate and gas phase is denoted by T. The number of molecules adsorbed at the surface of area A will be denoted by N_a.

For a two-dimensional phase, the Gibbs adsorption relation:

$$A\,\mathrm{d}F = N_a d\mu^a \qquad (1)$$

holds (Gibbs, 1961), where μ^a is the chemical potential of the adsorbate. Expressed in terms of the degree of coverage θ, where

$$\theta = A_0/A$$

Eq. (1) reads:

$$\mathrm{d}F = \frac{\theta}{a_0}d\mu^a, \qquad (2)$$

$_{a0}$ being the molecular area in a close-packed monolayer.

In equilibrium, the thermodynamic potential of a component is constant throughout the system. Equation (2) may then be used to relate F to p:

$$\mathrm{d}F = \theta/a_0 kT \,\mathrm{d}\ln(p) \qquad (3)$$

The 2-D pressure F only acts parallel to the surface. If two 2-D phases of different density are present at the same surface, the equilibrium requires the equality of 2-D pressures. On the other hand, if two adsorbent surfaces are spatially separated, no equality of 2-D pressures is required (de Boer and Broekhoff, 1967c). Heterogeneous surfaces constitute a separate problem. For the patch model popularized by Ross and Olivier (1964a), where a heterogeneous surface is regarded to be consisting of distinct, in itself homogeneous, regions, each patch has to be considered as an independent surface. There is no equality of 2-D pressure at different patches. For other types of heterogeneity, where patches are too small to accommodate more than a single or a few molecules at most, the use of 2-D pressures loses its meaning and the whole surface again has to be treated as a single thermodynamic system (Hill, 1949; Gordon, 1968). Whether phase transitions on a single surface of this type in principle are possible, is still a matter of speculation. Recent investigations do not exclude such transitions theoretically.

For a collection of in itself homogeneous surfaces, the phase rule may be formulated as (de Boer and Broekhoff, 1967c):

$$V = C - P + 2 - \sum_j (n_j - 1) \tag{4}$$

where: V = the variance of the system

C = the number of chemical components

P = the number of distinguishable *three-dimensional phases*

n_j = the number of 2-D phases present at the *same* surface.

Identical surfaces are only taken into account once. Adsorption itself does not invalidate the Gibbs Phase Rule. Only the occurrence of 2-D coexisting phases reduces the variance of the system. For the adsorption of a gas on an inert adsorbent, there can never be more than two coexisting 2-D phases present at distinguishable surfaces at the same time. Even for this situation, the variance equals zero. It is thus immediately clear, that 2-D phase transitions may only be found with adsorbents exhibiting highly homogeneous surfaces. Only a few adsorbents meeting this requirement are known at present, highly graphitized carbon, boron nitride (Ross and Olivier, 1964a) and certain carefully prepared inorganic halides (Fisher and McMillan, 1957; Hinchen, 1962) being among the most important ones. The study of adsorption on these substances is of great importance, as it may lead to a better understanding of the 2-D state.

The phase rule (4) remains valid for multilayer adsorption, as long as the multilayer may be taken to exist of a sequence of independent 2-D phases, stacked on top of each other. Over a fairly large relative pressure region, the multilayer adsorption of krypton on graphitized carbon blacks may be described by this picture. In general, however, the mutual dependence of adsorbed layers in the multilayer excludes the existence of real 2-D condensation phenomena, although pseudo-mono-variance during the condensation of a certain layer in the multiphase may be observed under favourable conditions.

The occurrence of 2-D liquid-solid transitions and 2-D triple points may not be excluded theoretically (Alder and Wainwright, 1962). Experimental evidence for such transitions deserves furthur study. (Duval and Thomy, 1964). Theoretically, a 2-D liquid-solid transition has been predicted for hard-sphere molecules even in the absence of inter-molecular attractions. In practice, transitions are observed from a 2-D gas phase to a 2-D *condensed* phase. The existence of a 2-D *critical point* possibly justifies the use of the term 2-*D* liquid for this condensed phase.

Tsien and Halsey (1962) consider a condensed localized 2-*D* phase as 2-*D* solid. In view of the existence of a 2-*D* critical point for localized adsorption, this seems questionable. A *true* 2-*D* phase should have no degrees of freedom perpendicular to the adsorbent surface. Actually there always is a vibrational movement perpendicular to the surface. It has been shown by de Boer (1956) and Kruyer (1955b), that there is a close connection between the vibrations corresponding to partition function and the mean time of residence of the adsorbed molecules on the surface. At present, we will assume that for the 2-*D* phases under consideration this partition function is equal to one. In localized adsorption, although the hopping of the molecules from one region of the surface to another is considered not to be contributing to entropy, vibrations parallel to the surface are not necessarily negligible and may even be dependent on surface coverage. Nothing is known with certainty about such vibrations, and they have to be neglected at present. The same applies to possible changes in the internal degrees of freedom upon adsorption of poly-atomic molecules, see, however, the work by Kruyer (1955a).

B Prediction of Phase Transitions

The occurrence of phase transitions may be predicted from models of the two-dimensional phase, if expressions for the 2-*D* pressure and thermodynamic potential are available over the whole region of possible values of θ. Denoting the more dense 2-*D* phase by the index L, the other by the index G, the equilibrium requirements for the occurrence of a 2-*D* phase transitions may be formulated as follows:

$$F_L = F_G \tag{5}$$

$$\mu_L^a = \mu_G^a \tag{6}$$

From the simultaneous solution of these two equations, two values θ_L and θ_G may be found below a certain value of the temperature, T_c. For $T = T_c$, θ_L and θ_G coincide, whereas above T_c no solutions may be obtained from Eqs (5) and (6). Equation (6) may also be written as:

$$p_G = p_L \tag{7}$$

For the application of Eqs (5)–(7) it is not necessary to have one single function describing F or μ^a as a function of θ. It may happen that two distinct functions describe the condensed and the gaseous phase respectively. If there exists one single function describing the whole 2-*D* density range, then an additional equilibrium requirement may be obtained from Eq. (3) by integrating between the boundaries set by Eq. (7) (de Boer and Broekhoff, 1967d):

$$\int_{p_G}^{p_L} \theta \, \mathrm{d} \ln (p) = 0, \text{ for } p_L = p_G \tag{8}$$

which is identical to:

$$\ln (p)(\theta_L - \theta_G) = \int_{\theta_G}^{\theta_L} \ln (p) \, \mathrm{d}\theta \tag{9}$$

Equation (9) enables us to solve the coexisting densities at the coexistence pressure from the adsorption equation itself. It is clear that Eq. (9) requires the adsorption isotherm to be S-shaped, exhibiting metastable and unstable parts, see Fig. 1. Equation (9) simply requires the shaded areas in Fig. 1 to be of equal magnitude. It is the 2-D analogue of Maxwell's well-known equal area rule (Maxwell, 1875). In the critical point, where θ_L and θ_G coincide, θ_c is given by the requirements:

$$\left.\begin{array}{l} \dfrac{\mathrm{d}F}{\mathrm{d}\theta} = 0; \text{ resp. } \dfrac{\mathrm{d} \ln (p)}{\mathrm{d}\theta} = 0, \ \dfrac{\mathrm{d}p}{\mathrm{d}\theta} = 0 \\[2mm] \dfrac{\mathrm{d}^2 F}{\mathrm{d}\theta^2} = 0; \text{ resp. } \dfrac{\mathrm{d}^2 \ln (p)}{\mathrm{d}\theta^2} = 0, \ \dfrac{\mathrm{d}^2 p}{\mathrm{d}\theta^2} = 0 \end{array}\right\} \tag{10}$$

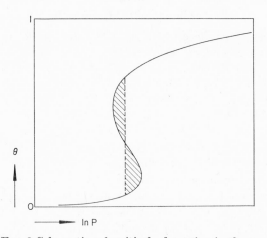

FIG. 1 Schematic sub-critical adsorption isotherm.

It is clear that in general the prediction of critical conditions requires either F or p to be expressible as one single function of θ over the whole θ-region. We are faced here with the same problem that exists in three dimensions, where it is often found, that specific models may be set up either for the condensed state or for the gaseous state, and so not suitable to include the critical region. In the present discussion, we will restrict ourselves to relative simple models, enabling the prediction of phase transitions and of critical conditions. Such a procedure, although unsatisfactory from a purely theoretical point of view, facilitates the analysis of experimental data and will be shown to lead to a better understanding of the adsorbed state.

III Models for the Two-Dimensional State and their Respective Adsorption Equations

A Introduction

As stated in Section II A we may discriminate between localized and mobile models for the 2-D state. In the simplest model of localized adsorption, a random distribution of N_a molecules over N_s surface sites, arranged in a regular lattice, is considered. By means of simple statistical thermodynamics, the 2-D pressure of such a phase may be shown to be equal to (Fowler and Guggenheim, 1939a):

$$F = N_s/A \; kT \ln \left(\frac{N_s}{N_s - N_a} \right) \tag{11}$$

From our definition of a_0, it is clear

$$a_0 = A/N_s.$$

Defining θ as N_a/N_s, we may write Eq. (11) as:

$$F = kT/a_0 \cdot \ln \left(\frac{1}{1-\theta} \right) \tag{12}$$

For μ^a the following expression is found:

$$\mu^a = kT \ln \left(\frac{\theta}{1-\theta} \right) - E^0 \tag{13}$$

where E^0 is the adsorption energy.
For the ideal 3-D gas phase, μ^g equals*

$$\mu^g = kT \ln (p) - kT \ln (kT) - kT \ln (\Lambda^{-3}) \tag{14}$$

where Λ stands for $h/(2\pi mkT)^{\frac{1}{2}}$ (Hill, 1960).
From Eqs (13) and (14) the adsorption equation is found to be:

$$p = kT\Lambda^{-3} \; \frac{\theta}{1-\theta} \exp(-E^0/kT). \tag{15}$$

---

* Rotational and vibrational degrees of freedom have been neglected in the 3-D as well as in the 2-D state. This is admitted as long as there is no change in these degrees of freedom during adsorption.

This is the well-known Langmuir equation, usually written as:

$$p = K_{loc}^0 \,\frac{\theta}{1-\theta}\, \exp(-E^0/kT) \tag{16}$$

where K_{loc}^0 is given by

$$K_{loc}^0 = kT\,\Lambda^{-3}. \tag{17}$$

It is to be realized that in Eq. (17) all vibrations of the adsorbed molecules on their adsorption sites and all changes in internal degrees of freedom upon adsorption are neglected.

The simplest mobile adsorption model views the adsorbed phase as an ideal 2-D gas, its 2-D pressure being given by

$$F = kT/a_0\theta. \tag{18}$$

The corresponding mobile expression for μ^a is:

$$\mu^a = -kT \ln (\Lambda^{-2}a_0) + kT \ln (\theta) - E^0 \tag{19}$$

From Eqs (14) and (19), the adsorption equation follows:

$$p = \frac{kT\theta}{\Lambda a_0}\, \exp(-E^0/kT) \tag{20}$$

commonly written as:

$$p = K_{mob}^0 \,\theta\exp(-E^0/kT) \tag{21}$$

where K_{mob}^0 is given by

$$K_{mob}^0 = kT/(\Lambda a_0). \tag{22}$$

In analogy to gas absorption, Eq. (21) is frequently called the *Henry equation* (Gregg and Sing, 1967b). It is to be noted, that for very low coverages, Eq. (16) for localized adsorption, only differs from Eq. (21) in the magnitude of K^0. A proportionality between p and θ for low coverages in itself is *not* an indication of mobile adsorption. In the present treatment, K_{mob}^0 will be called the Henry constant, as opposed to the Langmuir constant K_{loc}^0. Equations (16) and (21) have been derived by de Boer (1953a) and by de Boer (1956) and Kruyer (1955b) from kinetic considerations. The relation between K^0 and the mean residence time of an adsorbed molecule at zero degree of coverage and energy of adsorption has been established by these authors on statistical grounds. A very important result is, that even if there is no net energy of adsorption, there is a finite time of adsorption for molecules hitting a surface. This time factor plays an important role in the theory of transport of gases through porous solids at low pressures (Knudsen diffusion and surface diffusion phenomena). For details the reader is referred to the original publications of de Boer and Kruyer.

Both the Eqs (16) and (21) are only valid as limiting cases for low surface coverage where interactions between the molecules may be neglected as well as effects caused by the finite dimensions of the adsorbed molecules themselves. At present there is no completely satisfactory theory of the condensed state either in three or in two dimensions. The equation of state of a mobile one-dimensional liquid has been formulated, at least in principle, for interacting compressible particles (Henderson and Davison, 1967). For one- and two-dimensional "lattice gases", Onsager (1944) has given an exact treatment which is too complicated to be useful as a starting point for an adsorption equation. For mobile 2-D liquids, several simplifying approximations have to be made. In many cases it is necessary to approximate real molecules by incompressible spheres or disks and to separate molecular interactions rigorously from molecular repulsion effects. Such a separation of course is artificial. The simplest mobile model in this class is that of van der Waals. De Boer (1953b) has studied the 2-D van der Waals analogue in detail and has shown how many phenomena, such as 2-D condensation and 2-D supercritical densification, may be derived from such a treatment (see Section III C). Another simple model of the liquid state in this class is the "free-volume" conception of Eyring and Hirschfelder (1937), which may directly be adapted to the 2-D state (see Section III D). In Section III E we derive a 2-D equation of state from the exact virial coefficients for a hard disks fluid. All three approaches directly lead to relatively simple adsorption equations for mobile adsorption. For localized adsorption, taking into account intermolecular interaction has led to two adsorption equations, viz. that of Fowler and Frumkin (1925; 1926) and the refined treatment of Fowler and Guggenheim (1939c). Both equations will be treated in the next section (III B). In Section III F the theoretical behaviour of these five different models will be compared, whereas in Section IV the application of experimental data and the information obtained from the different models will be treated in detail.

B Equations for Localized Adsorption

As stated before, Onsager's (1944) exact treatment of 2-D lattice gases does not lead to an explicit expression for the equation of state. The most simple one of the approximate solutions to the 2-D lattice gas problem is originally due to Frumkin (1925; 1926), although it is commonly known as the Fowler equation (Fowler and Guggenheim,

4*

TABLE I. Critical constants for various equations of state

Ia

1-D
Hard Rods
All Mobile Models Eq. (54)

l_0/l_c	0·3333
$(k_1^m)_c$	6·7500
$(pl/kT)_c$	0·3750

Ib

2-D

	Mobile Hard Disks			Localized Lattice Gases	
	van der Waals Eq. (54)	SFA approach Eq. (68)	VE approach Eq. (84)	Fowler-Guggenheim Eq. (12)	q.c. Eq. (37)
a_0/a_c	0·3333	0·2944	0·2333	0·5	0·5
$(k_1)_c$	6·7500	11·830	10·724	4	4·8654
$(Fa/kT)_c$	0·3750	0·4448	0·3662	0·3862	0·2933

Ic

3-D

	Mobile Hard Spheres		
	van der Waals Eq. (54)	Eyring Eq. (77)	VE approach Eq. (85)
v_0/v_c	0·3333	0·2791	0·2018
$(k_1^m)_c$	6·7500	16·842	13·688
$(pv/kT)_c$	0·3750	0·5358	0·3590

1939a). Essentially, this is a first order correction to the Langmuir equation, taking into account the effect of nearest neighbour-interactions between adsorbed molecules, while retaining the assumption of complete randomness of distribution. If the interaction energy of a molecule with all other molecules at neighbouring sites is denoted by $2w$, then the canonical ensemble partition function for such a 2-D lattice gas is known to be given by (Fowler and Guggenheim 1939a),

$$Q = \frac{N_s!}{N_a!(N_s - N_a)!} \exp(-E^0 N_a/kT - N_a^2/N_s \cdot w/kT). \tag{23}$$

From Eq. (23), by standard methods of statistical thermodynamics, the following expressions for F and μ^a are found:

$$F = kT/a_0 \cdot \left[\ln\left(\frac{1}{1-\theta}\right) - \theta^2 w/kT \right] \tag{24}$$

$$\mu^a = kT\left[\ln\left(\frac{\theta}{1-\theta}\right) - \frac{E^0}{kT} - 2w\theta/kT \right]. \tag{25}$$

From (25), (14) and (17) the adsorption equation is obtained as:

$$p = K_{\text{loc}}^0 \frac{\theta}{1-\theta} \exp\left(-E^0/kT - k_1^l \theta\right) = K_{\text{loc}} \frac{\theta}{1-\theta} \exp\left(-k_1^l \theta\right) \tag{26}$$

where k_1^l is given by:

$$k_1^l = 2w/kT \tag{27}$$

and k_{loc} is given by $K_{\text{loc}} = K_{\text{loc}}^0 \exp\left(-E^0/kT\right)$.

From Eqs (25) and (26) the conditions for a 2-D phase transitions are found to be:

$$\ln\left(\frac{1}{1-\theta_G}\right) - \frac{k_1^l}{2} \theta_G^2 = \ln\left(\frac{1}{1-\theta_L}\right) - \frac{k_1^l}{2} \theta_L^2 \tag{28}$$

$$\ln\left(\frac{\theta_G}{1-\theta_G}\right) - k_1^l \theta_G = \ln\left(\frac{\theta_L}{1-\theta_L}\right) - k_1^l \theta_L \tag{29}$$

From these equations, k_1^l may be readily eliminated, resulting in:

$$\ln\left(\frac{\theta_G}{\theta_L} \frac{(1-\theta_G)}{(1-\theta_L)}\right) = \frac{2}{\theta_L + \theta_G} \ln\left(\frac{\theta_G}{1-\theta_G}\right) \tag{30}$$

It may be easily verified that

$$\theta_G = 1 - \theta_L \tag{31}$$

is a solution of (30).

Elimination of θ_G from (31) and (29) yields:

$$\ln\left(\frac{\theta_L}{1-\theta_L}\right) = k_1^l \left(\theta_L - \tfrac{1}{2}\right) \tag{32}$$

from which θ_L may be solved as a function of k_1^l by means of standard numerical methods (see Table II and Figs. 4 and 5).

Denoting the pressure p corresponding to a degree of coverage θ by $p(\theta)$, $p(\frac{1}{2})$ from Eq. (26) is found to be:

$$p(\tfrac{1}{2}) = K_{\text{loc}}^0 \exp\left(-E^0/kT - k_1^l/2\right) \tag{33}$$

so Eq. (32) is identical to:

$$p(\tfrac{1}{2}) = K_{\text{loc}}^0 \frac{\theta_L}{1-\theta_L} \exp\left(-E^0/kT - k_1^l\,\theta_L\right) \tag{34}$$

In general

$$p(\theta_L) = p(\theta_G) = p(\tfrac{1}{2}) \tag{35}$$

As shown by Fowler and Guggenheim (1939a) Eqs (31) and (35) are direct consequences of the fact that Eq. (26) is an odd function of $(\theta - \frac{1}{2})$. The critical value of θ from Eq. (31) obviously is $\frac{1}{2}$. From Eq. (32) it follows that $\theta_L \to \frac{1}{2}$ leads to:

$$(k_1^l)_c = 4, \text{ viz. } w/kT_c = 2. \tag{36}$$

It has recently been shown by de Boer and Broekhoff (1967e) that the analysis of experimental 2-D condensation data is greatly facilitated by a detailed knowledge of θ_L and θ_G as a function of k_1. From experimental data of V_L and V_G, the volumes adsorbed at the extremes of the 2-D coexistence line, the ratio θ_L/θ_G may be deduced. This ratio is a unique function of k_1^l. In combination with p_c the pressure of 2-D condensation, the experimental values for E^0 and of V_m, the volume adsorbed at complete coverage may also be deduced. As in Section IV we will make extensive use of this mode of analysis, an extensive table of θ_L and θ_G as a function of k_1^l is presented in Table II.

This over-simplified treatment regards the distribution of N_a molecules over N_s surface sites as completely random. The probability of occupance for a certain site is taken to be completely independent of the occupance of neighbouring sites.

A first refinement of this crude localized treatment is known as the quasi-chemical (q.c.) treatment. A detailed discussion has been given by Fowler and Guggenheim (1939c). Here, the most important features of the quasi-chemical treatment will be summarized. It has been shown that the 2-D pressure F of the lattice gas in the q.c.-treatment is given by:

$$F = kT/a_0 \cdot \ln\left(\frac{1}{1-\theta}\right) - \frac{z}{2}\ln\left(\frac{\beta+1-2\theta}{(\beta+1)(1-\theta)}\right) \tag{37}$$

where β is defined as:

$$\beta = [1 - 4\theta\,(1-\theta)(1-\exp(k_1^l/z))]^{\frac{1}{2}} \tag{38}$$

TABLE II. Two-dimensional densities θ_L and θ_G of the coexisting phases and corresponding reduced pressures $(p/K)_{\text{loc}}$ as a function of k_1^l for the Fowler-Guggenheim equation

k_1	$(p/K)_{\text{loc}}$	θ_L	θ_G
9·000	0·01111	0·9877	0·0123
8·000	0·01832	0·9788	0·0212
7·500	0·02352	0·9718	0·0282
7·000	0·03020	0·9621	0·0379
6·700	0·03508	0·9546	0·0454
6·500	0·03877	0·9486	0·0514
6·400	0·04076	0·9453	0·0547
6·300	0·04285	0·9418	0·0582
6·200	0·04505	0·9379	0·0621
6·100	0·04736	0·9338	0·0662
6·000	0·04979	0·9293	0·0707
5·900	0·05234	0·9244	0·0756
5·800	0·05502	0·9192	0·0808
5·700	0·05784	0·9135	0·0865
5·600	0·06081	0·9073	0·0927
5·500	0·06393	0·9005	0·0995
5·400	0·06721	0·8931	0·1069
5·300	0·07065	0·8850	0·1150
5·250	0·07244	0·8806	0·1194
5·200	0·07427	0·8760	0·1240
5·150	0·07615	0·8712	0·1288
5·100	0·07808	0·8662	0·1338
5·050	0·08006	0·8608	0·1392
5·000	0·08208	0·8552	0·1448
4·950	0·08416	0·8493	0·1507
4·900	0·08629	0·8430	0·1570
4·850	0·08848	0·8363	0·1637
4·800	0·09072	0·8293	0·1707
4·750	0·09301	0·8218	0·1782
4·700	0·09537	0·8138	0·1862
4·650	0·09778	0·8052	0·1948
4·600	0·10026	0·7961	0·2039
4·550	0·10280	0·7862	0·2138
4·500	0·10540	0·7756	0·2244
4·450	0·10807	0·7641	0·2359
4·400	0·11080	0·7515	0·2485
4·350	0·11361	0·7376	0·2624
4·300	0·11648	0·7223	0·2777
4·250	0·11943	0·7050	0·2950
4·200	0·12246	0·6854	0·3146
4·150	0·12556	0·6623	0·3377
4·100	0·12873	0·6339	0·3661
4·080	0·13003	0·6203	0·3797
4·070	0·13068	0·6128	0·3872
4·060	0·13134	0·6047	0·3953
4·050	0·13199	0·5957	0·4043
4·040	0·13266	0·5858	0·4142
4·030	0·13332	0·5745	0·4255
4·020	0·13399	0·5610	0·4390
4·010	0·13466	0·5432	0·4568
4·000	0·13534	0·5000	0·5000

TABLE III. Two-dimensional densities θ_L and θ_G of the coexisting phases and corresponding reduced pressures $(p/K)_{loc}$ as a function of k_1^l for the quasi-chemical approximation

k_1^l	$(p/K)_{loc}$	θ_L	θ_G
12·000	0·00248	0·9973	0·0027
11·400	0·00335	0·9962	0·0038
10·800	0·00452	0·9948	0·0052
10·200	0·00610	0·9927	0·0073
9·600	0·00823	0·9898	0·0102
9·000	0·01111	0·9855	0·0145
8·400	0·01500	0·9792	0·0208
7·800	0·02024	0·9696	0·0304
7·200	0·02732	0·9547	0·0453
6·600	0·03688	0·9305	0·0695
6·000	0·04979	0·8881	0·1119
5·940	0·05130	0·8822	0·1178
5·880	0·05287	0·8758	0·1242
5·820	0·05448	0·8690	0·1310
5·760	0·05613	0·8617	0·1383
5·700	0·05784	0·8538	0·1462
5·670	0·05872	0·8496	0·1504
5·640	0·05961	0·8453	0·1547
5·610	0·06051	0·8407	0·1593
5·580	0·06142	0·8360	0·1640
5·550	0·06235	0·8311	0·1689
5·520	0·06239	0·8259	0·1741
5·490	0·06425	0·8205	0·1795
5·460	0·06522	0·8184	0·1852
5·430	0·06620	0·8089	0·1911
5·400	0·06721	0·8027	0·1973
5·370	0·06822	0·7961	0·2039
5·340	0·06925	0·7892	0·2108
5·310	0·07030	0·7820	0·2180
5·280	0·07136	0·7742	0·2258
5·250	0·07244	0·7661	0·2339
5·220	0·07353	0·7574	0·2426
5·190	0·07465	0·7481	0·2519
5·160	0·07577	0·7381	0·2619
5·130	0·07692	0·7274	0·2726
5·100	0·07808	0·7157	0·2843
5·070	0·07926	0·7030	0·2970
5·040	0·08046	0·6890	0·3110
5·010	0·08168	0·6733	0·3267
4·980	0·08291	0·6555	0·3445
4·950	0·08416	0·6347	0·3653
4·920	0·08543	0·6090	0·3910
4·908	0·08595	0·5966	0·4034
4·896	0·08647	0·5820	0·4180
4·890	0·08673	0·5736	0·4264
4·884	0·08699	0·5640	0·4360
4·878	0·08725	0·5527	0·4473
4·872	0·08751	0·5379	0·4621
4·869	0·08764	0·5277	0·4723
4·866	0·08777	0·5097	0·4903
4·8654	0·08803	0·5000	0·5000

and z stands for the coordination number of the surface sites itself, being equal to 6 for a triangular lattice.

The corresponding equation is

$$p = K_{loc}^0 \exp\left(-E^0/kT\right) \frac{\theta}{1-\theta}\left(\frac{2-2\theta}{\beta+1-2\theta}\right)^z = K_{loc} \frac{\theta}{1-\theta}\left(\frac{2-2\theta}{\beta+1-2\theta}\right)^z \tag{39}$$

From Eqs (5) and (7), it may be verified, that Eqs (31) and (35) also hold for the q.c.-approximation.*

The degrees of coverage at phase transition may be directly calculated from the relation:

$$\frac{\theta_L}{1-\theta_L} = \left(\frac{\beta+1-2\theta_L}{\beta-1+2\theta_L}\right)^{z/(2-z)} \tag{40}$$

The critical temperature for the phase transition is dependent on w, the pair interaction energy and may be calculated from

$$(k_1^l)_c = 2z \ln\left[z/(z-2)\right]. \tag{41}$$

For a triangular lattice ($z = 6$), this critical value for k_1^l is equal to 4·87, somewhat higher than that given by Eq. (36) for the crude localized treatment. In Section IV, we will have the opportunity to compare the results of both localized treatments on application to experimental data. For the analysis of data, a table of θ_L and θ_G as a function of k_1^l for the q.c.-approximation is quite useful. For the convenience of the reader, such a table is presented in Table III (see also Figs 4 and 5).

C The 2-D van der Waals Equation

The van der Waals equation of state (van der Waals, 1873) is, historically speaking, the first equation to take into account both intermolecular interactions and the finity of the molecules. However, the agreement with observed behaviour of a real gas is rather more qualitative than quantitative. The description of the liquid state and the transition region, especially, are poor. This, of course, is a consequence of the assumptions and approximations in the derivation of the van der Waals equation.

Many attempts have been made to give a better description of the

---

* The relations $\theta_L = 1-\theta_G$ and $p_L = p_G = p(\frac{1}{2})$ have been shown to be valid even for Onsager's exact treatment. On the other hand Honig has shown that these relations only hold if the adsorbed molecule is allowed to occupy only one surface site at the time. For branched molecules, the subcritical isotherms are no longer symmetrical around $\theta = \frac{1}{2}$, and one of the most prominent characteristics of 2-D phase transitions in localized systems disappears.

gas and liquid state (Hirschfelder *et al.*, 1954a). Three groups of equations of state can be distinguished: first the equations based on a
rather simplified model, like the van der Waals equation and the
free volume equation of Eyring (Eyring and Hirschfelder, 1937).
These equations can easily be transformed to apply to 2-D fluids. In
the second place there are the pragmatic equations of state of which
the only purpose is to give an empirical description of gas or liquid
properties as close as possible (for example, the Benedict-Webb-Rubin-
equation and the Kamerlingh-Onnes virial type of equation of state).
It is obvious that this group is of no interest for our present purpose,
since such equations cannot provide information about the nature of
adsorption. The more recent theories (Henderson and Davison, 1967;
Barker and Henderson, 1967) of the gas and liquid state may be
considered as a third group, since they are characterized by a more
refined treatment of the hard sphere fluid and by the use of electronic
computers.

So far most attention has been paid to the theoretical hard sphere
problem and the approximation of the radial distribution function
(the ratio of the local density at a distance r from a certain molecule
and the average density). The various equations of state for hard
spheres were compared to "experimental" properties obtained by simulating a hard sphere fluid on a computer (Alder and Wainwright, 1960;
1962). Barker and Henderson (1967) superimposed molecular interactions
over the hard sphere fluid, using the few known short range radial
distributions (Throop and Bearman, 1965) and applied their method
to argon data quite successfully. However, this method is not yet
fit for application to a 2-D fluid, since too little is known about the
2-D radial distribution function. The lack of knowledge of the 2-D
state forces us to resort to the more simplified equations.

A van der Waals gas consists of hard spheres with superimposed
molecular interactions. In the 2-D case, so for a *hard disk* fluid, this
yields for the partition function (Hill, 1948):

$$Q = \frac{\Lambda^{-2N_a}}{N_a!} A_f^{N_a} \exp\left(\frac{-\frac{1}{2}\phi N_a + N_a E^0}{kT}\right). \tag{42}$$

The interaction energy of one pair of molecules θ according to Barker
and Henderson (1968), is:

$$\phi = \int_{d_0}^{\infty} u(r) \frac{N_a}{A} g(r) 2\pi r \, dr \tag{43}$$

where: $u(r)$ = the intermolecular potential, and

$g(r)$ = the radial distribution function.

In a very dilute 2-D gas the molecules are distributed completely at random. Consequently, $g(r)$ may be set at 1. Defining:

$$a_2 = -\tfrac{1}{2} \int_{d_0}^{\infty} u(r) 2\pi r \, dr \qquad (44)$$

the partition function becomes

$$Q = \frac{\Lambda^{-2N_a}}{N_a!} A_f^{N_a} \exp\left(\frac{a_2 N_a^2 / A + E^0 N_a}{kT} \right) \qquad (45)$$

The thermodynamic potential can be obtained from Eq. (45) by differentiation of $\ln (Q)$ with respect to N_a:

$$-\mu^a / kT = \ln\left(\frac{A_f}{N_a}\right) + \frac{N_a}{A_f}\frac{\partial A_f}{\partial N_a} + \frac{2a_2 N_a}{AkT} + \frac{E^0}{kT} - 2\ln \Lambda \qquad (46)$$

Since in equilibrium the chemical potential of the adsorbed layer equals the chemical potential of the bulk gas phase (Eq. (14)), the adsorption equation can be written as:

$$\ln\left(\frac{p\Lambda}{kT}\right) + \frac{E^0}{kT} = -\ln\frac{A_f}{N_a} - \frac{N_a}{A_f}\frac{\partial A_f}{\partial N_a} - \frac{2a_2 N_a}{AkT} \qquad (47)$$

From Eq. (45) the spreading pressure F can be found from

$$\frac{F}{kT} = \frac{\partial \ln Q}{\partial A} \qquad (48)$$

or,

$$\frac{F}{kT} = \frac{N_a}{A_f}\frac{\partial A_f}{\partial A} - \frac{a_2 N_a^2}{kTA^2} \qquad (49)$$

Various approximations are possible for the "free area" A_f/N_a, the area available for one molecule. At very low coverages, when only bi-molecular collisions occur, A_f can be represented by the total area diminished with a constant (Boltzmann, 1898) denoting the finity of the hard disks:

$$A_f = A - N_a b_2^0 \qquad (50)$$

According to van der Waals, b^0 in three dimensions is equal to four times the proper volume of a molecule, whereas in two dimensions it can easily be verified to equal twice the proper area of a molecule (de Boer, 1953c; Tonks, 1936). Substitution of Eq. (50) in Eq. (47) and Eq. (49) yields for the adsorption equation and the 2-D equation of state respectively:

$$\ln\left(\frac{p\Lambda}{kT}\right) + \frac{E^0}{kT} = \ln\left(\frac{N_a}{A - N_a b_2^0}\right) + \frac{N_a b_2^0}{A - N_a b_2^0} - \frac{2a_2 N_a}{AkT} \qquad (51)$$

and

$$F = -a_2\frac{N_a^2}{A^2}+\frac{N_a kT}{A-N_a b_2^0}, \text{ viz. } \left(F+\frac{a_2 N_a^2}{A^2}\right)(A-N_a b_2^0) = N_a kT \quad (52)$$

Introductions of the coverage $\theta = A_0/A$ with $A_0 = N_a b_2^0$ leads to

$$\ln\left(\frac{p}{K_{\text{mob}}}\right) = \ln\left(\frac{\theta}{1-\theta}\right)+\frac{\theta}{1-\theta}-k_1^m\theta$$

where:

$$K_{\text{mob}} = K_{\text{mob}}^0 \exp\left(-E^0/kT\right)$$

and

$$k_1^m = \frac{2a_2 N_a}{A_0 kT} = \frac{2a_2}{b_2^0 kT} \quad (53)$$

analogously the equation of state (52) can also be written as:

$$\frac{b_2^0 F}{kT} = \frac{\theta}{1-\theta}-\tfrac{1}{2}k_1^m\theta^2 \quad (54)$$

The equation for mobile physical adsorption can also be found by integration of Eq. (52) with the aid of the Gibbs-adsorption equation (de Boer, 1953d). Equation (52) is subjected to a detailed consideration in the well-known book of de Boer "The Dynamical Character of Adsorption" (1953a), where the reader will find a wealth of information on the behaviour of the 2-D van der Waals analogue. Ross and Olivier (1964a) extensively used this Hill-de Boer equation in their analysis of physical adsorption data on homogeneous and rather heterogeneous surfaces and confirmed experimentally the properties of Eq. (53) predicted by de Boer.

The van der Waals constants a and b^0 may be considered as two adjustable parameters, varying from substance to substance and even depending upon the temperature. In the 3-D case these two parameters can be evaluated without difficulty from the critical point or from compressibility data. However, the adsorption equations have three adjustable parameters, namely K_{mob}, k_1^m and N_m, the number of molecules adsorbed in a completely filled monolayer. From k_1^m the ratio a_2/b_2^0 can be calculated. In order to be able to calculate the heat of adsorption E^0 from K_{mob} and the surface area S from N_m the value of either b_2^0 or a_2 must be known, since it is not possible to evaluate both values from the adsorption isotherm independently.

The values of a_2 and b_2^0 can be calculated from a_3 and b_3^0, since they relate to the same substance. Therefore, we define the intermolecular potential $u(r)$ to be given by the Sutherland potential:

$$u(r) = \infty \text{ when } r < d_0 \text{ and}$$

$$u(r) = -u_0 \left(\frac{d_0}{r} \right)^6 \text{ when } r \geqslant d_0 \tag{55}$$

This function shows a hard core repulsion and a London attraction branch. The relations between the van der Waals constants in 1, 2 and 3 dimensions and the parameters u_0 and d_0, are shown in Table V, which also displays the comparable parameters of the other adsorption equations discussed in this chapter.

TABLE IV. Comparison of the van der Waals constant b^0 with the geometrical "volume" in closest packing of hard rods, disks and spheres

	Configuration	(A_0)van der Waals$/(A_0)$real
1-D	Line	1
2-D	Simple squares	1·5708
	Triangular	1·8138
3-D	Simple cubes	2·0944
	FCC	2·9619

The Sutherland parameters can be obtained from the critical temperature and pressure, according to

$$u_0 = 3 \cdot 375 k T_{c3} \text{ and } d_0 = 0 \cdot 3908 \left(\frac{k T_{c3}}{p_{c3}} \right)^{\frac{1}{3}}. \tag{56}$$

The value of u_0 is independent of the number of translational degrees of freedom. Therefore, in the ratio of the critical temperatures of the 3, 2 or 1-dimensional state,

$$T_{c3} : T_{c2} : T_{c1} = \left(\frac{k_1}{k_{1c}} \right)_{3\text{-}D} : \left(\frac{k_1}{k_{1c}} \right)_{2\text{-}D} : \left(\frac{k_1}{k_{1c}} \right)_{1\text{-}D} \tag{57}$$

the u_0/kT-factors in k_1 (see Table V) are cancelled out. With Table 1 it follows for the van der Waals equation:

$$T_{c3} : T_{c2} : T_{c1} = 1 : 0 \cdot 5 : 0 \cdot 2 \tag{58}$$

It is obvious that at infinite pressure the free volume or free area equals zero. This yields the value of A_0 to be $N_a b_2^0$. However, since

TABLE V. Characteristic parameters of various mobile equations of state according to the Sutherland intermolecular potential

Va

1-D Hard Rods

All Models Eq. (54)

l_0	d_0
a_1	$\frac{1}{5}d_0 u_0$
k_1^m	$\frac{2}{5}u_0/kT$

Vb

2-D Hard Disks		

van der Waals Eq. (54)	SFA-approach Eq. (68)	VE-approach Eq. (84)
a_0	$\frac{1}{2}\pi d_0^2$	$\frac{1}{2}\sqrt{3}d_0^2$	$0\cdot8667d_0^2$
a_2	$\frac{1}{4}\pi d_0^2 u_0$	$\frac{1}{4}\pi d_0^2 u_0$	$\frac{1}{4}\pi d_0^2 u_0$
k_1^m	u_0/kT	$\frac{1}{3}\pi\sqrt{3}u_0/kT$	$1\cdot8125u_0/kT$

Vc

3-D Hard Spheres		

van der Waals Eq. (54)	Eyring Eq. (77)	VE-approach Eq. (85)
v_0	$\frac{2}{3}\pi d_0^3$	$\frac{1}{2}\sqrt{2}d_0^3$	$0\cdot8121d_0^3$
a_3	$\frac{2}{3}\pi d_0^3 u_0$	$\frac{2}{3}\pi d_0^3 u_0$	$\frac{2}{3}\pi d_0^3 u_0$
k_1^m	$2u_0/kT$	$\frac{4}{3}\pi\sqrt{2}u_0/kT$	$5\cdot1582u_0/kT$

TABLE VI. Two-dimensional densities θ_L and θ_G of the coexisting phases and corresponding reduced pressures $(p/K)_{mob}$ as a function of k_1^m for the van der Waals equation of state

k_1^m	$(p/K)_{mob}$	θ_L	θ_G
15·000	0·00356	0·8417	0·0037
14·500	0·00440	0·8350	0·0047
14·000	0·00542	0·8276	0·0058
13·500	0·00667	0·8195	0·0072
13·000	0·00819	0·8106	0·0091
12·500	0·01005	0·8007	0·0113
12·000	0·01230	0·7897	0·0142
11·500	0·01502	0·7773	0·0178
11·000	0·01830	0·7633	0·0224
10·500	0·02224	0·7472	0·0282
10·000	0·02696	0·7287	0·0358
9·900	0·02801	0·7246	0·0376
9·800	0·02910	0·7204	0·0395
9·700	0·03022	0·7160	0·0415
9·600	0·03139	0·7115	0·0436
9·500	0·03260	0·7069	0·0458
9·400	0·03384	0·7020	0·0482
9·300	0·03513	0·6970	0·0506
9·200	0·03647	0·6918	0·0533
9·100	0·03785	0·6864	0·0561
9·000	0·03928	0·6808	0·0591
8·900	0·04076	0·6749	0·0622
8·800	0·04229	0·6688	0·0656
8·700	0·04387	0·6624	0·0692
8·600	0·04550	0·6558	0·0731
8·500	0·04718	0·6488	0·0772
8·400	0·04892	0·6414	0·0816
8·300	0·05072	0·6337	0·0863
8·200	0·05257	0·6256	0·0914
8·100	0·05449	0·6171	0·0969
8·000	0·05647	0·6080	0·1028
7·900	0·05850	0·5983	0·1093
7·800	0·06061	0·5881	0·1163
7·700	0·06277	0·5771	0·1240
7·600	0·06501	0·5652	0·1325
7·500	0·06731	0·5524	0·1419
7·400	0·06968	0·5384	0·1524
7·300	0·07212	0·5230	0·1643
7·200	0·07464	0·5058	0·1779
7·100	0·07723	0·4861	0·1939
7·000	0·07989	0·4630	0·2133
6·900	0·08263	0·4340	0·2385
6·880	0·08319	0·4271	0·2447
6·860	0·08375	0·4196	0·2514
6·840	0·08431	0·4113	0·2589
6·820	0·08488	0·4021	0·2673
6·800	0·08545	0·3914	0·2773
6·780	0·08602	0·3782	0·2896
6·770	0·08631	0·3699	0·2975
6·760	0·08660	0·3592	0·3079
6·750	0·08689	0·3333	0·3333

the molecules are fixed in a regular array at infinite pressure, the real value of A_0 can be obtained from d_0 by simple geometrical considerations. Table IV shows the ratio $(A_0)_{\text{van der Waals}}/(A_0)_{\text{real}}$ for several configurations of arrays of rods, disks and spheres. For hard disks and spheres this ratio is considerably greater than unity, which shows clearly that—except for hard rods—the van der Waals constant b^0 must depend strongly upon the density in reality. In Section III E this dependence will be considered. The critical point can be found by putting the first and second derivate of $\ln (p)$ with respect to θ equal to zero. Thus:

$$\frac{\partial \ln (p_c)}{\partial \theta_c} = \frac{1}{\theta_c(1-\theta_c)^2} - k_1^m = 0 \tag{59}$$

$$\frac{\partial^2 \ln (p_0)}{\partial \theta_c} = \frac{3\theta_c - 1}{\theta_c^2(1-\theta_c)^3} = 0. \tag{60}$$

From Eq. (60) it follows that $\theta_c = 1/3$. The critical value of k_1^m amounts 6·75. A $\ln (p)$ versus θ graph always shows a point of inflection at $\theta = 1/3$ independent of the value of k_1^m, whereas the inflection point in a linear p versus θ plot occurs at values of θ less than 1/3 and even vanishes when k_1^m is smaller than 2. So, if an adsorption isotherm does not show a point of inflection it does not *a priori* indicate the absence of adsorbate-adsorbate interactions or the presence of surface heterogeneity.

The conditions for 2-D condensation, derived in Section II B, must be applied to Eq. (53) and Eq. (54), since the adsorption isotherm is S-shaped at k_1^m values greater than 6·75. The coverages of the coexisting 2-D gas and liquid phase can be obtained by solving simultaneously

$$\ln\left(\frac{\theta_L}{1-\theta_L}\right) + \frac{\theta_L}{1-\theta_L} - k_1^m\theta_L = \ln\left(\frac{\theta_G}{1-\theta_G}\right) + \frac{\theta_G}{1-\theta_G} - k_1^m\theta_G \tag{61}$$

$$\frac{\theta_L}{1-\theta_L} - \tfrac{1}{2}k_1^m\theta_L^2 = \frac{\theta_G}{1-\theta_G} - \tfrac{1}{2}k_1^m\theta_G^2 \tag{62}$$

Eq. (62) can be reduced to:

$$(1-\theta_L)(1-\theta_G)(\theta_L+\theta_G) = \frac{2}{k_1^m} \tag{63}$$

It is obvious that these equations only can be solved numerically. The results are shown in Table VI and in Figs 4 and 5.

D   The "Free Area" Approach to the 2-D State

The van der Waals equation of state, as summarized in the preceding section, may be described as a first attempt to take into account the dependence of the effective volume (3-D) or area (2-D) available for a molecule on the 2-D liquid or gas-density, while retaining the essential characteristics of a kinetic theory. It has been shown there, that only at low densities, the effective free volume or area may be obtained by subtracting from the total volume a constant amount for each molecule present. At higher densities, the "packing" of molecules in more or less ordered structures (3-D) and arrays (2-D) results in a more complicated dependence of free volume and area on density. A very simple, but surprisingly successful, theory of liquids has been developed by Eyring and Hirschfelder (1937) and Hirschfelder et al. (1954b) under the name "free volume theory". In this theory, the packing in ordered structures is emphasized and the mobility of molecules in gases and liquids is considered only as a secondary factor. This is in sharp contrast to the van der Waals conception, where mobility and disorder are completely retained. Nevertheless, as in the most simple "free volume" theories the conception of a "smoothened" intermolecular potential field, independent of position and directly proportional to the overall concentration, is retained, the resulting equations resemble closely those of the van der Waals conception.

The "free volume" approach in fact is an oversimplified form of a cell theory of liquids and gases (Barker, 1963). The molecule is supposed to translate freely within a cage constituted by its nearest neighbours. The dimensions of this cage are determined by the mean distance between the molecules, corrected for the hard sphere diameter of the molecules themselves. Each cell is always occupied by one single molecule. The effective volume or area of a single cell not only is dependent on the mean molecular distance but also on the symmetry of the packing. In many respects, such a "free volume" liquid or gas, resembles a solid (Barker, 1963), if the vibrations of the molecules in the solid are replaced by translations along the axis of the cell, restricted by the finite dimensions of the cell. Moreover, the molecules are supposed to be mutually exchangeable and a factor e^N is included in the partition function to account for communal entropy (Hirschfelder et al., 1954b). Extrapolation of the free volume or free area approach to the region of gaseous densities is inconsistent with the inherent disorder of the gaseous state. Nevertheless, the equations of state following from this type of approach reduce to the ideal gas law at infinite dilution (strictly speaking the same is not true for the entropy). In the liquid density range, the free volume (Hirschfelder et al., 1954b) and free area (Tonks, 1936) approach are probably better approximations than the van der Waals type of approach. In the gaseous density range the free area approach, though not exact, may be useful as a first approximation.

In analogy to the *3-D* partition function for a "free volume" liquid, the *2-D* free area partition function may be defined as:

$$Q = \Lambda^{-2N_a} a_f^{N_a} N_a \exp\left(N_a + N_a^2 a_2/(AkT) + N_a E^0/kT\right) \quad (64)$$

where the total intermolecular potential, in analogy to that of the van der Waals equation, is approximated by $N_a a_2/A$. The free area a_f for a hard disk liquid (molecular diameter d_0) may be deduced from

FIG. 2

The fundamental cell in the
SFA-approach.

FIG. 3

The fundamental cell in the
RFA-approach according to
Wang *et al.* (1965).

Fig. 2. The central molecule cannot be within a distance d_0 of the walls of the cell. The mean molecular distance d determines the area a^* of the main hexagon. The effective free area a_f is the area of the inner hexagon. The total area a^* of the hexagon equals

$$a^* = 2\sqrt{3}d^2$$

whereas the free area a_f is given by

$$a_f = 2\sqrt{3}(d-d_0)^2 = 4(\sqrt{a}-\sqrt{a_0})^2 = 4a_0(1/\sqrt{\theta}-1)^2. \quad (65)$$

The corresponding *2-D* pressure and thermodynamic potential μ^a may be computed from Eq. (65) by the relations:

$$F = -kT/a_0(\theta^2/a_f \cdot da_f/d\theta + k_1^m \theta^2/2) \quad (66)$$

$$\mu^a = -kT(1 - 2\ln\Lambda + E^0/kT + \ln(a_f) + \theta/a_f \cdot da_f/d\theta + k_1^m \theta) \quad (67)$$

to be equal to:

$$Fa_0/kT = \frac{\theta}{1-\sqrt{\theta}} - \frac{k_1^m \theta^2}{2} \quad (68)$$

$$\mu^a/kT = \ln\left(\frac{\Lambda^2}{4a_0}\right) - E^0/kT + 2\ln\left(\frac{\sqrt{\theta}}{1-\sqrt{\theta}}\right) + \frac{\sqrt{\theta}}{1-\sqrt{\theta}} - k_1^m \theta \quad (69)$$

Upon combining (14) and (69) the adsorption isotherm is obtained:

$$p = \frac{K^0_{\text{mob}}}{4} \frac{\theta}{(1-\sqrt{\theta})^2} \exp\left(\frac{\sqrt{\theta}}{1-\sqrt{\theta}} - k^m_1\theta - E^0/kT\right) \tag{70}$$

The adsorption isotherm Eq. (70) in general appearance resembles that of the 2-D van der Waals adsorption equation. Its critical value $(k^m_1)_c$ is 11·83, whereas θ_c equals 0·2944. In the critical point $(p/K_{\text{mob}})_c$ equals 0·14155 and $(Fa/kT)_c = 0.4448$ (see also Table I).

TABLE VII. A comparison between the predicted coexisting densities θ_L and θ_G at a certain value of k^m_1 for the SFA approach, the RFA approach and the combined SFA van der Waals approach

	SFA		RFA	
k^m_1	θ_L	θ_G	θ_L	θ_G
27·207	0·8309	0·00046	0·8297	0·00036
25·393	0·8164	0·00095	0·8149	0·00077
23·579	0·7990	0·00194	0·7972	0·00162
21·766	0·7778	0·00447	0·7755	0·00340
19·952	0·7513	0·00771	0·7481	0·00717
18·138	0·7168	0·00151	0·7122	0·0155
16·324	0·6701	0·0297	0·6626	0·0359
14·510	0·6010	0·0602	0·5893	0·1268
12·697	0·4779	0·1363	0·4897	0·2170

For k^m_1 larger than 11·83, two-dimensional condensation occurs. The coexisting two-dimensional densities θ_L and θ_G may be calculated from the relations (5) and (6):

$$\frac{\theta_L}{1-\sqrt{\theta_L}} - \frac{\theta_G}{1-\sqrt{\theta_G}} = k^m_1(\theta^2_L - \theta^2_G)/2 \tag{71}$$

and

$$\ln\left[\frac{\theta_L(1-\sqrt{\theta_G})^2}{\theta_G(1-\sqrt{\theta_L})^2}\right] + \frac{\sqrt{\theta_L}(1-\sqrt{\theta_G})}{\sqrt{\theta_G}(1-\sqrt{\theta_L})} = k^m_1(\theta_L - \theta_G) \tag{72}$$

Data of coexisting densities for θ_L and θ_G as a function of k^m_1 are presented in Table VIII. The choice of free area according to Fig. 2 is a rather intuitive one. A geometrical more exact choice of a_f has been proposed recently by Wang *et al.* (1965) and is presented in Fig. 3. From this figure, the following expressions for a_f may be derived:

$$\left. \begin{aligned} a_f &= 3\sqrt{3}d^2/2 - 2\pi d_0^2 \\ &= 3a_0(1/\theta - 4\pi\sqrt{3}/9) \end{aligned} \right\} \quad \text{if } d > 2d_0 \tag{73}$$

$$\left. \begin{aligned} a_f &= 12(\sqrt{3}/8d^2 - 1/8d\sqrt{4d_0^2 - d^2} - \phi d_0^2/2) \\ &= 3a_0(1/\theta - 1/\theta\sqrt{4\theta/3 - 1/3} - 4\phi/\sqrt{3}) \end{aligned} \right\} \quad \text{if } d < 2d_0 \tag{74}$$

where ϕ and θ are related by

$$\phi = \arccos{(1/(4\sqrt{\theta}) + \sqrt{3/4 - 3\theta/16})}$$

F and μ^a may directly be calculated from Eqs (66) and (67) after differentiation of Eq. (73) with respect to θ. The resulting forms are too lengthy to be recorded here, so we will restrict the discussion to some special features of this Refined Free Area approach (RFA). It might be anticipated from Fig. 3 that there is some dis-continuous behaviour of the free area around the point $\theta = \frac{1}{4}$, where $d = 2d_0$. Indeed the first and second derivative of a_f with respect to θ in this point are not uniquely defined. As a consequence, the usefulness of the Refined Free Area approach vanishes in the region $\theta = \frac{1}{4}$, which in fact is the critical region. This rather disturbing behaviour of the Refined Free Area approach is still under investigation. It has been remarked that the idea of free space as the nooks and crannies left over by incompressible spheres is obsolete and misleading (Moellwynn-Hughes, 1961). The results of the present discussion seem to substantiate this view. For the present, the RFA approach may be used at low reduced temperatures $(T \ll T_c)$. In this region, coexisting 2-D densities have been calculated with the aid of Eqs (15) and (16). A comparison between the data obtained from the RFA and the SFA (Simple Free Area) approach is presented in Table VII. At low reduced temperatures, the differences between the results of both treatments are surprisingly small.

In Section III C the van der Waals equation of state has been used to describe the whole density region. As the SFA treatment may be unsatisfactory in the gaseous density region, we have investigated the coexistence of a condensed SFA phase with a diluted 2-D van der Waals gas. Consistency requires to replace the relation $a_0 = b_2^0$ by the appropriate one:

$$a_0 = \sqrt{3b_2^0/\pi}, \quad k_1^m = \pi k_1^m/\sqrt{3}$$

(see also Table V).

TABLE VIII. Two-dimensional densities θ_L and θ_G of the coexisting phases and corresponding reduced pressures $(p/K)_{mob}$ as a function of k_T^m for the SFA approach

k_T^m	$(p/K)_{mob}$	θ_L	θ_G
25·000	0·00120	0·8129	0·0011
24·000	0·00179	0·8033	0·0016
23·000	0·00267	0·7927	0·0024
22·000	0·00397	0·7808	0·0036
21·500	0·00482	0·7743	0·0043
21·000	0·00586	0·7674	0·0052
20·500	0·00710	0·7600	0·0063
20·000	0·00859	0·7521	0·0076
19·500	0·01038	0·7436	0·0091
19·000	0·01251	0·7344	0·0110
18·500	0·01506	0·7245	0·0132
18·000	0·01810	0·7138	0·0159
17·500	0·02170	0·7022	0·0192
17·000	0·02595	0·6894	0·0231
16·800	0·02787	0·6840	0·0249
16·600	0·02991	0·6783	0·0268
16·400	0·03209	0·6724	0·0289
16·200	0·03411	0·6662	0·0312
16·000	0·03689	0·6598	0·0337
15·800	0·03953	0·6531	0·0363
15·600	0·04234	0·6461	0·0392
15·400	0·04534	0·6387	0·0424
15·200	0·04852	0·6310	0·0458
15·000	0·05191	0·6229	0·0495
14·800	0·05550	0·6143	0·0536
14·600	0·05933	0·6053	0·0581
14·400	0·06338	0·5957	0·0630
14·200	0·06768	0·5855	0·0684
14·000	0·07223	0·5746	0·0744
13·800	0·07706	0·5630	0·0810
13·600	0·08216	0·5505	0·0884
13·400	0·08756	0·5370	0·0968
13·200	0·09327	0·5223	0·1062
13·000	0·09929	0·5061	0·1169
12·900	0·10242	0·4974	0·1229
12·800	0·10564	0·4881	0·1294
12·700	0·10895	0·4783	0·1364
12·600	0·11234	0·4677	0·1441
12·500	0·11582	0·4564	0·1526
12·400	0·11940	0·4440	0·1620
12·300	0·12306	0·4304	0·1727
12·200	0·12682	0·4151	0·1850
12·100	0·13067	0·3974	0·1996
12·000	0·13462	0·3760	0·2180
11·900	0·13867	0·3464	0·2445
11·880	0·13949	0·3382	0·2521
11·870	0·13990	0·3335	0·2565
11·860	0·14031	0·3282	0·2615
11·850	0·14073	0·3219	0·2675
11·840	0·14114	0·3136	0·2755
11·830	0·14155	0·2944	0·2944

The coexistence requirements (5) and (6) may then be written as

$$\frac{\theta_L}{1-\sqrt{\theta_L}} - \frac{\theta_G}{1-\pi\theta_G/\sqrt{3}} = k_1^m/2(\theta_L^2-\theta_G^2) \ , \tag{75}$$

$$-\ln(4)+2\ln\left(\frac{\sqrt{\theta_L}}{1-\sqrt{\theta_L}}\right)+\frac{\sqrt{\theta_L}}{1-\sqrt{\theta_L}}$$

$$-\ln\left(\frac{\theta_G}{1-\pi\theta_G/\sqrt{3}}\right)-\frac{\pi\theta_G/\sqrt{3}}{1-\pi\theta_G/\sqrt{3}} = k_1^m(\theta_L-\theta_G) \ . \tag{76}$$

In this "realistic" interpretation of the van der Waals equation of state, these equations are valid at low 2-D gas densities and thus at low reduced temperatures. Numerical results indicated that there is hardly any difference between the SFA approach and the present treatment. Consequently, we will adopt the SFA approach over the whole density region. Its validity in the critical region of course remains questionable, but the present results indicate that the SFA approach may be extrapolated with reasonable accuracy to the gaseous 2-D density region.

The three-dimensional analogue of Eq. (68), may be written, according to Hirschfelder *et al.* (1954b), as:

$$\frac{pv_0}{kT} = \frac{\theta}{(1-\theta^{1/3})} - \frac{\theta^2(k_1^m)_3}{2} \tag{77}$$

where θ is equal to v_0/v and $(k_1^m)_3$ is the 3-D analogue of k_1^m.

From Eq. (77) the predicted critical constant may be determined. It turns out that θ_c equals 0·2791, whereas $p_c v_c/kT_c$ equals 0·5358. This is only slightly higher than the ratio $p_c v_c/kT_c$ as calculated from the Lennard-Jones and Devonshire theory of the liquid state (Lennard Jones and Devonshire, 1937; 1938), viz. 0·519. Both values are in very poor agreement with the observed ratio for inert gases: ~0·29 (see also Section III F) (Barker, 1963). It must be concluded that in three dimensions the "free volume" approach gives a poor description of the critical region. Therefore, it is improbable that values for effective molecular dimensions may be determined successfully from critical data. In principle, the hard sphere diameter d_0, for example, may be calculated from the 3-D p_c and T_c by (see Tables I and V):

$$u_0 = 2\cdot8431 \ kT_{c3} \text{ and } d_0 = 0\cdot5958\left(\frac{kT_{c3}}{p_{c3}}\right)^{\frac{1}{3}} \tag{78}$$

So the values of d_0, and consequently of a_0 calculated in this way are higher than the corresponding ones as calculated from the van der Waals equation of state. This is not surprising in view of the difference in the predicted ratio $p_c v_c / kT_c$ for both treatments. A second ratio of interest T_{2c}/T_{3c}, may be calculated from Eq. (57) to be equal to 0·4359, considerably lower than that predicted by the van der Waals equation (see Eq. (58)). In view of the unsatisfactory behaviour of the *3-D* equation (77) in the critical region, the importance of this number seems doubtful.

E Extrapolation of the 2-D Virial Equation of State

An equation of state can be written as an expansion in inverse powers of A, resulting in a virial equation of state.

$$FA/(N_a kT) = 1 + B_2(N_a b_2^0/A) + B_3(N_a b_2^0/A)^2 + B_4(N_a b_2^0/A)^3 + \ldots \qquad (79)$$

where b_2^0 is the original van der Waals constant of Eq. (50).

For hard disks and spheres the virial coefficients are independent of the temperature. Eq. (52) can be written as:

$$FA/(N_a kT) = \frac{1}{1-(N_a b_2^0/A)} - N_a a_2/(AkT) \qquad (80)$$

Expansion of (80) shows that all virial coefficients (except the second) in the van der Waals equation are equal to one. Van der Waals himself (1897) already noticed that this cannot possibly be correct and calculated the third virial coefficient to be 15/32 for hard spheres. However, he made a mistake, as was pointed out by Boltzmann (1898), who showed that $B_3 = 5/8$. Tonks (1936) showed that for hard disks $B_3 = 4/3 - \sqrt{3}/\pi$. In case of hard spheres B_4 was calculated by van der Waals (1898), van Laar (1899) and Boltzmann (1899).

For about half a century no further calculations were performed, because of the insuperable mathematical difficulties. It is the electronic computers, that provide the possibility of calculating higher virial coefficients. Ree and Hoover (1964) computed the higher virial coefficients up to the sixth and gave a reliable estimate of the seventh and eighth coefficient, for both hard spheres and disks (see Table IX). These virial coefficients offer the possibility to obtain a better approximation of the van der Waals constants b_2 and b_3. Suppose the area dependence of b_2 can be represented by:

$$b_2(A)/b_2^0 = c_2 + c_3(N_a b_2^0/A) + c_4(N_a b_2^0/A)^2 + c_5(N_a b_2^0/A)^3 + \ldots \qquad (81)$$

Substitution of (81) in (80) yields with (79):

$$\frac{1}{1 - \sum_{i=2} c_i(N_a b_2^0/A)^{i-1}} = 1 + \sum_{i=2} B_i(N_a b_2^0/A)^{i-1} \qquad (82)$$

TABLE IX. Exact virial coefficients for a hard sphere and a hard disk fluid,
as computed by Ree and Hoover (1964)

	Disks	Spheres
B_2	1	1
B_3	0·7820	0·6250
B_4	0·5324 ± 0·0003	0·2870
B_5	0·3338 ± 0·0005	0·1103 ± 0·0003
B_6	0·1992 ± 0·0008	0·0386 ± 0·0004
B_7	0·115	0·0127
B_8	0·065	0·0040

From this equation the constants c can be calculated with help of the recursion formula:

$$c_2 = B_2$$
$$c_3 = B_3 - B_2 c_2$$
$$c_4 = B_4 - B_3 c_2 - B_2 c_3$$
$$c_5 = B_5 - B_4 c_2 - B_3 c_3 - B_2 c_4, \text{ etc.} \tag{83}$$

The results are listed in Table X.

TABLE X. Constants of Eq. (81) for the VE approach

	Disks	Spheres
c_2	$+1$	$+1$
c_3	$-0·2180$	$-0·3750$
c_4	$-0·3161\ 10^{-1}$	$+0·3695\ 10^{-1}$
c_5	$+0·3482\ 10^{-2}$	$+0·2078\ 10^{-1}$
c_6	$+0·2697\ 10^{-2}$	$-0·7963\ 10^{-2}$
c_7	$-0·2448\ 10^{-4}$	$-0·1622\ 10^{-3}$
c_8	$+0·3736\ 10^{-4}$	$+0·8768\ 10^{-3}$

Replacing b_2^0 in Eq. (80) by $b_2(A)$ from Eq. (81) yields

$$FA/(N_a kT) = \frac{1}{1 - N_a b_2(A)/A} - N_a a_2/(AkT) \tag{84}$$

Analogous, the 3-D case becomes:

$$pV/(NkT) = \frac{1}{1 - N b_3(V)/V} - \frac{N a_3}{VkT} \tag{85}$$

It is obvious that expansion of the first term in the right hand part of Eq. (84) reproduces the original hard disks virial coefficients. Moreover, it yields an infinite number of higher virial coefficients, which are all positive and rapidly decrease at increasing number. Since no negative higher virial coefficients occur, Eq. (84) does not show the transition from fluid to solid phase at very high density, that was "observed" by Alder and Wainwright (1960; 1962) from their molecular dynamical simulation of hard spheres or disk fluids. There is no proof that such a phase transition exists in reality. The possibility should not be excluded that this phase transition is a mere consequence of simulating a finite system, consisting of a great number of molecules, by a small number of molecules in a system with permeable boundaries.

There is no *a priori* reason for writing an equation of state in the virial rather than in the reciprocal form, because when all virial coefficients are known, both forms are identical. However, the reciprocal form has the advantage, that at a certain value of the density the pressure goes to infinity. This is an important feature of adsorption equations, since adsorption in the monolayer region shows a very definite saturation effect.

The minimum area A_0 in Eq. (84) and the minimum volume V_0 in Eq. (85) can be obtained by solving

$$N_a b_2(A_0)/A_0 = 1 \text{ and } N b_3(V_0)/V_0 = 1$$

This yields

$$A_0 = N_a b_2^0/1{\cdot}8125 \text{ and } V_0 = N b_3^0/2{\cdot}5791 \tag{86}$$

Table IV shows that the theoretical close packing corresponds to the factors $1{\cdot}8138$ and $2{\cdot}9619$ respectively. So, the deviation for hard disks is less than $0{\cdot}1\%$, which is very good, seeing the uncertainties in the computed virial coefficients. For hard spheres considerable improvement is achieved, although the limiting density is about 15% less than theoretically predicted. The values of the critical constants resulting from Eqs (84) and (85) are listed in Table I.

The relation between the one-, two- and three-dimensional temperatures, corresponding to the VE (virial extrapolation) equations of state derived in this section, can be evaluated from Eq. (57).

$$T_{c3}{:}T_{c2}{:}T_{c1} = 1{:}0{\cdot}4485{:}0{\cdot}1572. \tag{87}$$

According to Eq. (87), the *2-D* and *1-D* critical temperatures are considerably lower than the values predicted by the van der Waals equation (see Eq. (58)). There is some experimental evidence that the *2-D* critical temperature is about $0{\cdot}45$ rather than $0{\cdot}5$ times the *3-D* critical temperature.

The Sutherland parameters can be calculated from the critical temperature and pressure according to

$$u_0 = 2 \cdot 6535 k T_{c3} \text{ and } d_0 = 0 \cdot 4468 \left(\frac{k T_{c3}}{p_{c3}} \right)^{1/3} \tag{88}$$

The numerical values of a_0, a_2 and k_1^m can be calculated with the formulae listed in Table V.

The adsorption equation corresponding to Eq. (84) can be derived with the help of the Gibbs adsorption equation (see Eq. (3)), which after partial integration may be written as:

$$\int d \ln(p) = \frac{FA}{N_a k T} - \int \frac{F}{N_a k T} dA$$

Elimination of F by substitution of Eq. (84) yields:

$$\int d \ln(p) = \frac{A}{A - N_a b_2(A)} - \frac{N_a a_2}{A k T} + \frac{N_a a_2}{k T} \int \frac{dA}{A^2} - \int \frac{dA}{A - N_a b_2(A)}. \tag{89}$$

Defining a function

$$f(A) = 1 - N_a b_2(A)/A \tag{90}$$

yields for Eq. (89)

$$\int d \ln(p) = \frac{1}{f(A)} - \frac{2 a_2 N_a}{A k T} - \int \frac{dA}{A f(A)} \tag{91}$$

Since the coverage θ per definition equals A_0/A, with Eq. (86) it follows that

$$\theta = \frac{N_a b_2^0}{1 \cdot 8125 \, A} \tag{92}$$

Thus, Eq. (91) becomes

$$\int d \ln(p) = \frac{1}{f(\theta)} - k_1^m \theta + \int \frac{d\theta}{\theta f(\theta)} \tag{93}$$

where

$$k_1^m = \frac{2 a_2 N_a}{A_0 k T} \tag{94}$$

Substitution of Eqs (92) and (81) in (90) yields

$$f(\theta) = 1 - 1 \cdot 8125 \, \theta + 0 \cdot 7162 \, \theta^2 + 0 \cdot 1882 \, \theta^3 - 3 \cdot 758_{10^{-2}} \theta^4 \tag{95}$$
$$- 5 \cdot 274_{10^{-2}} - \theta^5 + 8 \cdot 682_{10^{-4}} \, \theta^6 - 2 \cdot 401_{10^{-3}} \, \theta^7$$

or, written as a product of factors

$$f(\theta) = (1-\theta)(1 - 1 \cdot 3562 \, \theta + 0 \cdot 4974 \, \theta^2)(1 + 0 \cdot 5847 \, \theta + 0 \cdot 1307 \, \theta^2)$$
$$(1 - 0 \cdot 0409 \, \theta + 0 \cdot 0369 \, \theta^2) \tag{96}$$

The integration of the right hand part of Eq. (93) can be performed by means of partial fractions. The integration constant is chosen in such a way that the obtained adsorption equation reduces to the Henry equation at very low coverage. The resulting adsorption equation becomes (van Dongen, to be published),

$$\ln (p/k_2^m) = \ln (\theta) - 4 \cdot 1319 \ln (1-\theta) - k_1^m \theta + \frac{1-f(\theta)}{f(\theta)} + 1 \cdot 6374 \ln$$

$$(1 - 1 \cdot 3562\theta + 0 \cdot 4974\theta^2) + 0 \cdot 1182 \ln (1 + 0 \cdot 5847\theta + 0 \cdot 1307\theta^2) +$$

$$0 \cdot 8103 \ln (1 - 0 \cdot 0409\theta + 0 \cdot 0369\theta^2) + 0 \cdot 1987 \arctan \left(\frac{0 \cdot 2172\theta}{1 + 0 \cdot 2923\theta} \right)$$

$$- 0 \cdot 7741 \arctan \left(\frac{0 \cdot 1939\theta}{1 - 0 \cdot 6781\theta} \right) - 0 \cdot 1395 \arctan \left(\frac{0 \cdot 1911\theta}{1 - 0 \cdot 0205\theta} \right)$$

where

$$K_{\mathrm{mob}} = K_{\mathrm{mob}}^0 \exp \left(-E^0/kT \right) \qquad (97)$$

This lengthy equation can be approximated with surprising accuracy by

$$\ln (p/K_{\mathrm{mob}}) = \ln (\theta) - 4 \cdot 7243 \ln (1-\theta) - k_1^m \theta - 5 \cdot 2169\theta - 2 \cdot 7477\theta^2 -$$
$$0 \cdot 9812\theta^3 - 1 \cdot 6392\theta^4 + 4 \cdot 1258\theta/(1-\theta) \qquad (98)$$

The difference in the pressure calculated with Eq. (97) or with Eq. (98) is always less than $0 \cdot 02\%$ at coverages less than $0 \cdot 9$. The constants in Eq. (98) were computed from Eq. (97) by means of least squares curve fitting technique. For sake of convenience Eq. (98) can be used in comparison with experimental data.

At k_1^m values greater than $10 \cdot 724$ two-dimensional condensation will occur. The values of θ_L and θ_G can be computed from Eqs (5) and (6) applied to Eqs (97) and (84). The results are shown in Table XI and in Figs 4 and 5. A remarkable feature of the coexistence region is the small value of θ_L even at low temperature. However, there is little absolute significance in this, since the volume adsorbed at a coverage $\theta = 1$ depends strongly upon the model used to calculate the monolayer volume (see Section V). The phase transition predicted by Alder and Wainwright (1962) would start at a coverage $\theta = 0 \cdot 762$. Such a high coverage can be reached only at high pressure, where multimolecular adsorption will have set in, or at very low (reduced) temperature, where the equilibrium pressure is too low to measure adsorption isotherms with the required accuracy. So, if such a phase transition exists, it is no wonder that it has not been found experimentally.

5

TABLE XI. Two-dimensional densities θ_L and θ_G of the coexisting phases and corresponding reduced pressures $(p/K)_{\text{mob}}$ as a function of k_1^m for the VE approach

k_1^m	$(p/K)_{\text{mob}}$	θ_L	θ_G
25·000	0·00067	0·7309	0·0007
24·000	0·00096	0·7208	0·0010
23·000	0·00138	0·7098	0·0014
22·000	0·00196	0·6977	0·0020
21·000	0·00277	0·6844	0·0029
20·000	0·00390	0·6697	0·0042
19·000	0·00544	0·6532	0·0060
18·000	0·00753	0·6347	0·0085
17·500	0·00884	0·6245	0·0102
17·000	0·01035	0·6135	0·0122
16·500	0·01209	0·6018	0·0146
16·000	0·01408	0·5891	0·0175
15·800	0·01496	0·5837	0·0188
15·600	0·01588	0·5781	0·0202
15·400	0·01686	0·5724	0·0217
15·200	0·01789	0·5664	0·0234
15·000	0·01897	0·5602	0·0252
14·800	0·02011	0·5538	0·0272
14·600	0·02131	0·5471	0·0293
14·400	0·02257	0·5402	0·0316
14·200	0·02389	0·5329	0·0341
14·000	0·02528	0·5253	0·0368
13·800	0·02673	0·5174	0·0398
13·600	0·02826	0·5091	0·0431
13·400	0·02985	0·5003	0·0467
13·200	0·03153	0·4911	0·0507
13·000	0·03327	0·4814	0·0550
12·800	0·03510	0·4710	0·0599
12·600	0·03700	0·4600	0·0653
12·400	0·03898	0·4482	0·0714
12·200	0·04105	0·4355	0·0782
12·000	0·04320	0·4217	0·0860
11·900	0·04431	0·4144	0·0904
11·800	0·04544	0·4066	0·0951
11·700	0·04659	0·3985	0·1001
11·600	0·04776	0·3898	0·1056
11·500	0·04896	0·3806	0·1117
11·400	0·05017	0·3707	0·1183
11·300	0·05141	0·3600	0·1257
11·200	0·05267	0·3483	0·1342
11·100	0·05395	0·3353	0·1439
11·000	0·05525	0·3204	0·1554
10·950	0·05591	0·3119	0·1622
10·900	0·05658	0·3024	0·1700
10·850	0·05725	0·2915	0·1792
10·800	0·05793	0·2782	0·1908
10·780	0·05820	0·2716	0·1966
10·760	0·05847	0·2638	0·2037
10·750	0·05861	0·2591	0·2081
10·740	0·05875	0·2533	0·2135
10·724	0·05899	0·2333	0·2333

F Comparison of Models

Five different models for the uni-molecular adsorbed phase have been discussed in some detail. Two of these, the Fowler-Guggenheim model (Fowler and Guggenheim, 1939a; Frumkin, 1925; 1926) of localized adsorption and its first order refinement the quasi-chemical approximation (Fowler and Guggenheim, 1939c), suppose adsorption to be restricted to specified lattice sites at the surface of the solid and have been characterized as models of localized adsorption. The three other models are derived from the assumption of in principle mobile molecules. In the cell models of adsorption, such as the SFA approximation, this mobility is rather restricted: molecules are freely mobile only within the boundaries set by the walls of their cages. Yet, the general appearance of the adsorption isotherm predicted by the SFA approximation, is that of a mobile adsorbed layer rather than a localized adsorbed layer. This is apparent from the following considerations:

1. The point of inflexion of the simplest mobile model isotherm in which interaction is taken into account, the van der Waals equation, is located at $\theta = 0.3333$ (Table I). This is considerably lower than the point of inflexion corresponding to the localized treatments, 0.5. The point of inflexion from the VE equation, an equation based on the virial treatment of complete mobile hard sphere gases, is situated at even lower coverages, $\theta = 0.2333$. The SFA treatment leads to a coverage in the point of inflexion of 0.2944, intermediate between that of the van der Waals treatment and the VE equation and thus more in line with the mobile models than with the localized ones.

2. The general appearance of the locus of coexisting two-dimensional densities as a function of reduced temperature T/T_{2c} and reduced two-dimensional condensation pressure p/p_{c2} (see Figs 4 and 5) for the three mobile isotherms is quite different from that for the two localized isotherm models. The symmetry of the localized adsorption models is completely lacking for the mobile models.

It is to be noted that the localized model is seen to predict a high surface density for the condensed phase at temperatures only slightly below the critical temperature. The variation of surface density in the condensed phase with pressure and with temperature is rather weak for localized adsorption as compared to mobile adsorption at temperatures well below the 2-D critical temperature. For mobile adsorption, even at temperatures well below the critical one, the condensed phase just after condensation still corresponds to a rather loose surface packing and increase of the 3-D pressure continues to result in a substantial increase in surface density over a long range of relative pressures (see Figs 6 and 7). On the other hand, for mobile adsorption isotherms, a surface coverage of 0·9 is only reached at very high *3-D* pressures and a situation approaching a completely covered surface in

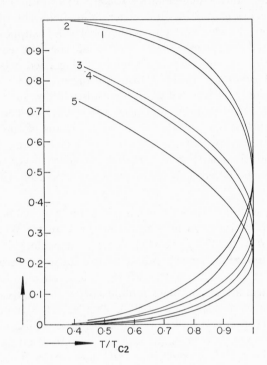

FIG. 4 Locus of coexisting two-dimensional densities as a function of the reduced temperature T/T_{c2}.

1. Fowler-Guggenheim.
2. quasi-chemical.
3. van der Waals.
4. SFA approach.
5. VE approach.

the first adsorbed layer is hardly realizable in practice. For localized adsorption on the other hand, there seems to be no problem in realizing surface coverages θ very near to unity at sufficiently low temperatures. This directly leads to the problem of the definition of monolayer volume. Although in all treatments, the monolayer volume is completely defined by the size of the adsorbed molecules or the size of the adsorption sites respectively, it appears that the direct physical significance of the monolayer volume concept is rather more vague in mobile

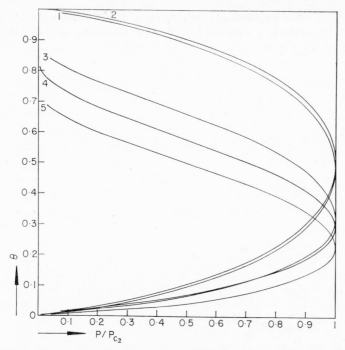

FIG. 5 Locus of coexisting two-dimensional densities as a function of the reduced pressure of condensation p/p_{c2}. Legend: see Fig. 4.

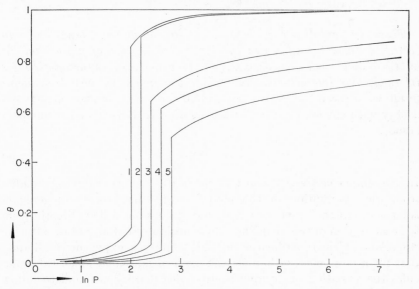

FIG. 6 Examples of theoretical adsorption isotherms in the sub-critical range ($T/T_{c2} = 0.8$). Legend: see Fig. 4.

adsorption than in localized adsorption. We want to stress, that in mobile adsorption something like a completed monolayer is not realizable physically.

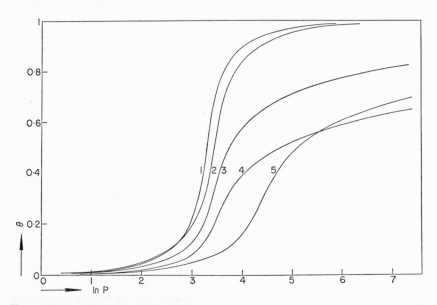

FIG. 7 Examples of theoretical adsorption isotherms in the super-critical range ($T/T_{c2} = 25$). 1·Legend: see Fig. 4.

These clear-cut differences between mobile and localized behaviour may be traced down to differences in differential entropy of adsorption for localized and mobile adsorption, not to differences in accounting for intermolecular interactions. Except for the quasi-chemical treatment, in all cases the interaction is accounted for by a variation of internal energy with coverage in the form according to Barker and Henderson (1968):

$$U_{\text{int}} = -C\theta N_a \qquad (99)$$

In the simple van der Waals treatment this equation directly follows from the assumption of the model, as in the Fowler-Guggenheim treatment. In the other models, Eq. (99) does not follow directly from the assumption of the model and its inclusion essentially is an intuitive step. An empirical justification for this step is the experimental finding that for a large class of liquids composed of non-polar spherical molecules the variation of internal energy with density is found to follow approximately an equation of the type (99) (Hirschfelder *et al.*, 1954b).

For the sake of simplicity, we will restrict ourselves to a comparison between the differential entropy of localized adsorption according to the simple Fowler-Guggenheim model and that of mobile adsorption according to the simple van der Waals equation of state.

For simple localized adsorption, the differential entropy of adsorption is given by:

$$dS/d\theta = -kN_s \ln\left(\frac{\theta}{1-\theta}\right) \qquad (100)$$

Whereas for mobile adsorption this differential entropy in case of the van der Waals equation is given by:

$$dS/d\theta = -kN_m\left[\ln\left(\Lambda^2/b_2^0\right) + \ln\left(\frac{\theta}{1-\theta}\right) + \frac{\theta}{1-\theta} - 1\right]. \qquad (101)$$

Apart from the constant terms Eq. (101) contains the additional term $\theta/(1-\theta)$, which is due to the assumption of complete mobility within the effective free volume and which tends to infinity when θ approaches unity at a far larger rate than the logarithmic term common to both equations. For mobile adsorption the quick decrease in entropy of the adsorbed phase at increasing superficial density is a powerful factor in inhibiting the formation of a high-density condensed phase. Although for other adsorption models, the expression for the differential entropy of adsorption is far more complicated, the same trend persists throughout. An important conclusion to be drawn from this behaviour is, that it must be possible to obtain information concerning the mobility of the adsorbed phase from its two-dimensional condensation behaviour and from the compressibility behaviour of the condensed phase upon increasing $3\text{-}D$ pressure.

It thus is seen that there is a consistency in the behaviour of the adsorption isotherms within the group of mobile equations on the one hand and of localized equations on the other hand. In spite of this, the differences in detailed behaviour between different models in the group of mobile equations, is quite large. This is illustrated by the predicted properties of the critical phase for different equations (Table I). As a characteristic property we may take the predicted value of the Kamerlingh-Onnes constant $p_c V_c/RT_c$.

In three dimensions, for many simple gases its experimental magnitude is found to be about 0·29. The simple van der Waals theory, for example, predicts a value of 0·375. A slight but significant improvement towards the experimental value is achieved by the VE approach. The simple free volume approximation of Eyring leads to a value very remote from the experimental one. In this respect it resembles the behaviour of the Lennard Jones and Devonshire (1937; 1938) cell model with a predicted value of 0·591. The recent application of computer calculatory techniques to the simulation of hard sphere and hard disk gas behaviour, the Monte-Carlo (Metropolis *et al.*, 1953) and Molecular dynamics (Alder and Wainwright, 1960; 1962) representation of 2-*D* and 3-*D* gas behaviour, has led to the idea that the simple cell theories, as well as the cell theories of the Lennard Jones and Devonshire type describe a solid state rather than a liquid state. At lower coverages the cell theories would thus describe metastable states. It is not impossible that at high coverages on the other hand, cell theories are useful approximations. The virial theory on the other hand, and especially the virial expansion extrapolation as discussed in Section III E, clearly describes a densified gas state rather than an ordered state. No negative virial coefficients result from the extrapolation technique described and so no ordered high-density phases are included. The cell-theories probably over-estimate such an ordering whereas the virial extrapolation theory possibly under-estimates it. In two dimensions, no experimental value for the Kamerlingh-Onnes constant is known. This is due to two causes:

(a) Completely homogeneous adsorbents are still very rare and few data on such adsorbents are available over a sufficient range of temperatures.

(b) The 2-*D* critical conditions are even more hard to establish experimentally than the 3-*D* ones.

No direct observation of the 2-*D* phase is possible and the experimental uncertainties in adsorption isotherms render interpretations of measured adsorption curves in the critical region very difficult. All two-dimensional critical temperatures found in the literature are to be considered as quite rough approximations. Nothing is known about 2-*D* critical pressures and surface densities. The predicted 2-*D* Kamerlingh-Onnes constants follow the same trend as their 3-*D* ones. If adsorption is mobile and if, moreover, the 2-*D* gas in practice behaves as its related 3-*D* one in the critical region, then we may expect the virial extrapolation to be the most accurate description of a 2-*D* gas at high densities as yet available.

A remarkable property of this last model is the attainment of a density corresponding very close to that of a hexagonal close packing at infinite 2-*D* pressure. Such a behaviour does not follow from any of the assumptions made in the derivation. In the simple free area model the attainment of hexagonal close packing in the limit of 2-*D* pressure has merely been a starting point, whereas in the simple van der Waals-treatment the area per molecule at infinite pressure, b_2^0, may only be identified empirically with a dense close-packed state. If the constant b_2^0 is identified with two times the hard disk area of the molecules, as would follow from theoretical considerations, then all surface coverages exceeding 0·55 are to be excluded as physically unattainable. It has been argued by de Boer (1953e), that b_2^0 in fact turns out to be a reasonable measure of the area occupied by non-hard disk molecules in a nearly close-packing. Indeed, it is striking that in many cases b_2^0 is very close the area occupied per molecule which may be calculated from the 3-D bulk liquid density. Striking as this may be, the agreement seems essentially accidental. The neglect of finite repulsive forces between molecules is a serious short-coming of all theories treated here. We may therefore expect all treatments to lead to semi-quantitative predictions at best. It is worthwhile recollecting that at this very moment no satisfactory treatment of 3-D liquids and high density gases is available in spite of the introduction of more realistic intermolecular forces than the hard-sphere and hard-disk approximation used throughout here (Henderson and Davison, 1967).

In localized adsorption, a severe complication is the necessity to introduce specific assumptions about the surface of the adsorption, i.e. the number of discrete adsorption sites at the surface. The pair interaction energy between adsorbed molecules, for example, may not be predicted a priori, but is dependent on the distance of the adsorption sites at the surface.

A problem common to all models considered, is the onset of multi-layer adsorption. As will be shown in the next section, even less is known about multilayer adsorption. The stacking of 2-D layers at the moment seems to be the most promising attack but is to be considered as a first approximation only. Yet, it has been justly realized by de Boer that insight into the character of adsorption may only be gained by an exhaustive study of the behaviour of 2-D liquids and gases both theoretically and experimentally. The present contribution is no more than a first step. In the remainder of this chapter we will show what conclusions may be drawn about the adsorbed state by application of the present views to experimental data on homogeneous and nearly homogeneous adsorbents. We may not expect these conclusions to be more than of semi-quantitative validity.

G The Multilayer Problem

It may be concluded from the preceding sections that no exact treatment of unimolecular adsorption has yet been developed, although useful equations may be derived from simple models. Even less is known about the formation of multilayers in physical adsorption.

_localized adsorption, the famous BET theory (Brunauer *et al.*, 1938; Brunauer, 1943) enjoys a great, if rather unfounded, popularity. If the derivation of this theory is based on statistical mechanics (Hill, 1946), then the BET theory is seen to be a logical extension of the Langmuir approach to localized adsorption. According to the BET theory the total surface coverage θ is given by:

$$\theta = \frac{Cx}{(1-x)(1-x+Cx)} \tag{102}$$

where C is a constant, and x stands for p/q (de Boer, 1953f), q being the pressure where θ approaches infinity.

By tradition q is identified with the saturation pressure p_0 of a *3-D* liquid at the same temperature. On theoretical grounds this identification is completely unfounded. If q is set equal to p_0, then for adsorption of nitrogen on non-porous inorganic oxides, carbons and salts the BET theory has been shown to cover only a relative pressure region between 0·05 and 0·35 (de Boer *et al.*, 1966). If q is set equal to about 1·3 p_0 (de Boer, *et al.*, 1966), then the BET equation may be used to describe the isotherm between 0·10 and 0·75 relative pressure. This may hardly be taken as a justification of the BET picture. The asymptotic approach of the isotherm to p_0 indicates a gradual transition to a *3-D* liquid at higher relative pressures. As the BET equation does not resemble any model of a liquid phase, it is incapable of describing such a transition. Its validity over the range $x = 0·05$ to $0·35$ probably is quite accidental, as it completely breaks down in the description of multilayer adsorption even over this restricted range if the adsorbent surface is sufficiently homogeneous. It appears that the BET equation is a useful empirical description of multilayer adsorption over this restricted pressure range on energetically heterogeneous surfaces (Young and Crowell, 1962b), although in its derivation heterogeneity was not taken into account. This interesting feature deserves more attention than it has hitherto received. For large values of θ, it seems logical to identify the multilayer with a liquid layer of a certain thickness t, which is stabilized by potential field emanating from the solid and decaying with distance. Representing this potential field by $F(t)$, we may formally write for the thermodynamic potential of the multilayer μ_a:

$$\mu_a = \mu_L - F(t) \tag{103}$$

where: $\mu_L =$ the thermodynamic potential of the bulk liquid. In equilibrium $\mu_a = \mu_g$, so the adsorption isotherm may formally be written as:

$$RT \ln (p/p_0) = -F(t), \tag{104}$$

If it is assumed that only London dispersion forces between the solid and the molecules in the adsorbed layer are operative, then the potential field of the solid may be taken to decrease inversely proportional to the third power of the distance to the solid as a first approximation. If the structure of the adsorbed layer were identical to the bulk liquid, then the relation:

$$F(t) = C/t^3 \tag{105}$$

would hold, and the resulting adsorption isotherm would be:

$$RT \ln (p/p_0) = -C/t^3 \tag{106}$$

Eq. (106) is generally known as the Frenkel-Halsey-Hill equation (Frenkel, 1946; Halsey, 1948; Hill, 1950). In practice, this equation does not describe multilayer adsorption satisfactorily. A better, if completely empirical, description is given by the related Halsey equation (Halsey, 1952):

$$RT \ln (p/p_0) = -C/t^n \tag{107}$$

where n has a value somewhere between 2 and 3.

A related empirical description is that of Jura and Harkins (1943)

$$\log (p/p_0) = B - A/t^2 \tag{108}$$

which gives a satisfactory description of the adsorption of, for example, nitrogen at $78°K$ over a relative pressure range of 0.08 to 0.8. The constants B and A in this instance turn out to be independent in the first instance of the chemical characteristics of the solid. This equation therefore is especially suitable for relative surface area determinations. For nitrogen A and B are equal to 13.99 and 0.034 respectively (de Boer et al., 1966).

A theoretical description of multilayer adsorption has already been given by de Boer and Zwikker (1929). They assumed induction of dipoles in the first adsorbed layer by the electrostatic field of the adsorbent. These dipoles in their turn induce dipoles in the second layer, and so on. In principle, these authors gave a rigorous treatment of multilayer adsorption according to this mechanism. The mathematical difficulties, however, were insuperable and simplifying assumptions had to be made. It was assumed that the adsorbed layer was essentially liquid-like in behaviour and under the influence of a potential field generated by the mechanism of dipole induction discussed before. As a first approximation $F(t)$ for such a field is given by:

$$F(t) = a\beta^n \tag{109}$$

and the adsorption isotherm then becomes:

$$RT \ln (p/p_0) = -a\beta^n. \tag{110}$$

Deviations from the liquid structure of the adsorbate were taken into account by introducing a third parameter γ:

$$RT \ln (p/\gamma p_0) = -\alpha \beta^n. \qquad (111)$$

This equation was found to be successful in describing, e.g. the adsorption of argon on SnO_2, and of water on certain minerals (Bradley, 1936). The induced dipole mechanism is probably only operative in selected cases of adsorption.

On the whole, the theory of multilayer adsorption had hardly grown out of the semi-empirical stage. Nevertheless the need is felt to extend the models for unimolecular adsorption presented in this chapter to the multilayer region. Experimentally the two cannot be separated and even at fairly low pressures the onset of the formation of at least a second layer complicates the interpretation of experimental data. It has been shown by de Boer and Broekhoff (1967a) that for the adsorption of krypton on carbon at $78°K$ a more or less satisfactory description of multilayer formation may be given by considering a stacking of 2-D van der Waals layers on top of each other and assuming the influence of the surface to be decreasing inversely proportional with the third power of the distance. For the adsorption of nitrogen this description failed beyond the formation of a second layer.

Nevertheless, such an approach may be useful as a first attack in correcting for multilayer adsorption. We will consider the multilayer picture as a stacking of 2-D mobile layers in some detail.

Consider a stacking of n two-dimensional mobile layers at a mutual distance d_0 (d_0 being the hard sphere diameter). In the jth layer N_j molecules are present. The partition function of a molecule in the jth layer then is given by:

$$q_j = \Lambda^{-2}(A_f)_j$$

The potential field working at a molecule in the jth layer is generated by

(a) *The solid*. Its magnitude is given by:

$$E_j = E^0/j^3$$

(b) *The n-1 other layers*. Its magnitude is dependent on the concentration in all layers. If we assume only London dispersion forces then in first approximation this contribution to the potential field amounts to:

$$\sum_{i \neq j}^{n} 2N_i a_2/[A(j-i)^4]^*$$

---

* Note that the factor 2 is omitted in Eq. (45); there are in total only N_iN_j pairs of interacting molecules in the ith and the jth layer respectively. Retaining the factor 2 would lead to taking into account each pair twice in the summation of the energy.

(c) *The jth layer itself.* The interaction between the molecules in the jth layer themselves, is equal to

$$N_j a_2/A.$$

The complete partition function for the whole adsorbed phase then becomes:

$$Q = \prod_j \frac{(q_j)^{N_j}}{N_j!} \exp\left[\frac{\sum_j N_j}{kT}\left(E^0/j^3 + \frac{a_2 N_j}{A} + \sum_{i \neq j} \frac{a_2 N_i}{(j-i)^4} \right) \right]$$

$$= \prod_j \frac{(q_j)^{N_j}}{N_j!} \exp\left[\sum_j N_j\left(\frac{E^0}{j^3 kT} + \frac{k_1^m}{2}\theta_j + \sum_{i \neq j} \frac{k_1^m \theta_i}{2(j-i)^4} \right) \right] \tag{112}$$

Next we determine the values of N_j in such a way that Q is maximal with respect to N_j at constant total number of moles adsorbed N_a. This leads to the expression:

$$-2 \ln A - \ln (N_j) + \ln (A_f)_j + N_j \, d \ln (A_f)_j/dN_j + E^0/(j^3 kT) +$$

$$k_1^m \sum_{i \neq j} \frac{\theta_i}{(j-i)^4} + k_1^m \theta_j = \text{const} = -\mu/kT \tag{113}$$

If we take for A_j the van der Waals expression $A_j = A - N_j b_2^0$, we may write for Eq. (113):

$$\ln (p/K_{\text{mob}}^0) = \ln\left(\frac{\theta_j}{1-\theta_j} \right) + \frac{\theta_j}{1-\theta_j} - E^0/(j^3 kT) - k_1^m \theta_j - k_1^m \sum_{i \neq j} \frac{\theta_i}{(j-i)^4} \tag{114}$$

There are for n layers a set of n equations of the type (114). These n non-linear equations have to be solved simultaneously for the set of values θ_j. No analytical procedure is known but numerical solution in practical cases is always possible. Equation (114) has been solved for a set of 7 layers, at a temperature about 1·2 times the 2-*D* critical temperature, so it is well below the 3-*D* critical temperature (see Fig. 8). It appears, that although the first and the second layer behave definitely supercritical, beyond the formation of the fourth layer subcritical behaviour sets in and higher layers are condensing despite of the fact that the temperature is well above the 2-*D* critical temperature. Clearly, this model shows a remarkable transition from 2-*D* to 3-*D* behaviour. On theoretical grounds, such a transition is not unexpected, but it has to be noted that no such behaviour is found in practice. The experimental transition from the 2-*D* to the 3-*D* state is far more gradual than predicted by the present theory. This may be caused by the break-down of the separate layer model.

The analogues of Eq. (114) for the other two-dimensional equations of state in the mobile cases are obvious. For localized adsorption, a similar procedure was applied by Hill (1947), to the Fowler-Guggenheim equation. However, Hill did not take into account either the dependence of the interaction with the adsorbent on distance nor the fact that a molecule on top of a molecule in the j-1th layer is not equidistant to all its $(z+1)$ nearest neighbours in that layer.

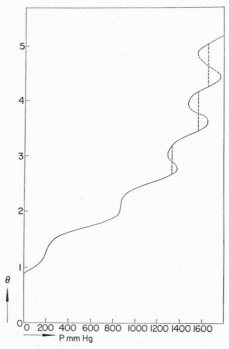

Fig. 8 Theoretical multimolecular adsorption isotherm for the van der Waals equation at a reduced temperature $T/T_{c2} = 1\cdot25$.

Taking into account these factors results in the following equation for the jth layer in the multilayer stacking:

$$\ln (p/K_{\text{loc}}^0) = \ln \left(\frac{\theta_j - \theta_{j+1}}{\theta_{j-1} - \theta_j} \right) - E^0/(j^3 kT) - k_1^l \theta_j - \frac{k_1^+}{z} - k_1^{++} (\theta_{j+1} + \theta_{j-1})$$

(115)

where: k_1^+ and k_1^{++} are analogues of k_1^l accounting for the interaction between two molecules stacked on top of each other and between a molecule and the nearest neighbours of the molecule on top of which it has been placed. In the special case where the distance between two adjacent layers is equal to the distance between two neighbouring sites, and only London dispersion forces are at play, the following relationships should hold:

$$k_1^+ = k_1^l, \qquad k_1^{++} = k_1^l/8 \qquad\qquad (116)$$

Equation (115) has not been tested experimentally. A test of Eq. (114) on the sorption of krypton and of nitrogen at 78°K on the homogeneous carbon black Sterling 2700°, showed that Eq. (114) for krypton described the experimental findings rather well up to the point where 2-D condensation sets in in the second layer. At higher gas pressures, the amount adsorbed predicted by Eq. (114) is definitely too low. For nitrogen, the same trend is found: at the 2-D densification of the second layer the usefulness of Eq. (114) breaks down. Apparently, Eq. (114) is only valid as a first order correction for the onset of multi-layer adsorption at a densified first layer in the low pressure region.   Among the several shortcomings of a treatment of the type given here, we may list the following:

1. Complete neglect of vibrational freedom in any layer, in a direction perpendicular to the surface. As the multilayer formation proceeds towards a three-dimensional bulk structure, we must expect this degree of freedom to become equally important to the lateral degrees of freedom in any layer remote to the surface.

2. Uncertainties in the dependence of the intermolecular interaction on distance. We have assumed that the interaction between a molecule at a distance d from the surface of the adsorbent and the adsorbent itself may be expressed by an equation of the type:

$$E_d = C/d^n$$

where according to the simple theory n should equal 3 for a semi-infinite bulk solid, or 4 for an infinite plane of adsorbing material. It has been shown by de Boer, that these exponents are approximations, valid only if the distance d to the plane or the surface of the solid is large in comparison to the intermolecular distances in the solid or the plane. More accurate numerical calculations indicate a value of n somewhat larger than 3 in the neighbourhood of the solid surface. On the other hand, an analysis of experimental multimolecular adsorption data recently showed that in order to describe the experimental data for adsorption of krypton and nitrogen at 78°K on the homogeneous carbon black Sterling FT a somewhat slower decay of the interaction energy with distance must be assumed than is predicted by the third power law. An extreme case of such behaviour is the adsorption of ethyl-chloride. Here a value of 2 for n has to be assumed in order to explain the experimental findings (de Boer and Broekhoff, 1967b).

3. Whereas Eq. (114) predicts a clearly distinguishable densification of separate layers, the behaviour shown by the adsorption of krypton at 2-D subcritical temperatures, the supercritical adsorption of nitrogen and argon beyond the formation of the second layer shows no sign of separate layer behaviour. Clearly the approximation of the multilayer as a stacking of separate layers breaks down beyond the second layer at supercritical temperatures. It is well to realize that beyond the second layer the influence of the adsorbent on the heat of adsorption becomes very small; the largest contribution to the heat of adsorption stems from the interaction with the layers already adsorbed. As a consequence, the effective heat of adsorption becomes nearly equal for all layers beyond the second layer. The transition to a bulk condensed phase at pressures near saturation will take over and all separate layer behaviour is bound to vanish.

IV   Interpretation of Adsorption Data on Adsorbents with Energetically Homogeneous Surfaces

A   Methods of Evaluating Adsorption Parameters from Adsorption Data

All adsorption equations discussed here are of the general form

$$\ln (p/K) = f(k_1, \theta)$$

where K and k_1 are constants, related to the interaction between adsorbent and adsorbate molecules and the interaction between the adsorbed molecules themselves, respectively. All adsorption data are recorded in terms of p and N_a or V_a, the number of molecules adsorbed or the volume adsorbed in ml S.T.P. respectively, on an adsorbent with fixed but unknown surface area. Therefore, a third parameter $V_m(N_m)$ is required to reduce V_a, (N_a) to θ. For all models discussed, V_m is the amount adsorbed in the monolayer at infinite two-dimensional pressure F. For mobile sorption equations, this amount is determined by the surface area S and the hard sphere diameter of the adsorbate molecule d_0, while for localized adsorption V_m is determined by S and by the area connected with one adsorption site at the surface s_0. It is to be stressed that there is no satisfactory independent method of estimating S (see also the extensive discussion in Section V of this chapter). For mobile equations, the hard sphere diameter d_0 in principle may be determined from the 3-D equation of state for each model separately. No such procedure exists for the estimation of the localized "site area" s_0. Therefore, there is no way of estimating V_m independently. Some authors (Pierce, 1968; Aristov and Kiselev, 1967; Cochrane et al., 1967; Fisher and McMillan, 1958) have adopted the convention of deriving V_m from the BET method. Such a procedure, of course, is obsolete. The BET equation is a localized equation of state, so BET monolayer volumes may never be used in interpretating adsorption data with the aid of mobile equations of state. Moreover, the BET equation deliberately neglects lateral interactions between adsorbate molecules, so its use in connection with either the Fowler equation or the q.c. equation is untenable on logical grounds. To the opinion of the present authors, V_m is to be treated as a separate parameter, to be derived from the adsorption data from the adsorption equations themselves. This is a complication in the evaluation of sorption data. Two methods have been developed in the Delft research group:

1. For supercritical isotherms a modified least square method has been developed. The theoretical isotherm equation is fitted to the experimental adsorption data in such a way that

$$\sigma = \sum [\ln (p)_{\text{obs}} - \ln (p)_{\text{calc}}]^2$$

attains a minimum value for the optimum choice of all three parameters K, k_1 and V_m. This method, a generalization of the well-known least-square method of fitting experimental points to a linear equation, uniquely defines the values of the parameters K, k_1 and V_m. The mathematics involved is somewhat complicated and calculations involve an iteration procedure most conveniently executed on a high-speed electronic computer.

2. For subcritical isotherms, parts of the isotherm equation are either metastable or unstable and never realized in experimental work. This somewhat complicated the application of the method described under 1. A method, devised earlier by de Boer (de Boer and Broekhoff, 1967e) was found to be useful. It is clear that for subcritical isotherms the ratio

$$V_L / V_G = \theta_L / \theta_G$$

uniquely determines the value of k_1 for a certain model. The ratio V_L / V_G may conveniently be evaluated from the vertical or nearly-vertical stretches in the adsorption isotherms and the corresponding value of k_1 may be read from one of the corresponding tables II, III, VI, VIII or IX. At a certain value of k_1, the ratio

$$(p/K)_{\text{cond}}$$

is uniquely defined (see tables) and K may be directly computed from the experimentally observed value of p_{cond}. Once the parameters k_1

and K are fixed in this way, the optimum value of V_m may be determined from the experimental isotherm and the appropriate isotherm equation with comparative ease.

A problem common to both supercritical and subcritical isotherms is the correction for the onset of multilayer adsorption. A reliable evaluation of the parameters k_1, K and V_m involves the processing of as many sorption data as available over a relatively large range of 3-D equilibrium pressures p. At higher coverages part of the experimentally observed adsorption undoubtedly is due to at least the start of the formation of a second layer on top of the first layer. On the other hand, it will be clear from the discussion in Section III G, that the theoretical description of multilayer adsorption is still in its first stage of development. In some cases, the separate formation of a second layer experimentally is clearly recognizable. This enables the evaluation of an empirical heat of adsorption for the second layer. Adsorption at higher coverages now may be viewed as a stacking of different layers and the coverage θ in each layer may be calculated from the appropriate equation of state. Such a procedure has been found to be satisfactory for the adsorption of nitrogen and krypton, provided the coverage in the second layer does not exceed the coverage in the inflexion point or the 2-D condensation coverage resp. In many cases, including nearly all supercritical isotherm data, experimental data on the densification of the second layer are lacking. An estimate of the contribution of the second layer to the adsorption at higher coverages may be made with the Eqs (114) and (115) respectively. A warning against over-confidential use of these equations, however, is necessary. Both equations are founded on a decay of attractive forces of the adsorbent inversely with the third power of distance. Experimentally such a third power law has been demonstrated to be satisfactory only for the 2-D van der Waals equation of state. Whether it also applies for the other equations of state is still doubtful. In general, for supercritical isotherms corrections for multilayer adsorption are small and the uncertainties in the correction for second-layer formation are of little consequence.

B   Evaluation of the Heat of Adsorption

Comparisons of experimental adsorption isotherms on energetically homogeneous surfaces with theoretical isotherm equations directly leads to a value of K. From this value of K we may immediately calculate E^0 either by Eq. (22) or by Eq. (17). Thus, two different values for E^0 may be obtained, depending on whether mobile or localized adsorption is assumed. Comparison with experimentally determined heats of adsorption may furnish us with important information on the character of adsorption, mobile or localized. However, it is well to realize the exact meaning of E^0. This last energy is the energy difference between the gaseous state and the adsorbed state extrapolated to zero degree Kelvin. It may easily be related to experimentally determinable heats of adsorption, e.g. the isosteric heats of adsorption, as we will show presently. In the discussion in Section III A we deliberately neglected all changes in vibrational and rotational entropies of adsorption, as well as the vibration perpendicular to the surface. Following Kruyer (1955a), we may take these changes into account by putting:

$$K^0_{\text{mob}} = \frac{kT \; q_{\text{rot}(g)} \; q_{\text{vib}(g)} \; \exp(-E^0/kT)}{Aa_0 \; q_{\text{rot}(a)} \; q_{\text{vib}(a)} q_\perp} \tag{117}$$

and

$$K^0_{\text{loc}} = \frac{kT \; q_{\text{rot}(g)} \; q_{\text{vib}(g)} \; \exp(-E^0/kT)}{A^3 q_{\text{rot}(a)} \; q_{\text{vib}(a)} q_\perp \; q_x \; q_y} \tag{118}$$

For monatomic gases we are of course only occupied with $q_\perp$, the vibrational partition function perpendicular to the surface, and in localized adsorption with q_x and q_y resulting from vibrations at the adsorption site in the plane of the adsorbent surface. The isosteric heat of adsorption Q_{st} is commonly defined at:

$$Q_{st} = kT^2 \partial \ln(p)/\partial T \tag{119}$$

and we will denote its limit at $\theta = 0$ by Q^0_{st}.

From this definition and from Eq. (20) it follows that for mobile adsorption of a monatomic gas the following relation holds:

$$Q^0_{st} = E^0 + 3/2kT - kT^2 \partial \ln(q_\perp)/\partial T \tag{120}$$

or in general for polyatomic molecules:

$$Q^0_{st} = E^0 + 3/2kT + kT^2 \sum_{\text{rot,vib}} \partial \ln\left[\frac{q_g}{q_a}\right] /\partial T - kT^2 \, \partial \ln (q_\perp)/\partial T \tag{121}$$

In the present treatment we have assumed $q_\perp$ to be equal unity, viz, a completely unexcited vibration. The other extreme at high temperature would be:

$$q_\perp = kT/h\nu$$

where ν is the characteristic frequency of the vibration perpendicular to the surface. In that case Eq. (120) would read:

$$Q^0_{st} = E^0 + 1/2kT \tag{122}$$

If this vibration were not excited, and, moreover, all rotations were lost upon adsorption, then we would have obtained from Eq. (121):

$$Q_{st}^0 = E^0 + 3/2kT + nkT \qquad (123)$$

where n would be the number of rotations and/or vibrations completely lost upon adsorption. In practice it seems unlikely that all vibrations and rotations are completely lost, so Eq. (123) has to be considered as an extreme. Moreover, it appears from Eqs. (120) and (123) that such a loss of degrees of freedom may be partially compensated by a gain of freedom of vibration perpendicular to the surface. As a first approximation we may therefore put:

$$Q_{st}^0 = E^0 + 3/2kT \qquad (124)$$

Exactly the same reasoning for localized adsorption leads to

$$Q_{st}^0 = E^0 + 5/2kT \qquad (125)$$

Q_{st}^0 may be determined either from calorimetric measurements or from the measured adsorption isotherms at different temperatures without the introduction of any specific adsorption model. On the other hand, E_0 may be determined at each temperature from the isotherm after introducing an appropriate adsorption equation. *Comparison of E^0 with the measured values of Q_{st}^0 should in principle lead to information concerning the validity of the chosen adsorption model.*

C   Examples of 2-D Densification and 2-D Phase Transition

As we have seen, all models for the 2-D state introduced here predict S-shaped isotherms and, at sufficient low temperatures, a 2-D phase transition.

S-shaped isotherms have been found experimentally in many cases, e.g. the adsorption of argon, nitrogen, xenon, ethyl chloride, ethane, chloroform and trichloro-fluoro-methane at graphitized carbon blacks. Two-dimensional phase transitions have been found for the adsorption of krypton, ethyl chloride, chloroform and trichloro-fluoro-methane at graphitized carbon blacks, and for krypton and methane on sodium- and potassium halides and related substances. This list is not exhaustive but contains the most pertinent examples. It is noteworthy, that at the time of publication of de Boer's monograph no well established example of S-shaped isotherm or of 2-D phase transitions were known. The phenomena predicted by him have now been established beyond any doubt. De Boer's treatment of these phenomena was centred at the application of the 2-D van der Waals equation of state. It has been the aim of the present authors to test the different model isotherms for the 2-D state now available against the experimental data.

As discussed before, the onset of multilayer adsorption is a serious complication in the interpretation of sorption data. After testing nearly all data now available, the present authors have come to the conclusion that the following conditions have to be imposed on the experimental data:

1. A large number of points on the isotherms has to be taken with as great an accuracy as possible.

2. The range of the adsorption isotherm has to extend from very small coverages up to as high a degree of coverage as consistent with the requirement of small coverages in the second layer.

Only a few of the published adsorption data meet this requirement. On account of this, relatively accurate adsorption data at the highly graphitized carbon black Sterling FT (2700) were taken, including the adsorption of argon, nitrogen and krypton.

A   *Argon on Sterling FT (2700) at 77·4°K*

The adsorption isotherm was taken over the pressure range 10^{-4} to 4 mm Hg. Over a hundred experimental points were taken. The experimental isotherm is given in Fig. 9. In Fig. 10 the same isotherm is

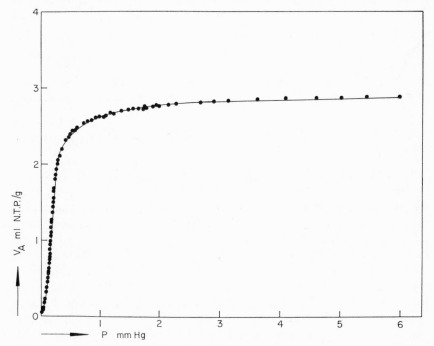

FIG. 9 Argon adsorption isotherm on Sterling FT at 77·4°K. Linear pressure scale.

plotted on a logarithmic pressure scale. This last figure demonstrates how difficult it is to secure sufficient adsorption data in the high relative pressure range before multilayer adsorption sets in. The most significant differences in the shape of the theoretical isotherms on a logarithmic scale (Figs 6 and 7) are becoming apparent only at relatively high pressures. In practice, multilayer formation sets in in this region.

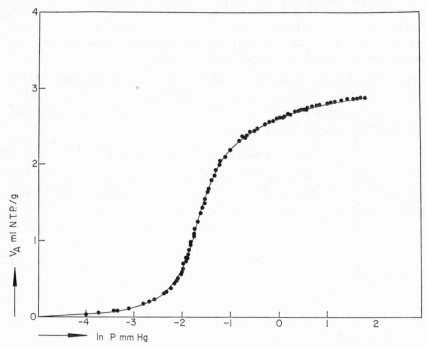

FIG. 10 Argon adsorption isotherm on Sterling FT at 77·4°K. Logarithmic pressure scale.

It was found that over the restricted region experimentally realizable in the monolayer region, all of the theoretical isotherm equations discussed in Section III could be fitted reasonably well into the experimental isotherm, except for the localized q.c.-approximation which failed in the highest relative pressure region (the experimental adsorption after correction for multilayer, there exceeded systematically the monolayer volume capacity predicted by the shape of the isotherm at lower relative pressures). The sequence of decreasing "closeness of fit" was found to be: 2-D van der Waals equation, VE approach, SFA approach, Fowler, q.c. (Fig. 11). The most significant adsorption parameters thus obtained for different models are collected in Table XII.

As a most striking result, E^0 for all three *mobile* equations of state is of the same order of magnitude, its mean value being 2·18 kcal/mole. The isosteric heat of adsorption was found to be equal to 2·35 kcal/mole (Sams *et al.*, 1962b). From Eq. (124) this would lead to a value of

TABLE XII. Adsorption parameters of argon adsorbed on Sterling FT at 77·4°K

	k_1	K	V_m	E^0	Q_{st}^0	$(k_1T)_{exp.}$	$(k_1T)_{theor.}$
	—	mm Hg	cc STP/ g	kcal/ mole	kcal/ mole	°K	°K
van der Waals	5·673	1·422	3·552	2·171	2·402	439·1	508·7
SFA approach	11·02	1·009	3·965	1·958	2·189	852·9	777·1
VE approach	9·584	2·015	4·499	2·166	2·397	741·8	724·9
Fowler-Guggenheim	2·404	0·8634	2·914	3·006	3·391	186·1	—
q.c.	2·886	0·9987	2·848	2·984	3·369	223·4	—

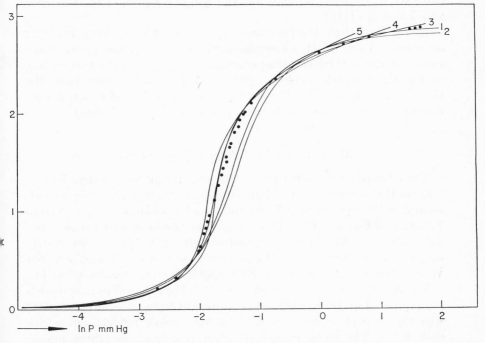

. 11 Argon adsorption isotherm on Sterling FT at 77·4°K. Logarithmic pressure scale. ⸱st Fit" theoretical adsorption isotherms compared to experimental data (dots) (see legend ʳig. 7).

E^0 of 2·12 kcal/mole, indeed very close to our value as derived from the isotherm equations.

On the other hand, the localized Fowler treatment yields a value for E^0 nearly 1·5 times the experimental found one. This striking result indicates that argon has retained its mobility upon adsorption completely. This conclusion is not inconsistent with that of Kruyer (1955a), who found a decrease in 2-D mobility only at higher coverages. This decrease in mobility on account of the finite "volume" of the molecules is taken into account automatically by the adsorption equation of Section III. The value of E^0 found from the mobile equation, moreover, is in excellent agreement with the mean value calculated by Kiselev (Avgul et al., 1959) from the interaction between one argon atom and the basal plane of graphite, viz. 2·22 kcal/mole. The value of V_m calculated from the isotherm is seen to depend strongly on the chosen model. This is not unexpected, as the characteristic hard sphere or hard disk diameter d_0 for each model has to be calculated from the appropriate 3-D equation of state in correspondence with measured 3-D p-V-T data. It turns out that also in 3-D the characteristic diameter d_0 depends strongly on the adopted equation of state (see also Table XVIII).

The 2-D critical temperatures T_{c2}, as calculated from $(k_1 T)_{\text{exp}}$, are listed in Table XVII, which also displays the T_{c2}-values based on the values of the 3-D critical temperatures. The $(T_{c2})_{\text{exp}}$-values, according to the three mobile models, agree mutually much better than the theoretical values. The average value of 69°K is quite acceptable, contrary to the value of 46°K, predicted by the localized equations.

B   Nitrogen on Sterling FT at 77·4°K

The adsorption isotherm was taken over the pressure range 10^{-3} to 1·2 mm Hg, including more than 90 experimental points. The experimental isotherm both on a linear and on a logarithmic scale is given in Fig. 12 and Fig. 13. All isotherm equations could be fitted reasonably well into the experimental isotherms, although there were clearly distinguishable differences. The sequence of best "fit" was: van der Waals equation, VE approach, SFA approach, q.c., Fowler (Fig. 14).

The adsorption parameters derived with the aid of different models are presented in Table XIII. As in the case of argon, it is surprising how well the adsorption energies E^0 from the mobile models agree with each other. The mean energy of adsorption from the three mobile models is 2·18 kcal/mole. The observed isosteric heat of adsorption is of the order of magnitude of 2·3 kcal/mole (Hellemans et al., 1967),

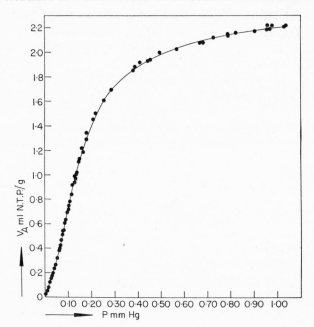

FIG. 12 Nitrogen adsorption isotherm on Sterling FT at 77·4°K. Linear pressure scale.

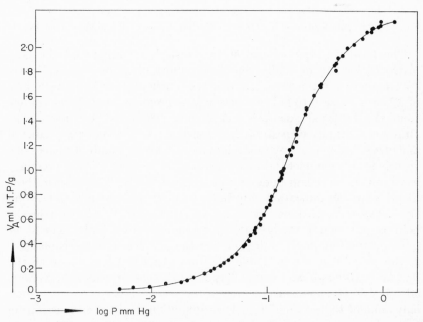

FIG. 13 Nitrogen adsorption isotherm on Sterling FT at 77·4°K. Logarithmic pressure scale.

which would lead to a predicted value of E^0 of 2·05 kcal/mole. The difference between this observed value and the predicted ones, might be due to some restriction of the rotation of the nitrogen molecule in comparison to the 3-D gaseous state. According to the studies of Kruyer, there are only minor indications of such a loss of rotational freedom upon adsorption.

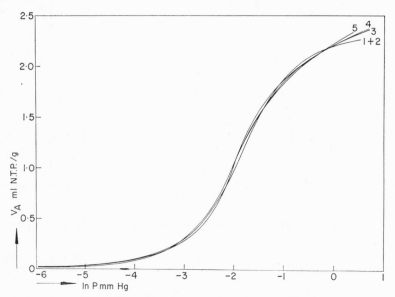

FIG. 14 Nitrogen adsorption isotherm on Sterling FT at 77·4°K. Legend: see Fig. 11.

The localized equations of state, Fowler's equation and the q.c.-approach lead to mutually consistent values of E^0 of 3·03 kcal/mole, 50% higher than the experimental ones. Their quantitative predictions of E^0 are thus seen to fail completely. The predicted monolayer volume from the localized adsorption equations 2·36 ml STP/g adsorbent, although mutually consistent, is significantly lower than the predicted monolayer volume of any of the mobile equations of state. On the same adsorbent, the complete adsorption isotherm at higher relative pressures has been measured in detail by de Boer et al. (1965). These authors found a distinct indication of formation and densification of the second layer. On a logarithmic pressure scale, the amount adsorbed in the point of inflexion of the second layer amounted to 4·3 ml/g. The localized adsorption equations predict that the coverage in the second layer in the point of inflexion is 0·5 (see Table I). Even if we assume the first layer to be already completely filled at that pressure, the volume adsorbed in the point of inflexion of the second layer predicted would only amount to 3·54 ml STP/g. This prediction deviates seriously from the experimental value. On the other hand, e.g. for the van der Waals equation of state, which predicts a coverage θ of 0·3333 in the second layer at the corresponding point of inflexion, the predicted amount adsorbed would be 4·20 ml STP/g, in much better agreement with the observed value. A more detailed analysis, which will be published elsewhere, confirms that the three mobile equations of state can describe the formation of the second layer on top of the first layer much better than the localized ones, as the predicted monolayer volumina for

TABLE XIII. Adsorption parameters of nitrogen adsorbed on Sterling FT at 77·4°K

	k_1	K	V_m	E^0	Q_{st}^0	$(k_1 T)_{exp}$	$(k_1 T)_{theor}$
	—	mm Hg	cc STP/ g	kcal/ mole	kcal/ mole	°K	°K
van der Waals	3·889	0·6322	3·152	2·265	2·496	301·0	425·3
SFA approach	9·162	0·4474	3·474	2·037	2·628	709·1	649·8
VE approach	6·745	0·8830	4·233	2·248	2·479	522·1	606·1
Fowler-Guggenheim	1·888	0·4359	2·360	3·030	3·415	146·1	—
q.c.	1·977	0·4533	2·356	3·024	3·409	153.0	—

TABLE XIV. Adsorption parameters of nitrogen adsorbed on Sterling FT at 78°K. Data of Avgul et al. (1959)

	k_1	K	V_m	E^0	Q_{st}^0	$(k_1 T)_{exp}$	$(k_1 T)_{theor}$
	—	mm Hg	cc STP/ g	kcal/ mole	kcal/ mole	°K	°K
van der Waals	3·648	0·6305	3·355	2·271	2·502	284·5	425·3
SFA approach	8·699	0·4313	3·743	2·068	2·992	678·5	649·8
VE approach	6·444	0·8862	4·519	2·268	2·599	502·6	606·1
Fowler-Guggenheim	1·725	0·4314	2·490	3·060	3·445	134·6	—
q.c.	1·808	0·4468	2·486	3·055	3·440	141·0	—

localized adsorption turn out to be too low to give a reasonable explanation of the densification of the first layer and the starting of the formation of the second layer at higher relative pressures. Here again, only the mobile equations of state are capable of giving a physically satisfactory description of adsorption at a homogeneous surface.

The only other data available on the adsorption of nitrogen of sufficient accuracy are those of Kiselev (Isirikyan and Kiselev, 1961). The adsorption parameters derived from these data are much the same except for the value of V_m (see Table XIV) which are somewhat higher over the whole region. This may be due to the fact that Kiselev's data are taken in a higher pressure region than those of the present authors. The conclusions concerning the mobility of nitrogen as given here remain equally valid.

A point of interest is, that the product k_1T, found experimentally, for the van der Waals and VE approach again is lower than the theoretical one derived from the 3-D gaseous state. It was found earlier by de Boer and Broekhoff (1967a) that at higher densities the van der Waals equation of state could describe the measured isotherm satisfactorily with the theoretical value of k_1 at 77·6°K, viz. 5·48. The more detailed analysis of the low-pressure region given here has led to adopting smaller values of k_1. It turns out that the exact value of k_1 is of little influence in describing the higher coverage region of the isotherm, whereas the lower part of the isotherm is quite sensitive to the choice of k_1. The 2-D critical temperature of about 50°K, according to the mobile models, seems more realistic than the T_{c2}-value of 35°K as predicted by the localized models (see Table XVII).

C   Krypton on Sterling FT at 77.4°K

At this temperature, the adsorption of krypton is definitely subcritical in behaviour and a distinct phase transition in the first and

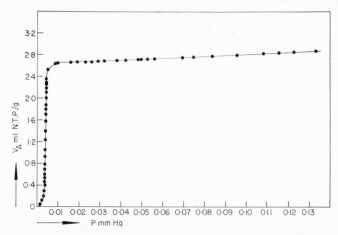

FIG. 15 Krypton adsorption isotherm on Sterling FT at 77·4°K. Low pressure region.

the second layer has been found by many authors. Our experimental data for the first layer are presented in Fig. 15, the higher pressure region is presented in Fig. 16.

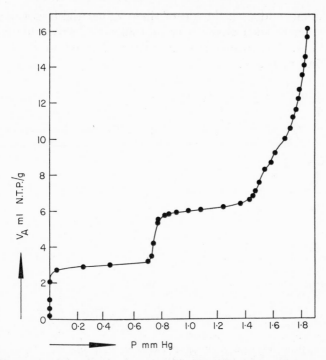

FIG. 16 Krypton adsorption isotherm on Sterling FT at 77·4°K. Higher pressure region.

From the experimental isotherm, a ratio θ_L/θ_G is found to be about 14·0. From this ratio, the acting value of k_1 may be derived for the different models with the aid of the Tables II, III, VI, VIII and XI. From these acting values of k_1 and the corresponding values of p/K, K

TABLE XV. Adsorption parameters of krypton adsorbed on Sterling FT at 77·4°K

	k_1	K	V_m	E^0	Q_{st}^0	$(k_1 T)_{\exp}$	$(k_1 T)_{\text{theor}}$
	—	mm Hg	cc STP/ g	kcal/ mole	kcal/ mole	°K	°K
van der Waals	9·33	0·1166	3·306	2·588	2·819	722·1	706·7
SFA approach	15·22	0·0840	3·597	2·373	2·604	1178	1080
VE approach	13·96	0·1584	4·076	2·591	2·822	1081	1007
Fowler-Guggenheim	6·09	0·0851	2·866	3·529	3·914	471·4	—
q.c.	6·66	0·1128	2·864	3·486	3·871	515·5	—

may be found, and with the aid of these values the best value of V_m corresponding to each model may be calculated, as was described in Section IV A. The adsorption parameters derived in this way are gathered in Table XV.

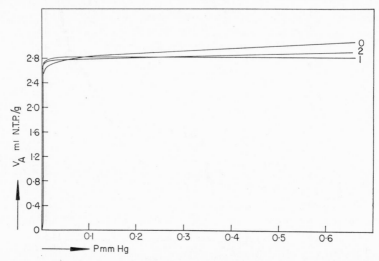

FIG 17a: Krypton adsorption on graphitized carbon black Sterling F.T., at 77·6 °K, as compared to localized adsorption models: O experimental line; 1 Fowler-Guggenheim; 2 q.c.

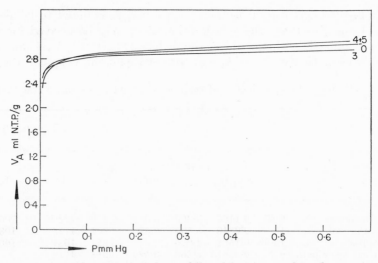

FIG. 17b: Same as fig. 17a, but for mobile adsorption models: O experimental line; 3 Van der Waals; 4 SFA; 5 VE.

It was found, that for the adsorption of krypton from 0·002 up to 0·7 mm Hg, the experimental data could be described reasonably well with all three mobile equations of state, but *not* with the localized ones. This is illustrated in Figs 17a and 17b. The intermolecular interaction for krypton at this temperature turns out to be much higher than that for either argon or krypton. As is apparent from Fig. 17, the localized adsorption models under these conditions predicted substantially lower compressibilities for the condensed phase than the mobile ones. The experimentally found compressibility is in reasonable agreement with the predictions of either of the mobile models, but incompatible with the localized ones. Unfortunately no isosteric heats of adsorption for krypton of sufficient accuracy are available. From theoretical considerations, Kiselev (Avgul *et al.*, 1959) predicted a value of 2·95 kcal/mole for the interaction energy with the surface which is somewhat closer to the ones found from the present treatment for mobile adsorption, than for the localized case. The value of T_{c2} seems to be some 100°K (see Table XVII).

It has been shown by de Boer and Broekhoff (1967b), that the van der Waals equation of state can give a reasonable description of the multilayer region. Similar calculations for the other equations of state have not yet been performed. Yet, it is clear from the very small value of V_m as derived from the localized equations of state, that no satisfactory description of multilayer adsorption can be based on localized models of adsorption. The compressibility in each layer formed is much larger than is consistent with the model of localized adsorption under these subcritical conditions.

Upon comparing the adsorption of argon, nitrogen and krypton on the same adsorbent and at the same temperature, it seems clear that mobile adsorption gives a much better representation of the most important features of adsorption than localized adsorption. A comparison reveals yet another interesting feature: if localized adsorption at certain specified points of the surface should be an adequate description of adsorption, then we would expect that the number of moles present in the monolayer for different gases at the same adsorbent would either be the same or show some simple ratio, depending on whether an adsorbed molecule occupies one or more specified sites. No indication of such behaviour is found in practice. It might be argued that such a picture of localized adsorption is too simple: sometimes it is contended that localization is equivalent to restriction of mobility itself. Such a restriction of mobility will always take place at higher coverages on account of the finite volume of the adsorbed molecules. Our models of mobile adsorption are attempts to account for such restrictions while retaining the essential features of mobility in two dimensions. It turns out, that all three attempts developed in practice account for such a restriction of mobility in a reasonably satisfactory manner.

The examples here may suffice as illustrations of the application of 2-D equations of state to the interpretation of sorption isotherms. We will restrict ourselves to a very short discussion of some interesting examples of adsorption on homogeneous surfaces.

D   Xenon at Different Temperatures on the Graphitized Carbon Black MT (3100)

Isotherms of xenon on this carbon black have been published recently (Cochrane et al., 1967) at four different supercritical temperatures. The isotherms were not presented in a sufficiently detailed manner to permit accurate analysis. Some general characteristics, however, are of interest. At all temperatures the E^0 of all mobile equations of state are all within the range of 4·2 to 4·5 kcal/mole. The application of localized equations of state leads to mutually consistent values of E^0 in the range of 6·9 to 7·3 kcal/mole. The extrapolation of the experimental heat of adsorption leads to a value of about 4·0 for Q_{st}^0, in reasonable agreement with the mobile equations of state (with possibly some contribution of vibration perpendicularly to the surface) and in very poor agreement with the localized picture. The best "fit" between experimental data and the theoretical adsorption isotherm equation is obtained by the van der Waals equation of state and the VE approach.

E   Benzene at Different Temperatures at the Graphitized Carbon Black P 33 (2700)

The isotherms were measured by Pierotti and Smallwood (1966) over the temperature range 273 to 323°K. The adsorption parameters are collected in Table XVI. It is seen that the formally temperature independent parameters V_m and $k_1 T$ more or less vary with temperature for all models. All mobile models predicted E^0-values of the order of magnitude of 9 kcal/mole. The extrapolated isosteric heat of adsorption is of the order of magnitude of 10 kcal/mole (Isirikyan and Kiselev), which according to Eq. (124) would correspond to an E^0 value approximately 9·2 kcal/mole, in excellent agreement with the prediction of the mobile models. On the other hand, the localized models lead to a mean value of the order of magnitude of 13·7 kcal/mole. According to Eq. (125) this would correspond with a value of Q_{st}^0 of approximately 15 kcal/mole. Again, the adsorption seems to be essentially mobile in character.

TABLE XVI. Adsorption parameters of benzene adsorbed on P33 at various temperatures. Data of Pierotti and Smallwood (1966)

	T_{obs}	k_1	K	V_m	E^0	Q_{st}^0	$(k_1T)_{exp}$	$(k_1T)_{theor}$
	°K	—	mm Hg	cc STP/ g	kcal/ mole	kcal/ mole	°K	°K
van der Waals	273	0·4148	0·4609	1·943	9·036	9·850	113·2	
	288	0·8101	1·537	1·945	8·888	9·746	233·3	
	298	0·6625	3·006	2·018	8·830	9·718	197·4	1896
	303	0·9813	4·350	1·974	8·463	9·366	297·3	
	323	0·7082	11·19	2·023	8·804	9·767	228·7	
SFA approach	273	5·036	0·3115	2·174	8·271	9·085	1374	
	288	5·559	1·0446	2·163	8·077	8·935	1601	
	298	5·395	2·031	2·239	7·995	8·883	1608	2896
	303	5·737	2·937	2·191	7·613	8·516	1738	
	323	5·681	7·930	2·212	7·868	8·831	1835	
VE approach	273	1·951	0·6503	2·652	8·982	9·796	532·6	
	288	2·666	2·183	2·616	8·828	9·686	767·8	
	298	2·308	4·261	2·756	8·768	9·656	664·7	2701
	303	2·951	6·172	2·645	8·399	9·302	591·1	
	323	2·341	15·72	2·763	8·742	9·705	756·1	
Fowler-Guggenheim	273	−0·5766	0·3145	1·422	13·40	14·77	−157·4	
	288	−0·4166	1·0304	1·443	13·53	14·96	−120·0	
	298	−0·4022	2·041	1·472	13·65	15·13	−119·9	—
	303	−0·2651	2·953	1·463	12·76	14·26	−80·3	
	323	−0·3002	7·719	1·467	14·07	15·67	−97·0	
q.c.	273	−0·3862	0·3157	1·421	13·40	14·77	−105·4	
	288	−0·4220	1·0301	1·444	13·53	14·96	−121·5	
	298	−0·4009	2·044	1·472	13·65	15·13	−119·5	—
	303	−0·2683	2·952	1·464	12·76	14·26	−81·3	
	323	−0·3034	7·719	1·468	14·07	15·67	−98·0	

F   Krypton Adsorbed at Different Inorganic Halides

The adsorption of krypton at sodium bromide has been studied by Fisher and McMillan (1958) at different 2-D subcritical temperatures. With the aid of the appropriate tables of coexisting phases k_1 and K may be estimated for all five 2-D models discussed here. The isotherms show, however, that a substantial part of the surface is heterogeneous in character, which complicates interpretation. In all cases the acting k_1-values were very near to the critical ones. With these values, the isotherms could be "fitted" to the isotherm equations only with moderate accuracy. No significant differences were found between mobile

6

and localized equations of state. The heterogeneous character of the isotherm does not permit to evaluate Q_{st}^0 from the low-coverage region of the isotherms. We have included this example to stress the necessity of completely homogeneous adsorbents. The inorganic halides are of potential interest, as we may expect localized adsorption if it occurs on this sort of adsorbent. A comparison between the data of Fisher and McMillan and our data on krypton on Sterling FT (2700) suggests that at this halide the 2-D critical temperature is substantially lower than at the graphitized carbon. For example, for the van der Waals equation of state, $k_1 T$ for krypton at Sterling FT is 722°K, whereas the data of Fisher and McMillan suggest a value of about 530°K which corresponds with a 2-D critical temperature of only 78·5°K on NaBr versus 107°K at Sterling FT.

Recent data of Taikaishi and Saito (1967) of adsorption of krypton on sodium-, potassium-, and rubidium-chloride lead to virtually the same conclusion. The effective 2-D critical temperature for adsorption of krypton on alkali halogenides seems to be much lower than the corresponding ones for adsorption at graphitized carbon blacks. More careful experimental data over a large region of surface coverages are needed to decide whether this is due to a difference in the character of the adsorption or whether this is caused by interaction between the adsorbent and the adsorbate molecules, e.g. polarization of the adsorbate by the ionic constituents of the adsorbent.

D Conclusions

For supercritical isotherms, the sigmoidal parts of the isotherm may be fitted to all of the models of the 2-D state discussed in Section III. The localized models, however, are not successful in describing the behaviour of adsorbed layer at higher 2-D densities. This characteristic of the localized adsorption isotherm is even more prominent at temperatures well below the 2-D critical temperature.

Moreover, comparison of calculated values of E^0, the interaction potential between one adsorbate molecule and the adsorbent at zero degrees Kelvin, with the isosteric heat of adsorption Q_{st}^0 indicates that in nearly all cases the adsorption is essentially mobile in character. The molecules behave as if only one translational degree of freedom is lost.

All three models discussed are reasonably successful in accounting for the formation observed of a unimolecular layer. As a surprising result, the simple van der Waals equation of state, simple both as a mathematical expression and as a physical picture of the adsorbed layer, gives, in general, the best description of most of the characteristics of physical adsorption at uniform surfaces. From a pragmatical point of view, we have found no gain in introducing refined expressions for the dependence of the effective "free area" in the 2-D equation of state. This may be partly due to the fact that unimolecular adsorption isotherms may be determined experimentally over a restricted range of relative pressures. The largest differences between the mobile models become apparent in their compressibility behaviour at high surface coverages.

TABLE XVII. Two-dimensional critical temperatures T_{c2} calculated from experimental k_1T values compared to theoretical T_{c2} values calculated from the three-dimensional critical temperature

	A		Kr		N_2		C_6H_6	
	Calc.	Theor.	Calc.	Theor.	Calc.	Theor.	Calc.	Theor.
van der Waals	65	75	107	105	45	63	29	281
SFA approach	72	66	100	91	60	55	138	245
VE approach	69	68	101	94	49	57	62	252
Fowler-Guggenheim	47	—	118	—	37	—	?	—
q.c.	46	—	106	—	31	—	?	—

V Surface Area Determination

A Introduction

The surface area S of an adsorbent can be defined as the accessible area for one adsorbate molecule or as the geometrical area of the solid. Only the first definition relates to physical adsorption. In general the accessible area will not be equal to the geometrical area, because of irregularities on the surface. Unless stated otherwise, the surface area S denotes the accessible area. The value of S, an important property of adsorbents and catalysts, is given by

$$S = a_0 N_m \text{ or } S = 0.269 a_0 V_m \qquad (126)$$

The latter formula yields S in m^2/g when a_0 is expressed in $Å^2/molecule$ and V_m in ml STP/g. The number of adsorbed molecules in a completely filled monolayer N_m must somehow be calculated from the adsorption isotherm with the help of an equation of state. The value of a_0, the area of one adsorbate molecule in such a filled monolayer, is not provided by the adsorption isotherm and must be obtained some other way, dependent on the type of equation of state used to calculate N_m.

Thus, the surface area determination depends strongly upon the adsorption equation. Therefore, we distinguish between adsorption on homogeneous and heterogeneous surfaces.

B The Molecular Area

Per definition a_0 is the area per molecule in a completely filled monolayer.* In case of localized adsorption s_0, the area per site, is fixed by the lattice properties of the adsorbate. It is independent of the size of the adsorbent molecules as long as one molecule only can adsorb on one site at a time (see the footnote on page 79). So, s_0 is the same for the Fowler-Guggenheim and the q.c. adsorption equation.

From the various models underlying the mobile adsorption equations discussed in Section III different relations emerge between a_0 and d_0, the collision diameter. These relations are listed in Table V. Hence, the value of d_0 also depends on the model and has to be calculated from the 3-D state somehow. The parameters u_0 and d_0 can easily be evaluated from the critical temperature and pressure using Eqs (56), (78) and (88). However, none of the 3-D equations of state describe the critical phenomena well, seeing the differences between predicted and observed value of the Kamerlingh-Onnes constant $(pV/RT)_c$ (see Table I). Moreover, the various 3-D equations of state lead to rather different values of d_0 and u_0 (see Table XVIII). The d_0 values calculated with the three-dimensional VE-approach seem to agree quite well with values obtained from application of the Lennard Jones intermolecular potential to gas viscosity or compressibility, whereas the d_0 corresponding to the van der Waals equation are considerably smaller. The 3-D Eyring equation, Eq. (77), gives rise to rather great collision diameters. It is noteworthy that the value of u_0 according to the van der Waals equation is some 30% greater than the value of u_0 as calculated with the 3-D Eyring and VE equation.

In the case of benzene, hexane and similar asymmetrical molecules the parameters u_0 and d_0 are very likely to change on going from three to two dimensions, since the rotation of such molecules will be highly restricted to rotation in a plane parallel to the adsorbate surface. In these cases a more reliable (relative) value of a_0 can be obtained by comparing the monolayer capacity of the particular adsorbate with the monolayer capacity of some standard adsorbate on the same adsorbent.

---

* This definition only makes sense in case of intermolecular potentional curves with a hard core repulsion branch. A soft core repulsion branch does not limit the number of adsorbed molecules per unit area. In the latter case a_0 can be defined arbitrarily.

C Heterogeneous Surfaces

A heterogeneous surface is characterized by a non-uniform heat of adsorption, which varies from place to place on the surface. This can be caused by irregularities in the crystal planes. There is some evidence (Taikaishi and Saito, 1967) that chemisorption of, for instance, water vapour leads to increased heterogeneity. Two extreme types of heterogeneity can be distinguished.

(a) First there is the possibility that the surface is a composition of a (great) number of homogeneous patches. So, each patch can be treated as a homogeneous surface. Ross and Olivier (1964a) showed that with the two-dimensional van der Waals equation as a local isotherm and with a gaussian energy distribution, a good description is given of adsorption in the monolayer region on rather heterogeneous surfaces. Adsorption on patch surfaces will be considered in Section V D since it does not differ fundamentally from adsorption on homogeneous surfaces.

(b) When the patches are so small that molecular dimensions are no longer negligible compared to the area of one patch, we have to deal with so called random energy distribution function (Hill, 1949; Gordon, 1968) in contrast to the patch energy distribution function. In the extreme case of a randomly distributed heat of adsorption on each patch only one molecule can adsorb. Mutual interactions of adsorbed molecules will depend strongly upon the coverage, being less important at low coverage, because of the great distances that may exist between the sites with comparable heat of adsorption. Moreover, multimolecular adsorption may occur on "hot spots" on the surface, whereas areas with a small heat of adsorption are not yet occupied. It is not surprising that an adsorption equation for heterogeneous surfaces, taking into account some acceptable (random) energy distribution, multimolecular adsorption and molecular interaction, is not yet available.

It is obvious, that the basic assumptions of the BET equation do not correspond to the features of heterogeneous adsorbents. However, it describes the shape of many adsorption isotherms quantitatively over a restricted pressure range. The monolayer capacity, predicted by the BET equation turns out to coincide with the B-point in many cases. Assuming that the density of the adsorbed film in the B-point has the same density as the bulk phase of the adsorbate at the considered temperature enables the value of a_0 to be calculated from the $3\text{-}D$ density. An impression of the reliability of the value of S_{BET} can be acquired by comparing the BET equation with the methods leading directly to S, without assuming a value of a_0, applied to the same heterogeneous adsorbent. Young and Crowell (1962c) summarized various independent methods.

Harkins and Jura measured heats of immersion of wetted anatase. Their results agree fairly well the S_{BET} obtained from nitrogen adsorption isotherms, whereas the BET method applied to argon and krypton adsorption isotherms show considerable deviation as long as one sticks to the a_0 values obtained from the liquid or solid state of the adsorbate.

On the other hand, it is not improbable that the Harkins-Jura anatase exhibited a surface texture in the sub-micropore range. A t-plot analysis of the sorption of nitrogen on anatase covered with one or more layers of presorbed water indicates that the surface area of the anatase decreases upon the adsorption of just one layer of water, pointing the blocking of micropores (see Chapter 1). In that case, the geometrical area of a thick film of liquid water will undoubtedly differ from the area accessible to one nitrogen molecule. Moreover, several investigators have found the existence of a contact angle between bulk water and anatase. This would complicate the interpretation of the Harkins-Jura experiments on the heat of immersion.

Surface areas calculated from the transport properties of gases through porous media seem to be only rough approximations. Interpretation of transport data involve severe approximations with respect to the porous structure of the material, making the results quite unreliable from an absolutist point of view.

"Geometrical" surface areas may be calculated in some instances from particle sizes and particle density, if a shape factor is assumed. The accuracy of the method depends, among other factors, on the particle size distribution. Particle sizes may be obtained from electron microscopy or X-ray diffraction line broadening. The results, in cases where the particles in itself are non-porous, are often of the same order of magnitude as the BET surface areas. No great accuracy may be expected from such methods, as, apart from the uncertainties in mean particle size and distribution of sizes, most energetically heterogeneous surfaces will exhibit some sort of surface roughness. All these complications may be expected to be of minor importance in the case of single crystals of such metals as copper. It seems possible to determine geometrical surface areas of single crystals with fair accuracy. Nevertheless "surface roughness" on account of "faceting" of certain crystal planes at the surface may not be ruled out *a priori*. Rhodin's very accurate adsorption measurements of copper single crystals contain indications of energetically homogeneous surfaces, pointing to geometrically "flat" surfaces. In all cases he found the BET surface area to be lower than the geometrical one. As the BET equation is not particularly suitable for the description of adsorption on energetically homogeneous surfaces, there is no reason to attach any special significance to the BET surface area above the geometrical one. All that may be said is the BET surface area probably is of the right order of magnitude. In other cases of adsorption on geometrically well-defined surfaces, the value of S_{BET} is found to exceed $S_{geom.}$ by about 30%. One is inclined to trust, in these cases, the geometrical area value rather than the BET value. It is to be realized that the BET method of surface area determination in reality is nothing but a convenient way to determine the B-point. Calculation of surface areas from the number of moles adsorbed at the B-point necessitates the assumption of a density of the adsorbed layer in the B-point. Commonly this density is taken to be equal to that of the liquid phase, although there seems to be no special reason for this assumption. For homogeneous surfaces we will show, in Section V D, that this assumption in many cases is grossly in error. For energetically heterogeneous surfaces the problem is even more complicated. In simple cases the actual surface may be thought to exist as a collection of in itself energetically homogeneous patches. It has been shown by de Boer and Broekhoff (1967b) that in such cases the density of the adsorbed layer in the B-point depends on the mean energy of adsorption and on the shape and the width of energy distribution function. On the other hand, a study of the liquid phase adsorption of lauric acids on inorganic oxides by de Boer et al. (1962) suggested that in these cases the assumption of bulk liquid density for the adsorption of nitrogen in the B-point leads to values consistent with those derived from the adsorption of lauric acid. Further comparative studies of the adsorption of inert gases and of adsorption specific to the surface, such as is the adsorption of lauric acids at oxides, would be of great value.

In the meantime, the BET method may be considered as a satisfactory relative method. Other relative methods, however, are often more convenient and may furnish us with additional information on the texture of the surfaces. This is particularly true for the t-method, as developed by de Boer et al., and which is treated in some detail in Chapter I of this book. We recall that it is based on the empirical finding that for a large class of non-porous substances the nitrogen adsorption isotherm may be reduced to a common curve over the whole of the multilayer adsorption region. In general the surfaces of these substances were energetically heterogeneous. In the present context it is particularly interesting that for the adsorption of nitrogen at the energetically homogeneous carbon blacks after the densification of the second layer the adsorption isotherm is completely reducible to the common t-curve. The surface area calculated from this part of the isotherm agrees somewhat better with that calculated from the low pressure region of the isotherm by means of the 2-D van der Waals equation, than the surface area obtained with the BET estimate. It seems that in these cases the S_t value is more trustworthy than the BET surface area (see also Section V D). Nevertheless, the t-method in general is restricted to energetically heterogeneous surfaces of oxides and graphites. A t-curve for other inorganic adsorbents, such as halogenides and chalcogenides has not yet been established experimentally. There are indications that the common t-curve of de Boer et al. (1962) does not apply to calcium fluoride.

A rational approach to the surface area determination from adsorption data on energetically heterogeneous surfaces is not possible unless more insight is gained into the fundamental characteristics of the adsorbed state itself. Therefore, adsorption studies on energetically homogeneous surfaces are absolutely essential to the development of the theory of surface area determination in the general case. A reasonable amount of experimental work on adsorption at homogeneous surfaces is now available, although not all of sufficient accuracy to enable thorough theoretical analysis. Theoretical analysis itself is only in its first stage. It is discouraging to note that quite a number of authors still use the BET equation to determine monolayer volumina from adsorption data on homogeneous surfaces and then proceed to test 2-D equations of state with the aid of the monolayer volume thus derived. The inconsistency of such a procedure will appeal to the reader.

A promising attack seems to be the high-temperature gas-adsorption method of Sams et al. (1962a) and of Barker and Everett (1962). These authors consider adsorption at low coverages and treat the adsorbed layer as a non-ideal two-dimensional gas. Surface areas may be calculated from the adsorption data and the assumption of a certain type of intermolecular potential. This method of attack is specially suited for homogeneous surfaces. Extension to higher coverages and lower temperatures is not yet possible and we have to revert to the methods described in the forthcoming section of this chapter.

D Homogeneous Surfaces

The method of evaluating the value of V_m from experimental adsorption data has been discussed in Section IV A for both sub- and supercritical adsorption in the low pressure region. The knowledge of adsorption in the multilayer region is not sufficient to evaluate a trustworthy monolayer capacity from experimental findings at higher pressures.

When the adsorbent surface consists of a number of in itself homogeneous patches, each with different heats of adsorption E, the adsorption equation can be written as (Ross and Olivier, 1964b):

$$V_a(p) = \sum_E \theta(E,p)v_m(E) \tag{127}$$

where $v_m(E)$ and $\theta(E,p)$ designate the local monolayer capacity and local coverage resp. Introduction of $\Delta F(E)$, denoting the fraction of the surface with a heat of adsorption q, into Eq. (127) leads to

$$V_a(E) = V_m \sum_E \theta(E,p)\Delta F(E).$$

Or, when the number of patches goes to infinity

$$V_a(p) = V_m \int f(E)\theta(E,p)\mathrm{d}E \tag{128}$$

$f(E)$ is the fraction of the surface with an adsorption heat between E and $E+\mathrm{d}E$. This differential distribution function can only be evaluated from experimental isotherms by means of numerical computation techniques.* These methods (Ross and Olivier, 1964a; Adamson et al., 1961; Adamson and Ling, 1961), by reducing Eq. (128) to Eq. (127) yield a series of $v_m(E)$ values. Hence, the total monolayer capacity V_m is given by

$$V_m = \sum_E v_m(E). \tag{129}$$

We will not go into detail in discussing the various methods of computing $f(E)$, since this does not fit in the present scope. The computation of $f(E)$ and of V_m is only possible for a given value of k_1, the molecular interaction parameter in the local isotherm, which must be calculated from the adsorption isotherm on a homogeneous sample of the adsorbent. Thus evaluation of V_m from adsorption isotherms on these patched surfaces is mathematically more complicated than in the case of a homogeneous surface, but it does not involve any basic changes in the theory of adsorption. Therefore, analysis of adsorption data on patchwise heterogeneous surfaces is not particularly fit for testing a local isotherm; deviations are easily hidden in a slightly different shaped distribution function and a different value for V_m. The great flexibility of

---

* When the Langmuir equation is adopted as a local isotherm, an analytical solution of $f(E)$ from Eq. (129) is possible (Sips, 1948), since in this case θ can be written explicitly as a function of p and E.

6*

TABLE XVIII. Molecular quantities d_0 (Å), a_0 (Å²), and u_0 (10^{-20}Joule) of various adsorbates, calculated from their critical 3-D temperature and pressure

	van der Waals Eq. (56)				SFA approach Eq. (78)				VE approach Eq. (88)			
	d_0	a_0	u_0	$(k_1T)_{c2}$ °K	d_0	a_0	u_0	$(k_1T)_{c2}$ °K	d_0	a_0	u_0	$(k_1T)_{c2}$ °K
A	2·945	13·62	0·7022	508·7	4·490	17·96	0·5916	951·9	3·367	9·825	0·5522	724·9
Kr	3·156	15·64	0·9757	706·7	4·811	20·04	0·8219	1323	3·608	11·28	0·7672	1007
Xe	3·433	18·52	1·350	977·9	5·235	23·73	1·1373	1858	3·926	13·36	1·062	1394
N₂	3·128	15·37	0·5872	425·3	4·768	19·69	0·4946	796·0	3·576	11·09	0·4617	606·1
CH₄	3·235	16·44	0·8884	643·4	4·932	21·06	0·7483	1204	3·699	11·86	0·6985	916·9
C₆H₆	4·569	32·79	2·617	1896	6·974	42·01	2·701	3547	5·224	23·65	2·058	2701
n-C₆H₁₄	5·187	42·26	2·367	1714	7·907	54·15	2·443	3208	5·931	30·48	1·861	2443
CHCl₃	4·327	29·41	2·498	1809	6·597	37·69	2·577	3387	4·948	21·22	1·964	2578
CCl₄	4·650	33·96	2·592	1878	7·089	43·70	2·675	3514	5·317	24·50	2·038	2676

Eq. (128), caused by $f(E)$ makes this equation rather insensitive with respect to k_1.

From the monolayer capacities of the various gases adsorbed on carbon black (see Section IV C and respective tables) the surface area S can be calculated with Eq. (126). The required values of a_0 were taken from Table XVIII, which displays the values of a_0 calculated from the 3-D critical temperature and pressure. In the case of the localized models we assumed that one argon, krypton or nitrogen molecule occupies three graphite unit hexagons, yielding for the area per site 15·74 Å². In the case of benzene we took the area per site equal to nine unit hexagons: 47·22 Å² (Ewing and Pierce, 1967). The results are listed in Table XIX.

TABLE XIX. Surface area of graphitized carbon blacks in m²/g. (a) Data of Avgul *et al.* (1959). (b) Data of Pierotti and Smallwood (1966). Average values (±2%) calculated from five isotherms at various temperatures

| | Sterling FT | | | P33 | |
	Kr	A	N_2	N_2^a	$C_6H_6^b$
van der Waals	13·9	13·0	13·0	13·9	17·5
SFA approach	19·3	18·6	18·4	19·8	24·8
VE approach	12·4	13·4	12·6	13·5	17·1
Fowler-Guggenheim	12·1	12·3	10·0	10·5	16·5
q.c.	12·1	12·1	10·0	10·5	16·5

Apart from the benzene data, Table XIX shows that each mobile adsorption model leads to reasonable consistent values of S for the various gases, whereas the deviations in the localized cases are significant. The agreement between the surface areas according to the van der Waals equation and the VE treatment is rather surprising. The SFA approach leads to considerably larger areas, because of the great values of a_0 which is due to the poor description of the 3-D critical state by the free volume treatment of Eyring (see also Eq. 77). An average value of 13·0 m²/g based on the van der Waals and VE treatment of adsorption on our sample of Sterling FT, would lead to the following values of a_0 in the case of the SFA approach:

krypton	13·5 Å²
argon	12·2 Å²
nitrogen	13·9 Å²
benzene	22·0 Å²

In the case of the van der Waals and VE approach we propose 24·4 and 18·0 Å² per molecule benzene resp.

The BET method, applied to our nitrogen adsorption isotherm, assuming a value of a_0 of 16·27 Å², yields a surface area of 12·1 m²/g. Apparently, the density of the adsorbed nitrogen film in the B-point, located by the BET equation, is less than the density of liquid nitrogen at 77°K. De Boer *et al.* (1965) applied the t-method to the adsorption isotherm of nitrogen on the same adsorbent and found a surface area of 13·3 m²/g, which agrees very well with the present result. It is remarkable that straight t-plots can be obtained in case of nitrogen adsorption on highly graphitized carbon blacks at relative pressures higher than about 0·35. This means that the multilayer region of the adsorption isotherm is similar to the adsorption on heterogeneous carbon blacks. It may be inferred from this resemblance that the influence of surface roughness and other causes of heterogeneity diminish rapidly at increasing thickness of the adsorbed layer. This confirms that the t-method is very useful for estimating the surface area of carbon blacks, since it is not affected by the degree of heterogeneity, contrary to the BET equation. Wolfe and Sams (1965) applied the virial theory of adsorption of Barker and Everett (1962) to adsorption data of some rare gases on P33. Using the Lennard Jones (6–12) parameters they found a surface area of 8·54, 8·68 and 8·2 m²/g in the cases of argon, xenon and krypton resp. The difference with the present finding is considerable. It should be noted, that the virial theory can only be applied to the low coverage region, where the deviations from the Henry equation are relatively small, whereas the adsorption equations discussed in Section III describe the adsorption isotherm up to considerably higher degrees of coverage. Therefore, the present methods of evaluating the surface area are much more sensitive with respect to the saturation at completion of the monolayer.

It is obvious that, as long as no adequate theory of the 2-D state exists, the problem of the surface area determination remains far from solved. A better description of the 3-D state is also required, since the molecular area can only be obtained from the properties of the adsorbate in its 3-D state.

VI Concluding Remarks

In his book "The Dynamical Character of Adsorption", de Boer succeeded in developing a complete picture of the adsorbed state, emphasizing the mobility of molecules in the adsorbed state. Most of the previous work on adsorption was based on Langmuir statistics and so implicitly on the picture of localized adsorption. Two-dimensional condensation phenomena had been predicted before by Fowler and Guggenheim, but only for localized adsorption. A theory of the two-dimensional liquid state had been developed by Devonshire, but, one gets the impression, rather as a theoretical "curiosum". The impact of these early theoretical investigations on the study of adsorption phenomena seems to have been rather small. The striking practical success of the multilayer theory of Brunauer *et al.* (1938) has led to a vast acceptance of the picture of adsorbed molecules adhering to certain surface sites or to sites formed by previously adsorbed layers. Doubtless, the BET theory has been a milestone in the development of the study of adsorption and of solid surfaces in particular, and therefore has been, and still is, of exceeding value. On the other hand, its success seems to have resulted in a preoccupation with the localized picture.

One of the great merits of de Boer's monograph has been not only the development of a picture of mobile adsorption but even more the convincing argumentation that led to the concept that in physical adsorption mobility must be expected to be the rule rather than the exception.

De Boer has used the 2-D van der Waals equation of state to demonstrate many of the fundamental characteristics of mobile adsorbed film, such as 2-D condensation phenomena and 2-D critical temperatures and the cooperation between primary adsorption forces and intermolecular interactions. At that time, none of these effects had been established experimentally, but during the subsequent experimental investigations nearly all of them have been demonstrated.

Of course, de Boer was well aware of the approximate character of the 2-D van der Waals equation of state. In the final remarks of his monograph, de Boer justifies this choice of a relatively simple model and stresses one of the most important features of his study by stating: "A complete picture which may be visualized by those who preferably think in pictures has been developed." In the present contribution, we have sought to introduce more sophisticated 2-D equations of state and to compare their behaviour to that of the 2-D van der Waals equation of state. These equations of state lack the mathematical simplicity of the 2-D van der Waals equation. We may consider them to be more satisfactory from a purely theoretical point of view, but at present they do not give a better description of experimental adsorption isotherms than does the van der Waals equation of state itself. In general, the localized equations of state tested were far less satisfactory, which is in complete agreement with de Boer's concept of 2-D mobility. Here also, further theoretical refinements did not lead to a better description of experimental isotherms: the q.c.-approach turned out to be no more satisfactory than the simple Fowler-Guggenheim equation of localized adsorption. For most purposes, the 2-D van der Waals equation of state seems to give an excellent description of adsorption phenomena at homogeneous surfaces, accounting both for mobility and for intermolecular interactions in a quantitative manner. There are, however, strong indications that values of a_2 (and possibly of d_0) as derived from the 3-D state in a number of cases are not satisfactory (see Sections IV and V). This situation is not improved by refining hard disk models of the 2-D state. This may be either due to inherent inadequacies of the equations of state themselves or to the influence of the solid surface on the state of the adsorbed molecules. In order to settle this question more and careful experimental work is needed in the field of adsorption with different adsorbates on different homogeneous adsorbents and at a wide range of experimental conditions.

VII List of Symbols

A	available, accessible area for N_a molecules
A_f	free area for N_a molecules
a_f	free area for one molecule
A_0	area occupied by N_a molecules in closest packing
a_0	area occupied by one molecule in closest packing
$a_{1,2,3}$	van der Waals interaction parameter for 1-D, 2-D and 3-D state
B	virial coefficient
$b_{1,2,3}^0$	van der Waals constant for 1-D, 2-D and 3-D state
d_0	molecular collision diameter
E^0, E	heat of adsorption
F	2-D pressure
ϕ	molecular pair interaction function
h	Planck's constant
k	Boltzmann's constant
k_1^m	interaction parameter of mobile adsorption equations
k_1^l	interaction parameter of localized adsorption equations
K_m^0 b	pre-exponential Henry constant
K_{loc}^0	pre-exponential Langmuir constant
K_{mob}	Henry constant
K_{loc}	Langmuir constant
N_a	number of adsorbed molecules
N_m	number of adsorbed molecules in a completely filled monolayer
N	number of molecules in the gas phase
P	number of 3-D phases in the system
p	pressure
p_0	condensation pressure
p_{c3}	critical pressure of 3-D state

p_{c2}	equilibrium pressure of critical 2-D state
Q,q	partition function
Q_{st}	isosteric heat of adsorption
r	intermolecular distance
S	surface area per gram adsorbent
S_{geom}	geometrical surface area
s_0	site area in localized adsorption
T	absolute temperature
$T_{c1,c2,c3}$	critical temperature for 1-D, 2-D and 3-D state
t	thickness of adsorbed layer
θ	degree of surface coverage, reduced surface density
θ_L,θ_G	reduced density of 2-D liquid and 2-D gas phase
u_0	molecular interaction parameter
μ^g	thermodynamic potential of the gas phase
μ^a	thermodynamic potential of the adsorbed layer
V_0	smallest possible volume for N molecules
v_0	smallest possible volume for one molecule
V_m	monolayer capacity
w	interaction energy between neighbouring sites in localized adsorption

VIII References

Adamson, A. W., Ling, I., Dormant, L. M. and Orem, M. (1961). *J. Colloid Interface Sci.* **21**, 45.

Adamson, A. W. and Ling, I. (1961). *Adv. Chem. Ser.* **33**, 51.

Alder, B. J. and Wainwright, T. E. (1960). *J. chem. Phys.* **33**, 1439.

Alder, B. J. and Wainwright, T. E. (1962). *Phys. Rev.* **127**, 359.

Aristov, B. G. and Kiselev, A. V. (1967). *Kolloid Zh.* **29**, 631.

Avgul, N. N., Kiselev, A. V., Lygina, I. A. and Poschkus, D. P. (1959). *Bull. Acad. Sci. USSR, Div. Chem. Sci.* 1155.

Bangham, D. H. and Farhouky, N. (1931). *J. chem. Soc.* 1324.

Barker, J. A. (1963). "Lattice Theories of the Liquid State", p. 29. Oxford University Press, Oxford.

Barker, J. A. and Everett, D. H. (1962). *Trans. Faraday Soc.* **58**, 1608.

Barker, J. A. and Henderson, D. (1967). *J. chem. Phys.* **47**, 4714.

Barker, J. A. and Henderson, D. (1968). *J. chem. Educ.* **45**, 2.

de Boer, J. H. (1937). "Elektronenemission und Adsorptionerscheinungen", p. 133. Verlag von Johann Ambrosius Barth, Leipzig.

de Boer, J. H. (1953a). "The Dynamical Character of Adsorption". Oxford University Press, Oxford.

de Boer, J. H. (1953b). "The Dynamical Character of Adsorption", Chapters VII–IX. Oxford University Press, Oxford.

de Boer, J. H. (1953c). "The Dynamical Character of Adsorption", p. 147. Oxford University Press, Oxford.

de Boer, J. H. (1953d). "The Dynamical Character of Adsorption", p. 170. Oxford University Press, Oxford.

de Boer, J. H. (1953e). "The Dynamical Character of Adsorption", p. 148. Oxford University Press, Oxford.

de Boer, J. H. (1953f). "The Dynamical Character of Adsorption", p. 64. Oxford University Press, Oxford.

de Boer, J. H. (1956). *Adv. Catalysis* **8**, 85.

144   J. C. P. BROEKHOFF AND R. H. VAN DONGEN

de Boer, J. H. and Broekhoff, J. C. P. (1967a). *Proc. Koninkl. Ned. Akad. Wetenschap.* **B70**, 342.

de Boer, J. H. and Broekhoff, J. C. P. (1967b). *Proc. Koninkl. Ned. Akad. Wetenschap.* **B70**, 352.

de Boer, J. H. and Broekhoff, J. C. P. (1967c). *Proc. Koninkl. Ned. Akad. Wetenschap.* **B70**, 326.

de Boer, J. H. and Broekhoff, J. C. P. (1967d). *Proc. Koninkl. Ned. Akad. Wetenschap.* **B70**, 317.

de Boer, J. H. and Broekhoff, J. C. P. (1967e). *Proc. Koninkl. Ned. Akad. Wetenschap.* **B70**, 333.

de Boer, J. H. and Kruyer, S. (1953). *Proc. Koninkl. Ned. Akad. Wetenschap.* **B56**, 415.

de Boer, J. H. and Kruyer, S. (1954). *Proc. Koninkl. Ned. Akad. Wetenschap.* **B57**, 92.

de Boer, J. H. and Zwikker, C. (1929). *Z. phys. Chem.* **B3**, 407.

de Boer, J. H., Houben, G. M. M., Lippens, B. C., Meys, W. H. and Walrave, W. K. A. (1962). *J. Catalysis* **1**, 1.

de Boer, J. H., Linsen, B. G. and Osinga, Th. J. (1965). *J. Catalysis* **4**, 643.

de Boer, J. H., Lippens, B. C., Linsen, B. G., Broekhoff, J. C. P., van den Heuvel, A. and Osinga, Th. J. (1966). *J. Colloid Interface Sci.* **21**, 405.

Boltzmann, L. (1898). "Vorlesungen über Gastheorie". Verlag von Johann Ambrosius Barth, Leipzig.

Boltzmann, L. (1899). *Versl. Koninkl. Ned. Akad. Wetenschap.* **VII**, 477.

Bradley, R. S. (1936). *J. chem. Soc.* 1799.

Brunauer, S., Emmett, P. H. and Teller, E. (1938). *J. Am. chem. Soc.* **60**, 309.

Brunauer, S. (1943). "The Physical Adsorption of Gases and Vapours". Oxford University Press, Oxford.

Cochrane, H., Walker Jr., P. L., Diethorn, W. S. and Friedman, H. C. (1967). *J. Colloid Interface Sci.* **24**, 405.

van Dongen, R. H. (to be published). Thesis, Delft University of Technology.

Duval, X. and Thomy, A. (1964). *C. R. hebd. Séanc. Acad. Sci. Paris*, **259**, 4007.

Ewing, B. and Pierce, C. (1967.) *J. phys. chem.* **71**, 3408.

Eyring, H. and Hirschfelder, J. O. (1937). *J. phys. Chem.* **41**, 249.

Fisher, B. B. and McMillan, W. G. (1957). *J. Am. chem. Soc.* **79**, 2969.

Fisher, B. B. and McMillan, W. G. (1958). *J. chem. Phys.* **28**, 549.

Fowler, R. H. and Guggenheim, E. A. (1939a). *In* "Statistical Thermodynamics", p. 426. Cambridge University Press, Cambridge.

Fowler, R. H. and Guggenheim, E. A. (1939b). *In* "Statistical Thermodynamics", p. 432. Cambridge University Press, Cambridge.

Fowler, R. H. and Guggenheim, E. A. (1939c). *In* "Statistical Thermodynamics", p. 441. Cambridge University Press, Cambridge.

Frenkel, J. (1946). "Kinetic Theory of Liquids". Oxford University Press, Oxford.

Frumkin, A. N. (1925). *Z. phys. Chem.* **116**, 466.

Frumkin, A. N. (1926). *Z.Phys.* **35**, 792.

Gibbs, J. W. (1961). "The Scientific Papers", Dover Publications, New York.

Gordon, R. (1968). *J. chem. Phys.* **48**, 1408.

Gregg, S. J. and Sing, K. S. W. (1967a). "Adsorption, Surface Area and Porosity", Chapter 6. Academic Press, London and New York.

Gregg, S. J. and Sing, K. S. W. (1967b). "Adsorption, Surface Area and Porosity", pp. 197, 221. Academic Press, London and New York.

Halsey G. D. Jr., (1948). *J. chem. Phys.* **16**, 931.

Halsey G. D. Jr., (1952). *Adv. Catalysis* **4**, 259.

Halsey G. D. Jr., and Singleton, J. H. (1954). *J. phys. Chem.* **58**, 1011.

Harkins, W. D. (1952). "The Physical Chemistry of Surface Films", New York.

Harkins, W. D. and Jura, G. (1944). *J. Am. chem. Soc.* **66**, 1362.

Hellemans, R., van Itterbeek, A. and van Dael, W. (1967). *Physica 's Grav.* **34**, 429.

Henderson, D. and Davison, S. G. (1967). In "Physical Chemistry" (H. Eyring, ed.), Chapter 7. Academic Press, New York.

Hill, T. L. (1946). *J. chem. Phys.* **14**, 441.

Hill, T. L. (1947). *J. chem. Phys.* **15**, 767.

Hill, T. L. (1948). *J. chem. Educ.* **25**, 347.

Hill, T. L. (1949). *J. chem. Phys.* **17**, 762.

Hill, T. L. (1950). *J. chem. Phys.* **54**, 1186.

Hill, T. L. (1960). "Introduction to Statistical Thermodynamics", p. 74. Addison-Wesley, London.

Hinchen, J. J., (1962). Thesis, Rensselaer Polytechnic Institute, Troy, New York.

Hirschfelder, J. O., Curtiss, C. F. and Bird, R. B. (1954a). "Molecular Theory of Gases and Liquids". John Wiley and Sons, New York, D 279.

Hirschfelder, J. O., Curtiss, C. F. and Bird, R. B. (1954b). "Molecular Theory of Gases and Liquids". John Wiley and Sons, New York.

Isirikyan, A. A., and Kiselev, A. V. (1961). *J. phys. Chem.* **65**, 601.

Jura, G. and Harkins, W. D. (1943). *J. chem. Phys.* **11**, 430.

Kruyer, S. (1955a). Thesis, University of Delft.

Kruyer, S. (1955b). *Proc. Koninkl. Ned. Akad. Wetenschap.* **B58**, 73.

Langmuir, I. (1918). *J. Am. chem. Soc.* **40**, 1361.

Lennard Jones, J. E. and Devonshire, A. F. (1937). *Proc. R. Soc.* **A163**, 53.

Lennard Jones, J. E. and Devonshire, A. F. (1938). *Proc. R. Soc.* **A165**, 1.

Maxwell, J. W. (1875). *Nature, Lond.* **11**, 357.

Metropolis, N., Rosenbluth., A. W., Rosenbluth, M. N., Teller, A. H. and Teller, E. (1953). *J. chem. Phys.* **21**, 1087.

Moellwynn-Hughes, E. A. (1961). "Physical Chemistry", p. 732. Oxford University Press, Oxford.

Onsager, L. (1944). *Phys. Rev.* **65**, 117.

Pierce, C. (1968). *J. phys. Chem.* **72**, 1955.

Pierotti, R. A. and Smallwood, R. E. (1966). *J. Colloid Interface Sci.* **22**, 469.

Ree, F. H. and Hoover, W. G. (1964). *J. chem. Phys.* **40**, 939.

Ross, S. and Olivier, J. P. (1964a). "On Physical Adsorption". Interscience, New York.

Ross, S. and Olivier, J. P. (1964b). "On Physical Adsorption", p. 125. Interscience, New York.

Sams, J. R., Constabaris, G. and Halsey, G. D. (1962a). *J. chem. Phys.* **36**, 1334.

Sams, J. R., Constabaris, G. and Halsey, G. D. (1962b). *J. phys. Chem.* **66**, 2154.

Sips, R. (1948). *J. chem. Phys.* **16**, 490.

Steele, W. (1967). *Adv. Colloid Interface Sci.* **1**, 3.

Taikaishi, T. and Saito, M. (1967). *J. phys. Chem.* **71**, 453.

Throop, G. J. and Bearman, R. J. (1965). *J. chem. Phys.* **42**, 2408.

Tonks, L. (1936). *Phys. Rev.* **50**, 955.

Tsien, F. and Halsey, G. D. (1967). *J. phys. Chem.* **71**, 4012.
van der Waals, J. D. (1873). Thesis, University of Leiden.
van der Waals, J. D. (1897). *Versl. Koninkl. Ned. Akad. Wetenschap.* **V**, 150.
van der Waals, J. D. (1898). *Versl. Koninkl. Ned. Akad. Wetenschap.* **VI**, 160.
van Laar, J. J. (1899). *Versl. Koninkl. Ned. Akad. Wetenschap.* **VII**, 350.
Wang, Y. L., Ree, T., Ree, T. and Eyring, H. (1965). *J. chem. Phys.* **42**, 1926.
Wolfe, R. and Sams, J. R. (1965). *J. phys. Chem.* **69**, 1129.
Young, D. M. and Crowell, A. D. (1962a). "Physical Adsorption of Gases",
    p. 238. Butterworth, London.
Young, D. M. and Crowell, A. D. (1962b). "Physical Adsorption of Gases",
    Chapter 6. Butterworth, London.
Young, D. M. and Crowell, A. D. (1962c). "Physical Adsorption of Gases",
    p. 212. Butterworth, London.

Chapter 3

SOME RECENT APPLICATIONS OF THE CALCULATION OF THE ENTROPY OF THE ADSORBED PHASE ACCORDING TO DE BOER

J. J. F. Scholten and S. Kruyer

Central Laboratory, N.V. Nederlandse Staatsmijnen/DSM, Geleen, The Netherlands

I Introduction

As a rule, heterogeneous catalysis goes through the same stages of development as normal three-dimensional chemistry. However, owing to the low "concentration of surface" sites (small number of surface sites per cm^3 of material) and the complicated structure of surfaces, the field is difficult to explore, both theoretically and experimentally.

This appears, for example, from the fact that the crystallography of bulk materials was widely studied in detail already during the thirties, whereas it was not until 1954 that research on surface crystallography was begun by Farnsworth, MacRae and Germer (low energy electron results; LEED). The same applies to the I.R.-study of the adsorbed phase, which has become of more general importance only after 1954 (Eischens, 1958) whereas in normal chemistry the development started already around 1935.

The work we are dealing with in this study originated in a period when the "alchemy-stage" of catalysis, which is taken to have lasted until the beginning of the present century, was already past. Once methods had been found for the determination of surface-areas, a start could be made with the kinetic and thermodynamic analysis of adsorption. Though we now seem to be entering the stage in which adsorption phenomena are being described on an atomic scale (I.R., LEED, field ion microscopy etc.), the *thermodynamic analysis* of adsorption has not yet lost its actuality.

The approach was pioneered by Kemball and Rideal (1946), Everett (1950) and de Boer (1952). De Boer's work is easily accessible and lends itself to a rapid orientation on the mobility of adsorbed layers. De Boer and Kruyer (1952, 1953, 1954, 1955), and Kruyer (1955) applied their method to many cases of physical adsorption of hydrocarbons, noble gases, nitrogen, hydrogen and oxygen on active carbon.

Afterwards, other pupils of de Boer frequently used the method also when dealing with strong physical adsorption or with chemisorption. It is the aim of the present authors to review these studies and show in what way the calculation of the entropy of adsorbed layers, in combination with other theories and experimental techniques, may contribute towards the drawing of conclusions on adsorption and catalysis phenomena. First however, we will present a brief outline of the procedure.

II Calculation of the Entropy of Adsorbed Molecules

When a gas is in equilibrium with n_a adsorbed molecules per gram of adsorbent at temperature T and pressure p, we have:

$$_g\mu(p,T) = \mu(n_a,T) \tag{1}$$

where μ is the chemical potential, and the indices g and a are related to the gas phase and the adsorbed phase respectively. As

$$\mu = H - TS \tag{2}$$

where H is the partial enthalpy and S the partial entropy,

$$_gS - _aS = (_gH - _aH)/T. \tag{3}$$

The enthalpy of an ideal gas is independent of pressure, and hence the difference $_gH - _aH$, i.e. the differential heat of adsorption—further indicated by $-\Delta H$—is equal to $_gH^0 - _aH$:

$$-\Delta H = _gH^0 - _aH \tag{4}$$

where $_gH^0$ is the enthalpy of the gas at standard pressure. The entropy of the gas is given by:

$$_gS = _gS^0 - R \ln p/p^0 \tag{5}$$

where R = molar gas constant and $_gS^0$ = the entropy of the gas at standard pressure. The difference $_gS^0 - _aS$ will be referred to as the differential adsorption entropy $-\Delta S$.

By substitution we find:

$$-\Delta S = \frac{-\Delta H}{T} + R \ln p/p^0 \qquad (6)$$

In cases where ΔS and ΔH are functions of θ, i.e. the degree of coverage of the adsorbed material, we have:

$$-\Delta S(\theta) = \frac{-\Delta H(\theta)}{T} + R \ln p/p^0. \qquad (7)$$

Hence, the heat of adsorption, the equilibrium-pressure and the temperature being known, the adsorption-entropy can be calculated.

From adsorption isotherms at various temperatures the differential heat of adsorption ΔH can be calculated by means of the Clausius-Clapeyron equation:

$$\Delta H = R \left[\frac{\ln p_1 - \ln p_2}{\dfrac{1}{T_1} - \dfrac{1}{T_2}} \right]_\theta . \qquad (8)$$

Eqs (7) and (8) give

$$-\Delta S(\theta) = R \frac{T_2 \ln p_2/p^0 - T_1 \ln p_1/p^0}{T_1 - T_2} \qquad (9)$$

Hence, from two adsorption isotherms at temperatures T_1 and T_2, and from the pressures p_1 and p_2 corresponding to the same degree of coverage θ, $\Delta S(\theta)$—the entropy of adsorption at coverage θ—can be calculated.

The experimental entropy values, calculated as outlined above, may be compared with theoretical values derived from various models of the adsorbed unimolecular layer on the basis of statistical thermodynamics. These models always are between two extremes. In the model of immobile adsorption, the atoms are firmly bound to the adsorption sites, and there are no translations or vibrations perpendicular or parallel to the surface. Then, the only entropy of the adsorbed layer still present is given by the entropy of a system of n particles distributed over n_0 sites, the so-called localization entropy:

$$_aS_{loc} = -R \ln \frac{\theta}{1-\theta} \qquad (10)$$

where $\theta = n/n_0$, the degree of coverage.

The other extreme case is a model corresponding to a two-dimensional ideal surface gas in which the degrees of internal rotation are retained too, and in which there is even an occasional possibility for the adsorbed particles to move perpendicular to the surface (super-mobility).

Of course, numerous intermediate situations can be imagined, and it is often difficult to decide which degrees of freedom actually contribute to the total entropy of adsorbed layer.

The various aspects of the statistical thermodynamics of adsorbed layers will not be treated here. The reader is referred to the original publications by de Boer and Kruyer. We shall only indicate (see following paragraphs) *which* statistical thermodynamic quantities are used for comparison with the experimental $-\Delta S(\theta)$ values.

III   Adsorption of N_2O_4 on Silica

In most heterogeneous catalytic processes the chemisorption of one or more of the reactants on to the surface is an essential step, resulting in a lowering of the activation energy of the reaction. In rare cases, however, the catalytic acceleration of a reaction can be ascribed to the increase in the concentration of the reactants on the catalyst surface caused by physical adsorption. A suitable name for this phenomena is *physical catalysis* (de Boer, 1956). One characteristic of this type of catalysis is that it takes place on every sufficiently large surface area, provided that the adsorbability of the reactants is high enough.

A clear example of this type of catalysis is found in the oxidation of nitric oxide over silica (Bokhoven and Zwietering, 1956). The mechanism of the reaction is not exactly known, whether in the gas phase or at the surface, but Scholten and Zwietering (1961) succeeded in showing that the observed acceleration factor on a silica catalyst can be theoretically calculated by means of Eyring's absolute reaction rate theory, i.e. on the basis of Gershinowitz and Eyring's three-body collision mechanism:

$$NO + NO + O_2 \rightleftharpoons N_2O_4^{\ddagger} \rightarrow N_2O_4 \rightleftharpoons 2NO_2,$$

which is supposed to be valid both in the gas phase and at the surface. Such a calculation, of course, can only be made if the partition-functions, F, of the reactants and of the transition states are known. To permit calculation of the partition function of the adsorbed reactants and the adsorbed transition state, the state of mobility of these species must be known. For this purpose use was made of de Boer and Kruyer's method. The calculation for adsorbed NO and O_2 is simple, and the result indicates that there is unrestricted two-dimensional mobility with fully-preserved rotation in either case (Scholten and Zwietering, 1961). As neither the structures of the activated complexes, nor the mobility of the adsorbed activated complex, are known, their partition functions cannot be calculated.

Therefore it was supposed that:

$$\frac{F_{N_2O_4^\ddagger}\text{adsorbed}}{F_{N_2O_4^\ddagger}\text{gas phase}} \simeq \frac{F_{N_2O_4}\text{adsorbed}}{F_{N_2O_4}\text{gas phase}} \tag{11}$$

which means that the ratios between the partition-functions of the activated states are about equal to those of the final states; the latter ratio has been calculated.

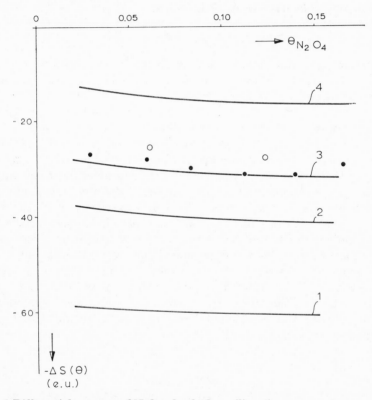

FIG. 1 Differential entropy of N_2O_4 adsorbed on silica, (in e.u. = entropy units), as a function of coverage, compared with the theoretical values for various degrees of freedom. $T = 296$–$313°K$.

○: experimental$-\Delta S(\theta)$-values: from isotherms of Reyerson and Wertz (1949).
●: experimental$-\Delta S(\theta)$-values from Bokhoven—Zwietering (1956).
curve 1: immobile adsorption; all translational and rotational degrees of freedom lost.
Curve 2: all rotational degrees of freedom lost; two degrees of translational freedom preserved.
Curve 3: two degrees of translational freedom with one preserved rotation parallel to the surface.
curve 4: as 3, but all rotations preserved.

The experimental differential entropy of N_2O_4 on silica as a function of coverage, calculated by means of Eq. (7), is given in Fig. 1. The experimental values have been compared with the theoretical statistical thermodynamic entropy changes expected for mobile, partly mobile and fully immobile adsorption.

In the case of fully immobile adsorption (Fig. 1, curve 1) all translational and rotational degrees of freedom are lost, and only the localization entropy $R \ln \theta/1-\theta$ is gained. Hence:

$$-\Delta S(\theta) = -\Delta S_{\text{trans.}} - \Delta S_{\text{rot.}} + R \ln \frac{\theta}{1-\theta} \qquad (12)$$

where $\Delta S_{\text{trans.}}$ denotes the statistical thermodynamic value for three degrees of translational freedom of N_2O_4 and $-\Delta S_{\text{rot.}}$ the corresponding values for three degrees of rotational freedom.

The theoretical curves 2, 3 and 4 in Fig. 1 have been calculated in the same way, further indicated in the caption to the figure. In the case of mobile adsorption the "localization entropy" $R \ln A^0/A_\theta$ is gained, where A^0 is the standard surface area for an N_2O_4 molecule, and A is the surface area available for an N_2O_4 molecule at coverage θ. As can be seen in Fig. 1, the experimental figures agree with the theoretical values for N_2O_4 molecules with two degrees of translational freedom, and with one preserved rotation parallel to the surface.

The mobility of the adsorbed reactants and transition states being known, the rate of the two-dimensional surface reaction on silica can be calculated. Comparing this rate with the rate of the gas phase reaction it can be established by how much the reaction is accelerated by the action of the silica. The theoretical values are in reasonable agreement with the experimental results (Bokhoven and Zwietering, 1956; Scholten and Zwietering, 1961).

Another approach, starting from the supposition that Bodenstein's mechanism:

(a) $2NO \rightleftharpoons (NO)_2$

(b) $(NO)_2 + O_2 \rightarrow N_2O_4$

is valid both in the gas phase and at the surface, yields approximately the same result. In this case, however, it is necessary to introduce the supposition that the heat of dimerization of NO approximately equals the activation energy of reaction (b) (Bokhoven and Zwietering, 1956).

The authors of this chapter do not regard Bodenstein's representation of the mechanism as a probable one because it considers dimerization of NO a condition for further reaction with oxygen. However, dimerization just deprives the NO molecule $\left[\dot{\underline{N}} - \overline{\underline{O}} | \leftrightarrow \overline{\underline{N}} = \dot{O} | \leftrightarrow \dot{\underline{N}} = \overline{\underline{O}} \right]$ of its highly reactive pseudoradical character.

There is still another mechanism (Benson, 1960) that involves an intermediate NO . O_2 and leads to reasonable theoretical values for the rate of the gas phase reaction according to Eyring's absolute reaction rate theory. This mechanism was not considered in calculating the catalytic acceleration of the reaction.

IV   Strong Physical Adsorption of Nitrogen on Nickel

A theoretical distinction between physisorption and chemisorption can be made quite well. Adsorption is called physisorption if the adsorption forces are of the van der Waals type. We are dealing here with dipole-dipole interaction (Keesom-forces), dipole-induced dipole interaction (Debye-forces) and the dispersion forces (London-forces). In these cases the electrons of the adsorbent and the adsorbate remain, to a first approximation, under the control of the same nuclei as before adsorption. In chemisorption there is electronic interaction (electron-transfer and/or sharing) between the adsorbate and the adsorbent.

Experimentally it is much more difficult to distinguish between the two types, and one has to apply a series of criteria before a decision can be made. It is risky to base such a decision on the value of the heat of adsorption alone, as was extensively argued by de Boer (1956) and, more recently, by Thomas and Thomas (1967). This is true also in using the activation energy of adsorption as a criterion.

The study of nitrogen-adsorption on nickel by van Hardeveld and van Montfoort (1966) is interesting in this respect. Whereas several authors (Beeck et al. 1941; Kokes and Emmett, 1960; Gundry et al., 1962; Schuit and de Boer, 1954) claimed the existence of reversible nitrogen chemisorption at $-183°C$ and $-78°C$, mostly on the ground of adsorption isotherms measurements, others (Wagener, 1957; Hickmott and Ehrlich, 1958; Trapnell, 1953), referring to adsorption measurements on evaporated films, concluded that nitrogen does not chemisorb on nickel at room temperature.

It remained doubtful, however, whether the nature of the adsorption was physical or chemical, since the influence of the adsorption of nitrogen both on the electrical conductivity (Suhrmann and Schultz, 1955) and on the surface potential of nickel (Mignolet, 1950) does not exceed the effect produced by the physical adsorption of xenon.

The infra-red work of Eischens and Jacknow (1965) drew new attention to this problem. These authors found that nitrogen adsorption on a nickel-on-silica catalyst produces an I.R. absorption band at 2202 cm^{-1}, which they attributed to the nitrogen-nitrogen stretching

vibration in a proposed structure of the shape Ni—N ≡ N. The molecular nature of the adsorbed nitrogen was proved by the observation
of *three* infra-red adsorption bands upon adsorption of an isotopic
mixture of $^{28}N_2$, $^{29}N_2$ and $^{30}N_2$.

These results could be confirmed by the infra-red work of van
Hardeveld and van Montfoort, who showed, however, that this type
of I.R.-active nitrogen adsorption occurs only when the diameter d
of the metal crystallites is within the range ~15 Å $< d <\sim70$ Å. This is

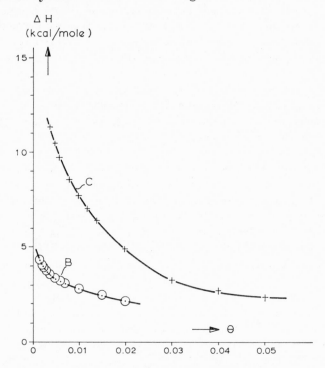

FIG. 2 Differential heat of adsorption, ΔH, of nitrogen on two types of nickel-on-
silica catalysts, as a function of the coverage of the total (nickel, plus silica)
surface area calculated from a set of adsorption isotherms between $-80°C$ and
$+40°C$.
B: nickel crystallites without B5-sites in the surface.
C: nickel crystallites with B5-sites in the surface.

because crystals within this range possess a large number of "rough
planes" which are absent, or much scarcer, on larger or smaller crystals.
The infra-red activity of nitrogen adsorbed on the special sites present
on these rough planes is due to the induction of a transition-moment
by the strong polarizing field of these sites, so formed that five Ni-

atoms in the surface contact the nitrogen molecule. A schematic representation of such sites, the so-called B5-sites, is given in Fig. 4. The observed I.R. absorption band at 2202 cm⁻¹ corresponds to the nitrogen Raman band (2331 cm⁻¹), which has shifted under the influence of the Stark effect.

To clarify the nature of the absorption band (physisorption, chemisorption or an intermediate case), it is worthwhile to make a closer study of the heat and entropy of adsorption in samples both with and without B5-sites. For this purpose, a set of nitrogen adsorption isotherms were measured on such samples, from which the differential heat of adsorption ΔH was calculated with the aid of the Clausius-Clapeyron equation. The result is given in Fig. 2, which clearly illustrates the difference in behaviour of these samples with regard to nitrogen adsorption; sample C adsorbs an amount of nitrogen with a high initial differential heat of adsorption, i.e. between $\sim$12 and 5 kcal/mole, whereas the highest value for sample B is only 4 kcal/mole. On both samples, however, ΔH tends towards the same low value of about 2 kcal/mole at higher coverage. It has to be remarked that the amount of nitrogen extra-strongly adsorbed on sample C corresponds with a nitrogen-coverage on the *nickel* part of the surface of the order of 10%.

The differential entropy of adsorption was calculated with the aid of Eq. (9).

The experimental values were compared with theoretical statistical thermodynamic entropy changes to be expected for mobile, partly mobile and fully immobile adsorption.

In the case of fully immobile adsorption, all translational and rotational degrees of freedom of the nitrogen molecules are lost, and only the localization entropy $R \ln \theta/1-\theta$ is gained (curve 1, Fig. 3). Hence:

$$-\Delta S(\theta) = -\Delta S_{\text{trans.}} - \Delta S_{\text{rot.}} + R \ln \frac{\theta}{1-\theta}. \tag{8}$$

In the case of mobile adsorption the nitrogen molecules still have two degrees of translational freedom ("ideal two-dimensional gas") and two rotational degrees of freedom (see curve 2, Fig. 3). Hence:

$$-\Delta S(\theta) = -\Delta S_{\text{one trans.}} + R \ln A^0/A_\theta \tag{10}$$

where $R \ln A^0/A_\theta$ is the "localization entropy" for a mobile layer, A^0 is the standard surface area of a nitrogen molecule, and A_θ the surface area available for a nitrogen molecule at coverage θ.

In Fig. 3 the results of the calculations are combined. It may be

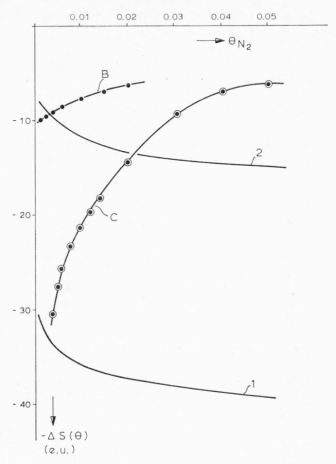

F IG . 3 Differential entropy of nitrogen adsorbed on two types of nickel-on-silica catalysts, as a function of coverage, at $T = 0°C$.

●: experimental differential entropy of nitrogen on nickel without B5-sites.

⊙: experimental differential entropy of nitrogen on nickel with B5-sites in the surface.

curve 1: theoretical differential entropy for immobile adsorption. All degrees of rotational and translational freedom lost.

curve 2: theoretical differential entropy for mobile adsorption. One degree of translational freedom lost.

concluded from this figure that initially, so at low coverage, the nitrogen on sample C (many B5-sites) is adsorbed to immobility, whereas at higher coverage, at $\theta = 0.02$, where the heat of adsorption has decreased from ∼12 kcal/mole to ∼5 kcal/mole, the adsorbed nitrogen is in the *mobile* or perhaps even super-mobile state. Nitrogen adsorption on sample B (no B5-sites) is always either mobile or super-mobile (see line B, Fig. 3).

It goes without saying that the immobility of the nitrogen adsorbed on nickel B5-sites, with a heat of adsorption of 10–12 kcal/mole and at a very low coverage, does not indicate a case of chemisorption, and hence we have to resort to still other criteria.

First, we draw attention to the non-specificity of adsorbed infra-red active nitrogen at room temperature to a particular metal; it is equally well found on platinum and palladium samples with B5-sites. Furthermore, immobile physisorption is quite within the range of possibilities, as indicated by Ehrlich and Hudda's field emission studies with the rare gases on tungsten (1959). These authors found that the rare gas atoms are adsorbed preferentially on to those sites where the ad-atom fits best into the structure of the surface, and that

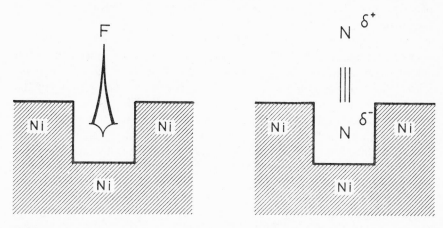

F

Fig. 4

this property determines the sequence of the bond strengths on the various surface sites. Now, looking at the geometry of a B5-site (schem-atic representation in Fig. 4), we see that a strong electric field may be present over short distances, owing to incomplete compensation of the positive and negative electric fields of the nuclei and the electron clouds of the metal atoms. In this case the relatively high heat of adsorption is accounted for as the sum of the Debye-contribution, resulting from the interaction of the electric field near the B5-site with the dipole induced in the nitrogen molecule, and the London contribu-tion; the latter may exceed that on a flat surface (B3-sites) by a factor two, owing to the greater coordination of the adsorbed molecule. This also furnishes an elegant explanation of the I.R. activity of the adsorbed nitrogen molecule, which is easily polarizable along its longer axis.

Further criteria for physisorption are:

1. there is no, or hardly any, influence on the ferromagnetic properties of the metal owing to physical adsorption and

2. a physically adsorbed nitrogen molecule is not "chemically activated", i.e. there is no possibility for synthesis of ammonia, or for nitrogen isotope exchange owing to this type of adsorption.

As to point 1, van Hardeveld (in press) shows that indeed there is no influence of the nitrogen adsorption on the E.P.R. signal of a nickel-on-silica catalyst with B5-sites; this is in agreement with the results of Andreev and Selwood (1967). However, a change in the E.P.R. signal is absent only if the nitrogen used is thoroughly freed of substances like oxygen and water by previously storing it over a nickel-on-silica catalyst.

As to point 2, van Hardeveld measured the rate of the nitrogen isotope exchange $^{28}N_2 + ^{30}N_2 \rightleftharpoons 2\,^{29}N_2$. At 350°C he indeed noted a small exchange activity over a nickel-catalyst with B5-sites. However, after thorough solvent extraction of the last traces (50 p.p.m.) of the *iron* in the nickel, the activity disappeared. The small exchange activity measured in the presence of 50 p.p.m. iron approximately agreed with the effect that might be expected from such an amount on the surface, in view of Kummer and Emmett's (1951) and McGeer and Taylor's (1951) measurements of the activity of *iron* for nitrogen isotope exchange. As all experiments conducted so far demonstrate that the kinetics of the nitrogen isotope exchange run parallel to those of the ammonia synthesis (Scholten, 1959) it is not expected that the Ni samples with B5-sites will be active for ammonia synthesis.

This allows us to conclude that we are dealing here with an example of strong immobile *physical* adsorption of nitrogen on the "rough planes" of nickel.

V The Mobility of Nitrogen Chemisorbed on a Singly-promoted Iron Catalyst

About ten years ago the adsorption and desorption kinetics of nitrogen on a singly-promoted iron ammonia-synthesis catalyst was extensively studied at the Central Laboratory of Dutch State Mines, Geleen.

Full details of this work are given in various standard treatises on catalysis and chemisorption, in a series of articles by Zwietering and

Roukens (1954), and in Scholten and Zwietering (1957), Scholten *et al.* (1955), and Scholten's thesis (1959).

Chemisorption isotherms were not measured by these authors. At adsorption equilibrium the rates of adsorption and desorption must be equal and hence the chemisorption isotherms can be found by equalizing the rate equations for adsorption and desorption valid in the same occupation range and in the same region of temperatures.

Putting the general equations for the adsorption and desorption kinetics equal to each other:

$$v_{\text{ads.}} = A(\theta)P_{N_2} \exp \frac{-E_{\text{ads.}}(\theta)}{RT} = \tag{13}$$

$$v_{\text{des.}} = D(\theta) \exp \frac{-E_{\text{des.}}(\theta)}{RT} \tag{14}$$

where $A(\theta)$ is the pre-exponential factor for adsorption and $D(\theta)$ for desorption, and considering that:

$$-\Delta H(\theta) = E_{\text{des.}}(\theta) - E_{\text{ads.}}(\theta) \tag{15}$$

and using Eq. (7) we get:

$$-\Delta S(\theta) = R \ln \frac{D(\theta)}{A(\theta)} \tag{16}$$

Hence, the experimental differential entropy could be easily calculated from the kinetic data and compared with the statistical thermodynamic values (for an extensive treatise see Scholten, 1959).

The calculations were first carried out on the basis of the supposition *that nitrogen is chemisorbed atomically*; the results are given in Fig. 5. We see from this figure that the experimental differential entropy values are in agreement with the theoretical figures for immobile dissociative adsorption of nitrogen at coverages below $\theta = 0 \cdot 1$ (see curve 4, Fig. 5). At higher coverage there is no agreement, neither with the values theoretically to be expected for mobile adsorption of nitrogen atoms (curve 1), nor with those for immobile dissociative adsorption (curve 4).

Theoretical calculations were made also for the case of *adsorption of di-atomic particles*, as it might be that pre-dissociative adsorption takes place, for instance in the form $\diagup^{N=N}\diagdown$. The relevant theoretical lines are also given in Fig. 5 (curves 2 and 3). It follows that at very low coverage nitrogen might be adsorbed to immobility in a pre-dissociative form. At coverages above $\theta \sim 0 \cdot 2$ $-\Delta S_{\text{exp.}}$ approaches the theoretical values, and at $\theta > 0 \cdot 25$ it is equal to the theoretical values calculated for mobile pre-dissociative adsorption of particles with one degree of rotational freedom perpendicular to the surface (curve 2).

This work furnished indications that nitrogen on these catalysts occurs in at least two forms; an immobile (atomic or di-atomic) form, and a mobile (di-atomic) form. It is interesting to note that comparison of the kinetic data with theoretical values from Eyring's absolute

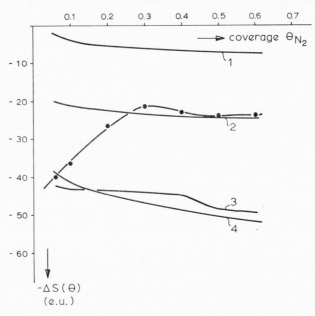

FIG. 5 Comparison of the experimental and theoretical differential entropies as functions of coverage for nitrogen chemisorbed on a singly promoted iron catalyst.
●: experimental ΔS-values.
curve 1: theoretical ΔS-values for mobile dissociative adsorption.
curve 2: as 1, for pre-dissociative mobile adsorption.
curve 3: as 1, for pre-dissociative immobile adsorption.
curve 4: as 1, for dissociative immobile adsorption.

reaction rate theory led up to the same conclusions for the mobility of the *transition states* in the adsorption and desorption processes of nitrogen on the iron catalyst (Scholten, 1959).

The recently-published work of Schmidt (1968) is interesting in this respect. This author attempted to apply field ion mass spectrometry to ionization of ammonia and nitrogen-hydrogen mixtures on iron, in order to determine which type of nitrogen particles exists at the surface. Field ionization makes it possible to ionize molecules that are interacting with a metal tip from the gas phase, and to analyse them mass-spectrometrically. The absence of NH_2^+, NH^+ and N^+ ions in the mass-spectra was remarkable. Detection of ions containing iron permitted direct analysis of chemisorption structures; structures containing atomic nitrogen were not found. According to Schmidt these results indicate that nitrogen enters the surface structure only in molecular form.

Shvachko et al. (1966) obtained the same result when investigating the synthesis of ammonia by the method of secondary ion-ion emission at temperatures up to over 400°C. They concluded that the first step in ammonia synthesis is the chemisorption of molecular nitrogen forming a surface-nitride FeN_2. In the second stage the chemisorbed nitrogen is hydrogenated, with the result that adsorbed particles of NH are formed. Subsequent hydrogenation of the NH-groups leads to formation of ammonia-molecules (the third step of the reaction).

From all this work one might conclude that the nitrogen at the surface is probably present in di-atomic form. Nevertheless, there is room for some criticism. The iron-nitrogen bond at low coverage is rather strong ($\sim$50 kcal/mole), and it is to be expected that at the field strength required for ionization of the nitrogen atom, iron-atoms or Fe—N^+ ions also desorb from the surface. In the gas phase such groups can react further with nitrogen molecules or with ions composed of N_2 and H atoms, to yield for instance $FeN_3H_n^+$-ions. Such a group of ions was indeed detected in Schmidt's mass-spectrum.

Even if we accept that the nitrogen present at the surface is largely in some diatomic form, it is not certain, as stated by Shvachko, whether the ammonia synthesis actually proceeds via such species. It is equally possible that there exists a surface equilibrium between a small concentration of surface nitrogen atoms and pre-dissociative nitrogen molecules. When the surface nitrogen atoms with hydrogen react to ammonia this equilibrium will shift towards the atomically bound form.

Shvachko et al. (1966) concluded from their work that ammonia synthesis goes via the surface steps:

1. $Fe + N_2 \rightarrow FeN_2$

2. $FeN_2 + H_2 \rightarrow Fe\Big\langle{}^{NH}_{NH}$

3. $Fe{}^{NH}\!\diagup + H_2 \rightarrow Fe—NH_3$

4. $Fe—NH_3 \rightarrow Fe + NH_3$

They state that this mechanism is in contradiction with Horiuti's school (Horiuti and Takezawa, 1961), which proposes the following mechanism:

7

$$(a) \qquad 2Fe + N_2 \rightarrow 2FeN_{ads.}$$
$$(b) \qquad 2Fe + H_2 \rightarrow 2FeH_{ads.}$$
$$(c) \qquad N_{ads.} + H_{ads.} \rightarrow NH_{ads.}$$
$$(d) \qquad NH_{ads.} + H_{ads.} \rightarrow NH_{2ads.}$$
$$(e) \qquad NH_{2ads.} + H_{ads.} \rightarrow NH_{3ads.}$$
$$(f) \qquad NH_{3ads.} \rightarrow NH_3.$$

The Japanese workers of Horiuti's school (see for instance Tanaka *et al.*, 1965) finally concluded that the stoichiometric number of the reaction $v_r = 1$, showing that reaction (a) is the rate-determining step. However, as Zwietering (1960) points out, the experimental result $v_r = 1$ does not definitely prove that the nitrogen chemisorption step is rate-determining. More steps with a stoichiometric number equal to unity can be imagined, for instance steps 2 and 3 in Shvachko's mechanism, all of which correspond to a rate-determining step occurring one time when the overall reaction $N_2 + 3H_2 \rightarrow 2NH_3$ occurs one time (i.e. $v_r = 1$).

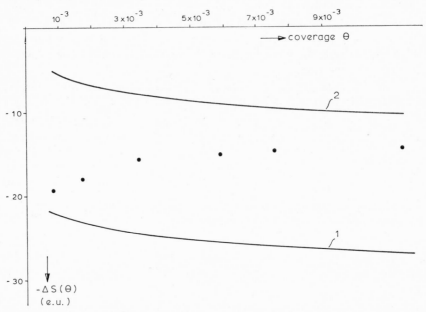

Fig. 6 Entropy of carbon monoxide on γ-alumina between $273 \cdot 2°$ and $293 \cdot 2°K$. Low pressure experiments; low coverages.

●: experimental—$\varDelta S$ values.

1: theoretical—$\varDelta S$ values for immobile adsorption.

2: theoretical—$\varDelta S$ values for mobile adsorption (mobile two-dimensional gas with preserved rotation).

As is well known, there are other strong arguments in favour of the view that the nitrogen chemisorption step is rate-determining (Scholten, 1959), including the observation that at a number of temperatures, pressures and nitrogen-coverages, the nitrogen adsorption rate was found equal to the ammonia synthesis rate.

VI The Entropy and Mobility of Nitrogen and Carbon Monoxide Adsorbed on Alumina

De Boer and Menon (1962) and Menon (1962) studied the adsorption of nitrogen and carbon monoxide on highly-dehydrated γ-alumina evacuated at temperatures up to 600°C. Isotherms were measured not only below one atmosphere but also at pressures up to 3000 atmosphere, which made it possible to investigate both the region of extremely low coverage and that of high coverage at temperatures relatively high for a physisorption process.

The results for carbon monoxide are very interesting. Fig. 6 com-

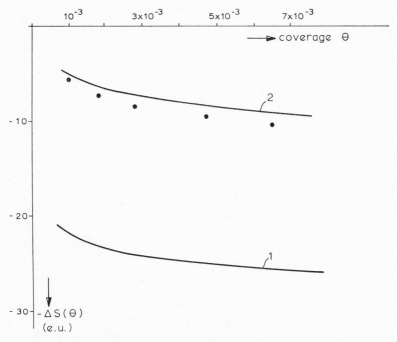

Fig. 7 Entropy of nitrogen adsorbed on γ-alumina between 273·2 and 293·2°K. Low-pressure experiments; low coverages.
●: experimental—ΔS-values.
1: theoretical—ΔS-values for immobile adsorption.
2: theoretical—ΔS-values for mobile adsorption.

pares the experimental differential entropy, $-\Delta S$, with theoretical statistical thermodynamical values for mobile and immobile adsorption. It is seen that at coverages below $\theta = 0\cdot001$ carbon monoxide (unlike nitrogen, see Figs 7 and 8) is adsorbed to immobility, which changes to hindered mobility between $\theta = 0\cdot001$ and $\theta = 0\cdot01$. The

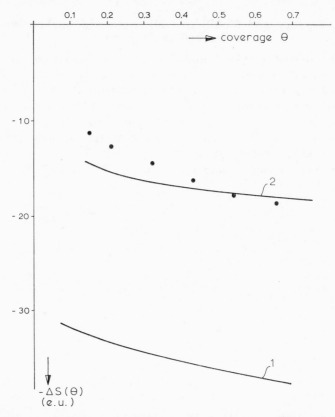

FIG. 8 Entropy of nitrogen adsorbed on γ-alumina between 272·4 and 298·16°K. High-pressure experiments; high coverages.
●: experimental—ΔS-values.
1: theoretical—ΔS-values for immobile adsorption.
2: theoretical—ΔS values for mobile adsorption.

adsorption seems to involve strong interaction with the surface, with the consequence that the adsorbed molecules are quite immobile and fixed to definite sites on the surface. The figures found at higher coverage (see Fig. 9) point to mobile adsorption, and beyond $\theta = 0\cdot6$ restrictions of the translations of carbon monoxide molecules on the surface gradually become noticeable.

Menon states that the small dipole moment (0·117 Debye unit) of carbon monoxide together with its larger quadrupole moment ($1·62 \times 10^{-26}$ against $1·29 \times 10^{-26}$ e.s.u. for nitrogen) and greater polarizability ($1·844 \times 10^{-24}$ for CO and $1·741 \times 10^{-24}$ cm^3 for nitrogen) as compared to nitrogen, apparently seems to have a profound influence

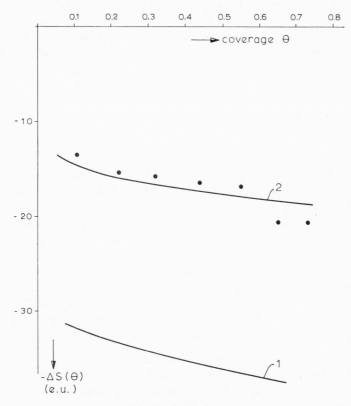

FIG. 9 Entropy of carbon monoxide adsorbed on γ-alumina between 272·4 and 298·16°K. High-pressure experiments; high coverages.
● : experimental—ΔS-values.
1: theoretical—ΔS-values for immobile adsorption.
2: theoretical—ΔS-values for mobile adsorption.

on the initial adsorption of carbon monoxide, making it a case of stronger physical immobile adsorption.

We think that these small differences are indeed the reasons for the stronger and somewhat less mobile adsorption of carbon monoxide as compared with that of nitrogen *over the whole range of coverages:* above $\theta = 0·1$ the heat of adsorption of carbon monoxide on alumina is

~2·6 kcal/mole, the figure for nitrogen being ~2·0 kcal/mole. The high *initial* heat of adsorption of carbon monoxide—7 to 8 kcal/mole at $\theta = 0.001$ against more than 3 kcal/mole for nitrogen—is not explained in this way. Perhaps it can be explained by Scholten and van Montfoort's observation (unpublished results) that on highly-activated γ-alumina a strong adsorption of carbon monoxide occurs, corresponding to $\theta = 0.002$, and related to a low surface concentration of Lewis sites. These Lewis sites result from the formation of a water molecule from two surface hydroxyl groups and are able to interact strongly with carbon monoxide. The sites responsible for this strong adsorption may be the same as those rendering the highly-activated alumina active for hydrogen-deuterium-exchange (Holm and Blue, 1951; Weller and Hindin, 1956).

VII Concluding Remarks

Reviewing the various applications of the de Boer and Kruyer method, we must conclude that, in combination with other theories and experimental data, it provides valuable information for a better understanding of adsorption and catalysis. The entropy differences not only in many cases are in good quantitative agreement with the theoretical values following from a given model of the adsorbed layer, but also often follow the trend of the theoretical entropy values as a function of coverage. Everett (1967) formulated the various conditions to be satisfied by the entropy variation in case the model of mobile adsorption is used. From thermodynamic considerations, if the model of an ideal two-dimensional gas is to be fully applicable it follows that:

1. the adsorption isotherm must be linear;
2. the heat of adsorption must be independent of coverage;
3. $\Delta S(\theta)$ must be linear function of $\ln A/A^0$ with slope R;
4. the order of magnitude of $\Delta S(\theta)$ must be equal to the expected theoretical value for adsorption of a two-dimensional gas.

In the work discussed in this chapter these conditions are frequently satisfied, e.g. for nitrogen dioxide adsorption on silica, for nitrogen adsorption on alumina, and for carbon monoxide adsorption on alumina. In some cases discussed here, Everett's conditions prove to be applicable only within a limited range of coverages. It is, of course, possible then to devise more refined models and calculate the theoretical entropy variation for these models. Everett did so for the non-ideal two-dimensional gas with and without intermolecular forces. His calculations show that introduction of these models at coverages below $\theta = 0 \cdot 5$ has only a minor effect on the theoretical entropy variation. Using de Boer and Kruyer's approach of course, one is not allowed to neglect the volume of the molecule itself. Therefore, in calculating the entropy of a two-dimensional layer adsorbed in the mobile state, one is compelled in fact, to use the Volmer equation,

$$F(A-n \cdot b) = nRT,$$

where F = two-dimensional pressure,

A = surface area available to a single adsorbed molecule,

n = number of adsorbed molecules,

b = surface area of one molecule.

The influence of this refinement is also small, notably in calculations worked out for low coverage. As a result of all these refinements, entropy differences of approximately two entropy units may occur at higher coverages, but these do not necessarily invalidate the choice between the various degrees of mobility, because the differences between the models used frequently amount to 20 entropy units or over.

Everett pointed out that a model of immobile adsorption may be imagined in which the contribution from the vibrations of the adsorbed molecules to the total entropy is so large as to increase the total entropy to the order of that of a two-dimensional adsorbed gas; this would make it impossible to conclude that the adsorption bears a mobile character. In view of the frequency of oscillation used by Everett in calculating the vibration entropy, viz. $10^{11}-10^{12}$ sec^{-1}, we must conclude, however, that this remark holds good only if the heat of adsorption is very low, as for example for argon on graphite (approx. 2 kcal/mole).

In only a few of the cases dealt with in this study could it be concluded that the adsorbed layer is in an immobile localized state, as in the adsorption of nitrogen on Ni-B5 sites and in the chemisorption of nitrogen on iron at low coverages. Since in such cases theory predicts a large entropy drop, which has been observed experimentally as well, here the conclusion seems to be unassailable. Given that at extremely low coverage carbon monoxide on alumina undergoes an entropy drop corresponding to the theoretical value for total immobility, it follows that even if the heat of adsorption is no more than 8 kcal/mole, the immobility may be complete. Consequently the contribution claimed by Everett for the vibration entropy cannot be large.

Thomas (1961) criticized the application of de Boer and Kruyer's method in the case of chemisorption. He states that in all adsorption studies entropy changes due to surface-structure changes in the adsorbent itself must be considered along with the entropy changes of the adsorbate. In physical adsorption the contribution of the first of these two entropy changes to the total entropy change is always likely to be insignificant compared to that of the second. In chemisorption, however, there is ample evidence that the entropy change due to surface-structure changes contributes significantly to the total entropy of adsorption.

We doubt this latter point, maintaining that during chemisorption the bond between surface and subsurface layer will be weakened, but not broken completely. The bonds between surface and subsurface layer are still so strong that the relating vibrations hardly can yield a considerable entropy gain.

VIII   References

Andreev, A. A. and Selwood, P. W. (1967). *J. Catalysis* **8**, 98.
Beeck, O., Smith, A. E. and Wheeler, A. (1941). *Proc. R. Soc.* **A177**, 62.
Benson, S. W. (1960). "The Foundations of Chemical Kinetics". McGraw-Hill, New York, Toronto, London.
de Boer, J. H. (1952). "The Dynamic Character of Adsorption". Clarendon Press, Oxford.
de Boer, J. H. (1956). *In* "Advances in Catalysis" (W. C. Frankenburg, V. I. Komarewsky, E. K. Rideal, eds). Vol. 8, p. 19. Academic Press, New York and London.
de Boer, J. H. and Kruyer, S. (1952) *Proc. K. ned. Akad. Wet.* **B55**, 451.
de Boer, J. H. and Kruyer, S. (1953). *Proc. K. ned. Akad. Wet.* **B56**, 67, 236, 415.
de Boer, J. H. and Kruyer, S. (1954). *Proc. K. ned. Akad. Wet.* **B57**, 92.
de Boer, J. H. and Kruyer, S. (1955). *Proc. K. ned. Akad. Wet.* **B58**, 61.
de Boer, J. H. and Menon, P. G. (1962). *Proc. K. ned. Akad. Wet.* **B65**, 17.
Bokhoven, C. and Zwietering, P. (1956). *Chem. Weekbl.* **52**, 83.
Ehrlich, G. and Hudda, F. G. (1959). *J. chem. Phys.* **30**, 491.
Eischens, R. P. and Puskin, W. A. (1950). *In* "Advances in Catalysis" (W. C. Frankenburg, V. I. Komarewsky, E. K. Rideal, eds). Vol. 10, p. 2.
Eischens, R. P. and Jacknow, J. (1965). *Proc. 3rd Int. Congr. Catal.* p. 627. North Holland, Amsterdam.
Everett, D. H. (1950). *Trans. Faraday Soc.* **46**, 453, 942, 957.
Everett, D. H. (1967). *Proc. chem. Soc.* 38.
Gundry, P. M., Haber, J. and Tompkins, F. C. (1962). *J. Catalysis* **1**, 363.
Hickmott, T. W. and Ehrlich, G. (1958). *J. phys. Chem., Solids* **5**, 47.
Holm, V. C. F. and Blue, R. W. (1951). *Ind. Engng Chem. ind. Edn.* **43**, 501.
Horiuti, J. and Takezawa, N. (1961). *J. Res. Catalysis*, Hokkaido, **8**, 170.
Kemball, C. and Rideal, E. K. (1946). *Proc. R. Soc.* **A187**, 53.
Kemball, C. and Rideal, E. K. (1947). *Proc. R. Soc.* **A190**, 117.
Kokes, R. J. and Emmett, P. H. (1960). *J. Am. chem. Soc.* **82**, 1037.
Kruyer, S. (1955). Thesis, Delft University of Technology, The Netherlands.
Kummer, J. T. and Emmett, P. H. (1951). *J. chem. Phys.* **19**, 289.
McGeer, J. P. and Taylor, H. S. (1951). *J. Am. chem. Soc.* **73**, 2743.

Menon, P. G. (1962). Thesis, Delft University of Technology, The Netherlands.
Mignolet, J. C. P. (1950). *Discuss. Faraday Soc.* 8, 105, 326.
Reyerson, L. and Wertz, J. E. (1949). *J. phys. Colloid Chem.* 53, 234.
Schmidt, W. A. (1968). *Angew. Chem. int. Edn.* 7.
Scholten, J. J. F. (1959). Thesis, Delft University of Technology, The Netherlands.
Scholten, J. J. F. and Zwietering, P. (1957). *Trans. Faraday Soc.* 53, 1363.
Scholten, J. J. F. and Zwietering, P. (1961). *Actes 2e Congr. Int. Catal.*, p. 389. Edition Technip, Paris.
Scholten, J. J. F., Zwietering, P., Konvalinka, J. A. and de Boer, J. H. (1955). *Trans. Faraday Soc.* 55, 2166.
Schmidt, W. A. (1968). *Angew. Chem. int. Edn.* 7.
Schuit, G. C. A. and de Boer, J. H. (1954). *J. Chim. phys.* 51, 48.
Shvachko, V. J., Fogel, Ya. M. and Kolot, V. Ya. (1966). *Kinet. Catal.* 7, 734.
Suhrmann, R. and Schultz, K. (1955). *Z. Naturf.* 109, 517.
Tanaka, K., Yamamoto, O. and Matsuyama, A. (1965). *Proc. 3rd Int. Congr. Catal.* p. 676. North Holland, Amsterdam.
Thomas, J. M. (1961). *J. chem. Educ.* 38, 138.
Thomas, J. M. and Thomas, W. J. (1967). "Introduction to the Principles of Heterogeneous Catalysis". Academic Press, London and New York.
Trapnell, B. M. W. (1953). *Proc. R. Soc.* A218, 566.
van Hardeveld, R. (in press). *J. Catalysis.*
van Hardeveld, R. and van Montfoort, A. (1966). *Surf. Sci.* 4, 396.
Wagener, S. (1957). *J. phys. Chem.* 61, 267.
Weller, S. W. and Hindin, S. G. (1956). *J. phys. Chem.* 60, 1506.
Zwietering, P. (1960). Presented at the Gordon Conference on Catalysis, New Hampshire, U.S.A.
Zwietering, P. and Roukens, J. (1954). *Trans. Faraday Soc.* 50, 178.

Chapter 4

ACTIVE ALUMINA

B. C. Lippens

European Research Center, Texaco Belgium N.V., Ghent, Belgium

and

J. J. Steggerda

University of Nijmegen, The Netherlands

I Introduction

The study of alumina is a subject of great importance because alumina is a large-volume product on the chemical market. Although the major part of it is used in the production of aluminium metal, an increasing amount is employed in other fields, e.g. ceramics, abrasives, medicinals, adsorbents and catalysts. Products for the last two applications are generally called "active alumina" and are the subject of this chapter.

The adsorptive and catalytic properties of alumina have been studied for some time and by 1945 an impressive mass of empirical information about the preparation and properties of aluminas was available. Insight into the fundamental problems, however, was lacking almost completely. Many studies were devoted to developing reliable methods for the determination of "activity", which was found to differ considerably not only from the various known adsorptive or catalytic processes but also from the many natural and synthetic alumina products available. Some of these methods gained widespread practical use; for instance, the classification of active aluminas for chromatographic purposes according to Brockmann and Schodder (1941). This method, still used today, was perfected and given a more rational base by Fortuin (1955) and in recent years modified for use in thin layer chromatography (Hermanek et al., 1961).

At the same time much effort went into elucidating problems concerning the thermodynamic and mechanistic aspects of adsorption and catalysis on alumina. But the contradicting results of most of these studies must be due primarily to a lack of detailed information about the origin and thermal history of the active alumina used. The title of Frary's paper (1946), "Adventures with Alumina", conveys a good idea of the situation at that time. But when strong interest for the more fundamental problems began considerable knowledge was achieved, possible because of improvements in X-ray and electron diffraction and in infra-red spectroscopic techniques. The development of the theory of physical adsorption has further stimulated deeper analysis.

It was shown that the important variables for the adsorptive and catalytic activities such as crystal structure, pore texture and the chemical nature of the surface were largely determined by rather detailed points in the preparation of the alumina. The understanding of this correlation between method of preparation and such properties of the final product as crystalline structure, pore texture and surface constitution is the central theme of this chapter.

Active alumina is prepared mostly by a thermal dehydration procedure. Because the properties of the activated products are strongly related to the structure and the morphology of the initial hydroxides, we shall discuss the relevant properties of these hydroxides in some detail in Section II.

Two of the more striking results of recent research are the elucidation of the complicated dehydration mechanisms of the hydroxides and the identification of a great number of crystalline forms of alumina, many of which can occur in "active alumina". These topics are dealt with in Section III.

The methods of investigation of the porous texture of adsorbents and catalysts have improved considerably in recent years, as Linsen and Broekhoff reported in Chapter 1. The resulting detailed pictures of such geometrical aspects as form, dimension and texture of the pore system will be discussed in Section IV.

The structure and chemical properties of the alumina surface are dealt with in Section V. Although much is still unknown, recent studies, especially those using infra-red-spectroscopic data, have contributed to a better understanding.

This chapter does not pretend to present an exhaustive survey of the literature on the subject. On the basis of their research experience in this field the authors selected from the very extensive material only what seemed to them to be of actual interest.

II Aluminium Hydroxides

Various modifications of aluminium trihydroxide $Al(OH)_3$ are described in the literature, the most common being gibbsite (in German and French studies called hydrargillite), bayerite and nordstrandite. Aluminium-oxidehydroxide ($AlO(OH)$) is known in two modifications, diaspore and boehmite. We shall use these simpler terms in accord with the recommendations of the International Nomenclature Symposium in Münster (Ginsberg et al., 1957). Besides these crystalline phases, which are rather well-defined and thoroughly studied, a number of new hydrates are claimed in recent years. Tucanite, a crystalline phase of composition $Al_2O_3 . 3\frac{1}{2}H_2O$ found in nature and also made synthetic-ally (Karsulin, 1963) is maintained to be a new modification, character-ized by a strong X-ray reflection with a spacing of 8·66 Å. A hydrate $5Al_2O_3 . H_2O$ called tohdite was later shown to be a form of Al_2O_3, containing 0·16–0·20 mol of adsorbed water (Torkar and Krischner, 1966). New phases of $Al(OH)_3$ were further mentioned by Shimizu et al. (1964).

These new forms have been incompletely described up till now, and in the following discussion we shall deal only with gibbsite, bayerite, nordstrandite, diaspore and boehmite. The description of these modifi-cations will illustrate how minor distortions in these structures may give rise to new forms, characterized by slightly different X-ray diffraction patterns. The incorporation of interlamellar water may furthermore cause deviations from the compositions $Al_2O_3 . 3H_2O$ and $Al_2O_3 . H_2O$. So some of the above-mentioned new forms may be genuine, and more claims can be foreseen for the future. A survey of the most characteristic X-ray spacings of the hydroxides is given in Table I.

TABLE I. Most characteristic d-spacings of aluminium hydroxides

Gibbsite		Bayerite		Nordstrandite		Boehmite		Diaspore	
d	I	d	I	d	I	d	I	d	I
4·82	100	4·716	100	4·785	100	6·112	100	4·70	3
4·35	30	4·370	110	4·33	15	3·160	53	3·97	8
4·28	15			4·205	15	2·343	50	3·20	3
3·35	7			4·156	10	1·979	6	2·54	6
3·30	14			3·928	2	1·857	24	2·37	2
3·16	10	3·207	40	3·892	6	1·847	17	2·33	8
3·10	5	2·708	5	3·184	10	1·768	8	2·32	6
2·455	20	2·468	3			1·661	14	2·12	6
2·410	6	2·361	7			1·526	9	2·08	4
2·378	25					1·452	14	2·06	10
2·284	4					1·435	7	1·90	2
2·239	8	2·224	140			1·430	7	1·81	3
2·160	11	2·160	3			1·410	1	1·72	2
2·079	0·5	2·078	3			1·402	3	1·71	3
2·043	19	1·986	4			1·382	9	1·67	2
1·988	13	1·974	2						
1·959	2	1·918	1·5						
1·913	10	1·841	2						
1·801	14	1·830	0·2						
1·748	14	1·770	0·5						
1·679	14	1·723	30						

A   Gibbsite

Gibbsite is the best known trihydroxide. It is the principal constituent of bauxites in North and South America. Technically it is the
most important because it is an intermediate for the production of
aluminium metal from bauxite (Bayer process). In this process a
concentrated sodium aluminate solution is slowly cooled in the presence
of crystal seeds. The gibbsite so obtained consists of almost spherical
crystal conglomerates which can be easily filtered. This procedure can
also be used for laboratory preparation (Sato, 1964).

In more suitable laboratory methods for the preparation of gibbsite
sodium aluminate solutions are neutralized with carbon dioxide.
For a successful result, a pure gibbsite product, the following reaction
scheme must be kept in mind (Oomes et al., 1961; Ginsberg, 1961 and
1962):

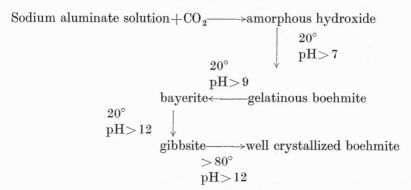

At temperatures above 20° the various transformations proceed at lower pH-values than indicated in the above diagram. The optimum conditions for the preparation of pure gibbsite are 40–60° and pH greater than 12. Below 40° gibbsite crystallizes in the form of hexagonal plates of about 1 μ diameter. At 60° and higher temperatures hexagonal rods of about $3 \times 3 \times 12\ \mu$ are obtained (Steggerda; 1955).

Natural and synthetic gibbsite has always been found to contain 0·2–0·3% Na_2O. Washing with dilute or even concentrated hydrochloric acid does not decrease the sodium content. Ginsberg et al. (1962) have reported the preparation of gibbsite to contain small amounts of K_2O instead of Na_2O. Although many authors state that alkali oxide is such an essential component of the gibbsite structure that without it gibbsite could not exist at all, this is not proven strictly. The experiments of Torkar and Krischner (1962) and those of Ginsberg et al. (1962), to prove that alkali is needed for the formation of gibbsite, can not be interpreted unequivocally, as the results can also prove that the transformation of bayerite into gibbsite needs a minimum pH to be of measurable speed.

The crystal structure of gibbsite, like those of bayerite and nordstrandite, is based on a double layer AB of closely-packed hydroxyl ions,* two-thirds of the octahedral holes being filled with Al-ions (Megan, 1934). As a consequence of the alternations of occupied and vacant octahedrons the lattice is somewhat deformed, the empty octahedrons being bigger, those filled being smaller. This leads to the structure of the double layers given schematically in Fig. 1 (Lippens, 1961).

The stacking of the double layers of gibbsite can be represented by

---

* In the following we shall use the term ion for the various constituents in the hydroxides and aluminas. This is done for the sake of convenience and does not pretend to describe the nature of the chemical bond in these compounds.

ABBAABBA etc. The double layers are kept together by hydrogen bonds between the OH-ions. The distance between two adjacent A or B layers is 2·81 Å compared with 2·03 Å as the distance between A and B. The real structure of gibbsite can be obtained by deforming the stacking in such a way that the double layers are displaced relative to each

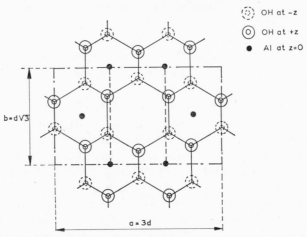

FIG. 1 Schematic representation of the structure of a trihydroxide double layer. Projection on (001) plane.

other over a short distance in the direction of the a-axis, so that OH⁻-ions of two different double layers come just above each other. This gives the monoclinic lattice. In gibbsite crystals from the Ural, Saalfeld (1960) observed triclinic crystals. In this modification the displacement of the stacking occurs in a different direction, giving a triclinic lattice. This direction is, however, crystallographically so similar to the a-axis, that the name gibbsite is still justified.

B Bayerite

Bayerite does not occur in nature but it can be made synthetically in different ways. It is often used as the starting material for the preparation of active alumina. As stated before, bayerite can be obtained as an intermediate during the preparation of gibbsite from aluminate solutions. It is, however, quite difficult to obtain pure bayerite in this way because it is usually contaminated with some boehmite, gibbsite and sodium oxide. Steggerda (1955) obtained a relatively pure product by bubbling carbon dioxide through a sodium aluminate solution at room temperature. By slightly modifying the experimental conditions of this method Sato (1962) got bayerites with different dehydration behaviour. A chemically very pure bayerite can be made by hydrolysing aluminium ethylate in water at temperatures below 70° (Torkar and Krischner, 1962). A simple method for the preparation of crystallographically pure bayerite has been given by Schmäh (1946). In this procedure amalgamated aluminium is oxidized by water at room temperature.

By treating precipitated gelatinous aluminium hydroxide with ammonia solutions products are obtained consisting for the greater part of bayerite. This procedure has been used by many investigators. Kraut et al. (1942) have shown that depending upon experimental conditions three distinct types of bayerite, viz. A, B and C could be obtained. Lippens (1961) has shown that this method is not suitable for the preparation of pure bayerite and that the three types mentioned by Kraut et al., are, respectively, nearly pure bayerite, bayerite and gibbsite, and bayerite and nordstrandite with possibly some gibbsite.

In contrast with gibbsite, bayerite can be made without any substantial amount of alkali. So there is no discussion about a possible stabilization of its structure by alkali oxide. The exact structure of bayerite is still not clear, X-ray work being difficult because no single crystals are available. The idea that bayerite is hexagonal, originally put forward by Montoro (1942) and later by Yamaguchi and Sakamoto (1958), has been questioned (Unmack, 1951; Lippens, 1961). Van Nordstrand et al. (1956) supposed bayerite to be a spiral-dislocation growth of gibbsite, parallel to the c-axis. Mostly recently Bezjak and Jelenić (1963) have proposed a triclinic space group P1.

Although a detailed picture of its structure can not be given at the moment, there is no doubt that bayerite is built in much the same manner as gibbsite. Double layers of hydroxyl ions with two-thirds of the octahedral voids filled with aluminium ions are stacked most probably as ABABAB etc. The atoms of the third layer are consequently placed above those of the first layer, just as in the brucite lattice. Within a double layer the distance AB is 2·07 Å (in gibbsite 2·03 Å). The double layers are held together by hydrogen bonds between adjacent hydroxyl ions; between two double layers the distance AB is 2·64 Å (in gibbsite 2·81 Å). Due to the stacking of the double layers the smallest 0–0 distance between two adjacent double layers is larger in bayerite (3·13 Å) than in gibbsite (2·81 Å). The density of bayerite is 2·50 as compared with 2·43 for gibbsite.

C Nordstrandite

Nordstrandite is named after van Nordstrand, who reported the preparation of this new form of $Al(OH)_3$ (van Nordstrand et al., 1956).

Since then it has been discovered to occur naturally in Serawa and Guam (Wall *et al.*, 1962; Hathaway and Schlanger, 1962 and 1965). Many authors have reported nordstrandite in mixtures with other hydroxide modifications. In recent years, however, some methods have been worked out to yield pure nordstrandite. In all of these methods gelatinous hydroxide is converted into nordstrandite by ageing in the presence of chelating agents, viz. ethylenediamine, ethyleneglycol and EDTA, under conditions which in the absence of these reagents would yield bayerite.

If the gel, obtained by adding ammonia to a solution of aluminium nitrate is suspended in a 70% ethylenediamine solution and this mixture is kept for 60 days at 58°, after filtration, washing with water and drying at 105° a pure nordstrandite is obtained (Hauschild, 1963).

Pure nordstrandite can also be obtained by Schmäh's method with amalgamated aluminium. If ethylenediamine is added to the water, nordstrandite is obtained instead of bayerite (Hauschild, 1963).

Hydrolysis of aluminium butoxide with 20% aqueous ethylene glycol and ageing the product at 60° in its mother liquor yields pure nordstrandite (Aldcroft and Bye, 1967). If the gel, obtained by adding ammonia to an aluminium nitrate solution is aged in a EDTA solution for 40 days at room temperature, nordstrandite is obtained (Benes *et al.*, 1966).

The exact determination of the crystal structure of nordstrandite has not been accomplished up till now. The Debye-Scherrer diagrams given by different investigators differ in minor details. Lippens (1961) assumed nordstrandite, like gibbsite and bayerite, to consist of double layers of hydroxyl ions, with aluminium in two-thirds of the octahedral holes. The stacking of the double layers could be ABABBABA, which is a combination of the stacking in bayerite and gibbsite. This is confirmed by infra-red spectra and by the general chemical resemblance of these hydroxides (Aldcroft and Bye, 1967). Recently Saalfeld and Mehrotra (1966) discussed X-ray data of a natural single crystal of nordstrandite. Their results fit a triclinic unit cell containing only a gibbsite stacking, which, however, is not identical with the triclinic form of gibbsite reported by Saalfeld (1960).

D Diaspore

Well-crystallized diaspore occurs in nature in some types of clay and bauxite. Laubengayer and Weisz (1943), Ervin and Osborn (1951) and Osborn and Roy (1952) have shown that between 275° and 425° and a water vapour pressure above 140 atm. all hydroxides and oxides are converted into diaspore, when a seeding of this form is present. Torkar and Krischner (1960c) have made diaspore without seeding by the hydrothermal conversion of active α-Al_2O_3 at 370–450° and 60–100 atm. water pressure. This active α-Al_2O_3 could be prepared by autoclaving metallic aluminium with water at 320–450°C and 14–100 atm. pressure. However, the preparations along this line were not always successful: sometimes boehmite was formed instead of diaspore.

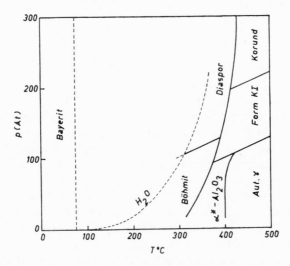

FIG. 2 The phase diagram of the system Al_2O_3—H_2O according to Torkar and Krischner (1963).

In Fig. 2 the most recent version of the phase diagram Al_2O_3—H_2O is given (Torkar and Krischner, 1963). This diagram should not be considered to be an equilibrium phase diagram; it is merely a schematic review of the products that can be obtained at different conditions of temperature and pressure. Questions concerning the thermodynamic stability of the various phases are not definitely settled at the moment. The success or the failure of a certain set of experimental conditions in the synthesis of one of the phases is very much dependent on kinetic factors, e.g. the rate of the hydrothermal formation of diaspore and corundum increases at higher pH (Yalman et al., 1960).

Although diaspore can be an interesting material for the preparations of α-Al_2O_3, it is so difficult to prepare that no application has been found so far. The structure of diaspore shall be dealt with in the next section.

E Boehmite

In the discussion of boehmite clear distinction should be made between well-crystallized boehmite and gelatinous boehmite, sometimes also called pseudo-boehmite. Well-crystallized boehmite can be made under hydrothermal conditions. It is the end product of the ageing of aluminium hydroxide gel at $pH > 12$ and $80°$ (Oomes et al., 1961). Gelatinous boehmite is the principal constituent of European bauxites. It can be prepared in various ways.

If solutions of aluminium salts are neutralized with ammonia, bulky amorphous precipitates containing large amounts of water and anions are formed. In contact with the mother liquor or with ammoniacal solutions this primary precipitate is transformed into a product, which gives an X-ray diffraction pattern of broad bands with spacings similar to the most intensive lines of well-crystallized boehmite. The product has a very extensive surface area and a water content of $1·3–1·8$ moles H_2O per mole Al_2O_3. It is usually called gelatinous boehmite or pseudo-boehmite. When the contact with the alkaline solution is too long, partial conversion into bayerite may occur. For detailed information of the experimental procedure the reader is referred to the original literature (Weiser et al., 1940 and 1952; Kraut, 1942). The morphology of these gels has been studied (Souza Santos et al., 1953; Moscou and van der Vlies, 1959; Lippens, 1961).

If amalgamated aluminium is oxidized with boiling water, boehmite is formed (Fricke and Jockers, 1947). If the pH of the water is lowered by bubbling carbon dioxide through the water, gelatinous boehmite can also be made at room temperature (Steggerda, 1955). By autoclaving solutions of basic aluminium salts under prescribed conditions of concentration, time and temperature (Bugosh, 1959), boehmite is formed. It consists of discrete, relatively uniform fibrils about 50 Å in diameter and 1000 Å long in the form of loosely-associated porous aggregates (Iler, 1961). The product, however, is impure, containing considerable amounts of anions.

Like the trihydroxides, the structures of the oxidehydroxides are closely related. The structure of diaspore has been determined by using natural single crystals. No boehmite crystals of sufficient size for single crystal X-ray diffraction are available. The corresponding iron compounds goethite and lepidocrocite are isomorphous with diaspore and boehmite respectively. This fact was used by Milligan and McAtee (1956) to estimate the structure of boehmite.

Neglecting H atoms, diaspore consists essentially of close-packed O atoms with Al atoms in certain of the octahedral holes. It may be regarded as being built up of infinite strips of the brucite type, linked up by sharing O atoms at the corners of AlO_6-octahedra. In boehmite the Al atoms are surrounded by a distorted octahedral group of O atoms, and these octahedral groups are linked together to form a complex layer structure. For instructive diagrams of the structure of diaspore and boehmite the reader is referred to Ewing's figures (Wells, 1962).

Van Oosterhout (1960) produced an easy method to describe the structures of the corresponding iron compounds, which we can use for the aluminium compounds. In the direction of the a-axis there are HO—Al—O chains schematically shown in Figs 3a and 3b. Two of

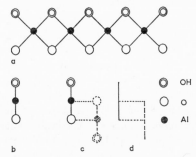

FIG. 3 (a) AlOOH chain; (b) Side view of AlOOH chain; (c) Side view of two antiparallel AlOOH chains; (d) Schematic representation of Fig. 7c.

these chains can be placed in an anti-parallel position to each other in such a way that the O atoms of the second chain are at the same level as the Al atoms of the first chain (Fig. 3c). Thus we obtain a kind of polymer double molecule

$$
\begin{array}{c}
\text{H} \\
\text{O} \\
| \\
\left(\begin{array}{cc} \text{Al} - \text{O} \\ | \quad\quad | \\ \text{O} - \text{Al} \end{array} \right)_n \\
| \\
\text{O} \\
\text{H}
\end{array}
$$

schematized in Fig. 3d. The chains give both modifications a repetition distance of 2·85Å in the direction of the a-axis. The difference between the two modifications is due to a different arrangement of the double molecules. In Figs 4a and 4b this is shown schematically: in both cases the *a*-axis is perpendicular to the plane of the drawing. The cleavage plane, indicated by *s*, is given by the position of the hydrogen bonds, just as in the case of the trihydroxides.

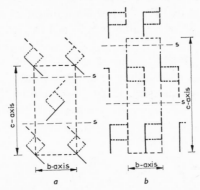

FIG. 4 Schematic representation of the crystal structures of (*a*) diaspore and (*b*) boehmite.

Infra-red (Jungmann *et al.*, 1963), nuclear magnetic resonance (Holm *et al.*, 1958) and selected area electron diffraction (Lippens, 1961) experiments indicate that the H-bond in boehmite is not symmetric and that the symmetry of boehmite is lower than generally accepted on the basis of X-ray evidence. Bezjak and Jelenić (1963) have started a new X-ray diffraction study of boehmite in order to settle some controversial points in the earlier studies.

For a description of the structure of gelatinous boehmite it is necessary to discuss the aging of an aluminium hydroxide gel in contact with an alkaline solution. In Table II (Lippens, 1966) the surface area,

TABLE II. Aging of aluminium hydroxide in contact with an ammoniacal solution of pH = 9 at 30° (Lippens, 1966)

Aging time hours	g H_2O per 100 g Al_2O_3	g SO_3 per 100 g Al_2O_3	Surface area m²/g Al_2O_3	X-ray pattern
0	81·3	23·2	<1	amorphous
1	40·2	13·1	12	gelatinous boehmite
44	27·8	4·0	201	*ibid.*
166	26·7	3·5	230	*ibid.*
290	26·2	3·0	242	*ibid.*+some bayerite
3 weeks	32·7	2·1	192	*ibid.*+bayerite
6 weeks	48·6	0·8	75	nearly pure bayerite
10 weeks	51·4	0·3	34	bayerite

the water content and the sulphate content are given as functions of the aging time for an aluminium sulphate solution precipitated with ammonia, kept at pH 9 and 30°. The initial amorphous material consists of spherical particles of 20–50 Å diameter, loosely aggregated to bigger units. Although the surface area should be large, it is, however, not accessible to nitrogen, so no BET surface can be measured. Per particle 10–20 SO_4-groups are present. During aging fibrils are formed in the aggregates, with a diameter about the same as those of the original spheres and with a length of some 100 Å. These fibrils give the X-ray pattern of gelatinous boehmite: strongly broadened diffraction lines, the tops of which almost coincide with the strongest lines of well-crystallized boehmite. The spacings of the (002) and the (103) reflections, however, are shifted with regard to well-crystallized boehmite. During the growing process, SO_4-groups located at the surface of the original spheres, are expelled. The gelatinous boehmite made in this way has a surface area of some 300 m^2/g and a water content appreciably higher than that of AlOOH. On the basis of the infra-red spectra of gelatinous boehmite Imelik *et al.* (1954) and Glemser and Rieck (1955, 1956) concluded that this extra water was not present as free water molecules but bonded with strong H bonds.

TABLE III. Recrystallization of gelatinous boehmite

Treatment	Moles H_2O per mole Al_2O_3	Spacing (002) refl.	c-axis Å*	Surface area m^2/g
fresh	1·74	6·70	13·02	490
24 h 20°	1·60	6·58	12·86	440
6 h 50°	1·50	6·51	12·82	395
6 h 120°	1·42	6·36	12·64	300
6 h 150°	1·36	6·31	12·58	255
6 h 170°	1·28	6·28	12·52	201
6 h 250°	1·12	6·16	12·30	64
24 h 250°	1·02	6·12	12·24	2·5

* After correction for continuous factors.

The study of the recrystallization of boehmite (Lippens, 1961 and 1966) provides further information on the nature of the differences between gelatinous and well-crystallized boehmite. By treating gelatinous boehmite with water at various temperatures, products were obtained with different water contents and surface areas, and with different shifts of the (002) reflection. The results are summarized in Table III and in Fig. 5.

In Fig. 5 the linear relation between the water content and the c-axis is demonstrated. By the uptake of 1 mole H_2O/mole Al_2O_3 above the stoichiometric composition of AlOOH the c-axis increases with 1·2 Å. The water containing silicates like vermiculite also shows such a relation between the length of one of the axes and the water content. In these cases the water enclosed between the silicate layers of the lattice can be expelled by heating, giving a simultaneous decrease of the interlayer distance. In the case of the silicates this process

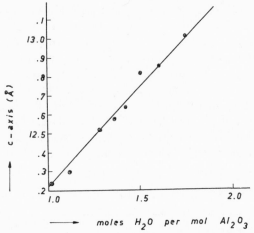

FIG. 5 The aging of gelatinous boehmite. The relation between water content and c-axis.

is reversible: by rehydration of the heated products water is again taken up and the original interlayer distance is restored. The changes in the c-axis of gelatinous boehmite, on the contrary, are irreversible. We assume that the extra water in the gelatinous boehmite is bound with strong H bridges between the layers of the boehmite. The extension of the lattice by this extra interlamellar water is irregular; the separate boehmite layers are stacked imperfectly. This model explains the shift in the 002 reflections as well as its breadth.

Jungmann et al. (1963) determined in the nuclear magnetic resonance spectrum of boehmite two lines, a broad component (5·3 gauss) and a narrow one (<0·2 gauss). The latter one disappears on prolonged evacuation at 100°, when the surplus water is removed. The broad resonance line does not change, which would mean that the basic structure of boehmite did not change appreciably with the removal of the extra water, in this respect resembling zeolitic water.

In contact with alkaline solutions the conversion of gelatinous into well-crystallized boehmite proceeds via bayerite and gibbsite. Considering the similarity between the two types of boehmite, this aging sequence is a puzzling phenomenon.

III The Formation and the Crystal Structure of Active Aluminas

A Classification of Aluminas

In studies of aluminas a great number of compounds are referred to as "aluminium oxide", although they often contain a relatively large amount of other compounds, such as water and alkali oxides or alkaline earth oxides. In order to distinguish among all of these "aluminium oxides" a number of letters of the Greek alphabet, extended with accents and asterisks were used. Some of these compounds fall outside the scope of this chapter, e.g. the alkali or alkaline earth oxides containing β-aluminium oxides, the lithium oxide containing ζ-oxide and the compounds obtained as films on aluminium by heating in air or by anodic oxidation (λ, μ, ν, ξ', ξ, ψ, ψ'). A survey of these is given by Newsome et al. (1960). We shall also exclude the form "autoclave γ", KI and KII prepared by Torkar and Krischner (1960a), as these forms have been investigated less completely.

The first more or less systematic classification of the aluminas was proposed by a group of European investigators at a symposium in Münster (Ginsberg et al., 1957). This classification, later modified by Lippens (1961), is based on the temperature at which the aluminas were obtained from the hydroxides:

(a) Low-temperature aluminas: $Al_2O_3 \cdot nH_2O$ in which $0 < n < 0.6$; obtained by dehydrating at temperatures not exceeding 600°C (called γ-group)

(b) high-temperature aluminas: nearly anhydrous Al_2O_3, obtained at temperatures between 900 and 1000°C (called δ-group).

To group (a) belong: ρ, χ, η- and γ-alumina, and to group (b) belong: κ, θ and δ-alumina.

Recently, Krischner (1966) proposed a classification based upon a more profound knowledge of the crystallographic structures of the aluminas. As these structures are all based on a more or less close-packed oxygen lattice with aluminium ions in the octahedral and tetrahedral interstices, Krischner distinguished three series, viz.:

α-series with hexagonal close-packed lattices, schematically ABAB,

β-series with alternating close-packed lattices, schematically ABAC-ABAC or ABAC-CABA,

γ-series with cubic close-packed lattices, schematically ABCABC.

The only representative of the α-series is α-Al_2O_3, either in the form of the stable corundum or as the decomposition product of diaspore. The β-series consists primarily of the alkali or alkaline earth oxides containing β-alumina and the decomposition products of gibbsite (χ and κ-alumina) which, according to Saalfeld (1960), have a related structure. The forms KI and KII (Torkar and Krischner, 1960a) probably belong to the same series. The γ-series consists of the decomposition products of the hydroxides bayerite, nordstrandite and boehmite and can be divided into a γ- or low-temperature group (η- and γ-alumina) and a δ- or high-temperature group (δ and θ-alumina). Some fully amorphous aluminas (e.g. ρ-alumina) may belong to this group as well, though there is no definite proof that these have a close-packed oxygen lattice.

In the following we shall use the first mentioned classification.

B   Characterization of the Aluminas by X-Ray Powder Diagrams

Table IV gives the X-ray powder data of the various forms of alumina. It should be kept in mind, however, that this list of spacings will give only a very limited picture of the X-ray diffraction pattern. As most of the aluminas are poorly crystallized, the lines are usually broadened. For a good characterization the line profiles must be taken into account.

A sharp distinction between different types of alumina is even more complicated when dealing with mixtures, which is normally the case. For instance, the dehydration of gibbsite in a high vacuum yields ρ-alumina, characterized by a single broad band at 1·40 Å, but some crystalline boehmite will be formed too. On further heating this boehmite decomposes to γ-alumina, which has also a strong diffraction band at 1·40 Å, thus preventing the further observation of ρ-alumina.

The diffraction patterns of γ- and η-alumina, which are very similar, differ in the following points:

(a) the 1·98 Å band is doubled in the case of γ, whereas that of η has only an asymmetric profile;

(b) the 4·6 Å band of γ is very broad, while that of η is sharp with a broadened base.

Kral (1966) tried to further distinguish γ and η by the difference between the ratios of the heights of the 2·40 Å and 2·28 Å peaks (which in fact indicate differences in line broadening, because the integrated intensities are equal), but with limited success. Especially in the case of very poorly crystallized material criterium (a) cannot be used because of the excessive line broadening of the γ-alumina. Differentiation between γ and η in this case can be made only with criterium (b).

TABLE IV. X-ray d-spacings and relative intensities of aluminas

$\chi(1)$ d	I	$\gamma(2)$ d	I	$\eta(2)$ d	I	$\kappa(3)$ d	I	$\delta(2)$ d	I	$\theta(2)$ d	I	$\alpha(4)$ d	I
								7·6	2				
						6·15	5	6·4	2				
								5·53	2	5·47	5		
								5·10	5	5·06	3		
4·46	m	4·6	12	4·57	16	4·50	5	4·57	8	4·57	10		
								4·07	8	4·00	3		
								3·61	2				
						3·16	5	3·23	2			3·479	74
						3·06	12	3·05	2				
						2·813	20	2·881	5	2·859	60		
		2·77	25	2·76	33			2·728	20	2·731	100		
						2·585	40	2·601	15			2·551	92
								2·460	40	2·462	80		
2·41	m	2·397	60	2·395	70	2·404	25	2·402	10			2·379	42
						2·321	15	2·315	5	2·314	40		
2·24	m	2·284	33	2·284	36			2·279	25	2·264	30		
2·12	s					2·127	30	2·160	3			2·165	<1
		1·990 } 65						1·986	50	2·028	80	2·085	100
1·96	ss	1·956 }		1·980	70			1·953	25			1·964	1
								1·914	8	1·913	40		
						1·877	10						
						1·834	5	1·827	3				
								1·810	5	1·800	5		
						1·753	5					1·739	43
						1·642	12	1·628	5				
								1·604	3			1·601	81
								1·538	5	1·538	20	1·546	3
		1·520	15	1·519	16			1·517	10			1·514	4
												1·511	7
										1·484	20		
						1·455	8	1·456	5	1·456	20		
						1·439	25			1·429	10		
								1·407	35	1·407	30	1·404	32
1·39	ss	1·407 } 100		1·396	100	1·395	45	1·396	65	1·392	100		
		1·395 }											
												1·373	48

(1) = Saalfeld (1960).
(2) = Lippens (1961); and Lippens and de Boer (1964b).
(3) = Tertian and Papée (1958).
(4) = Newnham and de Haan (1962).

The diagrams of δ- and θ-alumina consist of a great number of fairly sharp lines, many of which coincide. The most characteristic differences are:

(a) The different ratio of intensities between the 2·73 Å and 2·0 Å lines, which is greater for θ-alumina;

(b) the splitting of the 2·0 Å group of lines, which is double for θ (2·03 and 1·91 Å) and threefold for δ-alumina (1·99, 1·95 and 1·91 Å).

Here too, it will be clear that in the case of mixtures, particularly when some γ- or η-alumina is also present, differentiation will be difficult.

C   Dehydration Reactions

The aluminas are usually obtained by dehydration of the various hydroxides. Much controversy exists about the dehydration sequences, even in recent papers (e.g. Beretka and Ridge, 1967). Apart from the difficulties in characterizing the forms obtained, most of the confusion arises from insufficient information concerning the reaction conditions.

The work of Ervin and Osborn (1951) and of Torkar and Krischner (1960b; 1962) gives some idea of the phase diagram of the system aluminium oxide/water (see Fig. 2), but as mentioned in Section IID, such a diagram is of only limited use in predicting dehydration products, because kinetic factors are very important and true thermodynamic equilibrium is seldom reached. For instance, the stable modification at moderate water vapour pressure at a temperature of about 150°C is most probably boehmite, but it takes a very long time and hydro-thermal conditions to convert gibbsite completely into boehmite. As a consequence, gibbsite heated in air will decompose into a low-tempera-ture alumina (χ). Nevertheless, some boehmite usually is formed as well, because hydrothermal conditions exist in the interior of the particles (de Boer et al., 1954). This intragranular formation of boehmite will proceed till the increasing water vapour pressure creates a porosity reaching the outer surface of the granules. This explains why the particle size and the crystallinity of the hydroxide as well as such heating conditions as water vapour pressure and the speed of heating up, must be considered in observing the dehydration phenomena under a certain set of experimental conditions.

A   The Dehydration of the Trihydroxides

The dehydration of gibbsite in air or nitrogen gives a sequence of products different from that of bayerite or nordstrandite. As both the crystallinity and the particle size of gibbsite usually are much greater than those of bayerite and nordstrandite, up to 25% boehmite can be formed in gibbsite under the intragranular hydrothermal conditions, whereas in bayerite and nordstrandite usually less than 5% will be formed. However, very fine powders of bayerite (de Boer et al., 1954; Steggerda, 1955) and gibbsite (Tertian and Papée, 1958) do not form any boehmite at all.

The dehydration sequences in air can be represented as follows:

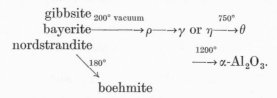

$$\text{gibbsite}\xrightarrow{250°}\chi\xrightarrow{900°}\kappa\xrightarrow{1200°}\alpha\text{-Al}_2\text{O}_3$$

$$\xrightarrow{180°}$$

$$\text{boehmite}\xrightarrow{450°}\gamma$$

$$\xrightarrow{180°}$$

$$\left.\begin{array}{l}\text{bayerite}\\ \text{nordstrandite}\end{array}\right\}\xrightarrow{230°}\eta\xrightarrow{850°}\theta\xrightarrow{1200°}\alpha\text{-Al}_2\text{O}_3.$$

In a vacuum the three trihydroxides decompose at low temperatures into an almost completely amorphous product (ρ-alumina), which at higher temperatures changes into γ- or η-alumina and further into θ-alumina.

$$\left.\begin{array}{l}\text{gibbsite}\\ \text{bayerite}\\ \text{nordstrandite}\end{array}\right\}\xrightarrow{200° \text{ vacuum}}\rho\xrightarrow{}\gamma \text{ or } \eta\xrightarrow{750°}\theta$$

$$\searrow 180° \qquad\qquad \xrightarrow{1200°}\alpha\text{-Al}_2\text{O}_3.$$

$$\text{boehmite}$$

ρ-alumina has the remarkable property that it will react with water to form bayerite, independent of the original trihydroxide from which it was obtained (Tertian and Papée, 1958).

B   The Dehydration of the Oxide Hydroxides

Diaspore is the only aluminium hydroxide that decomposes directly to α-Al$_2$O$_3$ (Deflandre, 1932), which initially shows line-broadening and high surface area, but soon recrystallizes:

$$\text{diaspore}\xrightarrow{450°}\alpha\text{-Al}_2\text{O}_3.$$

Although the α-Al$_2$O$_3$ is generally considered to be the most inert of all the oxides, Torkar and Krischner (1960c) showed that when made from aluminium metal at moderate water vapour pressures, an "active α-Al$_2$O$_3$" is formed that can be transformed into pure diaspore under hydrothermal conditions.

The dehydration sequence of boehmite depends on its crystallinity. Well-crystallized boehmite (crystal sizes $>1\,\mu$) decomposes according to:

$$\text{well-crystallized boehmite}\xrightarrow{450°}\gamma\xrightarrow{600°}\delta\xrightarrow{1050°}$$

$$\xrightarrow{1200°}\theta(+\alpha)\xrightarrow{}\alpha\text{-Al}_2\text{O}_3 \text{ (Lippens, 1961).}$$

The δ-region is strongly dependent on impurities and on the crystallinity of the boehmite. Traces of sodium favour the formation of θ, whilst Li and Mg stabilize δ-alumina and can even prevent the formation of θ. If the boehmite is less crystalline, the formation of δ is retarded and sometimes not observed at all.

Gelatinous boehmite (sometimes called pseudo-boehmite) decomposes at about 300°C into an alumina for which a doubling of the 1·98 Å and 1·4 Å diffraction no longer can be observed, due to the strong line broadening. For this reason, many authors refer to this form as a η-alumina. However, as the 4·6 Å band is extremely broad and does not show any sign of a sharp peak, we prefer to call it a γ-alumina. Due to the poor crystallinity of the pseudo-boehmite, formation of δ-alumina is observed hardly or not at all. Thus the dehydration scheme is:

$$\text{gelatinous boehmite (pseudo-boehmite)} \xrightarrow{300°} \gamma$$

$$\xrightarrow{900° \quad 1000°} \delta \xrightarrow{\quad} \theta + \alpha \xrightarrow{1200°} \alpha\text{-Al}_2\text{O}_3.$$

D   The Structure of the Aluminas

A   The Structure of γ- and η-Alumina

There is a little doubt that both γ- and η-alumina have a lattice closely related to that of spinel (MgAl_2O_4). The unit cell of spinel is formed by a cubic close packing of 32 oxygen atoms with 16 aluminium atoms in half of the octahedral interstices and eight magnesium atoms in tetrahedral holes. In γ-alumina only $21\frac{1}{3}$ Al-atoms have to be distributed over these 24 cation positions. Verwey (1935) deduced that the unit cell of γ-alumina has two and two-thirds vacancies on the octahedral positions and that eight aluminium atoms are distributed over the tetrahedral holes, corresponding with the notation Al_8 $[\text{Al}_{13\frac{1}{3}}\square 2\frac{2}{3}]\text{O}_{32}$. Jagodszinski and Saalfeld (1958) found by studying mixed crystals of spinel and γ-alumina that the two and two-thirds vacant cation positions in γ-alumina are probably octahedral positions, although Saalfeld (1960) is of opinion that in the γ-alumina obtained from boehmite, occupation of tetrahedral sites will occur hardly at all.

The doubling of the (400) and the (440) reflections in the powder pattern of γ-alumina clearly indicates that the spinel lattice is tetragonally deformed. η-alumina is often regarded as a cubic spinel; however, the asymmetric profile of the (400) band and selected area diffraction of single crystals show that a tetragonal deformation may exist here as well (Lippens, 1961). Yamaguchi and Yanagida (1962) showed that the tetragonal character of γ- and η-alumina increases with the water content.

The occurrence of sharp and diffuse lines in the diagrams of γ- and η-alumina (van Nordstrand, 1956) indicates that the lattices are strongly disordered. Lippens and de Boer (1964b) applied the selected area electron diffraction technique to the dehydration products of single crystals of bayerite and boehmite. They showed that the differences between γ- and η-alumina should be considered to be differences in the type of disorder and that these could be attributed to pseudo-morphosis relations between the hydroxides and the oxides. These pseudo-morphosis relations are summarized in Table V.

TABLE V. Pseudo-morphosis relations between some aluminium hydroxides and their dehydration products

Transforma-tion	Hydroxide		Alumina		Per cent shrink
	axis	d in Å	axis	d in Å	
bayerite→η	a	$8\cdot68 = 3\times2\cdot89$	$[01\bar{1}]$	$5\cdot58 = 2\times2\cdot79$	$-3\cdot3$
	b	$5\cdot06$	$[\bar{2}22]$	$3\cdot24 = \frac{2}{3}\times4\cdot86$	$-3\cdot9$
	c	$4\cdot72$	$[111]$	$4\cdot57$	$-52*$
boehmite→γ	a	$2\cdot85$	$[110]$	$5\cdot63 = 2\times2\cdot81$	$-1\cdot2$
	b	$3\cdot69$	$[001]$	$7\cdot82 = 2\times3\cdot91$	$+6\cdot0$
	c	$12\cdot24$	$[1\bar{1}0]$	$5\cdot63$	$-31*$
gibbsite→χ	a	$8\cdot64 = 3\times2\cdot88$	b	$5\cdot56 = 2\times2\cdot78$	$-3\cdot5$
	b	$5\cdot06$	a	$9\cdot64 = 2\times4\cdot82$	$-4\cdot8$
	$d(001)$	$9\cdot69$	c	$13\cdot44 = 3\times4\cdot48$	$-54*$

* Calculating the change of lattice dimension in this direction (perpendicular to the cleavage plane) the loss of OH-groups during the dehydration has been accounted for.

During the dehydration of bayerite to η-alumina the close-packed oxygen layers, which are parallel to the cleavage plane of bayerite, become the [111] plane of the spinel. Bayerite has a hexagonal close-packed stacking (ABAB . . .) whereas the spinel has a cubic close-packed stacking (ABCABC . . .). Moreover, half of the oxygen atoms have to disappear during dehydration. Cowley and Rees (1958) showed that under such conditions this will result in a one-dimensionally disordered stacking giving rise to abnormal reflections in single-crystal patterns (Jagodszinski and Laves, 1948). These were actually found by Lippens and de Boer (1964). Also the peculiar shape of many of the X-ray diffraction bands (sharp top and extra-diffuse base) could be explained in this way.

For boehmite the cleavage plane is parallel to an array of parallel rows of oxygen atoms. During dehydration this array remains in the spinel. Lippens (1961) showed that these parallel rows can only be stacked in one way (CDCD . . .) to form a cubic close-packed lattice. Consequently the oxygen lattice of γ-alumina should be fairly well ordered. In fact, this was found with single-crystal electron diffraction studies (Lippens and de Boer, 1964b; Saalfeld and Mehrotra, 1965). The reflections of γ-alumina in which the oxygen lattice plays a dominant role were sharp while the others were broad, especially those which came from aluminium atoms in tetrahedral interstices. Consequently, the disorder in the γ-alumina is determined mainly by disorder of the aluminium atoms, and especially those in tetrahedral positions. Saalfeld and Mehrotra (1965) determined the cation distribution by Fourier synthesis of the electron diffraction patterns and found that the octahedral aluminium sublattice was fully occupied and that the necessary vacant sites were randomly distributed over the tetrahedral interstices.

B   The Structure of δ- and θ-Alumina

There is some controversy about the X-ray pattern of δ-alumina. The data given by Rooksby and Rooymans (1961) differ from those given by Lippens (1961) and by Tertian and Papée (1958). The unit cell dimension calculated from the various data are accordingly somewhat different (see Table VI). It should be kept in mind that

TABLE VI. Unit cell dimension of δ-alumina

Authors	$a = b$ in Å	c in Å	c/a
Lippens (1961); Lippens and de Boer (1964)	7·94	23·50	2·96
Tertian and Papée (1958)	7·97	23·47	2·95
Rooksby and Rooymans (1961)	7·96	11·70	1·47

Rooksby and Rooymans prepared their δ-alumina by quenching vaporized or molten aluminium compounds at high temperatures whereas the other authors obtained their products by heating well-crystallized boehmite. Electron diffraction patterns of δ-alumina obtained from boehmite single crystals clearly show a long c-axis of 23·5 Å. δ-alumina has a lattice, which can be regarded as a super-structure of three Al_2O_3-spinel cells containing an integer number of aluminium atoms. The vacant positions probably are ordered on a fourfold screw axis parallel to the c-axis.

This long c-axis of δ-alumina with fairly well-ordered vacant cation positions may explain, why δ-alumina does not appear in the dehydration sequences of bayerite and of gelatinous boehmite (pseudo-boehmite). The [111] axis of η-alumina is the direction of the disorder in the stacking oxygen layers. This coincides with the c-axis of bayerite, so it is perpendicular to the cleavage plane of bayerite and to the plan parallel pore system after its dehydration (see Section IV B). The long c-axis of the δ-alumina should develop in a direction with an angle of about 35° to the [111] axis of η-alumina and consequently crosses the disordered oxygen layers and the pore system. Reorientation only will take place at such a high temperature that strong sintering occurs and θ-alumina will be formed instead of δ.

A similar explanation applies to the absence of δ-alumina in the dehydration sequence of pseudo-boehmite. The long c-axis is parallel to the b-axis of the original hydroxide. It has been shown (Lippens, 1961) that the pseudo-boehmite particles have short dimensions in the a- and b-direction (20–50 Å) so there is no possibility of formation of δ at relatively low temperatures. At high temperatures, when strong sintering occurs, the formation of θ is favoured.

The structure of θ-alumina is determined by Saalfeld (1960). It is monoclinic and isomorphous with β-Ga_2O_3, which structure is determined by Saalfeld (1960) and by Geller (1960). The lattice parameters are $a = 11\cdot24$ Å, $b = 5\cdot72$ Å, $c = 11\cdot74$ Å, $\beta = 103°\ 20'$. The oxygen lattice is still nearly cubic close-packed; the aluminium atoms are for the greater part in tetrahedral positions. Saalfeld (1960) is of the opinion that θ-alumina has still a true pseudo-morphism to the original spinel structure, which in the thermal history persists even to corundum. Lippens and de Boer (1964b), however, concluded from electron microscope observations that only preferred orientation (morphological relicts) exists after the transformation of δ- or η- to θ-alumina, and even less going to α-Al_2O_3.

C The Structures of χ- and κ-Alumina

The partial transformation of gibbsite into boehmite, which gives its own dehydration products upon further heating, greatly complicates the interpretation of X-ray measurements for the structure of χ- and κ-alumina. Saalfeld (1960) found that χ-alumina, obtained from relatively large single crystals of gibbsite, has a hexagonal lattice with $a = 5\cdot56$ Å and $c = 13\cdot44$ Å. This lattice is nearly cubic (described

8

as a rhombohedral lattice with $a_r = 7\cdot85$ Å, $\alpha = 90\cdot40°$) but definitely with a trigonal deformation. As in the case of η-alumina there is a one-dimensional disorder in the stacking of the oxygen layers perpendicular to the c-axis. The disorder is much stronger for χ than for η-alumina.

κ-alumina has also a hexagonal lattice, with $a = 9\cdot71$ Å and $c = 17\cdot86$ Å (Saalfeld, 1960). The close-packed oxygen layers parallel to the cleavage plane of gibbsite are persistent through χ- and κ-alumina and probably also in α-Al_2O_3 obtained at higher temperature. The stacking of the oxygen layers is different in the various forms. In gibbsite the oxygen atoms on both sides of the cleavage plane are perpendicular above each other (stacking sequence ABBAABBA). In χ there is a strong disorder in the stacking. The stacking of the oxygen layers in κ-alumina is very much like that of mica and of the sodium containing β-alumina, with a stacking sequence ABAC-ABAC or ABAC-CABA (Krischner, 1966). Finally in corundum the true hexagonal stacking ABAB is obtained.

D   Some Concluding Remarks

The persistency of the oxygen lattice during dehydration suggests that cation displacement in the lattice is the most important mechanism for the formation of the different forms of Al_2O_3. It is remarkable that going from the hydroxide stage to the corundum stage, both of which have aluminium atoms only in octahedral interstices, stages are passed that have aluminium in tetrahedral positions. It is obvious that during the diffusion of the aluminium ions through the oxygen lattice in small regions a special ordering of the Al-ions may temporarily exist, which will be manifested in the electron diffraction patterns. Such patterns are indeed found by Cowley (1963) and Brindley (1961). Whether these patterns must be considered as belonging to new forms of alumina is doubtful.

IV   The Porous Texture of Aluminas

A   The Experimental Methods

Surface area, pore volume, pore shape and pore size are the most important quantities with which the porous texture of a substance can be described. In this section we will deal with these geometrical aspects; the chemical nature of the surface will be discussed in Section V.

Direct information on the porous texture could in principle be obtained by direct observation in an electron microscope. However, the very small quantity to be used, the necessary high vacuum and the changes produced by the strong impact of high voltage electrons limit the applicability of this method and usually only qualitative results can be obtained. Similar difficulties are experienced with other "direct viewing" methods, such as field emission microscope studies, which can only be used for some very special materials.

One of the most powerful approaches has been to gradually fill the pore system with an adsorbate. Theories which can be used for the interpretation of adsorption phenomena are discussed elsewhere in this book and will be used in the following sections.

Small-angle X-ray scattering has been used to study the particle size of the solids (Brindley and Nakahira, 1959). The broadening of X-ray diffraction lines can give information about crystallite size and lattice defects (Beretka and Ridge, 1967; Levy and Bauer, 1967). Optical methods have been used with success to study the orientation of the pore system (Steggerda, 1955; de Boer et al., 1956).

None of the methods mentioned here will in itself give an unequivocal description of the porous texture; only a combination together with X-ray and electron diffraction methods discussed in the preceding section finally will develop a reasonably reliable picture.

B   Nitrogen Adsorption on Aluminas

A   Aluminas from the Trihydroxides

Nitrogen adsorption isotherms of the dehydration products of the trihydroxides were extensively studied to learn about their porous texture (for gibbsite: Steggerda, 1955, de Boer et al., 1956; for bayerite: Lippens, 1961, de Boer and Lippens, 1964, Lippens and de Boer, 1964a; for nordstrandite: Aldcroft and Bye, 1967).

The crystalline trihydroxides have a low surface area and pore volume; the shape of the isotherms is in agreement with a picture of loosely-packed non-porous particles with sizes of a few microns. When heated to just below the temperature at which the formation of low-temperature alumina starts, the adsorption isotherm shows that pores are formed. In this temperature region some well-crystallized boehmite is formed under intragranular hydrothermal conditions. In the case of gibbsite, which gives the highest quantity of boehmite, these pores have been described as "ink bottle" type pores, with a large volume but narrow openings. In the case of bayerite and nordstrandite these pores, as well as being much less abundant, are more slit-shaped in character.

Heated just above their decomposition temperature (250° for gibbsite, 230° for bayerite and nordstrandite) the nitrogen adsorption at low relative pressures increases enormously. If the Brunauer, Emmett and Teller theory is used to calculate the surface area, values of up to 500 m²/g are obtained. From the adsorption-desorption isotherm it can be concluded that only a small part of this surface area is present in pores wider than 20 Å. The rest of the adsorbed nitrogen is present in a micropore system, which we shall discuss later on. On further heating sintering results in a decrease of the total surface area.

When heated at a much higher temperature (above about 550°) the shape of the adsorption isotherms changes drastically. The BET surface area drops to about half of its highest value and the calculation of surface area and pore volume from the desorption isotherms shows that the micropore volume decreases to a very low value.

When a single crystal of gibbsite is dehydrated, the resulting product is optically birefringent, due to the pronounced texture of its pore system. The sign of birefringence, which can be determined under a polarizing microscope, changes when the dehydration temperature of the gibbsite crystal increases. At low temperature the birefringence is due to a system of plan parallel pores, parallel to the cleavage plane of the original gibbsite. These plan parallel pores form the micropore system, which disappears gradually by sintering at higher temperatures. Then an orientation of rod-like pores is dominant for the optical behaviour. These pores are all parallel and lie in the original cleavage plane (Steggerda, 1955; de Boer *et al.*, 1956). From electron microscope observations, Lippens (1961) came to a similar conclusion for bayerite.

B   Aluminas from the Crystalline Oxidehydroxides

On dehydration, the two crystalline oxidehydroxides boehmite and diaspore behave similarly with regard to the evolution of their surface area. Decomposition starts only at 400°. The formation of surface area is less dramatic than for the trihydroxides; the BET surface area has at about 500°C its maximum value of 90–100 m²/g. However, this BET surface area has no real significance because it applies to a micropore volume. Above about 550°C this micropore volume disappears, decreasing the BET surface area to 15–20 m²/g. Unlike the phenomena with the trihydroxides, the nitrogen isotherms do not show any appreciable change in type of pores. Even after heating well-crystallized boehmite to 750°C the pore system still retains the character of slit-shaped pores between plan parallel plates (Lippens, 1961; Lippens and de Boer, 1964). Density measurements show that after sintering at higher temperatures a part of the pore system is no longer accessible for the imbibition liquids (water and ethanol).

Various reasons can be found to explain the behaviour difference between the trihydroxides and the oxidehydroxides. Sasvári and Zalai (1957) and Lippens and de Boer (1964b) pointed to the differences in OH—OH distance across the cleavage plane for the various hydroxides. In boehmite this is much shorter than in bayerite. Dehydration would occur by interaction of two OH-groups at opposite sides of the cleavage plane in boehmite; in bayerite at the same side. Moreover, as already concluded from X-ray and electron diffraction observations, the oxygen layers of dehydrated boehmite fit much better than those of dehydrated bayerite.

C Aluminas from Gelatinous and Microcrystalline Boehmite

In general, the specific surface area of the different boehmites increases with decreasing crystallinity. On the other hand, dehydration produces a smaller increase in surface area the less crystalline the material is and eventually turns into a decrease of surface area for poor crystalline and gelatinous products (see Table VII).

TABLE VII. The surface area of boehmites of different crystallinity and of their dehydration products

| | Surface area in m^2/gram Al_2O_3 | | |
Type of boehmite	dried at 120°	dehydrated at 500°	increase
well-crystallized	1·3	65·3	+64
microcrystalline	64	100	+36
microcrystalline	68	99	+31
microcrystalline	100	101	+1
microcrystalline	201	180	−21
microcrystalline	255	208	−47
gelatinous	395	257	−138
gelatinous	490	316	−174
gelatinous	609	398	−211

In the case of gelatinous products the loss of surface area (expressed in m^2 per gram of Al_2O_3 in the sample) is almost completely due to the loss of water, causing a shrinkage of the particles. No new internal pores are formed, nor do the particles sinter together to any appreciable extent. In crystalline material the quantity of new pores produced by dehydration depends on the crystallinity of the original hydroxide.

The adsorption isotherms of the gelatinous products are of the mixed types A and E, which indicates pore systems consisting of the space between loosely-packed particles. The same type of pore is found in the unheated microcrystalline boehmites, but when heated the isotherms clearly form new pores.

C The Application of the t-method

The isotherms of the various aluminas were the first ones to which the Lippens-de Boer t-method was applied (Lippens and de Boer, 1965). This method is based on the experimental fact that, when dealing with

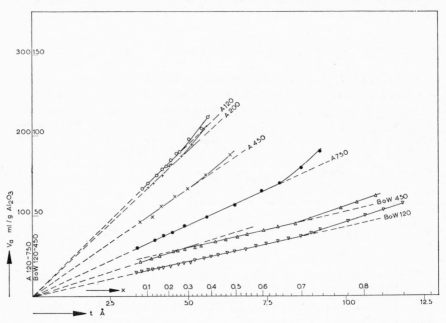

FIG. 6 V_a-t plots for gelatinous (A) and microcrystalline (BoW) boehmite, heated at various temperatures (the number in the code gives this preheating temperature) x = relative N_2-pressure.

multimolecular adsorption the adsorbed volume per unit surface area as a function of the relative pressure of the adsorbate can be represented by a single curve independent of the adsorbent. Necessary conditions for this to be valid are: no capillary condensation, no hindered adsorption in narrow pores and relative pressures higher than that required for a nearly filled monolayer. The adsorbed volume per unit surface area in fact represents the average or statistical thickness t of the adsorbed multilayer, hence the name t-curve for this function.

If the adsorbed volume (V_a in cm³/g) on a special adsorbent is plotted, not as a function of relative pressure, but as a function of the

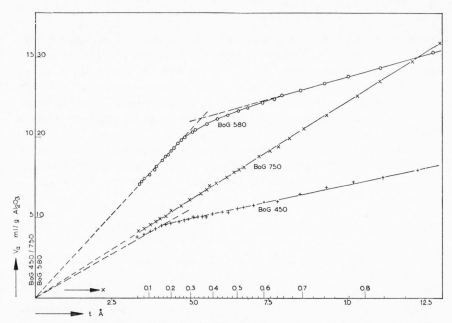

FIG. 7 V_a-t plots for well-crystallized boehmite, preheated at various temperatures (the preheating temperature is indicated by the number of the code) x = relative N_2-pressure.

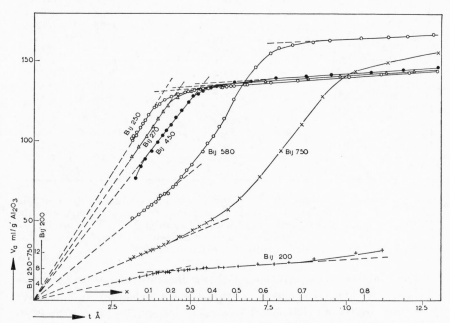

FIG. 8 V_a-t plots for bayerite, preheated at various temperatures (the preheating temperature is indicated by the number of the code) x = relative N_2 pressure.

corresponding t-value of the standard curve, a straight line going through the origin will be obtained in the case of unhindered, purely multimolecular adsorption. The slope will be a direct measure for the total surface area (S_t). If capillary condensation occurs this will be shown by an increase of the slope. Filling of narrow pores, which then will be inaccessible for further nitrogen adsorption, will be apparent from a decrease of the slope.

Typical examples of t-plots for various aluminas are shown in Figs 6, 7 and 8. They quantitatively confirm the qualitative conclusions from the adsorption isotherms. The numerical results are collected in Table VIII.

TABLE VIII. The surface area calculated with the BET equation and from the V_a-t plot for various alumina samples

Sample code		S	S_t	S_w	S_n	p/po at the beginning of capillary condensation	hysteresis
A	120	609	586	586	—	0·26	0·40
A	200	580	568	568	—	0·26	0·40
A	450	414	409	409	—	0·34	0·51
A	750	280	275	275	—	0·63	0·63
BoW	120	64·0	65·6	65·6	—	0·70	0·76
BoW	450	92·1	93·5	68·0	25·5	0·70	0·40
BoG	450	17·1	17·2	5·1	12·1	> 0·86	0·46
BoG	580	65·7	65·0	17·2	47·8	> 0·86	0·44
BoG	750	19·1	19·1	19·1	—	> 0·86	0·48
By	200	26·5	26·6	8·7	17·9	0·70	0·47
By	250	489	483	20·1	463	> 0·86	0·46
By	270	462	440	20·6	419	> 0·86	0·47
By	450	414	386	21·5	364	> 0·86	0·48
By	580	245	343	343	—	0·24	0·42
By	750	134	127	127	—	0·24	0·46

A = gelatinous boehmite, BoW = microcrystalline boehmite, BoG = well-crystallized boehmite, By = bayerite, the numbers in the coding apply to the preheating temperature, surface area are given in m^2/g Al_2O_3, S = surface area calculated with BET method, S_t = surface area, from initial slope of V_a-t plot, S_w = surface area of wide pores from V_a-t plot, $S_n = S_t-S_w$.

The samples obtained from gelatinous boehmite A120 to A450 (see Table VIII) show the onset of capillary condensation at a relative pressure lower than that corresponding to the beginning of hysteresis. This can be due to the presence of cones and wedges at the contact points of the particles, where reversible capillary condensation can take place (as was already pointed out by de Boer *et al.*, 1962). Heated to 750°C, noticeable sintering has already occurred (sample A750) and the sharp edges are rounded off; consequently, the onset of capillary condensation coincides now with the beginning of the hysteresis loop.

For many of the aluminas from the crystalline hydroxides (bayerite and boehmite) the *t*-plots show an appreciable amount of narrow pores (micropores) which are already completely filled with nitrogen at low relative pressures. The remaining surface area (in the wider pores) can be calculated easily from the slope of the V_a-t plot. This surface area S_w belongs to pores in which capillary condensation will start only at high relative pressures, whereas capillary evaporation occurs at a relative pressure of below 0·5. This points to either "ink bottle" type pores (wide pores with narrow openings) with pore openings of about 25 Å, or to slit-shaped pores with plan parallel walls and a wall distance of about 25 Å. Lippens (1961) calculated the average size of these wide pores from their pore volume and surface area. For dehydrated bayerite and well-crystallized boehmite samples this average was found to be about 22 Å. Thus it can be concluded that the pores are in fact slit-shaped. Only a small percentage of the pores have a much wider size, but these can exist only in some of the larger-sized particles. In coarse crystalline gibbsite de Boer *et al.* (1956) showed that these wide pores are much more abundant and are probably formed during the intragranular hydrothermal formation of boehmite.

D The Micropore Volume

In the preceding section it was shown that the crystalline hydroxides, heated just above their decomposition temperature, contain an appreciable micropore volume. That this micropore volume has a real existence could be shown by adsorption of lauric acid from pentane solution. If the pores of alumina are so wide that the surface is freely accessible 0·617 mmole of lauric acid can be adsorbed per 100 m² of surface area (de Boer *et al.*, 1962). Assuming that this is the case in the wide pores, the lauric acid adsorption in the micropores can be calculated as the difference between the total lauric acid adsorption and the calculated adsorption in the wide pores.

The results are summarized in Table IX. The average ratio between the micropore volume (V_n) and the quantity of lauric acid adsorbed in it (LA_n) is 0·227 cm³/mmole. This corresponds to a density of 0·882 g/cm³ for the lauric acid in the micropore volume. Comparing this with the density of solid and liquid lauric acid (0·883 and 0·868 g/cm³

8*

respectively), it can be concluded that the lauric acid completely fills the micropore volume, thus demonstrating its real existence.

TABLE IX. Lauric acid adsorption in the micropore volume

Sample code	S_w	V_n	LA_t	LA_w	LA_n	V_n/LA_n
BoG 450	5·1	0·0051	0·055	0·032	0·023	0·22
BoG 580	17·2	0·0260	0·219	0·106	0·113	0·23
By 200	8·7	0·0075	0·082	0·054	0·028	0·27
By 250	20·1	0·1965	0·998	0·124	0·874	0·225
By 270	20·6	0·1972	0·994	0·127	0·867	0·227
By 450	21·5	0·1982	1·003	0·132	0·871	0·228

Sample code: BoG = well-crystallized boehmite, By = bayerite, the preheating temperature is indicated by the code number.

S_w = surface area in the wide pores in m^2/g Al_2O_3, V_n = micropore volume in cm^3/g Al_2O_3, LA_t = total lauric acid adsorption in mmole/g Al_2O_3, LA_w = calculated lauric acid adsorption in wide pores in mmole/g Al_2O_3, LA_n = lauric acid adsorption in micropore volume, $LA_n = LA_t - LA_w$.

The width of the micropores will be smaller than 20–25 Å, as otherwise normal capillary condensation would occur. The extrapolated

TABLE X. Texture data of dehydration products of bayerite and well-crystallized boehmite

Sample code	V_{spec}	S_n	V_n	$\bar{d}_n$	$\bar{D}_s$
BoG 450	0·361	12·1	0·0051	8·4	545
BoG 580	0·302	47·8	0·0260	10·9	127
By 200	0·598	17·9	0·0075	8·4	670
By 250	0·336	465	0·1965	8·5	14·5
By 270	0·312	419	0·1972	9·4	14·9
By 450	0·302	364	0·1982	10·9	16·6

Sample code: BoG = well-crystallized boehmite, By = bayerite, the preheating temperature is indicated by the code number. V_{spec} = specific volume in cm^3/g Al_2O_3, S_n = surface area in the micropore volume in m^2/g Al_2O_3, V_n = micropore volume in cm^3/g Al_2O_3, $\bar{d}_n$ = average width of the micropores in Å, $\bar{D}_s$ = average thickness of the solid lamellae between the pores.

t-plots go through the origin so it might be assumed that the adsorption of nitrogen takes place in a normal way till the pores are filled by an adsorbed layer. Considering the pronounced cleavage plane in the hydroxides, the micropores can be expected to be slit-shaped. Assuming that such a pore will be filled when the thickness of the adsorbed layer on both pore walls equals half of the pore width, and assuming that adsorption will occur the same way as on a free surface, it is possible to calculate the micropore volume V_n, the average width of the narrow pores $\bar{d}_n$, and, with the aid of the specific volume of the alumina (V_{spec}), the average thickness $\bar{D}_s$ of the solid lamellae between the pores (Lippens, 1961; de Boer et al., 1965). The results of such calculations are given in Table X. The extreme thinness (about 15 Å) of the lamellae in the bayerite dehydration products is remarkable. Even if it is not allowed to calculate $\bar{d}_n$ in this manner, due to the uncertain meaning of S_n, the absence of any capillary condensation shows that $\bar{d}_n$ certainly will be smaller than 20 to 25 Å, which implies that $\bar{D}_s$ will be smaller than 30 to 40 Å. This throws a somewhat different light on the crystallographic texture of η-alumina: the one-dimensionally disordered stacking of the oxygen layers is due to the presence of numerous parallel pores which separate the oxygen layers.

V   The Surface Structure of Alumina

So far we have discussed the crystalline structure and the geometrical aspects of the pore system of active aluminas. Now we must consider the chemical nature of the surface of alumina, as this is predominantly significant in its catalytic and adsorptive properties. The accumulated results of crystallographic, electron microscope and adsorption studies must be combined with or form the basis of the interpretation of the results of those experimental techniques which are considered to give a more or less direct picture of the nature of the surface.

Active alumina is not pure Al_2O_3 but contains, depending upon temperature and water vapour pressure, from a few tenths to about 5% water. We shall deal with the role of this water in detail in the following paragraphs. Depending on preparative conditions, other components may be present too, e.g. alkali oxide, iron oxide and sulphate. The influences of these impurities have been recognized. The presence of even minute amounts of Na_2O was found to decrease the catalytic effect of alumina on the dehydration of propanol and butanol (e.g. Steinike, 1965; Dzis'ko et al., 1966). Rubinshtein et al. (1966) found that the apparent adsorption of hydrogen on Al_2O_3 is connected not with chemisorption but with the reduction of the Fe_2O_3 present in traces in the alumina. The presence of sulphate or other anion is generally considered to increase the "acidic nature" of the alumina, which results in a better catalytic activity for certain types of reactions. Although the effect of these substances is caused by their presence in the surface of the active alumina, we shall not deal with them in further detail.

Active alumina adsorbs water, either as hydroxyl ions or as water molecules on the surface, depending upon the temperature. When exposed to water vapour at about room temperature alumina adsorbs water as undissociated molecules bonded with strong hydrogen bonds to the underlying surface. At higher water vapour pressures more water is bonded in a multilayer physical adsorption process, but this water can be removed easily in a drying procedure at about 120° (de Boer *et al.*, 1963). Peri and Hannan (1960) presented infra-red spectroscopic evidence for the occurrence of undissociated water molecules at low temperatures and showed that during heat drying water molecules not desorbed and removed from the system react to form surface hydroxyl groups. This reaction is completed at about 300°.

At higher temperatures these OH⁻-ions are gradually expelled as H_2O but even at 800–1000°C and vacuum some tenths of a per cent. of water are still retained in the alumina. This phenomenon has been widely studied and discussed. The heat of adsorption of water greatly depends upon the water content. At low surface coverage it is reported (Cornelius *et al.*, 1955) to exceed 100 kcal/mole, while near complete OH⁻ coverage it is only about 20 kcal/mole. From the data of the residual water content as a function of temperature it can be concluded that the free energy of activation for desorption continues to increase with increasing degree of dehydration up to at least 800°.

The OH⁻-ions on the surface of alumina behave as Brönsted-acid sites. When on dehydration two neighbouring OH⁻-ions combine to give water, an oxygen ion is left on the surface which in earlier studies was described as a strained oxygen bridge:

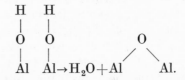

With a better understanding of the surface structure, the combination of two adjacent OH⁻-ions is now considered to leave behind an exposed Al-atom, which because of its electron-deficient character behaves as a Lewis acid site. The Brönsted and Lewis acid sites have always been looked upon as the active catalytic centres of alumina.

Many methods have been proposed for the determination of the amount and the acid strength of these sites, e.g. titration in benzene suspension with butylamine (Benesi, 1957) or with dioxane (Trambouze *et al.*, 1957). Interpretation of the experimental results is, however, difficult: the distinction between Brönsted and Lewis sites is rather obscure, and the adsorption of these rather big molecules can be restricted, as they cannot penetrate into the narrow pores often present in microporous samples. The adsorption of NH_3 from the gas phase is at present the most promising technique: the small dimensions of NH_3 give a minimum of steric hindrance even in the narrowest pores. Infra-red spectra of samples of alumina, on which NH_3 is adsorbed, provide information about the nature of the adsorptive sites (Peri, 1965c; Dunken *et al.*, 1966). A correlation between catalytic activity and "acidic character" is most straightforward when the "acidic character" is determined from the adsorption of NH_3 (Pohl and Rubentisch, 1966). Some results of these studies shall be dealt with later on.

In recent years the most important study of the alumina surface structure was made by Peri (Peri and Hannan, 1960; Peri, 1965a,b,c) using gravimetric and infra-red data as a guide and control in a computerized simulation of the dehydration. Although the sampling technique for his experimental work is rather complicated, and thus the thermal history as well as the crystallographic nature of the samples badly defined, the results can be considered more or less representative of the dehydration mechanism and the surface structure of alumina. Another serious limitation for the validity of Peri's model is the assumption that a spinel type alumina exposes only the (100) planes in the surface. Although strong evidence for this was given for the γ-Al_2O_3 formed by dehydration of crystalline boehmite (Lippens, 1961), significantly different situations may occur in other types of alumina. Especially for aluminas heated at high temperatures where sintering is considerable, the (111) plane of the spinel is from an energy point of view the most likely on the surface. Nevertheless, in view of the interest of Peri's approach, we shall give a short survey of its results.

On dry alumina, exposing a (100) plane, the top layer contains only oxide ions, as shown in Fig. 9*a*. At low temperatures a completely-filled monolayer of OH^--ions can be formed, giving a square lattice of OH^--ions, as represented in Fig. 9*b*. As in the (100) plane the surface of one oxide-ion is 7·9 Å^2, one water molecule is adsorbed (as two OH^--ions) on 16 Å^2 in the completely-filled monolayer. During dehydration adjacent OH^--ions are assumed to combine at random, but only two-thirds of the OH^--ions can be removed without disturbing local order (no two or more oxide ions are left on adjacent sites; no two or more adjacent sites are left vacant). Further dehydration requires the creation of oxide and/or vacancy disorder. Random removal of all hydroxyl pairs leave the surface as illustrated in Fig. 10. The remaining hydroxyl ions, covering about 10% of the surface, are found on five types of sites, having from zero to four nearest oxide neighbours

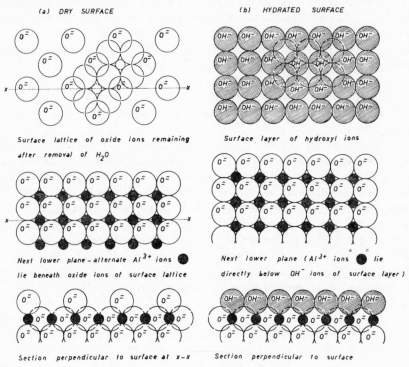

FIG. 9 Ideal (100) surface of the spinel-type alumina.

(see Fig. 10). The five isolated hydroxyl bands observed in infra-red spectra of heated alumina are assigned to stretching vibrations of these five types of sites. These five types of hydroxyl ion sites should vary in chemical properties, the A-site ions being the most basic and the C-site ions the most acidic. Peri has found such differences in chemical activity, e.g. in the rate of H–D exchange which is greatest for the C-sites. Carter et al. (1965) found, however, a different sequence of the rates for the various OH⁻-sites. Since the reasons for the difference between these two investigations are not clear, care should be taken in the interpretation of the experimental results.

Below a OH⁻-ion coverage of about 10% where no more adjacent

OH⁻-ion pairs are present, further dehydration is only possible when a
migration of surface ions is possible. Infra-red studies up to 800° indicate
that even at this temperature OH⁻-ions exist on distinct surface sites
and do not possess the mobility of a two-dimensional gas. But at this
high temperature protons migrate readily on the surface, and the gradual

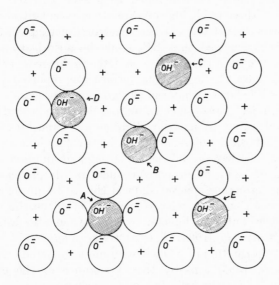

Fig. 10 Types of isolated hydroxyl ions (+denotes Al-ion in lower layer).

loss of surface area as well as the slow formation of high-temperature
forms of alumina indicate that also oxide and aluminium ion migration
occur. At this last stage of dehydration the number of defects on the
surface increases considerably, the major defects being two and three
directly adjacent vacancies and two and three directly adjacent oxide
ions.

In this model of the surface of alumina the "surface heterogenity"
is demonstrated clearly. Upon dehydration at increasing temperatures,
the Brönsted-acid sites, numerous at high water contents, are gradually
converted into Lewis-acid sites. In alumina, heated at about 600°
or higher, triple oxide vacancies occur which should be considered to
be easily-accessible, strong Lewis acid sites. The presence of these
various acid centres is clearly demonstrated by infra-red studies of
adsorbed NH_3 (Peri, 1965c; Dunken et al., 1966). The infra-red spectra
indicate the presence of NH_4^+, NH_3, NH_3^+ and NH_2^- bonded on Brönsted
sites, Lewis sites, very strong Lewis acid sites (triple vacancies) and

dissociatively adsorbed as NH_2^- en OH^- on adjacent acid-base sites respectively.

So far we have focused attention on the Brönsted and Lewis acid sites on the surface of alumina, which are generally considered to be the active centres for a great number of catalytic reactions. But from Peri's model it must be concluded that also pair and triple oxide defects (two or three oxide ions on directly adjacent sites) occur, which can be expected to behave as basic, electron-donating centres. Schwab and Kral (1965) showed that BF_3 could be adsorbed on alumina to an even greater extent than ammonia. Other evidence for this electron-donating character of the alumina surface was reported by Flockhart et al. (1965) who showed that the electron spin resonance spectrum of tetracyano ethylene, adsorbed on alumina, clearly indicated the presence of the radical anion. When the alumina was preheated above 500°, however, this radical anion could no longer be observed. At higher temperatures the electron-deficient character of alumina is dominant. When perylene was adsorbed on such highly-preheated samples electron spin resonance spectra showed this to be present as positive perylene ions. In contrast with tetracyano ethylene the perylene ion could, however, only be detected when oxygen also was present in the system (Scott et al., 1964). The reactivity of oxygen is demonstrated further by the formation of NO when alumina is heated in air (Parkyns and Patterson, 1965), and by the appearance of the characteristic infra-red bands of carbon dioxide when carbon monoxide is adsorbed on alumina.

Although we have now some sort of picture of the surface structure of active alumina, much work must be done. It is hoped that extending Peri's work to a great number of alumina samples, different in porous texture and crystallographic form, will also extend our knowledge. Moreover, the application of n.m.r. and e.s.r. techniques in the study of adsorbates on pure or doped alumina (van Reijen, 1964) might open new sources of information.

VI　References

Aldcroft, D. and Bye, G. C. (1967). Sci. Ceramics 3, 75.

Benes, L., Stoica, L., Nicolescu, A., Gruia, M. and Dardan, M. (1966). Rev. Roumaine Phys. 11, 489. (See Ceramic Abstr., 1966, 65, 17804.)

Benesi, H. A. (1957). J. phys. Chem., Ithaca. 61, 405.

Beretka, J. and Ridge, M. J. (1967). J. chem. Soc. A, 2106.

Bezjak, A. and Jelenić, I. (1963). Symp. bauxites, oxydes, hydroxydes Alumin. Zagreb. I, 105.

de Boer, J. H. (1958). *In* "The Structure and Properties of Porous Materials" (D. H. Everett and F. S. Stone, eds.), Butterworth, London.
de Boer, J. H. and Lippens, B. C. (1964). *J. Catalysis.* **3**, 38.
de Boer, J. H., Fortuin, J. M. H. and Steggerda, J. J. (1954). *Proc. K. ned. Akad. Wet.* **B57**, 170, 434.
de Boer, J. H., Steggerda, J. J. and Zwietering, P. (1956). *Proc. K. ned. Akad. Wet.* **B59**, 435.
de Boer, J. H., Houben, G. M. M., Lippens, B. C., Meys, W. H. and Walrave, W. K. A. (1962). *J. Catalysis.* **1**, 1.
de Boer, J. H., Fortuin, J. M. H., Lippens, B. C. and Meys, W. H. (1963). *J. Catalysis.* **2**, 1.
de Boer, J. H., Linsen, B. G., van der Plas, Th. and Zondervan, G. J. (1965). *J. Catalysis.* **4**, 649.
Brindley, G. W. (1961). *Am. Miner.* **46**, 771.
Brindley, G. W. and Ňakahira, M. (1959). *Z. Kristallogr.* **112**, 136.
Brockmånn, H. and Schodder, H. (1941). *Ber. dt. chem. Ges.* **24**, 73.
Bugosh, J. (1959). U.S. patent 2.915.475. (see *Ceramic abstr.*, April 1960, **39**, 99b.
Carter, J., Lucchesi, P., Corneil, P., Yates, D. J. C. and Sinfelt, J. H. (1965). *J. phys. Chem. Ithaca.* **69**, 3070.
Cornelius, E. B., Milliken, T. H., Mills, G. A. and Oblad, A. G. (1955). *J. phys. Chem., Ithaca.* **59**, 809.
Cowley, J. M. (1953). *Acta crystallogr.* **6**, 846.
Cowley, J. M. and Rees, A. L. G. (1958). *Rep. Prog. Phys.* **21**, 165.
Deflandre, M. (1932). *Bull. Soc. fr. Minér.* **55**, 140.
Dunken, H., Fink, P. and Pilz, E. (1966). *Chem. Technol.* **18**, 490.
Dzis'ko, V. A., Kolovertnova, M., Vinnikóva, T. S. and Bulgakova, Y. O. (1966). *Kinet. Katal.* **7**, 655.
Ervin, G. Jr. and Osborn, E. F. (1951). *J. Geol.* **59**, 381.
Flockhart, B. D., Naccacke, C., Scott, J. A. N. and Pink, R. C. (1965). *Chemy Comm.* 238.
Fortuin, J. M. H. (1955). Thesis, Delft University of Technology, The Netherlands.
Frary, F. (1946). *Ind. Engng Chem. analyt. Edn.* **38**, 129.
Fricke, R. and Jockers, K. (1947). *Z. Naturf.* **2**, 244.
Geller, S. (1960). *J. chem. Phys.* **33**, 676.
Ginsberg, H., Hüttig, W. and Strunk-Lichtenberg, G. (1957). *Z. anorg. allg. Chem.* **293**, 33, 204.
Ginsberg, H., Hüttig, W. and Stiehl, H. (1961). *Z. anorg. allg. Chem.* **309**, 233.
Ginsberg, H., Hüttig, W. and Stiehl, H. (1962). *Z. anorg. allg. Chem.* **318**, 238.
Glemser, O. and Rieck, G. (1955). *Angew. Chem.* **67**, 652.
Glemser, O. and Rieck, G. (1956). *Angew. Chem.* **68**, 182.
Hathaway, J. C. and Schlanger, S. O. (1962). *Nature, Lond.* **196**, 265.
Hathaway, J. C. and Schlanger, S. O. (1965). *Am. Miner.* **50**, 1029.
Hauschild, U. (1963). *Z. anorg. allg. Chem.* **324**, 15.
Hermanek, S., Schwarz, V. and Cekan, Z. (1961). *Colln. Czech. chem. Commun. Engl. Edn.* **26**, 3170.
Holm, C. H., Adams, C. R. and Ibers, J. A. (1958). *J. phys. Chem. Ithaca.* **62**, 922.
Iler, R. K. (1961). *J. Am. Ceram. Soc.* **44**, 618.
Imelik, B., Petitjean, M. and Prettre, M. (1954). *C. r. hebd. Séanc. Acad Sci. Paris* **238**, 900.
Jagodszinski, H. and Laves, F. (1948). *Schweiz. miner. petrogr. Mitt.* **28**, 456.

Jagodszinski, H. and Saalfeld, H. (1958). *Z. Kristallogr.* **110**, 197.

Jungmann, E., Klarić, K., Maricic, S. and Meić, Z. (1963). *Symp. bauxites, oxydes, hydroxydes Alumin.*, *Zagreb*. **I**, 137.

Karsulin, M. (1963). *Symp. bauxites, oxydes, hydroxydes Alumin.*, *Zagreb*. **II**, 37.

Kral, H. (1966). *Chemikerzeitung-chem. Appar.* **90**, 235.

Kraut, H. (1942). *Ber. dt. chem. Ges* **75**, 1359.

Kraut, H., Flake, E., Schmidt, W. A. and Volmer, H. (1942). *Ber. dt. chem. Ges* **75B**, 1357.

Krischner, H. (1966). *Ber. dt. keram. Ges.* **43**, 479.

Laubengayer, A. W. and Weisz, R. S. (1943). *J. Am. chem. Soc.* **65**, 247.

Levy, R. M. and Bauer, O. J. (1967). *J. Catalysis.* **9**, 76.

Lippens, B. C. (1961). "Structure and Texture of Aluminas", Thesis, Delft University of Technology, The Netherlands.

Lippens, B. C. (1966). *Chem. Weekbl.* **62**, 336.

Lippens, B. C. and de Boer, J. H. (1964a). *J. Catalysis.* **3**, 44.

Lippens, B. C. and de Boer, J. H. (1964b). *Acta crystallogr.* **17**, 1312.

Lippens, B. C. and de Boer, J. H. (1965). *J. Catalysis.* **4**, 319.

Megan, H. D. (1934). *Z. Kristallogr.* **A87**, 185.

Milligan, W. O. and McAtee, J. L. (1956). *J. phys. Chem. Ithaca.* **60**, 273.

Montoro, V. (1942). *Ricerca scient.* **13**, 565.

Moscou, L. and van der Vlies, G. (1959). *Kolloidzeitschrift.* **163**, 35.

Newnham, R. E. and de Haan, Y. M. (1962). *Z. Kristallogr.* **117**, 235.

Newsome, J. W., Heiser, H. W., Russel, A. S. and Stumpf, H. C. (1960). "Alumina Properties", Technical Paper 10b, Aluminium Company of America, Pittsburgh, Penn.

Oomes, L. E., de Boer, J. H. and Lippens, B. C. (1961). *In* "Reactivity of Solids" (J. H. de Boer, ed.), pp. 317–320. Elsevier, Amsterdam.

Osborn, E. F. and Roy, R. (1952). *Am. Miner.* **37**, 300.

Parkyns, N. D. (1967). *J. chem. Soc.* **A**, 1910.

Parkyns, N. D. and Patterson, B. C. (1965). *Chemy Comm.* 530.

Peri, J. B. (1965a). *J. phys. Chem.*, *Ithaca.* **69**, 211.

Peri, J. B. (1965b). *J. phys. Chem.*, *Ithaca.* **69**, 220.

Peri, J. B. (1965c). *J. phys. Chem.*, *Ithaca.* **69**, 231.

Peri, J. B. and Hannan, R. B. (1960). *J. phys. Chem.*, *Ithaca.* **64**, 1526.

Pohl, K. and Rubentisch, G. (1966). *Chem. Technol.* **18**, 496.

Rooksby, H. P. and Rooymans, C. J. M. (1961). *Clay Miner. Bull.* **4**, 234.

Rubinshtein, A. M., Slovetskaya, K. I., Brueva, T. R. and Federovskaya, E. A. (1966). *Dokl. Akad. Nauk. SSSR.* 167(6), 1308–10.

Saalfeld, H. (1960). *Neues Jb. Miner. Abh.* **95**, 1.

Saalfeld, H. and Mehrotra, B. B. (1965). *Ber. dt. keram. Ges.* **42**, 161.

Saalfeld, H. and Mehrotra, B. B. (1966). *Naturwissenschaften.* **53**, 128.

Sasvári, K. and Zalai, A. (1957). *Acta geol. hung.* **4**, 415.

Sato, T. (1962). *J. appl. Chem. Lond.* **12**, 553.

Sato, T. (1964). *J. appl. Chem. Lond.* **14**, 303.

Schmäh, H. (1946). *Z. Naturf.* **1**, 322.

Schwab, G. M. and Kral, H. (1965). *Proc. 3rd Congr. Catal.* Vol. 1, p. 433. North Holland, Amsterdam.

Scott, J. A. N., Flockhart, B. D. and Pink, R. C. (1964). *Proc. chem. Soc.* 139.

Shimizu, Y., Mitsui, N. and Funaki, K. (1964). *Kogyo Kagaku Zasshi.* **67**, 1190. (See *Ceramic Abstr.*, 1956, **63**, 1470.)

Souza Santos, P., Vallejo-Freire, A. and Souza Santos, H. L. (1953). *Kolloid Zeitschrift.* **133**, 101.

Steggerda J. J., (1955). Thesis, Delft University of Technology, The Netherlands.
Steinike, U., (1965). Z. anorg. allg. Chem. **338**, 78.
Tertian, R. and Papée, D. (1958). J. Chim. phys. **55**, 341.
Torkar, K. and Krischner, H. (1960a). Mh. Chem. **91**, 658.
Torkar, K. and Krischner, H., (1960b). Mh. Chem. **91**, 764.
Torkar, K. and Krischner, H. (1960c). Mh. Chem. **91**, 757.
Torkar, K. and Krischner, H. (1962). Ber. dt. keram. Ges. **39**, 131.
Torkar, K. and Krischner, H. (1963). Symp. bauxites, oxydes, hydroxydes Alumin. Zagreb. **I**, 25.
Torkar, K. and Krischner, H. (1966). Bull. chem. Soc. Japan. **39**, 1356.
Trambouze, Y., Perrin, M. and De Morgues, L. (1957). Adv. Catalysis. **9**, 44.
Unmack, A. (1951). Gen. Assembly int. Congr. int. Un. Crystallogr. Stockholm.
van Nordstrand, R. A. (1956). Proc. Symp. techniques catalyst Prep. Dallas, Texas, p. 43.
van Nordstrand, R. A., Hettinger, W. P. and Keith, C. D. (1956). Nature, Lond. **177**, 713.
van Oosterhout, G. W. (1960). Acta crystallogr. **13**, 932.
van Reijen, L. L. (1964). Thesis, University of Eindhoven, The Netherlands.
Verwey, E. J. W. (1935). Z. Kristallogr. **91**, 317.
Wall, J. R. D., Wolfenden, E. B., Beard, E. H. and Deans, T. (1962). Nature, Lond. **196**, 264.
Weiser, H. B. and Milligan, W. O. (1952). In "Advances in Colloid Science". Vol. 1. Interscience, New York.
Weiser, H. B., Milligan, W. O. and Purcell, W. R. (1940). Ind. Engng. Chem. analyt. Edn. **32**, 1487.
Wells, A. F. (1962). "Structural Inorganic Chemistry" (3rd ed.), p. 556. Oxford University Press, Oxford.
Yalman, R., Shaw, E. and Crown, J. (1960). J. phys. Chem. **64**, 300.
Yammaguchi, G. and Sakamoto, K. (1958). Bull. Chem. soc. Japan, **31**, 140.
Yamaguchi, G. and Yanagida, H. (1962). Bull. Chem. soc. Japan, **35**, 1896.

Chapter 5

POROUS SILICA

C. OKKERSE

Unilever Research Laboratory, Vlaardingen, The Netherlands

I Introduction

Porous silica* is one of the various forms of amorphous silica. Other forms are non-porous precipitates, silica hydrogels, pyrogenic materials like aerosil, the mineral opal, etc. These substances vary considerably in their appearance, hardness, and the degree of hydration, but they can all be considered as polycondensation products of orthosilicic acid, $Si(OH)_4$. The usual methods of preparation are precipitation with acids from silicate solutions (Vail, 1952) or hydrolysis of silicon derivatives such as silicon tetrachloride (Bartell and Fu, 1929) or

---

* This substance is often referred to as silica gel. To prevent confusion, we prefer to reserve the term "silica" for the dry material (xerogel) and to use "silica gel" for the product that has not yet been dried (hydrogel).

tetraethoxysilane, $Si(OC_2H_5)_4$. The pyrogenic silicas are mostly prepared by flame hydrolysis of silicon halides or by vaporization of silica.

This chapter will be concerned only with porous silica, although
much of it also applies to other forms of amorphous silica, especially
the discussion of the surface properties.

The discovery of silica is usually credited to Sir Thomas Graham
(1861), who prepared silica by dialysing dilute silica sols obtained by
mixing an aqueous solution of sodium silicate with hydrochloric acid.
Nowadays silica is manufactured commercially according to Patrick's
process, which consists essentially of gelation of an alkali metal silicate
by means of acid (White, 1959). Silica has found many applications:
as an adsorbent, a catalyst (e.g. for the oxidation of NO to NO_2), a
catalyst-carrier, and a filler. A new field of application of silica as a
selective adsorbent has been opened up by chemical modification of
the silica surface with organic substances. It has been found that the
surface hydroxyls can be replaced by ethoxy, phenyl, and other
organic groups (Iler and Pinckney, 1947; Kiselev and Kovaleva, 1959;
Deuel, 1959), and that this leads to pronounced changes in the adsorption properties. For example, a silica coated with ethoxy groups is
strongly water-repellent and organophilic, whereas normal silica is
sufficiently hydrophilic to be widely used as a drying agent.

A review of the state of knowledge in the field of silica up to 1955 has
been given by Iler (1955). Electron micrographs of silica show that the
physical structure can be described as a coherent aggregate of elementary particles of roughly spherical shape, with a diameter of the
order of 100 Å. The pore system within this aggregate is formed by the
open spaces between the elementary particles. The porous texture of
silica—as characterized by the specific surface area, the pore volume,
and the pores diameters—depends on the size and the packing of the
elementary particles. X-ray examination reveals that silica is not
crystalline. An elementary particle consists of an irregular three-
dimensional network of SiO_4 tetrahedra, each silicon atom being
linked to four oxygens and each oxygen being linked to two silicons.
At certain sites the elementary particles may be linked together by
Si—O—Si-bridges. The particle surface is covered with OH groups
which are responsible for the hydrophilic nature of normal silica.

The object of the present work is to survey the structure and texture
of porous silica and to explain the factors which contribute towards the
development of this structure during its preparation. The described
work is based mainly on investigations carried out under the guidance
of J. H. de Boer at the Delft University of Technology in the period
1956–62 (de Boer and Vleeskens, 1957, 1958; Vleeskens, 1959; Okkerse,

1961; Okkerse and de Boer, 1960a,b, 1962), and has been brought up to date by later publications in this field.

II Polycondensation of Silicic Acid

A Introduction

To understand the development of the porous structure of silica during its preparation it is necessary to examine first of all the poly-condensation of silicic acid. It is generally known that monomeric and polymeric silicic acid—formed, for instance, by neutralizing a solution of sodium metasilicate or water glass—can undergo a condensation reaction according to the scheme:

$$(HO)_3SiOH + HOSi(OH)_3 \rightarrow (HO)_3Si—O—Si(OH)_3 + H_2O$$

or, more generally:

$$(SiO_pH_q)_n—SiOH + HOSi——(SiO_rH_s)_m \rightarrow (SiO_pH_q)_n——Si—O—Si—(SiO_rH_s)_m + H_2O.$$

As a result of this condensation a macromolecular silicic acid is formed, which gradually grows into a polymeric or "elementary" particle of colloidal character. This particle consists of an irregular three-dimensional network of SiO_4 tetrahedra, each silicon atom being linked to four oxygen atoms and each oxygen to two silicons as already described. At sites where the condensation of OH groups has not yet taken place there will be silicon atoms that still carry one, two, or three OH groups. At a certain stage of the condensation gelation of the colloidal solution sets in, and finally a gel is produced. In the gelation stage condensation also takes place between the OH groups of different elementary particles. Carmen (1940) distinguished the pre-gelation stage from the gelation stage of the condensation reaction in the following way:

> In both stages the mechanism is the same, that is, condensation to form Si—O—Si links, but in the first stage condensation leads to particles of massive silica, while in the second, since it is not possible to fit two particles accurately together over a common face, the number of Si—O—Si linkages between particles is fewer in number than those within the particles themselves. They are merely sufficient to bind adjacent particles together, in a fixed position relative to one another. . . .

As long as the condensed polymeric particles are in colloidal solution or in the state of a (hydro-)gel, numerous water molecules are bound by the numerous OH groups of the structure. When this hydrogel is dried—during which process the condensation continues—a "xerogel" (porous silica) is obtained.

It has been known for a long time that the pH influences drastically the condensation of monosilicic acid. This appears, for example, from the variation of the gelling time of a silica sol with the pH of the sol (Okkerse, 1961; Okkerse and de Boer, 1960a,b, 1962) (see Fig. 1).

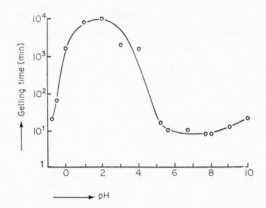

FIG. 1 Gelling time of a silica sol as a function of pH. SiO_2 concentration: 5% (pH 1–5, pH 8–10), $2\frac{1}{2}$% (pH 5–8).

The silica sols used in this investigation were prepared by the simultaneous addition of water glass and hydrochloric acid solution to water of pre-adjusted pH, in such a way that the pH of the liquid remained constant during the addition. It appears that in the region of pH about 2 the silica sols are most stable towards gelling, whereas below and above pH 2 the gelling time decreases. Above pH 8 the gelling time again begins to increase.

Linsen *et al.* (1960) and de Boer *et al.* (1960) investigated the condensation of silicic acid from a colloid-chemical point of view by means of viscosity and electrophoresis measurements. From the viscosity measurements on silica sols containing 0·5% SiO_2—prepared from sodium metasilicate—as a function of pH and time, it became clear that both the viscosity and the relative change of viscosity are minimal in the neighbourhood of pH 2 (Fig. 2).

The electrophoresis experiments showed that the particles in a 0·5% SiO_2 sol carry a positive charge at pH values lower than one and a negative charge at pH higher than 1·5. The isoelectric point of a 0·5% SiO_2 sol thus seems to be in between pH 1 and 1·5. In a similar way it was found that the isoelectric point of a 0·26% sol lies at about pH 2, so that the minimum in the viscosity curves seems to be related to the minimum charge on the sol particles. Since H^+ and OH^- ions are the potential-determining ions of silica sol particles, the observations of

Linsen *et al.* may indicate that the same ions—or the net charges that they produce—have a catalytic effect on the rate of condensation of silicic acid.

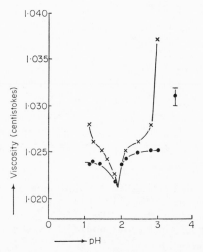

FIG. 2 Viscosity of 0·5% SiO_2 sols as a function of pH: (●) after 4 days, (×) after 13 days (after Linsen *et al.*, 1960). The vertical line indicates the spread of the viscosity values.

B Kinetic Measurements

To collect further evidence for the catalytic effect of H^+ and OH^- ions we investigated the condensation of silicic acid from the viewpoint of chemical kinetics (Okkerse, 1961; Okkerse and de Boer, 1960a,b, 1962). For this purpose the amount of low-molecular silicic acid present in silica sols (mainly monomeric+dimeric silicic acid = % lms) was determined as a function of the age of the sols (condensation time). The determination was carried out by means of a colorimetric method based on the formation of the yellow silicomolybdate complex. In the silica sols the pH, the initial SiO_2 concentration, and the salt concentration were varied. The results of these kinetic measurements are qualitatively in agreement with the results of the viscosity measurements reported by Linsen *et al.*: for each initial SiO_2 concentration the decrease of % lms with increasing condensation time appears to be smallest at about pH 2. By way of example, in Fig. 3 the % lms in 0·25% SiO_2 sols of various pH is shown as a function of the time of condensation. It may be seen that the rate of condensation is slowest at pH 2. This is revealed more clearly when profiles taken at fixed times of condensation are considered (Fig. 4).

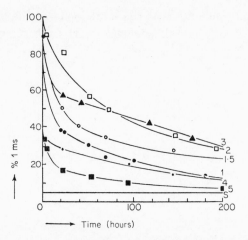

FIG. 3 Percentage low-molecular silicic acid (lms) in 0·25% SiO₂ sols as a function of the time of condensation. The pH's of the sols are indicated at the curves. S = solubility of silica (according to Iler (1955) S of amorphous silica at room temperature $\approx$ 120 mg/l which corresponds to 4·8% of a 0·25% SiO₂ sol).

Sols of other initial SiO_2 concentrations show an analogous behaviour; the maximum is always found between pH 2 and 3. No pronounced influence of the SiO_2 concentration or of the time of condensation on the position of the maximum could be detected, in contrast to Linsen's results.

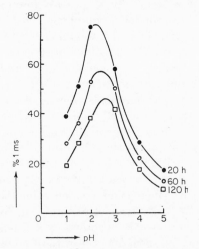

FIG. 4 Percentage low-molecular silicic acid (lms) in 0·25% SiO₂ sols as a function of pH at various times of condensation.

Systematic analysis of curves similar to those in Fig. 3 revealed that the rate of condensation is of second order on the concentration of low-molecular silicic acid at pH higher than two, and of third order at pH lower than two. The following rate equations were obtained from the experiments:

$$v = k_1[f(C_0)][H^+][C^3] \text{ at pH} < 2$$

and

$$v = k_h[f(C_0)][OH^-][C^2] \text{ at pH} > 2$$

where v = rate of condensation at time t, C = concentration of low-molecular silicic acid at time t, $C_0 = C$ at time $t = 0$.

C   Mechanism of the Reaction

The rate equations for the condensation in silica sols given in the previous section confirm in a more quantitative way what was already found qualitatively by Linsen *et al.*: the rate of condensation is minimal at about pH 2, increases linearly with the H^+ ion concentration at pH < 2, and with the OH^- ion concentration at pH > 2. Although we did not follow the condensation sufficiently long for the establishment of equilibrium between low-molecular and polymeric silicic acids, it can be concluded, for example, from Fig. 3 that the state of equilibrium is not affected by the pH. All curves approach the same final value corresponding to the solubility of amorphous silica in aqueous solutions at room temperature. Because the equilibrium does not depend on the pH, the influence of H^+ or of OH^- ions—or of the net charges that they produce—can be described as catalytic.

Baumann (1959) arrived at the same conclusion in his study of the condensation of monosilicic acid. Iler (1952) and Alexander (1954) explained the difference in the mechanism of the condensation in the two pH ranges by a catalytic effect of traces of fluorine at low pH and of OH^- ions at higher pH. There is no doubt about a catalytic effect of fluorine if the latter is added on purpose, but it seems very improbable indeed that the traces of fluorine present in sodium metasilicate would catalyse the condensation to the observed extent. Moreover, in the sodium metasilicate used by us we could not detect any traces of fluorine. According to our view, H^+ ions—or the positive charges that they produce—catalyse the condensation reaction at low pH.

On the basis of the experimental results the following mechanism was proposed (Okkerse, 1961; Okkerse and de Boer, 1960a,b, 1962) for the initial stage of the condensation: at pH < 2 there is a dynamic equilibrium between H^+ ions in the solution and OH groups on the surface of the silicate particles*:

$$\equiv\!Si-OH+H^+ \rightleftharpoons \equiv\!Si-\overset{+}{O}H_2.$$

Such a temporarily positively-charged site may attract an OH group of $Si(OH)_4$, and the following reaction may then occur:

$$\equiv\!Si-\overset{+}{O}H_2+HO-Si(OH)_3 \rightleftharpoons \equiv\!Si-\overset{+}{\underset{H}{O}}-Si(OH)_3+H_2O$$

whereupon the proton may be abstracted by an H_2O molecule. At $pH > 2$ the surface of the particles is covered with negatively-charged groups:

$$\equiv\!Si-OH+OH^- \rightleftharpoons \equiv\!Si-O^-+H_2O.$$

The negatively-charged particles may react with monosilicic acid in the following way:

$$\equiv\!Si-O^-+HO-Si(OH)_3 \rightleftharpoons \equiv\!Si-O-Si(OH)_3+HO^-$$

whereupon the OH^- ion may react with an H^+ ion, leading to the equilibrium required by the pH of the solution.

The proposed mechanism accounts for the existence of the isoelectric point and for the catalytic influence of electric charges on the condensation. Since the total quantity of charge is determined by the pH, the salt concentration, and apparently by the sol concentration, it is a constant for a given sol. Consequently, the H^+ or OH^- ion concentration and the sol concentration appear as time-independent quantities in the rate equations.

The above mechanism does not explain the different kinetics of the condensation at $pH > 2$ and at $pH < 2$. The different kinetics and their order might be explained by assuming a temporary change of the coordination number of silicon from four to six.† Furthermore, the logical assumption must be made that, especially at the beginning, the rate of condensation of low-molecular silicic acid with silicic acids of higher molecular weight is small with respect to the rate of condensation of low-molecular silicic acids with one another.

At pH values below two, the positive particle formed from silicic

---

† An alternative expression is that silicic acid acts as a Brönsted base at $pH < 2$ and as a Brönsted acid at $pH > 2$.

† It is well known that silicon may have a coordination number of six, for example in the ion SiF_6^{2-}. Since an OH^- ion is about as large as an F^- ion, it seems logical to assume that silicon can also be surrounded by six OH groups.

acid by taking up a H^+ ion may, by its attraction of two OH^- groups of two different molecules of silicic acid (by which the coordination number increases from four to six) facilitate the formation of the following "activated complex":

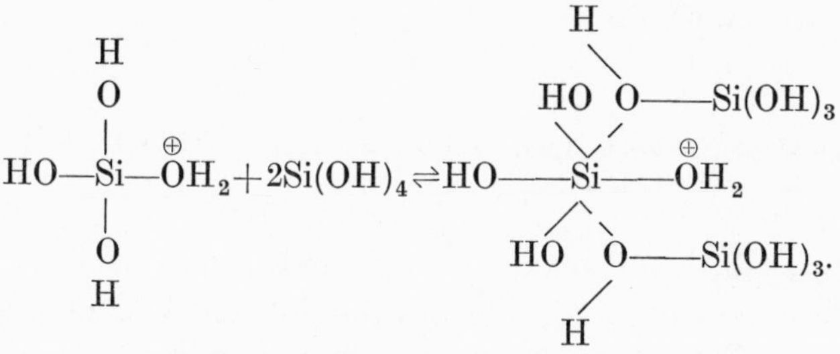

$$
\begin{array}{ll}
\text{H} & \\
\text{O} & \\
| \quad \oplus & \\
\text{HO—Si—OH}_2 + 2\text{Si(OH)}_4 \rightleftharpoons & \text{HO——Si——OH}_2 \\
| & \\
\text{O} & \\
\text{H} &
\end{array}
$$

In this complex the positive charge may be thought to be on the H_2O molecule or on the two HO—$Si(OH)_3$ molecules; the two limiting structures may both be written as:

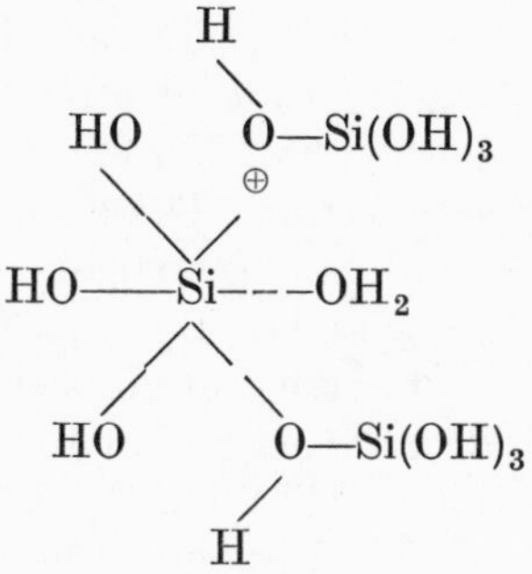

$$
\begin{array}{c}
\text{H} \\
\backslash \\
\text{HO} \qquad \text{O—Si(OH)}_3 \\
\backslash \quad \oplus \\
\text{HO——Si---OH}_2 \\
\diagup \quad \backslash \\
\text{HO} \qquad \text{O—Si(OH)}_3 \\
\diagup \\
\text{H}
\end{array}
$$

which may disintegrate into

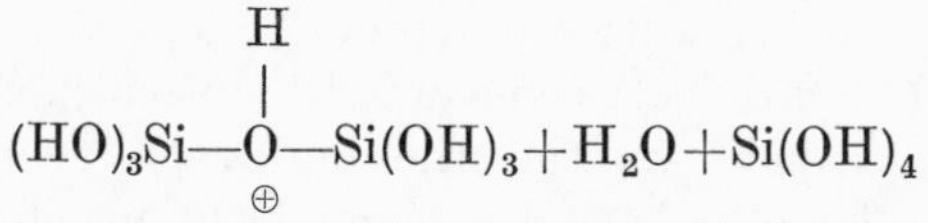

$$
\text{H} \\
| \\
(\text{HO})_3\text{Si—O—Si(OH)}_3 + \text{H}_2\text{O} + \text{Si(OH)}_4 \\
\oplus
$$

whereupon the proton may be removed by an H_2O or an $Si(OH)_4$ molecule.

At pH values higher than 2 the following scheme may apply:

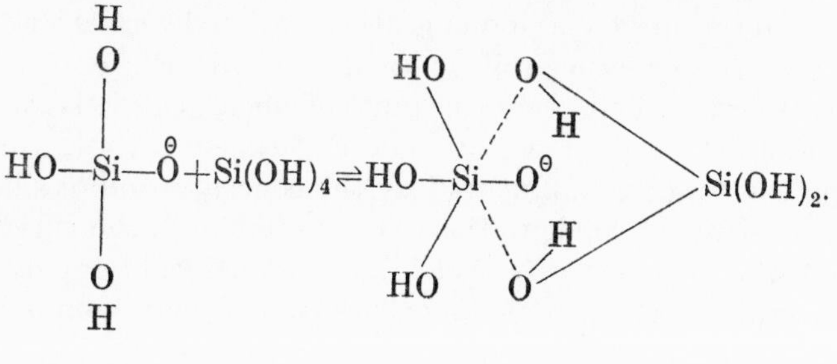

$$
\begin{array}{ll}
\text{H} & \\
\text{O} & \\
| & \\
\text{HO—Si—O} + \text{Si(OH)}_4 \rightleftharpoons & \text{HO—Si—O}^\ominus \quad \text{Si(OH)}_2. \\
| & \\
\text{O} & \\
\text{H} &
\end{array}
$$

In this case the formation of the activated complex is facilitated by the attraction between the negative charge on the oxygen atom and two hydrogen atoms of the OH groups, and by attraction between the negative charge and the silicon atom of one $Si(OH)_4$ molecule. It may disintegrate either into

$$(HO)_3Si \overset{O}{\diagup \diagdown} Si(OH)_3 + \overset{\ominus}{OH} \text{ or } (HO)_3Si \overset{O}{\diagup \diagdown} \underset{O^{\ominus}}{Si(OH)_2} + H_2O.$$

As this mechanism involves three molecules of silicic acid at pH <2 and two molecules at pH >2 it explains the different kinetic orders of the condensation in the two pH ranges. The hypothesis that the condensation mechanism involves a temporary increase of the coordination number of silicon from four to six was also advanced by Iler (1955).

From the kinetic equations it follows that at the same pH the rate of condensation of sols containing different initial silica concentrations increases with increasing concentration of SiO_2. Although the effect is not very pronounced, the addition of electrolytes also exerts an influence on the reaction rate. These concentration effects are also minimal at pH 2·0, and can be explained on a colloid-chemical basis (Okkerse, 1961; Okkerse and de Boer, 1960a,b, 1962). Apparently the key factor in the rate of condensation is the surface charge of the silica polymers, which is determined mainly by the pH and to a smaller extent by the concentration of silica and the electrolyte.

In a later publication Tai An-pang (1963) confirmed the above findings. He also supports the view that the polycondensation of silicic acid proceeds according to two different mechanisms, one in strongly acidic solutions (reaction between a neutral molecule and a monovalent positive ion of silicic acid) and the other in less acidic solutions (reaction between a neutral molecule and a monovalent negative ion of silicic acid). Starting from the equations for the ionization constants of silicic acid, Tai An-pang derived a general relationship between the gelling time and the pH. This relationship has the typical N-shape as shown in Fig. 1, and the curve maximum is also associated with the isoelectric point. From the experimental gelation time–pH curves the author calculated the three ionization constants of silicic acid. It is interesting to note that, in agreement with our experiments, these calculated ionization constants are influenced by the concentration of silicic acid and by the degree of condensation. The maximum in the curve occurs at pH 1·5 when hydrochloric acid is used as the acidifying agent and at pH 3·75 when acetic acid is used. The latter phenomenon is ascribed to substitution of the hydroxyl groups of silicic acid by the acetic acid molecule (comparable with the complex formation of silicon with fluoride ions), thus causing a change in the ionization behaviour of silicic acid and consequently in the position of the isoelectric point.

In a recent paper, Moulik and Mullick (1966) also report on the influence of the type of acid on the variation of pH for the maximum time of gelation in the cases of different acids. Like Tai An-pang, these authors observe that acetic acid shifts this pH to higher values. They do not associate the maximum in the gelling time with the isoelectric point, but believe that other species apart from H^+ and OH^-, such as ions and unionized acid molecules (e.g. acetic acid), can catalyse the polycondensation of silicic acid. Moulik and Mullick also report that cations like Na^+, Ca^{2+}, and Al^{3+} affect the gelling time differently in the acid region and not at all in the basic region, whereas anions like SO_4^{2-}, PO_4^{3-}, and Cl^- affect the gelling time differently in the basic region and not at all in the acid region. These observations support our views regarding the influence of colloid-chemical phenomena on the condensation reaction.

The following pattern emerges when all this information is taken into account. The essential condensation reaction of silicic acid is the reaction of unionized silicic acid with a positive monovalent silicic acid ion (which can be dimeric or polymeric) in the acid region and with a similar negative ion in the basic region. The reaction rate is therefore determined ultimately by the concentration of these negative or positive species. This concentration depends primarily on the pH, and to a smaller extent on the presence of other cations, anions, or even unionized acid molecules. These effects may be explained qualitatively on the basis of the Brönsted's general theory of acid-base catalysis, but the picture is complicated by the fact that during the reaction the size of the reaction species increases continuously from molecular to colloidal dimensions. More research is needed to clarify this general pattern more quantitatively.

In the subsequent sections it will be shown that the influence of the conditions of preparation on the final texture of porous silica can be understood and predicted on the basis of the principles developed above for the condensation of silicic acid.

III Relation Between the Texture of Porous Silica and the Conditions of its Preparation

A Influence of the pH of Formation

Systematic investigations (Okkerse, 1961; Okkerse and de Boer, 1960a,b, 1962; Sing and Madeley, 1953; Gärtner and Griessbach, 1958) into the relationship between the texture of porous silica and the conditions of its preparation have revealed that the rate of condensation of silicic acids is the essential variable in the preparation process.

Silica samples were prepared (Okkerse, 1961; Okkerse and de Boer, 1960a,b, 1962) by simultaneous addition of water glass solutions and hydrochloric solutions—dropwise and with vigorous mechanic stirring —to water of pre-adjusted pH, in such a manner that the pH of the liquid remained constant during the addition. The pH was measured with a pH-meter. The silica solutions or sols obtained in this way were left at room temperature until gelling had progressed to such a stage that a glass rod of a certain size placed in the gel at an angle of 20° did not fall over. The time required to reach this state was called the gelling time. After gelling the silica gels were washed with distilled water of pH 6 until the filtrate gave a negative reaction for chloride. The gels were dried by heating in an oven for 72 hours at 120°C. In this general procedure the SiO_2 concentration and the total condensation time were varied.

The texture of the samples was mainly characterized by the specific surface area as calculated from low-temperature nitrogen adsorption (S in m^2/g SiO_2), the pore volume (V_p in cm^3/g SiO_2) and the hydroxyl group occupation on the surface (N_{OH} = number of OH groups per 100 $Å^2$).

The pore volume was determined as the difference of the grain volume (V_g) and the specific volume of the solid (V_s). (All quantities are expressed per gram anhydrous silica.) The grain volume was measured pycnometrically by immersion in mercury at atmospheric pressure. As has been shown by Vleeskens (1959), the specific volume of silica may be calculated from :

$$V_s = 0.43 + 0.01W$$

where W is the percentage weight loss of silica, referred to heated silica (SiO_2), on heating at 1200°C after drying at 120°C. Thus the pore volume is given by:

$$V_p = V_g - 0.43 - 0.01W.$$

The number N_{OH} can be calculated from (Vleeskens, 1959):

$$N_{OH} = \frac{2 \cdot 10^3}{3} \times \frac{W}{S}.$$

Recent findings have shown that this formula only gives correct values if bulk H_2O and OH have been removed by heating at about 600°C.

Therefore the figures for N_{OH} given in this section—which are based on a drying temperature of 120°C—may not be very realistic (see Section V).

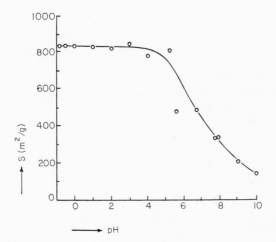

FIG. 5 Variation of the specific surface area (S) with the pH of formation.

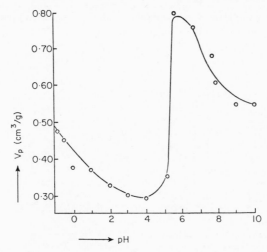

FIG. 6 Variation of the pore volume (V_p) with the pH of formation.

The effect of the pH of formation on the surface area is shown in Fig. 5. The pH-dependence of the gelling time of these samples has been shown in Fig. 1.

The change in pore volume with pH is demonstrated in Fig. 6. The variations of the surface area and of the pore volume with the pH

9

involve a large change in the shape of the nitrogen adsorption isotherms and the corresponding pore size distributions (Figs 7 and 8).

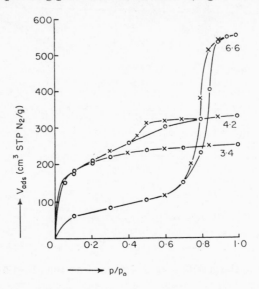

FIG. 7 Nitrogen-adsorption isotherms at $-196°C$ of silica samples prepared at various pH's: ($\bigcirc$) adsorption, ($\times$) desorption.

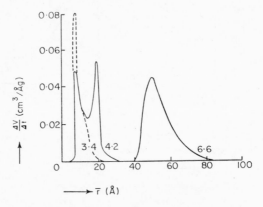

FIG. 8 Pore size distribution of silica samples prepared at various pH's.

To establish the influence of the total condensation time more independently of the gelling time, we subjected the gels to aging. The results of some of these experiments are given in Table I. The aging was carried out at 80°C in the mother liquor of the original gel for 94 hours before washing and drying.

The non-aged samples show qualitatively the same picture, as expected from the Figs 5 and 6. Aging of the gels has the effect of diminishing the specific surface area and of increasing the pore volume. The magnitude of these changes appears to be minimal at about pH 2. The mean pore radius $\bar{r}$ is smallest in the region of pH 2 independently of the aging treatment.

TABLE I. Influence of an aging treatment on the texture of silica

pH of formation	Non-aged aged	S (m²/g SiO₂)	V_p (cm³/g SiO₂)	W	$\bar{r}^*$ (Å)	N_{OH}
0	non-aged	729	0·53	5·1	14·5	4·7
	aged	628	0·69	5·0	20·4	5·3
3	non-aged	769	0·35	6·8	9·1	5·9
	aged	721	0·54	6·1	15·0	5·6
6	non-aged	552	0·43	6·1	15·6	7·4
	aged	360	1·03	3·6	57·2	6·7
7	non-aged	496	0·82	4·1	33·1	5·5
	aged	205	1·16	2·7	113·0	5·8

* $\bar{r}$ is the mean pore radius calculated from $\bar{r} = 2V_p/S$.

The experimental data indicate that the texture of silica is greatly influenced by the pH of formation and the total condensation time. This conclusion is supported by the results obtained by other investigators in this field (Sing and Madeley, 1953; Gärtner and Griessbach, 1958; Plank and Drake, 1947; Foster and Thorp, 1958). The question now arises, how can this influence be explained and how is it related to the influence of pH on the rate of condensation. The main factor determining the specific surface area of silica is the size of the elementary particles. These particles are formed by the condensation reaction in silica sols, and their ultimate size depends on the rate and duration of condensation. In the region of pH 2 the rate of condensation is minimal, which results in small elementary particles and consequently in relatively high specific surface areas. A fast condensation reaction, such as occurs in the region of pH 7, produces larger elementary particles and hence smaller specific surface areas. The rather surprising fact that the maximal specific surface area is not limited to pH 2 (see Fig. 5) is due to the other factor determining the size of the elementary particles, namely the reaction time. The reaction times of the samples were different because the gelling times were different. A low condensation rate and a long gelling time may lead to gels of the same particle size as a fast condensation rate and a short gelling time. Apparently our procedure of waiting until the sol is gelled (according to the definition chosen) gives gels of approximately equal particle size in the pH range from -1 to $+5$, because equal specific surface areas are found in this region. At higher pH the condensation rate is very fast and gelling progresses beyond the state at the moment of gelling before the reaction can be stopped by drying. Smaller surface areas are therefore obtained at pH>5.

The influence of pH on the particle size—and hence on the specific surface area—will be more pronounced with longer reaction times, or rather with reaction times of more comparable lengths. Therefore, the influence of pH appears more clearly from the experiments on the effect of aging the gel in the mother liquor (see Table I). For the aged samples the maximum specific surface area is found at about pH 2. In this region of pH the growth rate of the particles is small, and consequently the texture is affected only to a small extent by the aging treatment. At higher pH the condensation rate is large and an aging treatment at pH 5 and pH 7 results in a sharp decrease of the specific surface area. A similar effect—though less severe—is observed when the sol is aged at pH 0. It can be concluded that the rate and the time of condensation are the essential factors affecting the magnitude of the specific surface area of silica.

The influence of pH on the pore volume V_p is more complex, since the pore volume is a function of the packing, the size, and the size distribution of the elementary particles. In the region of pH 2 the silicas have smaller pore volumes than at higher and lower pH (see Fig. 6 and Table I). Aging of silica gel results in a larger pore volume owing to the growth of the larger elementary particles at the cost of the smaller ones. On the other hand, the detailed shape of the pore volume –pH curve is not well understood. In the pH region from -1 to $+5$ one might expect a more or less constant pore volume, because the average size of the elementary particles is about the same. The decrease of the pore volume with pH at pH>6 is also unclear. Apparently the pH of formation affects not only the size and size distribution but also the packing of the elementary particles. Undoubtedly, the influence of the pH on the packing of the particles is also connected with the repulsive forces between similar electrical charges. In view of the similarity between the graphs of Fig. 1 and Fig. 6 one might assume a more regular packing in the case of longer gelling times, due to a narrower size distribution of the particles. The fact that the pore size distributions (Fig. 7) become narrower with decreasing pH also points in this direction.

The results of Sing and Madeley (1953), who studied the influence of pH on the texture of silica between pH 3·7 and 5·8, are in agreement with our results in that region. Our results do not confirm the conclusion of Foster and Thorp (1958) that the finest pore structures are obtained at the lowest pH. It follows from our experiments that the mean pore radius is minimal at about pH 2. At lower (and higher) pH the average width of the pores increases.

Gärtner and Griessbach (1958) studied the influence of pH in the range from one to six on the texture by means of benzene adsorption. It is remarkable that they found the maximum specific surface area to occur at about pH 2, whereas we find this maximum in a pH range stretching from −1 to +5. This disagreement is probably associated with a different definition of the gelling time. The above authors considered a silica sol as gelled when syneresis occurred, and the time required to reach syneresis is much longer than the time required to reach gelling according to our definition. Strictly speaking, the above authors aged their gels in the mother liquor. This also appears from the specific surface areas given by Gärtner and Griessbach (1958): at pH 3—minimal rate of condensation—800 m²/g, and 250 m²/g at pH 6. The latter value is even smaller than the value obtained by us at pH 6 after 94 hours of ageing at 80°C (360 m²/g—Table I). As the influence of the pH becomes more pronounced with longer reaction times, larger differences in particle size at different pH values are obtained, which give rise to the maximum located at pH 2.

B Influence of pH During After-treatment of the Hydrogel—the Work of Neimark et al.

Neimark and Slinyakova (1956), Neimark et al. (1956, 1964a,b) and Sheinfain et al. (1961, 1963), whose work was reviewed by Mitchell (1966), studied extensively the influence of after-treatments of hydrogels with acid, including the pH of the wash water. They found that these after-treatments may exert a pronounced influence on the texture. For example, one portion of a hydrogel prepared in an acid medium was washed with water at pH 3·5 and the other portion with tap water at pH 6·6. Reference silicas from these two treatments were termed "finely-" and "coarsely-dispersed gels", with surface areas and pore volumes of 610 m²/g, 0·30 cm³/g and 400 m²/g, 0·82 cm³/g respectively. This alone gives some indication of the importance of the pH of the wash water. Steeping the hydrogels in acid emphasizes this point (see Table II, taken from Mitchell's paper, 1966).

Increasing the concentration of hydrochloric acid has very little effect on the surface area, but increases the pore volume. The inference that can be drawn from this is that this acid decreases the packing of the primary particles without materially affecting their size. A somewhat different result is obtained with sulphuric acid. This brings about a marked decrease in the surface area and an increase in the pore volume. Thus a sulphuric acid treatment of the finely-dispersed gel can increase the primary particle size and decrease the degree of packing to produce a coarsely-dispersed gel. On the other hand, sulphuric

TABLE II. Acid treatment of hydrogels (ambient temperature). Effect on xerogel structure

Acid	Concn., g-eqt./l	Surface area (m²/g)	Pore volume (cm³/g)
	Original finely-dispersed gel		
HCl	1·0	660	0·43
	5'0	620	0·60
	11·0	610	0·60
H₂SO₄	0·1	610	0·32
	1·0	450	0·50
	16·0	430	1·42
	Control	610	0·30
	Original coarsely-dispersed gel		
H₂SO₄	0·1	635	0·55
	0·5	500	0·55
	1·0	435	0·52
	16·0	450	1·50
	Control	434	0·71

acid treatment of the coarse gel can produce a relative increase in dispersity with a corresponding increase in the packing density. In fact, the surface area produced is similar to that of the finely-dispersed gel, but the density of packing is not as great and the pore volume is somewhat higher.

Provided that the hydrogel is not aged for too long, the changes of the surface area brought about by the acid treatment appear to be reversible: a hydrogel giving rise to a silica with a high surface area can be transformed into a hydrogel giving rise to a lower surface area and vice versa (Table III, taken from Sheinfain et al. (1963)).

The degree of packing appears to be irreversible: a hydrogel washed with water of pH 3·5 and then dried always gives a silica with a lower pore volume than when the hydrogel is first washed with water of pH 6·6, then treated with, e.g. 0·1 N H_2SO_4, and finally washed with water of pH 3·5 and dried. The surface areas in both cases are about the same (610 and 635 m^2/g), but the pore volume of the first sample is 0·30 cm^3/g and that of the acid-treated sample 0·55 cm^3/g.

In another series of experiments Neimark et al. (1964a) investigated the effect of the aging time of hydrogels in water of pH 6·8 before acid treatment. From this investigation it appears that with increasing age of the hydrogel the increase of the surface area brought about by acid treatment gradually decreases until after about 30 days of aging at 20°C acid treatment no longer has any influence on the texture.

TABLE III. Effect of acid treatment of hydrogels on the reversibility of xerogel structure

Specimen	Treatment conditions	Total pore volume V_p (cm^3/g)	Specific surface, S (m^2/g)	Effective pore radius r_p (Å)	Particle diameter, D (Å)
1	Hydrogel washed with water of pH 6·6; coarsely-dispersed	0·77	434	32	63
2	Hydrogel 1 after soaking in 6 N HCl, washing with water of pH 6·6	0·74	450	31	61
3	Hydrogel washed with water of pH 3·5; finely-dispersed	0·36	630	10	45
4	Hydrogel 1 after soaking in 6 N HCl, washing with distilled water to a pH of 3·5	0·80	675	23	40

Neimark and Sheinfain explain the above results on the basis of the following reasoning. When the hydrogels are soaked in acid, two competing effects come into play, hydrophilization (increased degree of hydration of the particles) and accelerated dehydration of the particles during drying. Increasing the degree of hydrophilic character leads to a decrease in the size of the micellar aggregates, causing closer packing on dehydration, with a consequent decrease in pore radius and an increase in the surface area. On the other hand, speeding up the dehydration by the acid treatment hinders mutual approach of the gel particles and gives a more open packing. In this case an increased pore volume would be expected. The hydrophilization is due to the fact that in the acid medium the bonds between the particles are strengthened because of the lowered dissociation of the silicic acid.

Hydrophilization is connected with breakdown of globules (peptiza-tion) into their primary particles, accelerated dehydration with aggrega-tion of the primary particles into larger particles, and with a decrease in the packing density. The differences between hydrochloric and sulphuric acid are explained by postulating that sulphuric acid shows a greater dehydrating ability than hydrochloric.

We believe that the results of Neimark $et\,al.$ (1964a,b) can be explained without difficulty on the basis of the condensation theory. The con-densation reaction proceeds as long as water is present in the system, and its rate is mainly determined by the pH. Thus, the condensa-tion reaction proceeds also during aging, washing, and drying of the hydrogel. As will be shown later, the condensation reaction proceeds even when solid silica is contacted with aqueous solutions, resulting in a growth of the elementary particles and thus in a decrease of the surface area. The rate of this decrease is again determined by the pH. The gelled state of a hydrogel, according to our definition, implies first a certain elementary particle size at that moment. When, for ex-ample, a hydrogel is prepared at pH 4, and then the pH of the gel is changed by washing with water of pH 6·6 and dried, the ultimate elementary particle size will be determined by a (time × condensation-rate function at pH 4)+(a time × condensation-rate function at pH 6·6). When a hydrogel is washed with water of pH 3·5 and dried in the same medium, the condensation reaction will be very slow in the washing and drying stage, resulting in a high surface area. If on the other hand the same hydrogel is washed with water of pH 6·6, the con-densation reaction will be very fast in the washing and drying stage, resulting in a lower surface area than the gel washed with water of pH 3·5.

The differences between the effects of hydrochloric and sulphuric acids on the texture might be explained on a colloid-chemical basis by assuming a difference between the effectiveness of chloride and sulphate ions in influencing the double layer round the sol particles, resulting in a difference in the charge of the particles and hence in the rate of condensation. A rather obvious explanation of the stronger effect of sulphuric acid might be that during the drying stage most of the hydrochloric acid is removed quickly by evaporation, whereas sulphuric acid will remain in the gel during the whole drying procedure (in the experiments of Neimark and Sheinfain the drying takes place in the presence of the acid applied). From our experiments too it follows that the stronger the acid the more open will be the packing, result-ing in a larger pore volume (see Fig. 6). As stated before, this effect is not understood in detail. The explanation of Neimark $et\,al.$—accelerated dehydration during drying in the presence of acids, thus

preventing better piling of the elementary particles—is in line with
the observations that will be mentioned later, that the manner of
drying influences strongly the pore volume and not so much the surface
area.

The so-called reversibility of the surface area of fresh gels by an
acid wash, which does not take place with aged gels, is in our opinion
an incorrect expression. Silica is a thermodynamically labile system
owing to its high surface energy, and for this reason its surface area

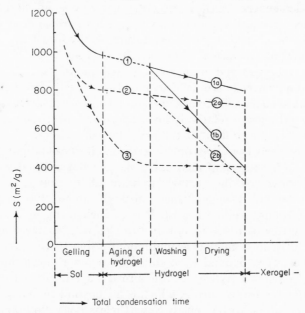

FIG. 9 Schematic and qualitative explanation of the effect of a continuing condensation reaction on the specific surface area of porous silica in various stages
of its preparation.

always tends to decrease. We therefore disagree with the conclusions
of Neimark and others (Wolf and Beyer, 1959) that the texture of
silica depends essentially on the manner of washing and drying and of
other after-treatments of the hydrogel. We believe that the properties
of silica can be affected in every stage of its preparation because they
depend on all factors influencing the condensation. This reaction proceeds—its rate being determined mainly by the pH—as long as water
and silica are together, thus including gelling, after-treatments of the
hydrogel by aging, washing, drying, and immersion of solid silica in
aqueous solutions. Very schematically and qualitatively, the whole
pattern is given in Fig. 9.

9*

Hydrogel 1 is prepared in an acid medium and not aged.

Hydrogel 1a is a fraction of hydrogel 1 washed with acid. During washing and drying the condensation remains low, so that a high surface area is produced.

Hydrogel 1b is a fraction of hydrogel 1 washed with water of pH 6·6. In this case the condensation is accelerated compared with the gelling stage and the surface area decreases drastically.

Hydrogel 2 is prepared in an alkaline medium and not aged. At this stage the elementary particles are still relatively small, and therefore an acid wash results in a silica having a high surface area (hydrogel 2a), whereas a normal water-wash results in hydrogel 2b, having a relatively low surface area.

Hydrogel 3 is prepared in an alkaline medium and aged. As a result, the elementary particle size is already rather large before the washing stage. A subsequent acid treatment stops condensation from proceeding, but nevertheless a relatively low surface area is produced.

It is interesting to note that the procedure of Neimark et al. leads to lower surface areas than does our procedure: all silicas prepared according to our method in acid medium, not aged but washed with water of pH 6·6, have specific surface areas of about 700 m²/g, whereas Neimark's method yields surface areas of about 400 m²/g under similar conditions. Neimark et al. had to include an acid wash or a wash with water of pH 3 to obtain samples with surfaces as high as 700 m²/g. This phenomenon is undoubtedly due to the fact that the gelling times were defined in a different manner: according to our definition Neimark's hydrogels are already aged, since the authors waited until syneresis occurred, which is far beyond the point at which we considered a sol to be gelled. Nevertheless both methods result in about the same size elementary particles. In our case growth of the relatively small elementary particles to larger ones, corresponding to a specific surface area of around 700 m²/g, takes place during the washing and drying stage; in the case of Neimark et al. the main growth takes place during gelling up to the point where syneresis occurs, and further growth during washing and drying is largely prevented by an acid wash.

The above reasoning indicates that silicas with the smallest possible elementary particles can be obtained by isolating the silica from a silica sol of pH 2 as early as possible, washing this material with water of about pH 2 and finally drying it at the lowest possible temperature in the shortest possible time. A similar method was followed by Dollimore and Heal (1962), who freeze-dried de-ionized silica sols or solutions of pH around two. Indeed, it appeared possible in this way to produce silicas in which the majority of the pores were smaller than 4·3 Å in diameter, indicating a very small elementary particle size.

C Influence of the SiO_2 Concentration, the Way of Drying the Hydrogel, and Hydrothermal Treatment of the Hydrogel

The SiO_2 concentration of the starting sol in the region from 0·2 to 1·0 moles SiO_2/l (1·2–6% wt SiO_2) did not affect the texture perceptibly in our experiments, although there was a considerable influence on the gelling time, or, obviously, on the rate of condensation. At higher SiO_2 concentrations, the condensation rate being faster, lower surface areas could be expected than at smaller concentrations, provided that the reaction times were comparable in the two cases. This was not true in our experiments, since the gelling time also decreases with increasing concentration, thus counteracting the effect of the increased condensation rate. Therefore, the effect of the SiO_2 concentration can be better examined by adopting the same total reaction time for different concentrations. No such studies have yet been reported.

TABLE IV. Influence of the pre-drying temperature of the gel

pH of formation	Pre-drying temp. (°C)	S	V_p	W	$\bar{r}$	N_{OH}
3·2	20	555	0·25	5·6	9·0	6·7
	40	630	0·28	6·0	8·9	6·3
	80	670	0·35	6·1	10·5	6·1
	120	675	0·38	6·1	11·3	6·0
7·0	20	330	0·59	3·7	35·8	7·5
	40	395	0·71	3·6	35·9	6·1
	80	345	0·78	3·6	45·1	7·0
	120	330	0·85	3·5	51·5	7·1

It was already mentioned that the way of drying the hydrogel influences the texture to a considerable extent. On the one hand the condensation continues during drying, causing a growth of the elementary particles, and on the other hand a considerable influence on the packing of the elementary particles may be expected.

Table IV presents some of our experiments regarding the influence of pre-drying the hydrogel to constant weight before drying at 120°C.

Since practically the same specific surface is found at different pre-drying temperatures, it can be concluded that the size of the elementary particles essentially is not affected by the pre-drying temperature. This conclusion is in agreement with our concepts regarding the formation of silica. On the other hand, the pore volume and hence the packing of the particles is strongly influenced by the pre-drying temperature. This effect is probably associated with the temperature dependence of the surface tension of water. The high surface tension of liquid water contained in the gel draws the structure together during drying. The effect is especially important after part of the water has been removed from the relatively wide spaces and the remaining water forms a meniscus between the skeleton units. Furthermore, the time in which the compressive force exerted upon the gel is operative increases with decreasing pre-drying temperature. Lower pore volumes can therefore be expected at lower drying temperatures, because the surface tension of water and the time of drying increase with decreasing temperature.

The action of the surface tension of water is avoided if the water of the gel is evaporated when frozen (freeze-drying) or if the water is replaced by alcohol and the alcohol is then evaporated. Under such conditions we obtained a white loose powder instead of grains of a few millimetres, which result from normal drying at 120°C. Vleeskens (1959) replaced the water in a hydrogel by alcohol, then the alcohol by ether, and finally he heated this material in an autoclave at 220°C (above the critical temperature of ether). When the tap of the autoclave was opened the ether evaporated very rapidly and a very fluffy product was obtained. After such treatment the pore volume was 4·8 cm^3/g SiO$_2$ and the specific surface area 960 m^2/g. If this product was subsequently immersed in water and then dried at 120°C, the pore volume was reduced to 0·7 cm^3/g SiO$_2$ and the specific surface area to 870 m^2/g SiO$_2$. This experiment demonstrates the enormous effect of the surface tension of liquid water on the ultimate pore volume.

Neimark and Sheinfain (1953) displaced the intermicellar water in hydrogels by various organic liquids before drying, and observed a qualitative relation between the surface tension of these liquids and the pore volume.

Chertov et al. (1965a) investigated the influence of hydrothermal treatment by heating the hydrogel in an autoclave at temperatures of 90–215°C for periods ranging from 2 to 40 hours. As a result of the most severe hydrothermal treatment the specific surface area decreased from 421 to 48 m^2/g and the pore volume increased from 0·76 to 1·96 cm^3/g. Apparently, and in agreement with the condensation theory, the elementary particles increase in size during hydrothermal aging. The higher pore volume indicates that for the growing particles in the hydrogel it is more difficult to achieve close packing. Apparently the hydrogel structure has already some firmness in this respect, so that the open space caused by material transported to the larger elementary particles is not (or only with greater difficulty) filled up by other elementary particles.

D General Conclusions

It has been shown that the texture of silica can be affected in every stage of its preparation, including gelling, after treatment of the hydrogel by aging and washing with various liquids, and drying. These influences can be qualitatively understood and predicted on the basis of the condensation theory, which attributes a major role to the rate of the condensation reaction of silicic acid in all stages during the development of the texture.

IV Stability of Porous Silica in Aqueous Media

A Introduction

In view of the influence of the condensation reaction on the development of the texture of silica during its preparation, it seemed interesting to investigate the effect on the texture when silica (xerogel) is soaked in various solutions and liquids. The following general procedure was used: three grams of silica were soaked in 50 ml of an aqueous solution in a polyethylene bottle, and the bottle was then placed in a constant temperature bath at 80°C for a certain time. After this treatment the sample was washed with distilled water until no more electrolyte could be detected in the filtrate. Finally the samples were dried in an oven at 120°C. The type of silica and the composition of the aqueous solution were systematically varied.

The modifications in the texture of the original silica were determined by measuring the specific surface area, the pore volume, and the number of OH groups per 100 $Å^2$ (N_{OH}). Complete nitrogen adsorption isotherms at $-196°C$ were determined on some selected samples.

Preliminary experiments were carried out with a number of silicas of different textures and with immersion liquids of various compositions. Some illustrative data are collected in Table V. The symbol $\bar{d}$ represents the mean diameter of the elementary particles, as calculated from $\bar{d} = 6V_s/S$. In the derivation of this relationship it is assumed that silica consists of spherical particles with a diameter $\bar{d}$. The specific volume (V_s) of the silica is calculated from the equation $V_s = 0.43 + 0.01\ W$ (see p. 224).

The data collected in Table V enable us to draw the following conclusions: the porous texture of silica is modified by treating silica with water or with electrolyte solutions at 80°C. The most striking phenomenon is the decrease in the specific surface area, whereas the pore volume remains nearly constant. Since the "chemical" water content

TABLE V. Characteristics of silicas after treatment in different liquids at 80°C

Silica sample	Immersion liquid	Immersion time (hours)	S	V_p	$\bar{r}$	W	N_{OH}	$\bar{d}$ (Å)
1	—	—	752	0·50	13	6·67	5·9	40
	conc. HCl	22	475	0·52	22	4·17	7·3	62
	conc. HCl	120	278	0·51	37	4·44	10·6	102
2	—	—	697	0·28	8	7·19	6·9	43
	conc. HCl	20	414	0·30	14	5·72	9·2	71
	conc. H_2SO_4	14	710	0·28	8	6·91	6·5	42
	1:1 H_2SO_4	28	309	0·28	18	6·33	13·7	95
	C_2H_5OH	14	704	0·27	8	—	—	—
3	—	—	324	0·73	45	3·16	6·5	85
	conc. HCl	240	297	0·73	49	3·46	7·8	94
4	—	—	731	0·49	13	5·71	5·2	40
	4M KCl-sol	94	462	0·51	22	4·77	6·9	62
	dist. H_2O	94	625	0·50	16	5·73	6·1	49

(W) decreases less than the specific surface area, the quantity N_{OH} increases.* The immersion treatment also increases the mean pore radius and the mean particle diameter. An aqueous immersion liquid appears to be an essential condition for the occurrence of the modifications, taking into account that neither concentrated sulphuric acid nor absolute ethyl alcohol has any effect. Salt and acid solutions appear to be more effective than pure water. Silicas with high surface areas change more rapidly than silicas with lower surface areas.

As a result of the treatment given, the adsorption isotherms undergo considerable changes (Fig. 10). However, the pore volume is not affected. The alterations in the shape and position of the isotherms and the hysteresis loops indicate an increase of the number of larger pores,

* The definitions of W and N_{OH} are given on p. 224.

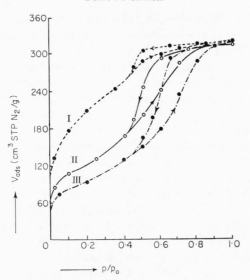

FIG. 10 Nitrogen-adsorption isotherms at −196°C: (I) original sample; (II) 94 hours in 4 M KCl at 80°C; (III) 94 hours in conc. HCl at 80°C.

whereas the smaller pores tend to disappear. This can be seen more conveniently from the pore-size distribution curves of Fig. 11.

The question that now arises is how the modification in the porous texture resulting from the immersion treatment may be explained. Since silica is a thermodynamically labile system, its surface area tends

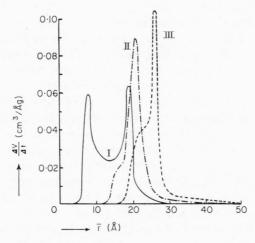

FIG. 11 Pore size distributions: (I) original sample; (II) 94 hours in 4 M KCl at 80°C; (III) 94 hours in conc. HCl at 80°C.

to decrease. This decrease can take place in an aqueous medium in which, as a result of the dissolution and deposition of the "silica", the larger elementary particles can grow at the expense of smaller ones. This process is somewhat similar to the coarsening of a precipitate in its mother liquor. The reactions involved are dissolution of "silica" from the surface (a decondensation reaction) and recondensation of the "silica" in solution with the OH groups on the surface of the solid.

A similar growth of the larger elementary particles at the expense of the smaller ones by steam at higher temperatures was observed by Adams and Voge (1957). These authors showed by means of electron micrographs that there is an essential difference between the effects of heating a silica-alumina cracking catalyst in dry air (thermal sintering) and in the presence of steam. Ries (1952) and also Schlaffer et al. (1957) came to the same conclusion on the basis of adsorption measurements. When the catalyst was heated below 800°C in the presence of steam there was a large reduction of surface area, whereas the pore volume decreased only slightly. Consequently the mean pore radius was considerably increased. Adams and Voge (1957) showed by electron micrographs that in this case matter is transported from the smaller to the larger elementary particles, which results in enlargement of the pores. The loss in surface area was quantitatively accounted for by the increase of the size of the particles. On the other hand, when the catalyst was heated at 900°C in dry air the pore volume decreased linearly with the surface area, and consequently the mean pore radius remained approximately constant. The pore-size distribution was also unaffected in this case.

There appears to be a strong similarity between the effect of a steam treatment at about 500°C on the cracking catalyst and the effect of heating silica in aqueous solutions at 80°C. It therefore looks as though the mechanisms of the two effects are the same, namely growth of the larger elementary particles at the expense of smaller ones, and possibly also a rounding off of the edges and corners of the elementary particles. The proposed mechanism accounts completely for the decrease in the specific surface area and the alterations of the isotherms. The transport of material from a small elementary particle to a larger one is of molecular character. The silica skeleton is not affected during this process, and therefore the pore volume does not change. This may be contrasted with thermal sintering, where complete particles sinter together, which causes a decrease in the specific surface area and in the pore volume. Since the surface energy of the elementary particles decreases with increasing particle diameter, the modification of the texture will be slower if the elementary particles are larger.

B   The Influence of pH

If the theory postulated for the modifications of the texture is correct, the differences observed in the rate of the process in immersion liquids of different compositions must be attributed to differences in the rates of condensation and decondensation in the various media. In view of this it seemed highly desirable to examine the influence of the pH of the immersion solution. These experiments were carried out in buffered solutions because the pH of a non-buffered solution in contact with silica tends to change as a result of the ion-exchange properties of silica. The results are shown in Fig. 12.

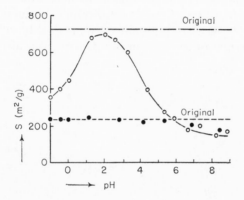

FIG. 12 Decrease of the specific surface area (S) of silica samples heated for 94 hours at 80°C in buffered solutions (0·2 mole/l) of various pH's: (– · – and ○) 5 W_a 0; (– – – and ●) 6 W_a 0.

It is found that the decrease of the specific surface area is minimal at pH 2, increasing at lower and higher values of the pH. The rate of the changes in texture thus depends on the pH in a similar way to the rate of condensation of silica sols. Apparently the rate of the condensation-decondensation reaction, and consequently the pH, is one of the essential factors influencing the stability of silica in aqueous solutions. The other essential factor is the texture of the original sample. The difference in behaviour between the submicroporous sample 5 W_a 0 and the macroporous sample 6 W_a 0 must be attributed to different surface energies of the two silicas. The surface energy of the submicroporous sample with a mean elementary particle diameter of 40 Å is so large that even at pH 2 there is a small decrease of the specific surface area. On the other hand, the elementary particles of the macroporous silica, having a diameter of roughly 125 to 150 Å, do not have a sufficiently large surface energy to cause a rate of attack by the reactions involved such that an appreciable effect on the specific surface area is noted.

The experimental evidence suggests that the rate of decondensation (i.e. the rate of dissolution of the silica) depends on the pH in the same way as the rate of condensation. This was verified by determining the amount of dissolved silica as a function of time and pH, using the silica-molybdate method as described by Alexander *et al.* (1954). Two types of silica—a submicroporous and a macroporous sample, with surfaces of 717 and 293 m²/g respectively—were suspended in buffered solutions of pH 2, 4, 6, and 8, kept at 60°C. The silica concentration in the suspensions was 9·0 g/l. At regular intervals samples were taken from the mother solution to determine the amount of dissolved silica. The solutions were only stirred immediately before taking the sample. The results of the measurements are given in Fig. 13.

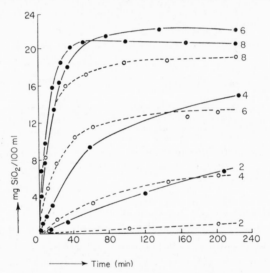

FIG. 13 Amount of silica dissolved at 60°C in solutions buffered at pH 2, 4, 6 and 8 (conc. 0·2 mole/l) as a function of time: (●) submicroporous sample, (○) macroporous sample.

It follows from Fig. 13 that the rate of solution is minimal at pH 2 and increases with increasing pH. Thus the rate of decondensation is affected by the pH in a similar way as the rate of condensation. It is interesting to note that the submicroporous sample shows a higher rate of solution than the macroporous sample, which is in agreement with what could be expected.

C The Influence of Electrolyte Concentration

In Section II it was reported that the rate of condensation increases with increasing salt concentration. It therefore seemed interesting to examine also the influence of the salt concentration on the stability of silica in aqueous solutions. For this purpose a submicroporous silica was treated with buffered sodium chloride solutions of different concentrations (Table VI).

TABLE VI. Influence of the salt concentration (0·189–3·189 mole/l) (temperature 80°C, time 94 hours, pH 7, solutions not stirred)

Na$^+$ ion concn. (eqt./l)	S
—	731*
0·189	188
0·239	174
1·189	165
3·189	135

* Original sample prepared at pH 3.

It can be concluded from Table VI and from Fig. 12 that the influence of the pH surpasses strongly the influence of the salt concentration in the region of 0·19 to 3·19 mole/l. Nevertheless, an increase of the salt concentration results in a slightly larger decrease of the specific surface area. Considering these results, it seemed very interesting to investigate the influence of salt concentrations smaller than 0·189 mole/l. Therefore, at small salt concentrations the pH was kept constant by an automatic titrator system. With the aid of this apparatus it was possible to neutralize automatically the H$^+$ ions liberated by ion exchange. The data summarizing these experiments are compiled in Table VII. Complete nitrogen adsorption isotherms were determined for some samples (Fig. 14).

From Table VII it follows that even at very small salt concentrations the pH determines mainly to what extent the texture is changed. Increasing the sodium-ion concentration at pH 3 by a factor of about 100 has no appreciable effect (AT 1 and AT 3), whereas an increase of the hydroxyl-ion concentration by a factor of 100 at the same sodium-ion concentration results in a large decrease of the specific surface area (AT 1 and AT 5). On the other hand, the addition of salt does accelerate the process (compare the experiments at the same pH but at different Na$^+$ ion concentrations), though to a smaller extent

243

lence of the electrolyte concentration (low concentrations)
mperature 80°C, time 24 hours, solutions stirred)

	pH	Na$^+$ concn. (eqt./l)	S	OH$^-$ added (m-eqt./g SiO$_2$)	H$^+$ added (m-eqt./g SiO$_2$)
0*	—	—	717	—	—
1	3	0·010	710	0	0
2	3	0·099	720	0	0
3	3	0·986	690	0·002	0
4	5	0·0015	560	0·019	0
5	5	0·010	548	0·027	0·003
6	5	0·089	452	0·027	0·008
7	7†	0·002	234	0·064	0
8	7	0·018	223	0·061	0
9	7	0·089	186	0·114	0·051
10	7	0·852	139	0·151	0·048
11	6·5→3·7‡	—	717	—	—

* Original sample.
† Distilled water, pH maintained constant.
‡ Distilled water, no base added.

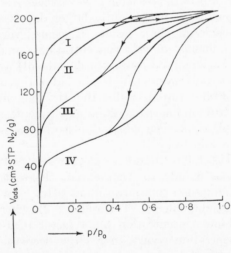

FIG. 14 Nitrogen-adsorption isotherms at −196°C: (I) original sample; (II) 24
hours at pH 5, 1 meqt. Na$^+$/l; (III) 24 hours at pH 5, 89 meqt. Na$^+$/l; (IV)
24 hours at pH 7, 89 meqt. Na$^+$/l.

than an increase in pH. This result is qualitatively the same as that obtained in the investigations concerning the influence of pH and of the salt concentration on the rate of condensation of silica sols (Section II), indicating once more that the rate of condensation is the basic factor determining the stability of silica in aqueous solutions. The fact that no change of texture could be observed in distilled water, which was not maintained at pH 7 (experiment AT 11), probably is due to the combined effect of the decrease in pH and the absence of salt. It is quite possible that the presence of a small amount of salt is required to build up the electrical double layer.

The isotherms given in Fig. 14 confirm the earlier result, namely that the number of larger pores increases and that the very small pores disappear, without affecting the pore volume. Isotherms III and IV show the effect of increasing the pH from 5 to 7 at a Na^+ ion concentration of 0·089 eqt./l, whereas isotherms II and III demonstrate the effect of increasing the Na^+ ion concentration from 0·001 to 0·089 eqt./l at pH 5.

Let us now consider the amounts of base and acid added by the automatic titrator to maintain the pH at the pre-set value (see Table VII). After the silica had been soaked in solutions of pH 5 and 7 there was a rapid consumption of base due to the formation of H^+ ions according to the ion-exchange reaction:

$$\equiv Si-OH+NaCl \rightleftharpoons \equiv Si-O^-+Na^++H^++Cl.$$

The rate of addition of the base decreased exponentially, and after about five hours the pH remained constant for about 10 hours without the addition of any base or acid. In some cases it was necessary to add a small amount of acid to maintain the pH at the given value during the remainder of the 24-hour period. Apparently OH^- ions are also formed during the experiments. To explain the formation of OH^- ions we start from the reasonable assumption that the surface charge density does not vary during the 24-hour period because this charge is determined by the pH and by the electrolyte concentration. As the surface area decreases during the proceeding condensation reaction, the total number of negative charges on the surface must also decrease, giving rise to the formation of OH^- ions in the solution by the condensation:

$$\equiv Si-O^-+Si(OH)_4 \rightleftharpoons \equiv Si-O-Si(OH)_3+OH^-$$
$$\text{in solution}$$

The rate of the ion-exchange reaction will be larger than the rate of condensation, so that initially more H^+ ions are produced by ion exchange than OH^- ions by the condensation. There will then follow a period in which the two reactions balance one another with respect to the H^+ and OH^- ion formation, but eventually more OH^- ions are produced by the proceeding condensation reaction than H^+ ions by the ion exchange. Evidently the condensation counteracts the consumption of sodium hydroxide. In spite of this, the amount of NaOH added per gram of silica increases both with increasing pH and increasing salt concentration. This means that the charge density increases in the same direction, in agreement with the theory about the catalytic condensation. At pH 3 hardly any H^+ ions or OH^- ions are formed, because the isoelectric point is situated in this region.

The experiments show that the stability of silica in aqueous solutions depends basically on those factors that influence the condensation reaction, i.e. the pH and the electrolyte concentration. This is in agreement with the "particle growth" hypothesis on the changes in the texture of silica in aqueous solutions given in Section IV A. In addition, the experiments give further support to our views on the formation of silica gels and silicas, namely the catalytic influence of positive or negative charges on the condensation reaction.

Mougey et al. (1958) investigated the influence of the adsorption of cations on the texture of silica. These authors immersed silicas in various non-buffered electrolyte solutions for a period of 45 minutes at room temperature, and the samples were then washed and dried at 150°C. A breakdown of the texture was observed, characterized by a decrease in the specific surface area and, to a smaller extent, a decrease in the pore volume. The authors do not give an explanation for the reported phenomena. Since the authors did not take into account the effect of the change in pH during the experiments it is difficult to correlate their results with ours, but it seems very probable that these phenomena too can be explained on the basis of particle growth. We did not determine the amount of cations adsorbed in our experiments. There is no doubt that immersion of silica in an aqueous solution at room temperature followed by washing and drying at 120°C results in a breakdown of the texture, because the condensation reaction proceeds also during the drying period. However, the textural changes observed by us cannot be due exclusively to the effect of the drying treatment because a longer period of immersion at 80°C, followed by the same drying procedure, results in a larger decrease of the specific surface area. This can be seen in Fig. 15, where the decrease in the specific surface area of a silica sample is shown as a function of the time of immersion in concentrated hydrochloric acid at 80°C.

Kiselev and co-workers (see Akshinskaya et al., 1962, 1963) investigated the changes occurring in the texture of silica under the action of water vapour in an autoclave at temperatures of up to 350°C (hydrothermal treatment), on steaming at high temperatures (round 850°C), and on heating in air at 850°C. As may be expected from the foregoing, the hydrothermal treatment led to a drastic decrease of the specific surface area, whereas the pore volume remained constant, thus resulting in enormous enlargement of the pores. For example, two hours at

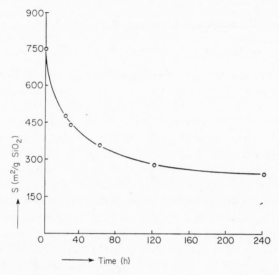

Fig. 15 Decrease in the specific surface area (S) of a submicroporous silica in concentrated HCl as a function of time.

40 atm. (340°C) reduced the surface area from 286 to 16 m²/g and the mean pore diameter was increased from 100 to 1600 Å. Thus also in this case particle growth occurred by molecular transport of silicic acid. The steam treatment at 850°C led to a decrease in the specific surface area and in the pore volume, in such a way that the average pore size was increased. The corresponding heat treatment without steam also resulted in a decrease of the specific surface area and of the pore volume, but here the size of the remaining pores was unaltered. In the last-mentioned case sintering took place: fusion together of two elementary particles whereby the identity of the original particles is lost. Thus here the observed decline in the surface area cannot be entirely explained by uniform growth of the larger elementary particles at the expense of smaller ones. Addition of small amounts of electrolytes, or the presence of impurities, greatly reduce the stability of the silica to hydrothermal treatment and steaming, which is in line with our

observations on the effect of electrolytes on the rate of condensation. The results of Schlaffer *et al.* (1965) are compatible with those of Kiselev (Akshinskaya *et al.*, 1962, 1963, 1964). These authors emphasize that silica is less stable to prolonged steaming than the silica-alumina cracking catalyst. This is probably due to the fact that the presence of alumina in silica reduces the rate of dissolution or decondensation, so that the transport of matter is impeded.

V   Surface Structure of Porous Silica

A   Distinction Between "Chemisorbed" and "Physisorbed" Water

Irrespective of the texture of silica as determined by the magnitude of the specific surface area and the pore-size distribution, the chemical nature of silica is determined by the number, distribution, and reactivity of the surface silanol groups. Since silica is amorphous to X-rays, it is impossible to derive the chemical nature of the surface from X-ray data, although Fourier analysis of such data might lead to better understanding (Fripiat *et al.*, 1963). Most of the studies devoted to the arrangement of the surface hydroxyls were done by thermogravimetric methods, adsorption of polar molecules, reactions of certain compounds with the surface hydrogels, and infra-red spectroscopy.

The first question is how to distinguish between chemisorbed and physisorbed water. The term "chemisorbed" or "bound" water refers to OH groups chemically bound to a surface silicon atom. It is possible to visualize a pattern in which a surface silicon carries one, two, or three hydroxyls. "Physisorbed" water is molecular water adsorbed on the silica surface. Various possibilities of the arrangements of the OH groups on the silica surface are indicated schematically in Fig. 16.

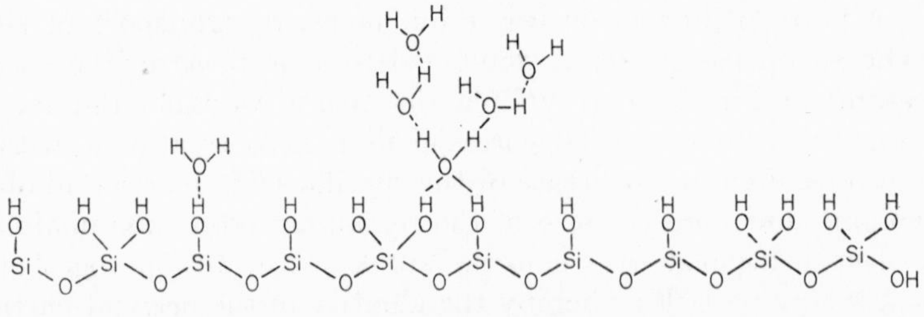

FIG. 16 Possible arrangements of the OH-groups on the silica surface.

Vleeskens (1959) showed that when wet silica (i.e. a sample containing both chemisorbed and physisorbed water) is heated at increasing temperatures under atmospheric conditions there is no particular point on the loss of weight/heating time curve (Fig. 17). Such a point would enable us to define precisely the temperature at which all physisorbed water has been removed while all chemisorbed water was still there.

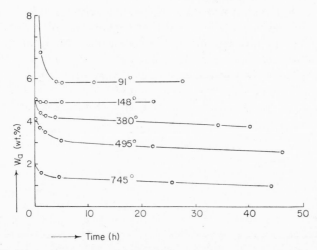

FIG. 17 Decrease in the water content (W_a) with heating time at various temperatures (°C) (W_a = loss of weight of silica referred to heated silica on heating at 1200°C).

According to de Boer and Vleeskens (1957, 1958) a silica dried at 120°C under atmospheric conditions has lost all physisorbed water and still contains all surface hydroxyls. Heating at higher temperatures partially depletes the surface of OH groups. The 120°C-criterion is based on the following arguments:

(a) Below 110°C the residual "water" content depends upon the water vapour pressure of the air in which the silica is dried; at 115°C this influence becomes negligibly small.

(b) Silica samples dried at 120°C under atmospheric conditions have the same water content (as determined by heating at 1200°C) as when they are pre-dried at 105°C and afterwards kept over P_2O_5, or when they are pre-dried at 105°C and then pumped off under high vacuum at room temperature.

The 120°C criterion for distinguishing physisorbed from chemisorbed water has not been generally accepted in the literature. Lange (1965) suggests that strongly physisorbed water (e.g. in very narrow micropores) requires drying temperatures approaching 180°C. On the other hand, Young and Bursh (1960) infer that at 180°C some chemically bound water has been evolved. Water vapour isotherms on silicas degassed at 180–200°C give rise to irreversibility in the hysteresis loop, indicating loss of silanol-derived water.

Since the work of Vleeskens in 1959, much attention has been given to the problem of distinguishing the two types of adsorbed water. The infra-red technique has proved to be particularly useful in this respect. Such measurements have revealed that surface silanols exhibit absorption in quite separate regions of the spectrum, namely at about 3750 cm^{-1} (2·66 μ), 3650 cm^{-1} (2·74 μ), 3500 cm^{-1} (2·86 μ), and 1640 cm^{-1} (6·1 μ). If physisorbed water is present a very broad band is obtained at 3400 cm^{-1} (2·95 μ) and the absorption at 1640 cm^{-1} is also increased. Figure 18, taken from Wirzing (1963), is given for the sake of illustration.

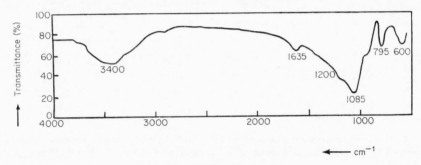

FIG. 18 Infra-red spectrum of silica (KBr technique).

Various interpretations of these patterns have been offered (for a review see Hockey, 1965). It is generally agreed that the absorption bands in the 3650–3750 cm^{-1} region are due to single surface hydroxyls, and that those appearing at 3400 cm^{-1} and 1640 cm^{-1} when molecular water is present are due to physisorbed water held on the surface by hydrogen bonding. However, there is no such agreement about the interpretation of the band at 3500 cm^{-1} and its associated absorption at 1640 cm^{-1}. Some workers suggest that it corresponds to strongly physisorbed, hydrogen-bonded water, while others correlate it with surface arrangements involving geminal hydroxyls (Si$\underset{\diagdown OH}{\overset{\diagup OH}{}}$). The former view appears to be irreconcilable with the experimental evidence obtained from water adsorption-desorption studies, since evacuation at room temperature completely removes the physisorbed water from pure silicas, and the 3400 cm^{-1} band then disappears completely, whereas higher temperatures of about 200°C–400°C are required before the surface species associated with the 3500 cm^{-1} band are removed.

Unfortunately, no full theoretical treatment of hydrogen bonding of the type involved in the present system is as yet available. However, it is an established fact that the stronger the hydrogen bond the greater the associated spectral shift from the non-bonded absorption wavelength. It follows that the absorption band at 3500 cm^{-1} can hardly be due to physisorbed water held more strongly by hydrogen bonding than that which produces a greater spectral shift to 3400 cm^{-1} and yet is more easily removed from the surface. For this reason, Hockey inclines towards the explanation that the band at 3500 cm^{-1} is due to surface silanol groups existing within an arrangement that allows "dimeric" hydroxyl interaction. Therefore, any distinction between chemisorbed and physisorbed water based on the presence or absence of a band at 3500 cm^{-1} seems to be very unreliable. The same can be

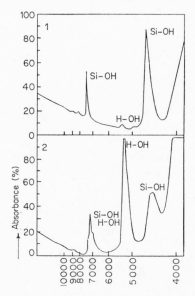

FIG. 19 Infra-red spectrum of silica with and without pre-adsorbed water (after Wirzing, 1963): (1) silica sample after degassing for 6 hours at $-196°C$; (2) after adsorption of water.

said about the band at 1640 cm^{-1}, since it is recognized that at this wave number, apart from physisorbed water, a harmonic of an SiO vibration (Fripiat and Uytterhoeven, 1962), and even an absorption due to geminal surface hydroxyls (Hockey, 1965) can be expected. Moreover, owing to the other overlapping bands (Bavarez and Bastick, 1965) it is difficult to assess quantitatively the band at 1640 cm^{-1}.

In view of these uncertainties it is not surprising that different authors who applied infra-red spectroscopy in the frequency region discussed came to different conclusions. Fripiat and Uytterhoeven (1962) believe that a temperature of 300°C is needed to remove all physisorbed water, although they admit that this temperature may vary with the type of the silica investigated. Davydov *et al.* (1964) state clearly that the drying temperature *in vacuo* must not exceed 150–200°C, because prolonged heating at higher temperatures results in appreciable dehydroxylation of the surface. Bavarez and Bastick (1965) favour a temperature of 240°C under vacuum; Fraissard *et al.* (1963) even believe that a temperature of about 450°C for aerogels, and of 600°C for xerogels, is needed to remove all molecular water. The latter authors make a distinction between "adsorbed" water (which, by definition, is removed at a temperature of 150°C under vacuum) and

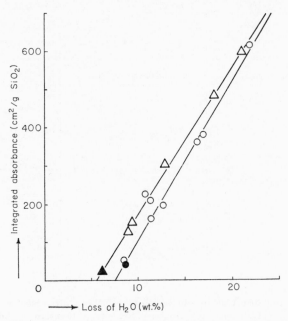

Fig. 20 Integrated absorbance as a function of weight after heating at 250°C (△) and at 120°C (○). ▲ and ● relate to the samples prior to water vapour treatment.

"constitutional" water, which is believed to cover the whole surface of a sample degassed at 150°C, and which is only removed by heating at temperatures in the region of 400–600°C.

It is rather surprising that up to now the work of Wirzing (1963) in this area has been more or less neglected; in our opinion this work provides the basis for an elegant solution of the problem of distinguishing chemisorbed and physisorbed water on silica. In view of the uncertainties in the interpretation of infra-red bands in the region between 1000 and 4000 cm^{-1}, Wirzing suggested the use of the combination band of water at 5265 cm^{-1} for the quantitative determination of physisorbed water. A typical spectrum in the region of 4000 to 10,000 cm^{-1} is shown in Fig. 19 on page 251.

Erkelens and Linsen (1969) applied this method to three types of silica. The samples were heated at various temperatures in the region of 120 to 800°C for 17 hours, and water adsorption was then carried out at 0·4, 1·2, and 4·0 mm Hg. The absorbance of the band having its maximum at 5265 cm^{-1} was recorded before and after adsorption of water. When the integrated absorbances were plotted against the weight loss on ignition at 1200°C a straight line intersecting the abscissa

TABLE VIII. N_{OH} values for Mallinckrodt silica and Aerosil samples pretreated at various temperatures

Sample	Temp. of heating (°C)	S_{BET} (m²/g SiO₂)	H₂O content rel. to SiO₂ (determined by ignition)	N_{OH} determined by Ignition	IR
Mallinckrodt silica	120	591	8·5	9·6	8·6
	200	634	8·2	8·6	7·6
	250	646	6·0	6·2	5·5
	300	623	4·9	5·2	5·1
	350	648	2·3	4·2	3·1
	450	599	2·2	2·4	2·1
	800 (8x)	166	1·3	5·2	4·0
Aerosil	250	320	2·3	4·8	4·4
	450	311	2·4	5·1	2·1
	120	218	2·1	6·7	4·6
	200	242	1·3	3·6	2·3
Mallinckrodt silica, pretreated with H₂SO₄/H₂O (l/l v/v)	120	225	7·8	23·2	20·2
	200	220	8·3	25·2	22·1
	300	245	6·5	17·7	17·4
	400	234	4·2	11·9	10·8
	500	283	3·4	8·0	7·1

was obtained. The point of intersection, indicating the absence of molecularly adsorbed water, determines the number of OH groups in the sample.

The integrated absorbance as a function of the water content is shown in Fig. 20, taken from Erkelens and Linsen (1969). Erkelens and Linsen compared the data obtained by the ignition method (drying at 120°C) with those obtained by Wirzing's method. This comparison is shown in Table VIII.

It can be seen from this table that for a number of Aerosil and Mallinckrodt samples the infra-red and ignition methods yield rather similar N_{OH} values, even in the case of the sample pre-treated at 120°C. This would suggest that the assumption made by de Boer and Vleeskens (1957, 1958) that this temperature would be sufficient to remove physically adsorbed water is in principle correct. Nevertheless, according to Erkelens and Linsen, the samples not pre-treated with water vapour also showed a certain absorption at 5265 cm^{-1} (see, e.g. the measuring points indicated by arrows in Fig. 20). This absorption is probably due to water in the interior of the elementary particles (bulk water). This water is not included in the N_{OH} value determined by the infra-red method in connection with the extrapolation procedure applied, but it is included in the weight loss due to ignition at 1200°C. It was therefore concluded that the N_{OH} determined by the infra-red method is more correct and slightly lower than that measured by the ignition method.

Since, according to Wirzing's method, the number of hydroxyl groups is calculated from determinations of the water content (by infra-red spectroscopy and by ignition), no conclusions may be drawn as to what proportions of the hydroxyl groups are present on the surface and in the bulk of the silica.

Summarizing, it can be said that Wirzing's method is best suited for distinguishing between chemisorbed and physisorbed water, and that the figures obtained from the simple ignition method of de Boer and Vleeskens after drying the sample at 120°C agree reasonably well with it, especially for xerogels (somewhat less so for aerogels).

B   Determination of the Number of Surface Hydroxyl Groups

As already mentioned in Section V A, Vleeskens did not take into account the possibility of the presence of internal water and/or internal hydroxyl groups within the elementary particles. Thus, he considered the chemical water content to be a measure of the number of surface hydroxyl groups, although during the last decade it became clear that in fact it is a measure of the total number of hydroxyl groups in the silica, including surface silanols, bulk silanol groups, and bulk water. Various methods have been examined for estimating only the surface hydroxyls, such as reactions with diborane, organometallic reagents, diazomethane, chlorosilanes, and D_2O exchange (for a review see Mitchell, 1966). Of these, the work of Fripiat with organometallic compounds and that of Kiselev with isotope-exchange methods have been most successful.

Fripiat and Uytterhoeven (1962) and Uytterhoeven *et al.* (1963, 1965) determine the total hydroxyl content by ignition at 800°C, the distinction between molecular water and OH groups being made by infrared spectroscopy in the region of 1600–3500 cm⁻¹. For the surface hydroxyls use is made of the following reaction:

$$\text{Si—OH} + \text{MeCH}_3 \rightarrow \text{Si—OMe} + \text{CH}_4 \atop \text{H}_2\text{O} + \text{MeCH}_3 \rightarrow \text{MeOH} + \text{CH}_4} (\text{Me} = \text{Li or MgI}).$$

According to these equations the amount of methane evolved is a direct measure of the content of surface hydroxyls, provided that molecular water is absent.

Some typical results obtained by Fripiat's technique for a xerogel are given in Fig. 21 (taken from Uytterhoeven *et al.*, 1963).

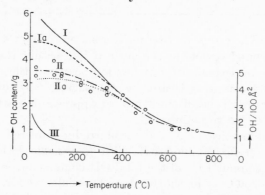

FIG. 21 Typical results for a xerogel: (I) total OH content by ignition; (Ia) total OH content by infra-red; (II) surface hydroxyls+surface H_2O by chemical reaction; (IIa) idem corrected for physisorbed water; (III) molecular water by infra-red.

From Fig. 21 it follows that for this xerogel:

(a) molecular water is removed completely only at a temperature of 400°C (curve III);

(b) the depletion of surface OH groups begins already at about 100°C (curve IIa);

(c) only a certain fraction of the hydroxyls is located at the surface, since the curves IIa and I do not coincide.

In Table IX the relative distribution of hydroxyls in two types of silica is given as a function of the heating temperature. These results are derived from Fripiat's paper.

TABLE IX. Relative distribution (in wt. %) of hydroxyls in silica

Temp. (°C)	Total OH (mmole/g)		Aerosil			Xerogel		
	Aerosil	Xerogel	Molecular water	Internal OH	Surface OH	Molecular H_2O	Internal OH	Surface OH
100	3·40	5·25	13	52	35	11	28	61
200	3·15	4·4	5	56	39	9	21	70
400	2·45	2·6	0	69	31	0	16	84
600	1·20	1·3	0	63	37	0	10	90
700	0·6	1·0	0	25	75	0	0	100

From Table IX it appears that for Aerosil up to 600°C the main part of the OH groups is not on the surface but within the elementary particles. For xerogels already at low temperatures the main proportion of the OH groups is located on the surface, although it is very clear that for this type of silica too an appreciable part of the OH groups may be said to be internal.

From the difference in N_{OH} determined by infra-red spectroscopy and by ignition for Mallinckrodt silica (see Table VIII) it can be concluded that about 10% of the total OH content in the temperature range of 100–200°C is in the form of molecular water, which is in agreement with the figure given for the xerogel in Table IX. Apparently a drying temperature of 120°C is too low to remove all molecular water. On the other hand, higher temperatures result in a small decrease of the surface hydroxyl content as is shown in Fig. 21.

Methods for the determination of the surface hydroxyl groups in silica with chemical reagents are often criticized, mostly because there is no exact proof for the postulated reaction mechanism—this refers, e.g. to the reaction with diborane (Fripiat and van Tongelen, 1967)—and/or of the accessibility of the surface for the reagent in question.

The latter possibility is excluded by Fripiat *et al.* for CH_3Li and CH_3MgI, since both compounds, although differing in molecular size, yield the same result.

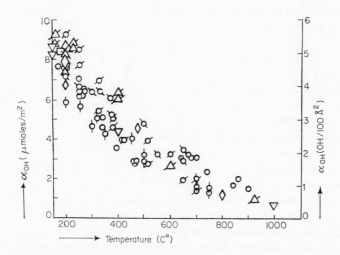

FIG. 22 Change in concentration of hydroxyl groups (a_{OH}) on the surface of different silica samples with rising temperature of treatment *in vitro* (taken from Davydov *et al.*, 1964).

Sample	Symbol	Reaction of SiOH with	Spec. surface area (m_2/g)
Silicagel V	□	D_2O	750
Silicagel A	◇	$MgCH_3I$	410
Silicagel VI	△	D_2O (20°C)	340
	◬	D_2O*	340
	◹	D_2O	340
Aerogel B	◖	$MgCH_3I$	220
Aerosil I	▽	D_2O	180
Aerosil D	○	$MgCH_3I$	178
	●	$LiCH_3$	178
Aerogel C	◗	$MgCH_3I$	135
Silicagel VII	◇	D_2O	39

* and $SiOD + H_2O$ (150°C)

A stronger argument in favour of Fripiat's technique for the determination of surface hydroxyls can be found in the works of Kiselev *et al.*

10

(Davydov *et al.*, 1964; Zhuravlev and Kiselev, 1963, 1965; Zhuravlev *et al.*, 1963). The Soviet workers have combined infra-red spectroscopy with isotope exchange. The surface OH groups are rapidly substituted by OD, making it possible to determine the surface concentration of hydroxyl groups by exchange between the investigated silica samples and D_2O vapour at ordinary temperature. The total amount of OH groups is determined by exchange between D_2O vapour and the entire quantity of water evolved when the sample is heated at 1200°C. The exchange is followed by mass spectroscopy and infra-red spectroscopy. Following D_2O exchange at room temperature, after pumping off the sample at 200°C to remove physisorbed water, the 3750 cm^{-1} band in the infra-red spectrum due from the free OH groups on the surface disappears and is replaced by a narrow band at 2760 cm^{-1} originating from free OD groups on the surface. By similar experiments, Kiselev *et al.* were also able to show that the OH groups in silica (aerogels and xerogels) are located partly on the surface and partly within the elementary particles. The ratio between the quantities of surface and bulk OH groups depends on the past history of the sample and on the size of the elementary particles (Davydov and Kiselev, 1963). Kiselev *et al.* determined the change of the surface hydroxyl group concentration as a function of the heating temperature by means of the isotope-exchange method for eight different silica samples (Fig. 22). Fripiat's results based on the use of CH_3Li and CH_3MgI are also shown in this figure.

In spite of the fact that the silica samples differ greatly both in their structural characteristics and in the method of preparation and subsequent treatment and analysis, the N_{OH} figures and their variation with temperature are much the same. This indicates that there is a great similarity between the surface structure of all samples investigated. The good agreement between Fripiat's and Kiselev's results can be considered definite proof for the validity of the two methods for the determination of the number of surface hydroxyls in silica.

C Structure of the Silica Surface

Vleeskens (1959) studied extensively the influence of temperature on the surface occupation by hydroxyl group occupation, defined by

$$\text{number of OH groups per 100 Å}^2 = \frac{W_{OH} \times 10^{-2} \times N}{S_{N_2} \times 10^{18} \times M/2} = \frac{2 \cdot 10^3 \times W_{OH}}{3 \times S_{N_2}}$$

in which N = Avogadro's number, M = molecular weight of the water, W_{OH} = loss of weight of the silica on ignition at 1200°C after drying at 120°C, in per cent. relative to dry matter (SiO$_2$), S_{N_2} = specific surface area from N_2 adsorption in m^2/g.

When silica was heated up to 1200°C the weight loss W_{OH} decreased drastically, e.g. from 4·8% at 120°C to 1·3% at 700°C. By rehydration in liquid water at 90°C it appeared possible to restore partially the original W_{OH}, provided that the sample had not been heated at a too high temperature, e.g. from 1·3% at 700°C, 3·6% is obtained on re-hydration compared with the original 4·8%. Water adsorption iso-therms of the dehydrated samples show the typical hydrophobic character of these materials. The hysteresis loop does not close, which indicates that during adsorption of water on similar dehydrated surfaces rehydration or formation of surface OH takes place. After complete rehydration in liquid water the water adsorption isotherms follow the normal hydrophilic course.

As a result of heating at, e.g. 700°C, the specific surface area also decreases, but relatively less so than the W_{OH}. Consequently, the N_{OH} determined by Vleeskens' procedure decreases when a silica is heated, e.g. from $N_{OH} = 6$ at 120°C to $N_{OH} = 0$ at 900°C. Even after full rehydration of a heated silica, N_{OH} appeared to have decreased if the silica sample had never been heated before. Vleeskens found that the N_{OH} tends to lower limit of 4·6 when silica is repeatedly heated above 450°C and is in each stage rehydrated by liquid water at 90°C. The higher the heating temperature the fewer stages are needed to reach the limiting value of $N_{OH} = 4·6$ (two stages at 650°C, only one stage at 890°C).

In their interpretation of the meaning of this limiting value, Vleeskens and de Boer assumed that OH groups on the surface are bound to Si atoms and that the surface is fully rehydrated, since it was not possible to increase the amount of chemisorbed water any further. It therefore seems logical to assume that the constant level of $N_{OH} = 4·6$ refers to a state in which all the Si atoms in the surface layer carry one OH group. Such a surface may be represented by the octahedral face of β-cristobalite, as well as by the basal and prism faces of β-tridymite, because these faces contain also 4·6 Si atoms/100 Å^2. Density measure-ments support this point of view. The density of anhydrous silica as determined from measurements with water and helium appears to be 2·28. Values ranging from 2·30 to 2·33 are reported for the density of β-cristobalite and β-tridymite, whereas the density of quartz is 2·65. In conclusion, Vleeskens' results indicate that some degree of ordering must be present in the solid lattice of silica and that the structure of the annealed silica surface is closely related to cristobalite or tri-dymite.

Although Vleeskens did not take into account the possibility of bulk water, as a result of which his N_{OH} figures should be considered critically, the value of $N_{OH} \approx 4\cdot6$ has been confirmed by various other investigators. From the investigations of Fripiat *et al.* and Kiselev *et al.* it follows that after evacuation at 200°C N_{OH} figures of about $4\cdot6$ result for all silicas investigated (see Fig. 22). It therefore seems that the surface structure of not only annealed silicas but of all types of silica is closely related to that of cristobalite or tridymite. The experiments of Fraissard and Imelik (1962) support this point of view. The latter authors showed by means of infra-red spectroscopy that the structure of xerogels may be described as a coherent aggregate of structural units, which resembles the structure of cristobalite or tridymite. On the other hand, the microstructure of aerogels seems to be more closely related to that of quartz.

Hockey and Pethica (1961) showed with infra-red spectroscopy that the Vleeskens' rehydration method after dehydration at a temperature higher than 400°C gives rise only to the free SiOH peak (3750 cm^{-1}) and this is consistent with one OH group per surface Si atom. When silica is heated up to 400°C there is a gradual sharpening of the 3750 cm^{-1} peak and a consistent decrease in the broad band associated with perturbed silanols (3650 cm^{-1}). Under such conditions no loss in surface area occurs, and this wide band can be restored on rehydration. At temperatures in excess of 400°C the band at 3650 cm^{-1} is not restored on rehydration, and only the peak of free SiOH (3750 cm^{-1}) appears.

At first sight it seems rather remarkable that although Vleeskens' general procedure for the determination of N_{OH} is not entirely correct, his results regarding the limiting value of $N_{OH} = 4\cdot6$ are supported by the results obtained by other investigators. Apparently the Vleeskens' dehydration-rehydration treatment produces samples that do not contain bulk OH. In other words, the procedure has the effect of removing bulk OH (Snijder and Ward, 1966). Another proof of this is given by the results of Uytterhoeven *et al.* (1963), who showed that the total hydroxyl content of silica is located at the surface as soon as the silica is annealed at a temperature of about 600°C or higher (see Table IX). Obviously for such cases Vleeskens' N_{OH} determination would yield correct results.

Let us now consider the meaning of the N_{OH} figures determined according to Vleeskens' method in the region of $N_{OH} > 4\cdot6$. When silica is treated with aqueous solutions at, e.g. 80°C, or when it is hydrothermally treated in an autoclave, N_{OH} increases drastically and may go up to 20 or even higher. Vleeskens explained values of $N_{OH} > 4\cdot6$

by assuming the presence of $-Si(OH)_2$ and/or $-Si(OH)_3$ groups on the surface, primarily on the sites of surface irregularities. During heating this broken up surface is smoothed out, while the particles stick together by interaction of OH-groups on the edge and flat parts of the surface, resulting in a decrease of the specific surface area and in removal of the $Si(OH)_2$ and $SiOH_3$ groups.

All evidence given in Section V B indicates that the above explanation of N_{OH} values greater than 4·6 is incorrect. As mentioned before, the essential reason for this is the presence of bulk water and bulk OH in unannealed silicas, which was not taken into account by Vleeskens.

As described in Section IV, treatment of silica with aqueous solutions or a hydrothermal treatment leads to a drastic decrease of the specific surface area and is accompanied by what we might now call a seeming increase of N_{OH} according to Vleeskens. It was suggested that N_{OH} values of, e.g. 13 (Okkerse and de Boer) might be explained by assuming the presence of $-Si(OH)_3$ groups on the surface. Chertov et al. (1965b, 1966) investigated how the surface and bulk hydroxyl content changes when silica is treated hydrothermally. These authors applied ion-exchange of hydrogen in the surface hydroxyls for Ca^{2+} from $Ca(OH)_2$ solutions and the reaction of Si—OH with lithium aluminium hydride to the determination of N_{OH}. Table X presents some of their results and compares them with N_{OH} values according to Vleeskens. The samples were obtained by hydrothermal treatment of the first sample.

TABLE X N_{OH} values for hydrothermally treated silicas according to Chertov and to Vleeskens

S (m²/g)	W_{OH} (wt. %)	N_{OH} acc. to Vleeskens (no./100 Å²)	N_{OH} acc. to Chertov (no./100 Å²)	Amount of bulk OH (wt. %)
425	4·72	7·4	6·0	0·90
166	2·47	9·9	6·1	0·96
73	1·53	13·9	5·3	0·95
21	1·03	32·6	5·4	0·85

It follows from this table that neither the surface OH occupation nor the bulk OH content increases on hydrothermal treatment; both remain virtually constant. The N_{OH} according to Vleeskens does increase, but this is only due to disregarding the presence of bulk OH groups.

In view of these results it is doubtful whether $-Si(OH)_2$ or $-Si(OH)_3$

may occur at all on silica surfaces. Indications for the presence of such groups from infra-red spectroscopy may also be ascribed to interactions of vicinal OH groups

as suggested by Snijder and Ward (1966).

In this concept the sharpening of the free OH peak at 3750 cm^{-1} and the decrease of the broad band at 3650 cm^{-1} (assumed to be due to geminal OH groups $-Si(OH)_2$) on annealing, may still be conceived as a smoothing out of the surface in such a way that the possibility of interaction of vicinal OH groups decreases owing to the removal of surface irregularities.

D   General Conclusions

In conclusion, amorphous silica is a system of polycondensed units of elementary particles, whose size and packing determine the geometrical structure or texture. Irrespective of the dispersity of the silica, the elementary particles consist of a SiO_4 network; at the surface the tetrahedral configuration of silicon is maintained by hydroxyl groups. In silica that has never been heated at high temperature, bulk hydroxyl (originating from SiOH and H_2O) occurs within the elementary particles, which is probably due to incompleteness of the condensation reaction. The surface structure of all silicas is closely related to that of cristobalite or tridymite. In a fully hydrated silica surface one OH group is probably always attracted to one surface silicon atom, and it is doubtful whether surface groups like $Si(OH)_2$ and $Si(OH)_3$ occur at all.

VI   References

Adams, C. R. and Voge, H. H. (1957). *J. phys. Chem.* **61**, 722.

Akshinskaya, N. V., Beznogova, V. E., Kiselev, A. V. and Nikitin, Yu. S. (1962). *Zh. fiz.-khim.* **36** (10), 1233.

Akshinskaya, N. V., Kiselev, A. V. and Nikitin, Yu. S. (1963). *Zh. fiz.-khim.* **37** (4), 927.

Akshinskaya, N. V., Kiselev, A. V. and Nikitin, Yu. S. (1964). *Zh. fiz.-khim.* **38** (2), 488.

Alexander, G. B. (1954). *J. Am. chem. Soc.* **76**, 2094.

Alexander, G. B., Heston, W. M. and Iler, R. K. (1954). *J. phys. Chem.* **58**, 453.

Bartell, F. E. and Fu, Y. (1929). *J. phys. Chem.* **33**, 676.

Baumann, H. (1959). *Kolloid Zh.* **162**, 28.

Bavarez, M. and Bastick, J. (1965). *C. r. hebd. Séanc. Acad. Sci., Paris*, **260**, 3939.

de Boer, J. H., and Vleeskens, J. M. (1957). *Koninkl. ned. Akad. Wet., Proc.* **B60**, 23, 45, 54.

de Boer, J. H. and Vleeskens, J. M. (1958). *Koninkl. ned. Akad. Wet., Proc.* **B61**, 2, 85.

de Boer, J. H., Linsen, B. G. and Okkerse, C. (1960). *Koninkl. ned. Akad. Wet., Proc.* **B63**, 360.

Carmen, P. C. (1940). *Trans. Faraday Soc.* **36**, 964.

Chertov, V. M., Dzambaeva, D. B. and Neimark, I. E. (1965a). *Kolloid Zh.* **27**, 279.

Chertov, V. M., Dzambaeva, D. B., Plashinda, A. S. and Neimark, I. E .(1965b). *Dokl. Akad. Nauk SSSR* **161**, 345.

Chertov, V. M., Dzambaeva, D. B., Plashinda, A. S. and Neimark, I. E. (1966). *Zh. fiz.-khim.* **40**, 520.

Davydov, V. Ya. and Kiselev, A. V. (1963). *Zh. fiz.-khim.* **37**, 2593.

Davydov, V. Ya., Kiselev, A. V. and Zhuravlev, L. T. (1964). *Trans. Faraday Soc.* **60**, 2254.

Davydov, V. Ya., Zhuravlev, L. T. and Kiselev, A. V. (1964). *Zh. fiz.-khim.* **38**, 2047.

Deuel, H. (1959). *Makromolek. Chem.* **34**, 206.

Dollimore, D. and Heal, G. R. (1962). *J. appl. Chem., Lond.* **12**, 445.

Erkelens, J. and Linsen, B. G. (1969). *J. Colloid Interface Sci.* **29**, 464.

Foster, A. G. and Thorp, J. M. (1958). *In* "The Structure and Properties of Porous Materials", p. 288. Butterworth, London.

Fraissard, J. and Imelik, B. (1962). *J. Chim. phys.* **59**, 415.

Fraissard, J., Solomon, I., Callait, R., Erlton, J. and Imelik, B. (1963). *J. Chim. phys.* **60**, 676.

Fripiat, J. J., Léonard, A. and Baraké, N. (1963). *Bull. Soc. chim. Fr.* p. 122.

Fripiat, J. J., and Uytterhoeven, J. (1962). *J. phys. Chem.* **66**, 800.

Fripiat, J. J. and van Tongelen, M. (1967). *J. Catalysis.* **5**, 158.

Gärtner, K. and Griessbach, R. (1958). *Kolloid Zh.* **160**, 21.

Graham, Sir Thomas (1861). *In* "Encyclopedia of Chemical Technology". Vol. 12 (1954). Interscience, New York.

Hockey, J. A. (1965). *J. Chem. Ind.* London, p. 57.

Hockey, J. A. and Pethica, B. A. (1961). *Trans. Faraday Soc.* **57**, 2247.

Iler, R. K. (1952). *J. phys. Chem.* **56**, 680.

Iler, R. K. (1955). "The Colloid Chemistry of Silica and Silicates". Cornell University Press, Ithaca, New York.

Iler, R. K. and Pinckney, P. S. (1947). *Ind. Engng Chem. ind. Edn.* **39**, 1379.

Kiselev, A. V. and Kovaleva, N. V. (1959). *Dokl. Akad. Nauk SSSR* **124**, 617.

Lange, K. R. (1965). *J. Colloid Sci.* **20**, 231.

Linsen, B. G., de Boer, J. H. and Okkerse, C. (1960). *J. Chim. phys.* **57**, 439.

Mitchell, S. A. (1966). *J. Chem. Ind.* London, p. 924.

Mougey, C., François-Rossetti, J. and Imelik, B. (1958). *In* "The Structure and Properties of Porous Materials", p. 266. Butterworth, London.

Moulik, S. P. and Mullick, D. R. (1966). *J. Polym. Sci.* **4**, 811.

Neimark, I. E., Piontkovskaya, M. A. and Slinyakova, I. B. (1956). *Kolloid Zh.* **18**, 61.

Neimark, I. E. and Sheinfain, R. Yu. (1953). *Kolloid Zh.* **15**, 145.

Neimark, I. E., Sheinfain, R. Yu., Kruglikova, N. S. and Stas, O. P. (1964a). *Kolloid Zh.* **26**, 595.

Neimark, I. E., Sheinfain, R. Yu., Lipkind, B. A. and Stas, O. P. (1964b). *Kolloid Zh.* **26**, 734.

Neimark, I. E. and Slinyakova, I. B. (1956). *Kolloid Zh.* **18**, 219.

Okkerse, C. (1961). "Macroporous and Submacroporous Silica", Thesis, Delft University of Technology, The Netherlands.

Okkerse, C. and de Boer, J. H. (1960a). *J. Chim. phys.* **57**, 534.

Okkerse, C. and de Boer, J. H. (1960b). *In* "Reactivity of Solids" (J. H., de Boer, ed.), p. 240. Elsevier, Amsterdam.

Okkerse, C. and de Boer, J. H. (1962). *Silic. ind.* **27**, 195.

Plank, C. J. and Drake, L. C. (1947). *J. Colloid Sci.* **2**, 399.

Ries, Jr., H. E. (1952). *Adv. Catalysis.* **4**, 87.

Schlaffer, W. G., Adams, C. R. and Wilson, J. N. (1965). *J. phys. Chem.* **69**, 1530.

Schlaffer, W. G., Morgan, C. Z. and Wilson, J. N. (1957). *J. phys. Chem.* **61**, 714.

Sheinfain, R. Yu. (1961). *Kolloid Zh.* **23**, 756.

Sheinfain, R. Yu., Kruglikova, N. S., Stas, O. P. and Niemark, I. E. (1963). *Kolloid Zh.* **25**, 732.

Sing, K. S. W. and Madeley, J. D. (1953). *J. appl. Chem.* **3**, 549.

Snijder, L. R. and Ward, J. P. (1966). *J. phys. Chem.* **70**, 394.

Tai An-pang (1963). *Sci. Sinica, Peking* **12** (9), 1311.

Uytterhoeven, J., Hellinckx, E. and Fripiat, J. J. (1963). *Silic. ind.* **28**, 241.

Uytterhoeven, J., Sleex, M. and Fripiat, J. J. (1965). *Bull. Soc. chim. Fr.* **6**, 1800.

Vail, J. C. (1952). "Soluble Silicates". Vols. 1 and 2. Reinhold, New York.

Vleeskens, J. M. (1959). Thesis, Delft, University of Technology,The Netherlands.

White, L. J. (1959). *Ind. Engng Chem. ind. Edn.* **51**, 232.

Wirzing, G. (1963). *Naturwissenschaften* **30**, 13, 466.

Wolf, F. and Beyer, H. (1959). *Kolloid Zh.* **165**, 151.

Young, G. J. and Bursh, T. P. (1960). *J. Colloid Sci.* **15**, 361.

Zhuravlev, L. T. and Kiselev, A. V. (1963). *Kolloid Zh.* **24**, 22.

Zhuravlev, L. T. and Kiselev, A. V. (1965). *Zh. fiz.-khim.* **39**, 453.

Zhuravlev, L. T., Kiselev, A. V., Naidina, V. P. and Polyakov, A. L. (1963). *Zh. fiz.-khim.* **37**, 2258.

Chapter 6

ACTIVE MAGNESIA

W. F. N. M. DE VLEESSCHAUWER*

Laboratory of Chemical Engineering, Technological University of Delft, The Netherlands

I Introduction

In 1961 J. H. de Boer edited the book "The Mechanism of Heterogeneous Catalysis". In a chapter of this book dealing with the decomposition of formic acid on oxides, Mars (1961) reviewed formic acid decomposition on several oxidic catalysts. He pointed out that all such catalysts showed the same selectivity for both the decomposition of formic acid and for alcohol. Mars collected the literature data in a graph. On the vertical axis was plotted the selectivity for the ethanol decomposition, on the horizontal axis the selectivity for the formic acid decomposition. In

---

* Present Address: Texaco Belgium N.V., European Research Centre, Ghent, Belgium.

both cases the selectivity was expressed as the ratio of the dehydrogenation rate to the total decomposition rate. In this selectivity diagram the different oxides could be located around the diagonal line going from the "100% dehydration origin" to the "100% dehydrogenation corner".

From this diagram it was apparent that the oxides not only showed a comparable selectivity for both reactions, but moreover—provided the preheating temperature of the oxides was not too high—the selectivity could be considered as a characteristic property of the oxides. The position of magnesia in this diagram was diametrically opposed to that of alumina. Magnesia showed a 100% dehydrogenation selectivity while for alumina the dehydrogenation to dehydration rate was almost zero. It was this controversial behaviour that induced the start of research on active magnesia in de Boer's Delft group. Following the tradition of his school, the investigation of the texture itself and of the parameters which control the ultimate texture of the active material received great emphasis, but also the catalytic aspects for one of the above mentioned reactions, alcohol decomposition, was investigated. This reaction was studied in order:

1. to determine the selectivity and the intrinsic activity of magnesia for this particular reaction;
2. to find out whether the selectivity is really a characteristic property of the oxide, or whether it is influenced by the texture of the solid.

The opinion that the selectivity is influenced by the texture is held by Schwab and Schwab-Agallicles (1949) who believe that the dehydrogenation reaction takes place on a flat surface and the dehydration reaction in narrow pores.

A part of this research on active magnesia is communicated in the following sections. The reader who may be interested in more details may be referred to a previous publication (de Vleesschauwer, 1967).

II Principles of the Activation Method

In Chapter 1 of this book, contributed by Broekhoff and Linsen, four major methods for the preparation of active solids or microporous systems are given: thermal decomposition, leaching of substances, sublimation and precipitation. The first three methods were already known in the seventeenth century and were mentioned by the English empiricist Francis Bacon. Among the methods given by Bacon was "calcination" or, in more general terms, thermal decomposition of compounds of which at least one of the dissociation products is volatile. This is the appropriate method for the preparation of active magnesia. This activation method takes advantage of two features:

1. the resulting oxide is invariably more dense than the reactant; and
2. the external shape and volume of the reactant particles are largely retained.

As a consequence the volume of the volatile material which leaves the reactant upon heating, is to a great extent converted into pore volume. The extent of this pore volume production depends upon the amount of contraction of the original particles or crystals. Examples of active magnesia generators are the hydroxide, carbonate, carbonate hydrates, basic carbonates, oxalate, etc., of magnesium. The volatile dissociation products are thus water, carbon dioxide and in the case of the oxalate also carbon monoxide. When the heat treatment would not be accompanied by any shrinkage, the pore volume might be calculated from the difference of the specific volume of the starting material and the solid product. In the case of magnesium hydroxide the theoretically possible porosity amounts to 54%, whereas in the case of the pentahydrate of magnesium carbonate, a porosity as high as 89% would be possible in theory. In practice, the porosity created by this activation method proves seldom higher than 60%. In the preparation of active solids by calcination, there are several factors to be considered. The major variables are:

(a) chemical composition and structure of the starting material,
(b) heating temperature,
(c) heating period,
(d) atmosphere in which the activation is carried out.

Moreover, effects of size or packing of the sample or effects of heating rate or extent of ventilation are often observed. These effects are generally due to a pressure build-up of the released volatile components, by which the gas composition at the reaction interface can be different from that of the main body of the gas phase. Essentially, these effects are covered by item (d).

In the next two sections, both the effect of the starting material and the heating temperature will be discussed for two "active magnesia generators", i.e. crystalline magnesium carbonate (magnesite) and crystalline magnesium carbonate trihydrate (nesquehonite). Both starting products were well-crystallized, with crystal dimensions in the μ-range. A rather long heating period (24 hours) was employed to ensure that any short-term effects during the heat treatment would be obviated in most cases. The intention was to prepare rather stable products which would not age too rapidly. This condition is best fulfilled when the heat treatment is carried out in air.

III Active Magnesia Prepared from Magnesite

A Preparations

The starting material was synthetic magnesite, prepared by hydro-thermal treatment of crystalline $MgCO_3 . 3H_2O$ (nesquehonite) in an autoclave at 150°C. The magnesite was obtained in the form of well-shaped rhombohedral crystals with an average size of 1 μ and a specific surface area of 2·9 m^2/g. From this powdery material pellets were made varying in size between 1·2 and 2·0 mm.

Separate batches of this material were heated in air for 24 hours at temperatures of 400, 500, 550, 600, 700 and 800°C. These preparations are indicated as M-450, M-500, M-550, etc.

B Investigation of the Calcination Products of Magnesite

A Decomposition Degree

From the loss on ignition, determined by heating the preparations at 1200°C till constant weight, the degree of dissociation can be calcu-lated. From these values the "dissociation curve" given in Fig. 1 was made.

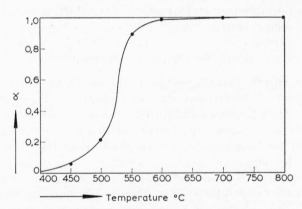

FIG. 1 Degree of decomposition of magnesite as a function of calcination tempera-ture.

It can be seen that only above 500°C a marked CO_2 loss sets in. The last traces of carbon dioxide are difficult to remove as is apparent

from the slow approach of the degree of decomposition to the 100%
value. The exact figures are 98·6% at 600°C, 99·4% at 700°C and 99·7%
at 800°C.

B   X-ray Powder Patterns

The X-ray patterns of preparations M-450 and M-500 are still identical
with that of the original magnesite. M-550 already shows the presence
of MgO, although some strong magnesite reflections can still be dis-
cerned. At higher preparation temperatures only the MgO pattern is
shown, the diffraction lines of which become sharper at increased
temperatures.

C   Microscopic Investigation

Using normal light it is impossible to detect whether magnesite has
been decomposed into magnesia or not. The microscopic pictures of
M-450 and M-550, for 5·8 and 89·1% decomposition respectively,
do not show any difference. This observation demonstrates the pseudo-
morphous character of the dissociation process.

By using polarized light, however, the distinction between decomposed and undecomposed crystals can easily be made. Between crossed
nicols magnesite shows its distinct birefringent character. On decomposition into the regular magnesia, birefringence disappears. For M-500
all crystals are still birefringent, whereas for M-550 only a few birefringent crystals are left. The decomposed crystals are translucent
between crossed nicols instead of opaque as would be expected for
isotropic material. The disperse state of the magnesia formed is responsible for this anomalous behaviour. On wetting the specimen on the
microscope slide with acetone, the decomposed crystals rapidly lose
their translucency. The rapidity with which the relics of the magnesite
crystals turn opaque shows that the pore structure formed on decomposition is easily accessible for acetone molecules.

D   Specific Volume of the Preparations in Alcohol

To verify the latter conclusion, the specific volume of the decomposition products was determined by imbibition of small diameter
molecules. For this purpose water is often used. Its affinity for active
magnesia is so high, however, that magnesium oxide can be converted
into magnesium hydroxide even by water vapour. For that reason
ethyl alcohol was used. This molecule is less reactive and only a few

ångstrom bigger than the water molecule. The specific volumes expressed per gram MgO, since the various preparations contain different amounts of CO_2-, were compared with the specific volumes calculated from their compositions by means of the relation

$$V_{spec} = \frac{1}{40 \cdot 32} (V_{MgO} + x V_{CO_2}) \text{ cm}^3/\text{g MgO} \qquad (1)$$

where x is the molar fraction of CO_2 contained in the sample. V_{MgO} and V_{CO_2}, the molar volumes of MgO and of CO_2 as bound in magnesite, were derived from literature data, assuming the molar volume of MgO in active magnesia and as bound in magnesite to be equal.

The agreement between the experimental and the calculated specific volumes is quite good. For preparation M-450 both figures are 0·672 and 0·663 cm³/g MgO, respectively, for M-500, 0·608 and 0·598 and for M-550, 0·328 and 0·324 cm³/g MgO. These figures demonstrate that the pores formed during the decomposition are fully accessible for molecules of the size of ethyl alcohol. This fact suggests that the densities determined in ethyl alcohol are closely related to the true density of the solid materal. The above-mentioned agreement is apparent from Fig. 2, where the experimental specific volumes of the different products are given versus their degree of dissociation. The full line represents the theoretical line, obeying Eq. (1).

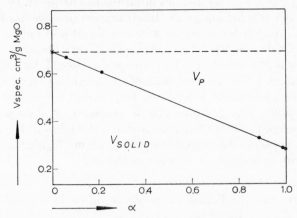

FIG. 2 Specific volume of the M preparations versus the degree of decomposition.

The vertical distance between this full line and the horizontal dotted line, in the same graph represents the theoretically possible pore volume, which will be obtained when no contraction or shrinkage of the original magnesite crystals takes place. On full decomposition this maximum pore volume amounts to 0·36 cm³/g, which value corresponds with a porosity of 60·3%.

To what extent this condition is actually fulfilled, together with more information about the pore structure, can be derived from the nitrogen sorption isotherms.

E Analysis of the Nitrogen Sorption Isotherms

A powerful tool for the investigation of pore structure and pore genesis in the preparation of active solids is offered by nitrogen sorption isotherms measured at liquid nitrogen temperature. Theoretical backgrounds and experimental set-up are considered in detail elsewhere in this book. Quantitative texture data which can be obtained from a sorption isotherm concern pore volume, surface area, mean pore radius and pore volume distribution. Moreover, qualitative information can be obtained on the shape of the pores. Typical isotherms of the decomposition products of well-crystallized magnesite are depicted in Figs 3a,b and c.

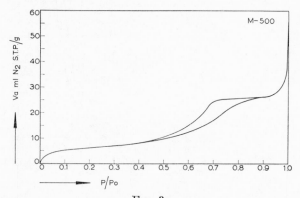

FIG. 3a

FIG. 3a Nitrogen sorption isotherm for magnesite decompositions product: M-500.

(a) *Pore Volume*. Generally the volume of micropores, or transitional pores, as they are termed in the Dubinin classification, is given by the volume of liquid adsorbate at a pressure close to the saturation pressure. The desorption branches of the depicted sorption isotherms show a more or less horizontal part and this volume corresponds to filling with liquid nitrogen, the pores formed within the original magnesite crystals. This pore volume is called the *intra*crystalline pore volume to distinguish it from the *inter*crystalline pore volume, which is made up by the voids between the relic magnesite crystals within the pellets. Figure 4 shows the course of the intracrystalline pore volume with the preparation temperature.

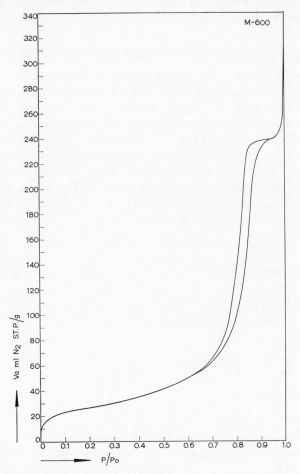

FIG. 3*b* Nitrogen sorption isotherm M-600.

Two parts can be distinguished: a rising part in the decomposition stage, and a falling part which must be related to sintering phenomena accompanied by shrinkage of the parent crystals. The maximum recorded pore volume is 0.370 cm^3/g for preparation M-600. This value corresponds with an intracrystalline porosity of 56.8%, which value is not far below the theoretically possible value of 60.3%.

To get an idea of the volume of the intercrystalline pores, the void volume of the pellets of M-600 was determined. This volume was

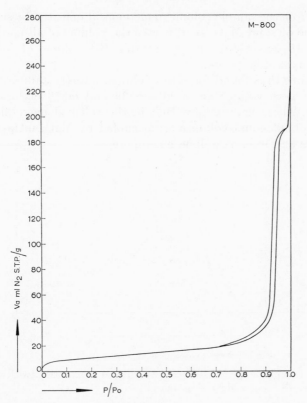

FIG. 3c Nitrogen sorption isotherm M-800.

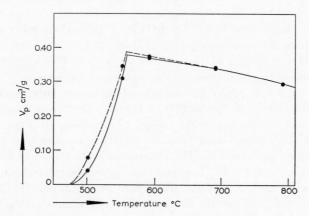

FIG. 4 Intracrystalline pore volume as a function of the calcination temperature.
$---$ per g MgO, $\underline{\quad\quad}$ per g.

obtained from the sample volume in mercury at one atm. by subtracting the volume of solid MgO. In this way the volume of all pores up to a radius of 15 μ is obtained, representing the volume of both intra- and intercrystalline pores.

The figures thus found for pellet volume, intercrystalline and intra-crystalline pore volume are 1·001, 0·339 and 0·376 cm³/g MgO, respectively. These figures show that in the calcined magnesite pellets of M-600 about equal volumes are occupied by MgO, intracrystalline micropores and intercrystalline macropores.

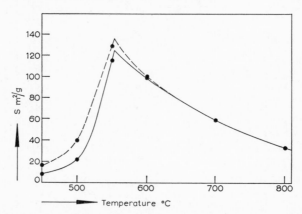

FIG. 5 Variation of the specific surface area of the M preparations with calcination temperature. – – – per g MgO, —— per g.

(b) *Surface Area.* The surface areas were calculated in the usual way from the lower reversible parts of the sorption isotherms using the BET equation. The value adopted for the area taken up by a nitrogen molecule was 16·27 Å². In Fig. 5 the calculated values are plotted versus the calcination temperature of the preparations, while in Fig. 6 the variation of the surface area (and the intracrystalline pore volume) with the degree of decomposition, are shown.

Both graphs can again be considered as being composed of two distinct parts, i.e. a rising branch in the decomposition range, and a falling branch in the sintering range. Comparison of Figs 4 and 5 shows that the surface area is more sensitive to sintering than the intracrystalline pore volume. The maximum surface area of 115·3 m²/g is obtained at 550°C. By lowering the decomposition temperature, products with higher surface areas can be obtained. This can be achieved by carrying out the decomposition in vacuum, as was shown for natural magnesite by Razouk and Mikhail (1961).

In Fig. 7 the adsorption isotherms are given in the form of "*t*-plots".

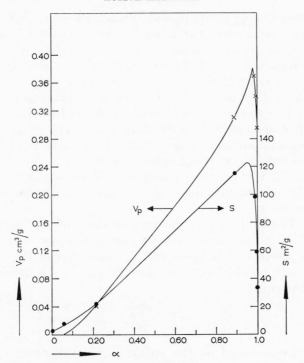

FIG. 6 Dependence of the surface area (●) and intracrystalline pore volume (×) on the decomposition degree of magnesite.

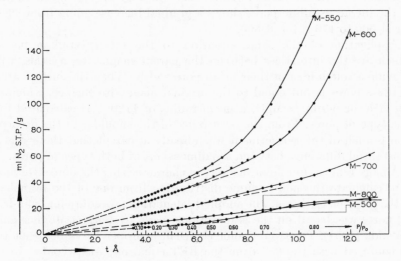

FIG. 7 V_a–t graphs for the M preparations.

After an initial linear region passing through the origin—showing that in this range the master t-curve is followed—deviations in an upward direction occur, demonstrating that the material takes up more adsorbate than corresponds to the volume of the multilayer; hence pointing to the onset of capillary condensation.

From these V_a–t graphs the absence of submicropores may be concluded. The specific surface areas calculated from the linear part are in perfect agreement with the BET values. The relative pressure, where reversible capillary condensation sets in, shifts to higher values with higher calcination temperatures, indicating a smoothing of the surface. In the V_a–t graph of preparation M-800 no deviations from the straight line through the origin are observed in the investigated pressure range.

(c) *Pore Radius.* It is apparent from the shift of the hysteresis loop to higher relative pressures that the pore dimensions increase with a rise in the calcination temperature. A rough idea of the mean pore radius $(\bar{r}_p)$ can be obtained from pore volume (V_p) and surface area (S) using the equation:

$$\bar{r}_p = \frac{2V_p}{S}. \tag{2}$$

This equation is based on the presence of non-intersecting tubular pores of uniform size. In practical cases these conditions are seldom fulfilled. The values calculated by means of Eq. (2) are plotted as a function of the calcination temperature in Fig. 8. The mean radius of the intracrystalline pores shows a gradual increase going from 39 Å for M-500 to 176 Å for M-800.

Application of the same equation to the intercrystalline pores, which are the interstices between the parent magnesite crystals, will provide a rough idea of their mean pore width. When the surface area of these pores is put equal to the original magnesite surface, which is 2·9 m²/g or 6·0 m²/g MgO, a mean radius of 1130 Å is calculated for this type of pores. From the occurrence of the shoulder in the desorption branch of the isotherms it was already apparent that there was a substantial difference between the dimensions of both types of pores.

A more refined, but laborious way of characterizing the pore structure is to calculate the pore volume distribution from one of the branches of the sorption isotherm. The adopted calculation procedure for cylindrical pores was based on the assumptions made by Barrett, Joyner and Halenda (1951). The troublesome choice of a proper "c-value" (not to be confused with the "c" from the BET equation) was avoided by a straightforward elaboration of the assumptions of Barrett *et al.*, leading to an equation where the volume of pores (V_{p_n}) with certain radius $(\bar{r}_{p_n})$ is given by:

$$V_{p_n} = A_n \Delta V_n - B_n \sum_1^{n-1} S_i + C_n \sum_1^{n-1} L_i \text{ (de Vleesschauwer, 1967)} \qquad (3)$$

where for a particular step n:

A_n, B_n and C_n are constants;

ΔV_n = the volume desorbed;

$\sum_1^{n-1} S_i$ = the total surface area of all previously emptied pores;

$\sum_1^{n-1} L_i$ = the total length of all pores emptied in previous steps.

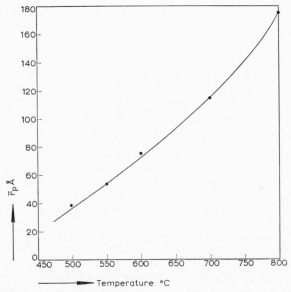

Fig. 8 Variation of the mean pore radii of the intracrystalline pores with the calcination temperature of magnesite.

The results of these calculations, as far as the pore volume distribution is concerned, are depicted in Fig. 9. The distribution curves for these preparations obtained from magnesite are rather symmetrical. There is a trend to a sharper distribution for preparations made at lower temperatures.

(d) *Shape of the Pores.* In the analysis of the desorption branches of the isotherms by use of Eq. (3) the cumulative surface areas obtained at the end of the distribution calculation, considerably exceed the corresponding BET surface areas. In the case of preparation M-550 for example $S_{cum}S_{BET}S_{cum}S_{BET}$ was as high as 1·64. The fact that S_{cum} is considerably higher than S_{BET} might be attributable—provided that the assumptions which rest on the basis of these calculations are justified—to either one of the following effects: (a) a non-uniform pore width along the length of the pores, (b) intersections of pores.

With regard to (a), when the cross-section of a pore is not constant, but varies along the length, the pore will lose its capillary condensate

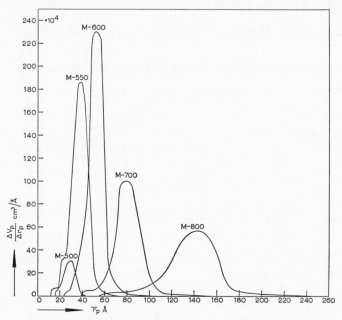

FIG. 9 Pore volume distributions of the M preparations. Analysis is based on the nitrogen desorption isotherm.

at a relative pressure which corresponds to a width that is smaller than the average or hydraulic radius of the pore. Consequently the volume present in the wider parts of the pore will be attributed to a pore of smaller radius and, accordingly, the surface area calculated according to equation

$$S_n = \frac{2V_{p_n}}{\bar{r}_{p_n}} \tag{4}$$

will be too high.

Allowance can be made for the fact that the hydraulic radius of a pore is greater than the critical radius (r_k+t), where emptying of the pore occurs, by putting the hydraulic pore radius $<r_p>$ equal to

$$<r_p> = m(r_k+t) \tag{5}$$

where the factor $m(m>1)$ is a measure of the uniformity of the pore cross-section. By trial and error, a value for m can be evaluated, for which the following conditions are best fulfilled:

1. $S_{cum} = S_{BET}$
2. $V_{cum} = V_p$
3. $V_{p_n} = 0$, at that relative pressure, where the V_a–t plot shows the end of pure multilayer adsorption (no capillary condensation anymore).

For the magnesias prepared from magnesite the pore uniformity factor obtained in this way varies between 1·3 and 1·6. The higher the calcination temperature, the lower is the uniformity factor. The evidence obtained here suggests the presence of tubular pores with narrower and wider parts.

With regard to (b) above, when intersection of pores occurs, there is a certain amount of pore volume, i.e. the intersection space, without the full corresponding surface area. Accordingly, the surface area of a group of pores, calculated with the above-mentioned equation, will be too large. It was shown that in the case of intersections of two pores (singular intersections) the surface area of such a pore is given by

$$S_p = \frac{2V_p}{r_p} \times \frac{1-3/4\epsilon}{1-1/2\epsilon} \tag{6}$$

where ϵ is the intracrystalline porosity.

Contrary to the equation given by Wheeler (1955) and by Steggerda (1956), this equation accounts both for common volume of the pores in their intersections and for the presence of surface area in the intersected volume (de Vleesschauwer, 1967). In the case of intersections of three pores (twofold intersections) the intersection factor reduces to $(1-\epsilon)/(1-2/3\epsilon)$.

Taking into account the effect of singular as well as twofold intersections, the cumulative surface area obtained in the analysis of the desorption isotherms, still exceeds the corresponding BET value. Hence the occurrence of pore intersections only, is not sufficient to explain the observed differences. From analysis of the adsorption isotherms, further evidence was obtained that these deviations are due mainly to the presence of pores with wide and narrow parts along their lengths, while the occurrence of pore intersections also must be considered.

The correspondence between pore shape and type of hysteresis loop was thoroughly analysed by de Boer (1958). Twenty-one shape groups of pores were distinguished giving rise to five different types of hysteresis loops. In view of the nature of the underlying pores being the interstices between randomly-packed magnesia crystallites, two shape groups are obvious here. These are groups II and XV of de Boer's classification (Fig. 10). Pores belonging to shape group II give rise to an A-type hysteresis loop, while group XV pores cause an E-type loop. The isotherms of the magnesias obtained at the higher calcination temperatures have an A-type loop and those of the products obtained at the lower temperatures show some E-character. The nature of the hysteresis loop, and information obtained from the cumulative calculations in the analysis of the sorption isotherms, suggest that for the magnesias made from magnesite the shape of the pores can best be

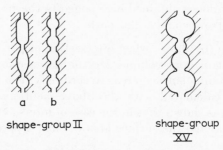

shape-group II   shape-group XV

FIG. 10 Pores representing shape group II (*a* and *b*) and shape group XV, after J. H. de Boer (1958).

represented by group II, being tubular pores with somewhat widened parts. An analysis of the widths of the hysteresis loops suggests that group IIb enjoys preference to IIa. The widened parts are then more or less spheroidally shaped.

F Size of the Magnesia Crystallites

It has been mentioned already that X-ray diffractions showed line broadening, which decreased with an increase in the calcination temperature of the preparations. Apart from the width inherent with the instrument, the width of the diffraction profile is determined by the size of the crystallites and by variation of the lattice parameter, often denoted by lattice strain. These two causes of line broadening can be distinguished by making use of the fact that both effects depend differently on the Bragg angle. In practice, this is established by measuring the line broadening for different diffractions and making a plot of $\beta_i \cos \theta$ versus $\sin \theta$, where β_i is the integral width of the pure diffraction profile and θ is the Bragg angle. When line broadening is due only to the small dimensions of the crystallites a horizontal line is found. The intercept on the vertical axis is inversely proportional to the crystallite size. When line broadening is due solely to lattice strain, a straight line is obtained which passes through the origin. Its slope is a measure of the variation in lattice parameter.

The experimental data are collected in Fig. 11.

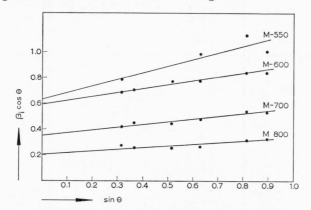

FIG. 11 $\beta_i \cos \theta$ versus $\sin \theta$ plots for active magnesias prepared from magnesite.

It is apparent from the graphs that the main cause of line broadening is the small crystallites size. Their size increases with increase of calcination temperature. The values calculated from the intercepts were the following: 154 Å for M-550, 165 Å for M-600, 278 Å for M-700 and 485 Å for M-800.

C Conclusions

The pore volume of the solid substances obtained by pyrolysis of synthetic magnesites proved fully accessible to ethyl alcohol molecules. The volumes determined by imbibition of alcohol, therefore correspond with the true densities of the solid material. Since a nitrogen molecule is smaller than an ethyl alcohol molecule, nitrogen will likewise be able to penetrate into all pores. By adding the volume of the solid material and the volume of the intracrystalline pores, the volume of the parent magnesite crystals ($V_{crystal}$) will be obtained:

$$V_{crystal} = V_{solid} + V_{p\ intracrystalline} \tag{7}$$

These values with other characteristic data of the preparations are recorded in Table I.

From the fifth column of this table it is seen that $V_{crystal}$ undergoes a decrease during heat treatment. From the difference of the crystal volume relative to the starting material, the extent of shrinkage was

TABLE I. Texture properties of the preparations of the M series

Preparations	Decomposition degree %	V_{solid} cm³/g MgO	V_p, intra-crystalline cm³/g MgO	$V_{crystal}$	Shrinkage Vol. %	Intra-crystalline porosity Vol. %	S_{BET} m²/g	Pore radius $\bar{r}_p$ Å	Crystallite size D Å	$S_{cryst.}$ m²/g
M	—	0·705	—	0·705	—	—	2·9	—	—	—
M-450	5·79	0·672	—	—	—	—	8·1	—	—	—
M-500	21·11	0·608	0·078	0·686	2·7	11·4	21·6	39	—	—
M-550	89·11	0·328	0·347	0·675	4·3	51·4	115·3	54	154	115
M-600	98·62	0·286	0·376	0·662	6·1	56·8	98·7	75	165	102
M-700	99·39	0·281	0·342	0·623	11·6	54·9	59·5	114	278	60
M-800	99·66	0·280	0·296	0·576	18·3	51·4	33·6	176	485	34

calculated (column 6). The relics of magnesite prove to contract progressively with rise of temperature. The overall shrinkage, however,
is not drastic. At 800°C it is only 18·3% by volume, causing the intracrystalline porosity of M-800 to be 51·4% instead of 60·3%. Qualitative
information on the presence of tiny magnesite crystals was obtained
from microscopic investigation of the preparations. This information
was confirmed with quantitative data from line broadening of X-ray
diffractions. The crystallite sizes ranged from 154 to 485 Å. In view of
the rather high porosity values ($> 50\%$) it is likely that the crystallite
faces will be available to a great extent for adsorption. When the
crystallites are assumed to be compact cubes, the total surface area
of the exposed faces can be calculated from their size and density by
means of the relation

$$S_{cryst} = \frac{6 \times V_{solid}}{D} \times 10^4 \tag{8}$$

where S_{cryst} = total specific surface area of the crystallites in m^2/g;

V_{solid} = true specific volume of the crystallites in cm^3/g;

D = crystallite size, in Å.

The values for S_{cryst} are collected in the last column of the given
table. Comparison of these crystallite areas with those available
for nitrogen adsorption (S_{BET}) yields a remarkable agreement. This
agreement suggests that the packing of the crystallites within the
aggregates is very loose. These aggregates, which have the same shape
and almost the same dimensions of the original magnesite crystals,
consist of ill-fitting magnesia crystallites, held at corners and edges
by weak van der Waals forces. Theoretically such a situation would be
obtained by removing every second building stone in a three-dimensional structure. The remaining building stones are likely to be orientated
in such a case. No orientation of the magnesia crystallites with respect
to the original magnesite lattice could be found by selected area electron
diffraction, so the crystallites are stacked in a random manner within
the parent magnesite crystals. With increase of calcination temperature
the magnesia crystallites grow bigger and the specific surface areas
show a corresponding fall. The mean crystallite size increases, whereas
the total number of crystallites decreases. This means that the larger
crystallites grow at the expense of the smaller.

The decrease of the pore volume, which is not so drastic as the fall
of the surface area, has to be related to the contraction of the original
crystal volume. In this conception it is apparent that the pore dimensions will increase at higher preparation temperatures, because the
crystallites become bigger and hence the voids between the crystallites

will become bigger too. The fact that the increase of the mean pore size lags behind the increase of the crystallite size—ratio pore diameter to crystallite size is 0·91, 0·82 and 0·71 for M-600, M-700 and M-800 respectively—has to be ascribed again to the shrinkage of the parent crystals.

From analysis of the sorption isotherms based on the presence of tubular pores, it appeared that the calculated cumulative data were in agreement with the experimental data, when it was assumed that

(a) the pores were not uniform but their cross-section varied along the pore, and

(b) intersections of pores occurred.

This conclusion is compatible with the idea of pores formed by packing of particles, where interstices of varying size will be met when a porous relic magnesite aggregate is transversed in an arbitrary direction, while in many interstices it will be possible to choose a path in a different direction.

IV Active Magnesia Prepared from Nesquehonite

A Introduction

On decomposition of nesquehonite, crystalline magnesium carbonate trihydrate, two volatile components, water and carbon dioxide, escape. Pore genesis will appear less straightforward than in the case of magnesite.

B Preparations

Nesquehonite was prepared by a homogeneous precipitation method, starting from a solution containing bicarbonate and magnesium ions. Exposed to air this solution is unstable at room temperature. A slow disproportionation of bicarbonate into carbonate and carbon dioxide occurs. Carbon dioxide is released and the trihydrate of magnesium carbonate gradually precipitates in a crystalline form. The snowy nesquehonite thus obtained consists of well-shaped birefringent needle-like crystals. Indexing of the obtained diffraction data showed that nesquehonite belongs to the monoclinic system. The dimensions of the unit cell are $a_0 = 12·11$ Å, $b_0 = 5·37$ Å, and $c_0 = 7·70$ Å, while $\beta = 90·42°$. The unit cell contains four molecules. With β so close to 90°, it is not surprising that nesquehonite is often considered to be ortho-rhombic. The powdery material was pelletized to spherical granules of 1·4–2·0 mm in a revolving drum by the wetting technique.

Separate portions of these nesquehonite granules were heated for 24 hours in air at different temperatures varying between 100 and

800°C. The granules were spread out as thinly as possible on a porcelain dish to prevent pressure build-up effects during the decomposition process. Temperature was raised at a slow rate to the desired value, after which the heat treatment was continued for 24 hours. The products thus obtained will be referred to further as N-150, N-200, N-250, etc. In this designation the number indicates the heating temperature.

C   Decomposition Route of Nesquehonite

The decomposition at relatively low temperature is illustrated in Fig. 12, where the H_2O/MgO and CO_2/MgO molar ratios of various

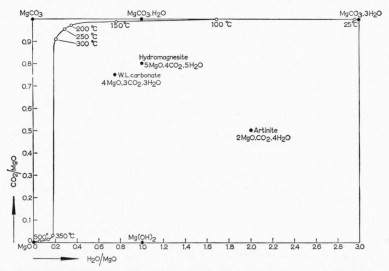

Fig. 12 Molecular composition of the calcination products of nesquehonite.

decomposition products are plotted, and the corresponding heating temperatures are indicated. From this diagram it is seen that the decomposition takes a rather selective route. Three stages can be distinguished:

1. loss of water, till a residual water content of about 0·2 mole is reached;
2. release of carbon dioxide (practically all carbon dioxide is released within a relatively small temperature range);
3. loss of residual water (the last traces of carbon dioxide are given off here as well).

Initial loss represents water of hydration. The progress of this process is clearly visualized in the DTA curves of the various products (Fig. 13).

The upper DTA trace recorded with the original nesquehonite

sample shows in the low temperature range (150–260°C) a broad unresolved endothermic peak. With increasing preparation temperatures this dehydration peak becomes smaller and smaller and has disappeared completely after preheating at 200°C.

The DTA curve of N-100 already shows a single dehydration peak. The X-ray diffraction pattern of N-100 is quite different from that of

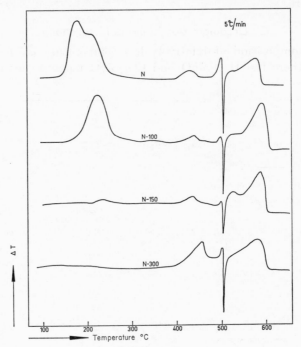

FIG. 13 DTA curves of nesquehonite and partially dehydrated nesquehonite preparations.

nesquehonite, although several spacings show some agreement with those of nesquehonite. This pattern also is obtained at 150°C, although less marked. The occurrence of this diffraction pattern in the dehydration sequence of nesquehonite has on various occasions been ascribed to a lower crystal hydrate, the mono or the dihydrate. The former enjoys generally preference. This matter has been discussed by Dell and Weller (1959).

Evidence for this lower hydrate is provided by the occurrence of the shoulder in the DTA dehydration peak. When the resolution is increased by carrying out the DTA at a lower heating rate, two maxima are found. Up to now, however, attempts to synthesize this lower hydrate have not been successful.

In the X-ray patterns of N-200, N-250 and N-300 all original diffraction lines have disappeared. Only a diffuse halo in the low angle range occurs to demonstrate that these products are amorphous to X-rays. The powder pattern of N-300 shows moreover a few faint lines of a basic carbonate (W.L. carbonate, see Section V B). All the products obtained at temperatures higher than 300°C show only the magnesium oxide pattern. The originally rather diffuse diffractions grow sharper at higher temperatures. At 800°C the material is well-crystallized to permit resolution of the α_1–α_2 doublet for the back reflections. Nesquehonite releases carbon dioxide to form magnesium oxide, at a much lower temperature than magnesite, showing that the carbonate ion in nesquehonite is much less stable.

As in the case of magnesite a "dissociation curve" may be inferred from the loss on ignition data (Fig. 14). The three stages, dehydration,

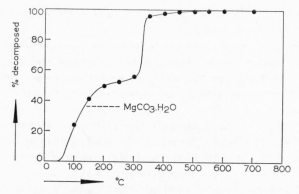

FIG. 14 Decomposition curve of nesquehonite.

decarbonation and loss of residual water, can be distinguished clearly. The dehydration presumably occurs via a lower hydrate, to form an X-ray amorphous hydrous carbonate. This intermediate releases carbon dioxide at relatively low temperatures, with formation of hydrous magnesia. At higher temperatures well-crystallized magnesia is formed and most of the residual water is released.

D   Texture of the Nesquehonite Decomposition Products

A   Availability to Ethyl Alcohol

As with the preparations of the magnesite series, specific volumes of the samples were determined in ethyl alcohol. An initial densification is observed with increase of preparation temperature ($d_4^{20} = 1 \cdot 835$

g/cm³ for N and 2.049 g/cm³ for N-100); thereafter the densities decrease to a minimum value of 1·758 g/cm³ for N-250. Decarbonation is accompanied by a sharp increase of the density from 1·775 for N-300 to 3·328 for N-350. The sintering range shows a further densification to a value of 3·594 for N-800. It is remarkable that beyond 50% decomposition the density has fallen to a value which is even lower than that of the starting material.

A comparison of the specific volumes calculated from the composition of the products and the experimental specific volumes gives more information on this peculiar phenomenon. The calculation presumes the molar volumes of magnesia, carbon dioxide and water to be additive, as expressed by the following equation:

$$V_{\text{spec}} = \frac{1}{40 \cdot 32} \left(V_{\text{MgO}} + x V_{\text{CO}_2} + y V_{\text{H}_2\text{O}}\right) \text{ cm}^3/\text{g. MgO} \tag{9}$$

where x and y are the molar amounts of water and carbon dioxide in the corresponding preparations.

The molar volume of water, 15·88 cm³/mole, is calculated from the difference in molar volume between nesquehonite and magnesite. A density of 1·14 g/cm³ for the water of hydration corresponds to this value. A further assumption is that at temperatures of 200°C and above, the residual water is no longer water of hydration but hydroxyl water, i.e. in the form in which it occurs in the hydroxide. The corresponding value for $V_{\text{H}_2\text{O}}$ (13·29 cm³/mole) is obtained from the difference in molar volume of the hydroxide and the oxide of magnesium. The density of hydroxyl water, corresponding to this value is 1·36 g/cm³; hence considerably higher than that found for the water of hydration. Similarly the molar volume of carbon dioxide (16·55 cm³/mole) is obtained from the molar volume of magnesite and magnesium oxide. Experimental calculated specific volumes and those calculated from Eq. (9) are recorded in Fig. 15.

From both graphs it is apparent that during the dehydration stage an appreciable deviation between both values arises. This difference disappears as soon as magnesium oxide is formed. It is remarkable that for preparation N-100, which already has lost 1·3 mole of water, there is hardly any difference between the experimental values and calculated values. This suggests that the initial dehydration stage occurs in a different way from the rest of the dehydration reaction. For all preparations made at temperatures above 300°C, which are all active magnesia preparations, there is no difference between the two specific volumes.

The deviations observed for some intermediate nesquehonite decomposition products, however, does not prove the presence of pores not available for the alcohol molecule. The reason is that V_{CO_2} is derived from magnesite, where as experimentally no magnesite formation is observed. The observed differences are so large that it might

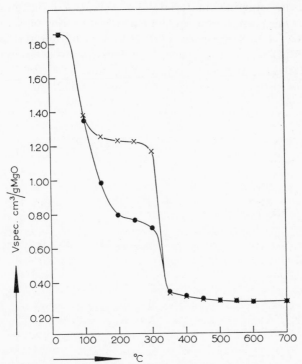

FIG. 15 Variation of the specific volumes of the nesquehonite decomposition products with heating temperature.

× measured in ethyl alcohol
○ calculated from the chemical composition

well be possible that some internal, i.e. non-accessible, pore volume is formed after the first dehydration stage of nesquehonite. The only definite conclusion which can be drawn is that all active magnesias obtained here, and also N-100, have no pores that are too small for the alcohol molecule to enter.

B Specific Surface Areas

The specific surface area of the starting material nesquehonite is only 1·2 m²/g. This figure represents the external area of nesquehonite needles. For N-100, with a degree of decomposition of 24%, the same

11

surface area is found. Since the preparations contain different amounts of volatile material, all surface areas should—for a better comparison—be quoted per gram of reference material, for which magnesium oxide is taken here. Thus N-100 shows an even slightly smaller area than its starting material: 3·4 versus 4·1 m²/g MgO. The three following preparations in the calcination series have comparable surface areas, i.e. N-150 with 14·0, N-200 with 15·6 and N-250 with 18·7 m²/g MgO. Hence the onset of the deviation between experimental and calculated specific volumes is accompanied by a certain increase of the specific surface area. Between N-300 and N-350 an enormous

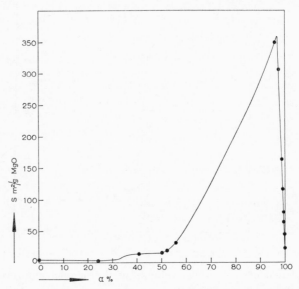

Fig. 16 Specific surface area of the decomposition product of nesquehonite versus the degree of decomposition.

increase from 31·0 to 350 m²/g MgO is recorded. With increased preparation temperatures, the effect of sintering is manifested. At 550°C the surface area has already fallen to 81 and at 800°C to 23 m²/g MgO. The course of specific surface areas with degree of decomposition is shown in Fig. 16. From this graph it is obvious that the first half of the decomposition is accompanied by only a modest gain in surface area.

At the end of the previous section it was concluded for preparation N-100 that any pores that might have been formed in the early dehydration stage must necessarily be accessible to ethyl alcohol. They therefore also will be accessible to nitrogen, which has a smaller "diameter" (4·3 Å) than the alcohol molecule (5·2 Å). Consequently, the formation of pores would have resulted in an enlargement of the specific surface area. Since there was no increase of surface area, it can be concluded that no pores were formed. Accordingly, the decrease of specific volume must be fully accounted for by a shrinkage of the parent crystals during the initial dehydration. It can be calculated that the extent of shrinkage for N-100 is as much as 26% by volume. This value observed after a decomposition degree of only 24% already exceeds the maximum value of 18% observed for the decomposition products of magnesite, discussed in Section III.

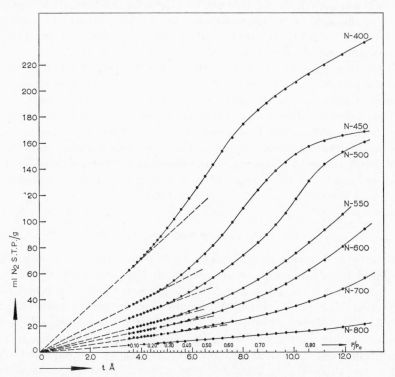

FIG. 17 V_a-t graphs of active magnesias prepared from nesquehonite.

The increase of the specific surface area to about $16\,m^2/g\,MgO$, when the dehydration is continued beyond 100°C, must be due to the development of some intracrystalline porosity. The corresponding pore volume of $0.016\,cm^3/g\,MgO$ is rather small. This suggests that further decrease of the specific volume in the second dehydration stage has to be ascribed mainly to a further contraction of the parent crystals. Taking into account the observed pore volume, a contraction of 33% by volume can be calculated for preparation N-250, as compared with 26% for N-100. The value of 33% is considered a minimum value, since pore volume not available for ethyl alcohol, if any, may be accessible to the smaller nitrogen molecule.

Decomposition of the intermediate amorphous carbonate occurs within a narrow temperature range, compared with the range where water of crystallization is released. Release of carbon dioxide is accompanied by production of magnesia of great activity. The specific surface area is 350 m²/g for N-350. The shape of the original nesquehonite needles is always retained. When this active magnesia is supposed to consist of an agglomeration of submicroscopic crystallites, it can be calculated that in each already microscopically small nesquehonite crystal some tens of millions of magnesium oxide crystals are generated.

When the preparation temperatures are higher, the surface area decreases rapidly. An increase of 100°C in the calcination temperature results in a decrease of the surface area by a factor of about two.

The easy accessibility of the porous structure for nitrogen is apparent from Fig. 17, where the V_a–t graphs for the magnesias of the nesquehonite calcination series are given. The reversible capillary condensation which can take place, e.g. in the cones and wedges formed by the planes of crystals touching each other, sets in at lower relative pressures than with the corresponding M preparations.

C   Pore Volume and Pore Radius

Four typical sorption isotherms characteristic of the active magnesias prepared from nesquehonite are shown in Figs 18a,b,c and d. Their desorption branches allow one to distinguish between the intra- and intercrystalline pore volume. Maximum intracrystalline pore volume of 0·54 cm³/g MgO is obtained for N-350. This value corresponds to an intracrystalline porosity of 61%. Due to the marked shrinkage in the preceding dehydration stage, porosity is—as to be expected—far below the theoretically possible value which is here 85%. At higher preparation temperatures the intracrystalline porosity of active magnesium oxide prepared from nesquehonite shows a considerable decrease.

For preparation N-800 the intracrystalline pore volume has fallen to 0·18 cm³/g MgO with a corresponding porosity of 39%. This sharp fall demonstrates that nesquehonite relics are subject to a greater shrinkage after the decomposition stage than is the case for the decomposition products of magnesite. From the intracrystalline pore volume and from the true volume, or the apparent specific volumes when the true specific volume is not known, the extent of contraction was calculated for the different preparations. The result of this calculation is shown in Fig. 19.

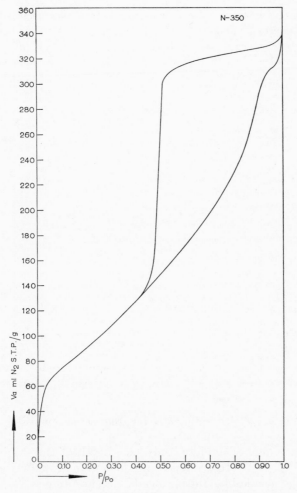

FIG. 18a Nitrogen sorption isotherm for magnesia N-350 from nesquehonite.

It can be seen that the first dehydration stage, where 1·3 mole water is released without development of any porosity, shows an appreciable contraction of 26%. It is followed by only a relatively small contraction of the nesquehonite framework in the subsequent dehydration stage. The actual activation, where the intermediate X-ray amorphous carbonate is transformed into magnesia, shows a further contraction of the original nesquehonite crystals to 53%. The shrinkage involved in the sintering range is apparent from a further increase to 76% for

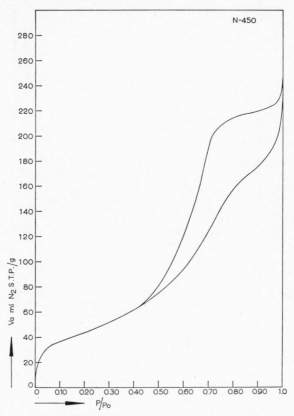

FIG. 18b Nitrogen sorption isotherm N-750 from nesquehonite.

preparation N-800. Therefore, only one-fourth of the original crystal volume is left after a treatment of nesquehonite at 800°C for 24 hours, although the needle-like appearance is largely retained.

From the intracrystalline pore volumes and surface areas, the mean pore radius can be obtained by use of Eq. (2). Since the surface areas are more affected by higher calcination temperatures than the corresponding pore volumes, the mean pore radius will increase with higher preparation temperatures. The values thus found are collected with other characteristic data in Table II. The mean pore radii range from 31 Å for preparation N-300 to 156 Å for preparation N-800.

As already mentioned, the powdery starting material was transformed into pellets. The apparent specific volume of these pellets was measured by immersion in mercury, which cannot enter into the voids between the original crystals. On account of the heat treatment the volume of the pellets appears to be subject to shrinkage as well. The same effect is found for the macro or intercrystalline pore volume that is

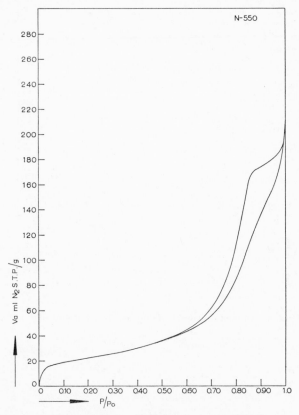

FIG. 18c Nitrogen sorption isotherm N-550 from nesquehonite.

given by the difference of pellet and crystal volume. When from this macropore volume and pellet volume the macroporosity or intercrystalline porosity is calculated by:

$$\Theta_{\text{intercrystalline}} = V_{p\ \text{intercrystalline}} / V_{\text{pellet}} \qquad (10)$$

all the calcination products show an almost constant macroporosity of 61–68% throughout the temperature range investigated. This remarkable phenomenon shows that during heat treatment the

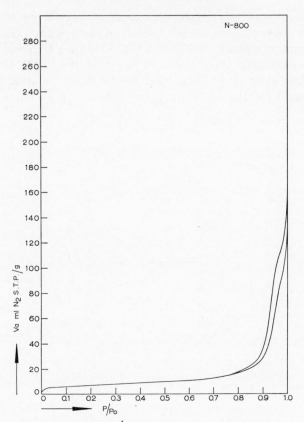

FIG. 18d Nitrogen sorption isotherm N-800 from nesquehonite.

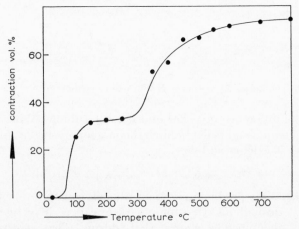

FIG. 19 Contraction of the original nesquehonite crystals as a function of the calcination temperature.

TABLE II. Characteristic data of the preparations of the N series

Preparations	Decomposition degree %	Chemical Composition		V_{solid}	V_p intra-crystalline cm³/g MgO	$V_{crystal}$	Shrinkage % by vol.	Intra-crystalline porosity %	S_{BET} m²/g MgO	$\bar{r}_p$ Å	D Å	$S_{cryst.}$ m²/g
		H_2O/MgO	CO_2/MgO									
N	—	2·96	1·00	1·856	0	1·856	—	0	4·1			
N–100	24·1	1·68	1·00	1·379	0	1·379	25·7	0	3·4			
N–150	40·8	0·76	0·99	1·254					14·0			
N–200	50·0	0·35	0·97	1·231					15·6			
N–250	52·2	0·30	0·95	1·224	0·016	1·240	33·2	1·3	18·7			
N–300	55·6	0·21	0·91	1·165					31·0			
N–350	95·8	0·17	0·03	0·340	0·535	0·875	52·9	61·1	349·8	31	45	412
N–400	97·2	0·13	0·01	0·319	0·490	0·809	56·4	60·6	360·8	32	54	332
N–450	98·7	0·074	0·007	0·296	0·336	0·632	66·0	53·2	163·8	41	97	178
N–500	99·0	0·053	0·004	0·290	0·329	0·619	66·7	53·2	119·1	55	133	128
N–550	99·5	0·032	0·002	0·285	0·264	0·549	70·5	48·1	81·0	65	162	104
N–600	99·6			0·283	0·242	0·525	71·8	46·1	64·1	76	194	87
N–700	99·8			0·282	0·217	0·499	73·1	43·5	44·7	97	286	59
N–800	100·0			0·278	0·178	0·456	75·5	39·0	22·8	156	648	26

arrangement of the parent crystals within a pellet does not change essentially and that the shrinkage of the pellets proceeds parallel to the contraction of the parent crystals.

The mean pore radius of the macropores range from 710 Å for preparation N-350 to 480 Å for preparation N-800. The difference between intracrystalline and intercrystalline pore dimensions is less marked here than in the case of the magnesias prepared from magnesite. This can also be seen from a comparison of their sorption isotherms.

It is apparent that an active magnesia pellet prepared in this way is highly porous. About 64% of its volume is occupied by intercrystalline voids between the parent crystals, and of the remainder, 40-60%, depending on the calcination temperature, is taken up by intracrystalline pores (voids between the magnesia crystallites). The total porosity of such a pellet accordingly varies between 79 and 86%.

D   Pore Size Distribution and Pore Shape

For the active magnesias the cumulative surface areas obtained from the analysis of the adsorption isotherms are given in Fig. 20 as a function of pore radius. The values thus obtained exceed the corresponding BET surface areas by 2–24%.

Analysis of the desorption isotherms showed considerably greater discrepancies between S_{cum} and S_{BET}. For N-350 a value as high as 1.99 was found for the S_{cum}/S_{BET} ratio, whereas in the M calcination series the maximum value was 1·64. The uniformity factor m, introduced in Section III BE, ranged between 1·7 and 1·3 in the order of increasing calcination temperatures. The lower value was obtained for N-800. This behaviour can be attributed to the occurrence of pores with a variable cross-section along their lengths. At higher preparation temperatures the cross-section of such a pore would become more uniform, which means a more regular stacking of the magnesia crystallites.

The sorption isotherm of N-350 displays a typical E-type hysteresis loop. With increase of calcination temperature, a gradual change towards A-type character is observed. When the E-type hysteresis loop is caused by tubular pores with appreciable variations in width— denoted by shape group XV in de Boer's classification—a change of the E-type loop into the A-type, can be explained by an equalization of the pore width, thus converting the pores from shape group XV into shape group II (see Fig. 10).

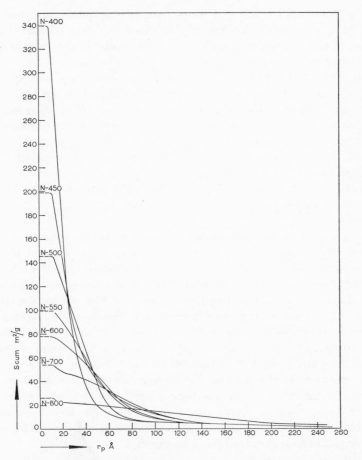

FIG. 20 Cumulative surface area plots for magnesias of the N series. Analysis is based on the nitrogen adsorption isotherms.

E   Size of the Magnesia Crystallites

The pure diffraction widths of the magnesias made from nesquehonite were processed in the same way as described for those of the M series. The crystallite sizes varied between 45 and 650 Å. The former value was obtained for N-350 and the latter for N-800 (see Table II, penulti-mate column). The specific surface areas of the crystallites calculated from these data using Eq. (8) are generally about 20% higher than the corresponding BET values (see Table II). Taking into account the accuracy of the crystallite size determinations, which is seldom estimated to be better than 20%, and the assumptions underlying

Eq. (8), the overall agreement is not bad. It is probable, however, that these unidirectional deviations may be attributed to a certain agglomeration of the magnesia crystallites, which results in the surface of the crystallites being not entirely available for adsorption.

The magnesias prepared from magnesite show some lattice strain, which is not observed for magnesias prepared at corresponding temperatures from nesquehonite. It is assumed that this lattice strain in the case of the M preparations has to be related to the formation of magnesia from a compound with a well-defined crystal structure, whereas in the case of nesquehonite, the magnesia crystallites are obtained via an intermediate carbonate which is amorphous to X-rays. It is likely that the crystallites formed from this intermediate carbonate with its poorly-ordered structure will not be subjected to lattice stresses.

From an electron diffraction pattern obtained from a pseudomorphically decomposed nesquehonite crystal, it is apparent that the magnesium oxide crystallites show no orientation with the crystallographic axes of the parent crystal, but are orientated at random.

In the sintering range the growth rate of the crystallite sizes is greater than that of the pore dimensions. For N-350 the ratio pore diameter to crystallite size is 1·36, whereas for N-800 this ratio has fallen to 0·48. This sharp fall is indicative of the great extent of shrinkage, which the parent crystals of nesquehonite undergo also in this stage. This shrinkage is the reason why magnesias prepared from nesquehonite show a lower intracrystalline porosity than those prepared at similar temperatures from magnesite, although the theoretically possible value for magnesias from nesquehonite is by a factor of 1·7 greater than those prepared from magnesite.

V   Effect of Calcination Parameters on Texture and Decomposition Route

A   Effect on Texture

In the two preceding sections pore genesis and sintering were followed for two reagents which produced magnesium oxide in a highly disperse condition via different decomposition routes. In these sections the mutual differences often received more attention than the points of correspondence. The common features are dominant, however, as will appear from the summary below.

1. Active magnesias are pseudo-morphous after their parent crystals.
2. Within the framework of these parent crystals millions of magnesia crystallites are stacked in a random way.

3. Since the extent of shrinkage is smaller than the volume originally taken up by the released volatile material, a porous skeleton remains with pores of the packing type.
4. The packing of these crystallites is so loose that almost the entire crystallite surface area is available for adsorption.
5. Sintering is manifested by a reduction of surface area, on account of an increase of the mean crystallite size at higher temperatures. The intra-aggregate pore dimensions also show an increase during sintering.
6. Thermal treatment is accompanied by a decrease of the dimensions of the parent crystals. The extent of contraction can differ appreciably for various starting materials.

The above characteristics are not only limited to both starting materials discussed here, but apply as well to other active magnesia generators. Also magnesium hydroxide, having a layer-like lattice, yields no fissure-type pores as might be expected, but under normal conditions a random crystallite agglomeration with pores of the packing type again is obtained. In some cases, however, e.g. when the decomposition of magnesium hydroxide is carried out in the vacuum of an electron microscope by electron bombardment, highly-orientated magnesium oxide crystallites are obtained, as was demonstrated by Goodman (1958). The preferred orientation may vanish again when after decomposition irradiation is continued at increased beam intensity.

The absence of any orientation effects in calcined magnesias is general and quite different from the phenomena observed in the decomposition of well-crystallized trihydroxides and oxide hydroxides of aluminium (see Chapter IV). It suggests that the activation of magnesia is of a lower degree compared to the formation of active alumina, where not only the external shape, but also structural aspects of the parent crystals are retained. The general absence of orientation effects with activated magnesia is possibly due to statistical formation of the crystallites at those spots where a sufficient number of carbonate or hydroxyl ions has dissociated or has condensed. Another possibility is that the crystallites are indeed formed in an orientated position but that bulk movement of the solid occurs so that the initial orientation of the crystallites might disappear shortly after their formation. This process of bulk movement cannot be explained by lattice diffusion, since it occurs far below the Tamman temperature (1325°C). It is likely that material transfer takes place by diffusion along the surface of the crystallites. Anderson and Morgan (1964) assume that especially in the case of magnesium oxide, surface diffusion is facilitated by the presence of water vapour. Adsorption with the formation of two hydroxyl groups and subsequent desorption of the water molecule might provide a mode of transport for surface oxygen ions. The cation migration would therefore be rate controlling. The greater effect of water vapour on the sintering rate for magnesium oxide compared with alumina and silica might thus be due to the low charge and the correspondingly high mobility of the magnesium ions. Whether or not it may also explain the absence of any orientation of the magnesia crystallites remains an open question.

From the above, it is clear that for the preparation of active magnesias the choice of the starting material is not a very decisive parameter. By a selection of the preparation temperature, however, the activity as expressed by the specific surface area and the texture expressed by the mean pore radius and the size of the magnesia crystallites can be varied, though not independently, almost at will. The maximum obtainable surface area, however, depends largely on the selection of the starting material. The lower its decomposition temperature, the higher will be the maximum surface area that can be obtained.

B   Effect on Decomposition Route

In Section II the major variables which are important in the preparation of active solids were discussed. One of these variables was the atmosphere in which the activation is established. It was pointed out that sample size, heating rate, etc., may influence this parameter, and therefore also the activation process or the decomposition route.

A typical example of this behaviour is found when the decomposition of nesquehonite is carried out under DTA conditions. Figure 21 shows the DTA curve of nesquehonite recorded at a heating rate of 5°C/min. The initial part of this curve, where dehydration takes place, was discussed in Section IV C.

The decarbonation reaction, which starts above 400°C in the DTA curve, shows a rather complex course. The small endothermic peak beginning at 400°C is accompanied by release of carbon dioxide from the X-ray amorphous carbonate. Here the first magnesium oxide is formed. At 490°C this reaction becomes more important. The dissociation pressure of the carbonate presumably reaches atmospheric pressure at this temperature, so that the released carbon dioxide can freely escape, and the decarbonation reaction is no longer controlled by the diffusion of carbon dioxide out of the sample holder. At 510°C this fast decarbonation reaction is interrupted by a sudden exothermic reaction, which is the transformation of the remaining amorphous carbonate into crystalline magnesite. The first correct interpretation of this exothermic peak was given by Dell and Weller (1959). The very steep, almost vertical, slope of this peak indicates that the exothermic reaction must proceed almost instantaneously. At 510°C a rearrangement of the metastable amorphous carbonate to the stable magnesite modification occurs. With increase of temperature this modification also becomes unstable. Its dissociation gives rise to the last endothermic peak.

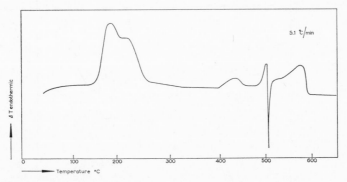

FIG. 21 DTA curve of nesquehonite.

The decomposition route shown here is thus quite different from that described in Section IV, where the decomposition was studied under less dynamic heating conditions. No evidence was obtained in that case for intermediate formation of magnesite, since the amorphous carbonate was already entirely converted into magnesium oxide at a temperature as low as 350°C.

With modern sensitive DTA equipment permitting the use of small samples, it could be shown that no crystallization of amorphous magnesium carbonate occurred when a sample of 20 mg was decomposed in a dynamic nitrogen atmosphere and a heating rate of 10°C/min. When the same experiment was performed in a static nitrogen atmosphere the usual DTA curve with a sharp exothermic peak at 510°C was obtained. This suggests that the observed crystallization should not be ascribed mainly to the high heating rate but rather to a retardation of the decarbonation reaction due to a pressure build-up by the released carbon dioxide in the sample.

This conclusion is supported by the two graphs A and B in Fig. 22 representing thermograms of nesquehonite recorded at the low heating rate of 2°C in air and carbon dioxide respectively. The retarding effect of carbon dioxide on the decarbonation reaction is clearly shown. In the decarbonation branch of curve B an inflection is observed, which is caused by the crystallization effect. When this phase transition would not have occurred, the decarbonation reaction would follow curve C. Since magnesite has a higher stability a further shift of the decarbonation reaction to higher temperatures occurs and instead of curve C, curve B is obtained.

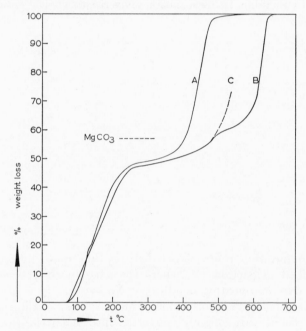

FIG. 22 Thermogram of nesquehonite recorded at a heating rate of 2°C/min.
   curve A: decomposed in air
   curve B: decomposed in CO_2

There is still another aspect in which the DTA decomposition route of nesquehonite differs from that observed under more steady heating conditions. X-ray powder patterns of samples withdrawn from a spare sample holder after the dehydration peak in the course of the DTA run showed that besides formation of the X-ray amorphous carbonate, a crystalline compound is formed. This compound gave rise to a faint but sharp diffraction pattern which could be indexed as a cubic structure with a cell constant of 8·518 Å. Its spacings showed good agreement with those reported by Walter-Lévy (1936) for a basic magnesium carbonate of the composition $4\,MgO$. $3\,CO_2$. $3H_2O$, which was obtained under hydrothermal conditions. The above pattern was only found when decomposition of nesquehonite was studied under DTA conditions. It is therefore reasonable to suppose that during a DTA run in the interior of the nesquehonite crystals hydrothermal conditions occur, which are responsible for the formation of this W.L. carbonate.

A similar conversion caused by internal hydrothermal conversion is observed in the dehydration of the aluminium trihydroxide, gibbsite. described by Lippens and Steggerda in Chapter IV.

All the above examples provide evidence that the transfer of the released volatile products from the interior of the crystals as well as from the exterior of the reacting interface can considerably affect the decomposition sequence in the activation of solids by calcination.

VI Catalytic Aspects of Magnesia for Alcohol Decomposition

A Introduction

In this section the catalytic activity and selectivity for the decomposition of isopropanol on active magnesias prepared at different temperatures will be considered.

The first systematic investigation of the catalytic properties of metal oxides for this type of reaction was made by Sabatier and Mailhe (1910), who studied the decomposition of ethyl alcohol. Their research covered magnesium oxide also. Although the investigation was mainly of a qualitative character it was clear that the selectivity of magnesium oxide for the dehydrogenation reaction was high, while its overall activity was low compared with other oxides.

Since secondary alcohols are more reactive than primary alcohols, and since the selectivity for primary and secondary alcohols is practically the same, the decomposition of the secondary alcohol, isopropanol, was taken here as a test reaction for the characterization of active magnesia.

B Experimental

1. *Materials:* M-450, M-500, M-550, etc., made by calcination of magnesite at different temperatures. The textural and structural characteristics of these preparations were given in Section III. The results of the catalytic experiments obtained with the preparations of the N series are practically identical with those obtained with the magnesias ex magnesite, and will not be discussed here.

2. *Apparatus:* The test reaction was made in a flow reactor coupled to a GLC. Use was made of a carrier gas, so that by changing the ratio of reactant and carrier gas the partial pressure of isopropanol could be

varied. The total flow rate through the reactor was kept constant for different isopropanol pressures. A schematic representation of the apparatus is given in Fig. 23.

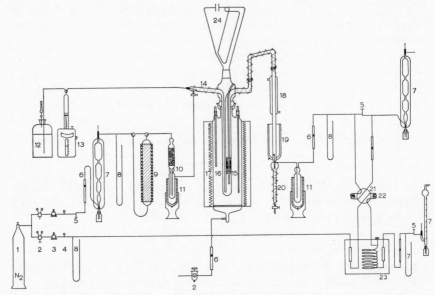

FIG. 23 Schematic representation of the apparatus for the catalytic test reaction.

1. N_2 cylinder	13. micro metering pump
2. pressure regulator	14. evaporator
3. mass flow controller	15. fixed-bed reactor
4. dial manometer	16. fluid-bed heating
5. needle valve	17. electrical furnace
6. rotameter	18. water-cooled jacket
7. soap film meter	19. dewar jacket
8. open manometer	20. receiver
9. BTS column	21. gas sampling valve
10. KOH tower	22. sample loop
11. cold trap	23. gas liquid chromatograph
12. storage bottle	24. cyclone

3. *Procedure:* All runs were made with the same amount of surface area of catalyst in the reactor ($\sim$34 m^2). The partial pressures of isopropanol were varied between 350 and 9 torr. The normal reaction temperature was 350°C. When starting a run it took a considerably long time before a steady decomposition rate was obtained. This period could be appreciably shortened by subjecting the catalyst to an oxygen pretreatment. When changing the partial pressure of isopropanol,

the following steady decomposition rate was obtained much faster in the case when the relative pressure was lowered than when it was raised. Therefore, kinetic measurements were started from high alcohol partial pressures. It has been shown that diffusion of isopropanol from the flowing gas phase to the external catalyst surface, and the internal diffusion into the pore system, was fast relative to the decomposition rate.

At the maximum partial pressure of isopropanol the degree of conversion was about 1·5%.

C Results

Two reactions were observed; dehydrogenation to acetone and hydrogen, and dehydration to propene and water. In the temperature range investigated (325–375°C) formation of di-isopropylether did not occur. Condensation products of acetone, such as mesityloxide, could not be detected in the gas phase. As stated before, selectivity is defined here as the ratio of the dehydrogenation rate to the total decomposition rate. The curves in Fig. 24 represent the dehydrogenation rate, expressed as μl H_2/m^2 min, as a function of the isopropanol pressure.

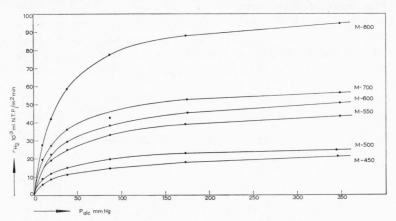

FIG. 24 Intrinsic dehydrogenation rates for the different magnesite calcination products at a temperature of 350°C.

Intrinsic dehydrogenation activity shows an increase with increasing preparation temperatures. For the dehydration reaction the reverse effect is observed for the lower temperature preparations. In that case the effect is much stronger. In Fig. 25, where the dehydration rates have been plotted, two different scales were necessary. For preparations made at temperatures of 550°C and higher, where magnesite is

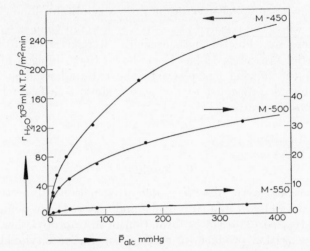

Fig. 25 Intrinsic dehydration rates at 350°C for some preparations of the M calcination series.

converted into magnesia, the dehydration rate is hardly affected by the preparation temperature.

The selectivity of this series preparations is governed by the great differences in dehydration activity. The variation of the selectivity factor with the calcination temperature is shown in Fig. 26. A break occurs at the temperature where magnesite is fully converted into

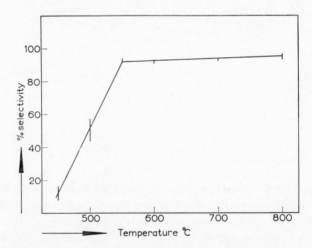

Fig. 26 Variation of the selectivity for the dehydrogenation reaction with the calcination temperature of the M preparations.

magnesium oxide. At lower temperatures, i.e. in the dissociation range of magnesite, a sharp increase of the selectivity for the dehydrogenation reaction is observed. At higher preparation temperatures, i.e. for the magnesia catalysts, the selectivity shows only a small increase. For the latter preparations the selectivity for the dehydrogenation reaction is invariably better than 90%.

The selectivity values showed some slight variations with the partial pressure of isopropanol. The extent of these variations, observed in the isopropanol pressure range investigated, are depicted in Fig. 26 by the length of a vertical line for the particular preparation. This variation is greatest for the partly decomposed magnesite preparation. The selectivity shows an increase with decreasing partial pressure of alcohol. It was shown that for these preparations this effect is not caused primarily by a different dependence of both parallel reactions on the partial pressure of isopropanol, but by a poisoning effect of one of the decomposition products of the dehydration reaction. Water proves to be a stronger poison for the dehydrogenation than for the dehydration reaction. Consequently the selectivity for the dehydrogenation reaction decreases with an increase of the partial pressure of water in the reactor. Such an increase of the partial pressure of water is produced indirectly by an increase of the isopropanol pressure. The above phenomena can be an indication that the nature of the active sites differ for both reactions.

It is clear from Figs 24 and 25 that the decomposition of isopropanol is of a variable order, being between first and zero order in isopropanol. This phenomenon can be explained by the assumption of variable adsorption of isopropanol on the active sites of the catalyst surface, probably in competition with the oxygen containing reaction products acetone and water.

The hydrogen production rate can be represented under steady state conditions by the relation:

$$r_{H_2} = k_2 \Theta_{alc} \tag{11}$$

where k_2 is the rate constant of the surface dehydrogenation reaction, and

Θ_{alc} represents the surface coverage of the active sites for this reaction.

A similar relation for the dehydration reaction is possible. There is ample evidence that hydrogen has no detectable influence on the kinetics of isopropanol dehydrogenation. Only a relatively small fraction of the surface will be covered by hydrogen which will escape immediately after it has been formed from isopropanol. Thus Eq. (11) will be valid also under non-stationary conditions.

At a reaction temperature of 350°C the reaction equilibrium for both reactions is far to the right. Thus the rate of the reverse reaction is negligible compared with that of the forward reaction, and has not to be considered.

The proportionality between reaction rate (r) and surface coverage of isopropanol, as expressed by the above equation, is in conformity with the adsorption isotherm character of the r versus p_{alc} plots. By extrapolation of the reaction rates to infinite partial pressure of alcohol, rate constants for both parallel reactions can be obtained. This extrapolation can be easily performed by plotting the reciprocal reaction rates versus the reciprocal values of the average partial pressure of isopropanol in the reactor. The intercept on the vertical axis yields the reciprocal value of the rate constant (k). This value is generally not identical with k_2 in Eq. (11). The latter is only the case when the Langmuir-Hinshelwood mechanism is obeyed, where the reaction partners are considered to be in adsorptive equilibrium with the surface, and the surface reaction is rate-determining. When, however, the adsorption and desorption processes are taken into account and no particular assumption is made on the nature of the rate-determining step, the dehydrogenation rate at infinite alcohol pressures is given by

$$r_{H_2} = k = \frac{k_2 k_3}{k_2 + k_3}$$

where k_3 is the desorption constant of acetone. For $k_2 \ll k_3$, the Langmuir-Hinshelwood mechanism is obeyed and $k = k_2$, whereas for $k_3 \ll k_2$, the desorption of acetone will be rate controlling with $k = k_3$.

The values of k thus obtained, proved to be independent of the partial pressures of the reaction products and were only dependent on reaction temperature and catalytic properties of the solids. Therefore, the value of k is an excellent parameter to characterize the catalytic properties of magnesia preparations for both parallel reactions. The values of the rate constants thus found are collected in Table III.

From the intrinsic reaction rates for both reactions, the selectivity factor for the dehydrogenation reaction was calculated. The corresponding values, given in the last column of Table III, show the high selectivity of the magnesia samples for the dehydrogenation reaction.

Figure 27 shows the variation of the intrinsic dehydration rate constant with the preparation temperature of the catalysts. The dehydration rate constant shows a sharp fall to become practically

TABLE III. Rate constants for the dehydrogenation and dehydration of isopranol in the presence of calcined magnesite preparations. Reaction temperature 350°C

Preparation	k_{H_2} $\mu l/m^2 min$	k_{H_2O} $\mu l/m^2 min$	k_{total} $\mu l/m^2 min$	Selectivity %
M–450	26·0	340	366	7·1
M–500	27·1	43·3	70·4	38·7
M–550	47·9	3·5	51·4	92·8
M–600	57·1	5·0	62·1	92·0
M–700	60·6	4·5	65·1	93·1
M–800	100	3·7	103·7	96·4

constant at 550°C when magnesite has been converted into magnesium oxide. The plot suggests a high dehydration activity for the starting material magnesite. In this research, magnesite indeed proved to be an active dehydration catalyst. Whereas activity for the dehydrogenation

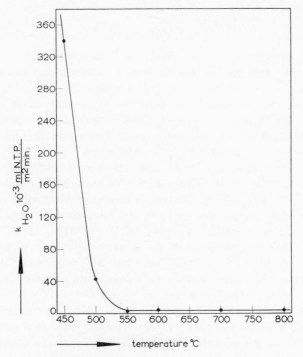

FIG. 27 Variation of the intrinsic dehydration rate constants with the calcination temperature of magnesite. Reaction temperature 350°C.

reaction was comparable with the magnesia catalysts, the selectivity for the dehydrogenation reaction was only 3·4%. Thus magnesite turned out to be a rather selective and active dehydration catalyst. Relative to the dehydrogenation reaction an increase of the rate constant with increase of calcination temperature is observed. This variation is modest and is only a factor of two for the magnesia preparations. On a weight basis the greatest dehydrogenation activity is shown by M-550 and M-600. The reduction of surface area by sintering cannot allow for the increase of the intrinsic dehydrogenation rate at higher temperatures.

From the variation of the intrinsic rate constant with temperature, activation energies for both parallel reactions were calculated. For M-700 values of 34·9 kcal/mole for E_{H_2} and 40·9 kcal/mole for E_{H_2O} were obtained. These activation energies are higher than those reported in the literature, which vary between 10·0–28·0 for E_{H_2} and between 14–30 for E_{H_2O}. Activation energies for the dehydration reaction exceed activation energies for the dehydrogenation reaction for all the reported data.

D Discussion

Magnesia proves to favour predominantly dehydrogenation of isopropanol. The activity for this reaction is between one and two orders of magnitude greater than for the dehydration reaction. Although large differences were noted for the textural quantities of the magnesias, the selectivity factor for the test reaction was almost constant. Only when structural effects played a part (presence of undecomposed magnesite) was the selectivity greatly affected.

May it, however, be inferred from the above that magnesia is an active catalyst for the dehydrogenation of alcohols? As a case in point let us take M-600, which catalyst is representative for the catalytic behaviour of magnesium oxide. For the intrinsic rate constant of the dehydrogenation reaction a value of $k_{H_2} = 57/\mu$l H_2/m^2 min was obtained. This figure means that at very high partial pressures of isopropanol $2·5 \times 10^{12}$ mole H_2/cm^2 sec are produced. When it is assumed that the entire surface participates in a uniform way in the reaction, and an adsorbed molecule occupies a surface area of 20 Å^2, 5×10^{-3} molecules of isopropanol will be dehydrogenated per site, per second. Thus it will take on an average 200 seconds, or over three minutes, before an adsorbed isopropanol molecule is converted into acetone and hydrogen. For a catalytic reaction this is quite a long time!

A very active catalyst for the dehydrogenation of alcohols is copper. For comparison the dehydrogenation of isopropanol was measured, therefore, on a Cu catalyst, for which the commercial BTS catalyst (BASF) was taken. Just the fact that the reaction temperatures had to be lowered by more than 200°C to 140°C to get about comparable reaction rates, points already to a great difference in activity between both catalysts. When the intrinsic dehydrogenation rate constant measured on preparation M-600 is reduced from 350° to 140°C by means of the determined value of the activation energy, the intrinsic activity of the magnesia catalyst proves to be as much as a factor of 10^7 less active than that of the Cu catalyst.

The catalytic properties of magnesia differ widely from those of alumina. Alumina is a well known dehydration catalyst for alcohols. Under normal reaction conditions no dehydrogenation takes place. de Boer et al. (1967) studied the decomposition of ethanol on γ and η-Al_2O_3 at a temperature of 307°C. The kinetics of ethene formation obeyed the Langmuir-Hinshelwood mechanism. In addition to ethene, di-ethylether was formed. The latter reaction predominated above pressures of 60 torr alcohol, and occurred mainly by the Rideal-Eley mechanism.

The rate constant for ethene formation was $k_{ethene} = 930 \ \mu l/m^2$ min on η-Al_2O_3. When this figure is compared with the rate constant of propene formation from isopropanol on magnesia (M-700) by extrapolation of the dehydration rate constant obtained at 350° to 307°C, the difference in activity is nearly a factor of 3000 in favour of alumina. For comparison of the dehydration character of magnesia and alumina this figure is not very realistic, however, since isopropanol is easier dehydrated than ethanol; the sequence for ease of dehydration being: isopropyl > isobutyl > n-butyl > n-propyl > ethyl alcohol.

The above comparisons are made to demonstrate that the catalytic properties of magnesia for both parallel reactions are poor. The selective character of magnesia for the dehydrogenation reaction is due to an almost complete lack of dehydration activity, probably on account of the basic character of the magnesia surface. For this reason the residual dehydrogenation activity, typical for all insulating metal oxides, is the prominent reaction for magnesia. This weak dehydrogenation activity is also likely to be found on aluminas. Alsop and Dowden (1954) suppose that the residual dehydrogenation activity for tervalent oxides is even higher than for bivalent oxides. Under normal reaction conditions this dehydrogenation activity is in case of alumina completely overshadowed by its outstanding dehydration properties.

VII References

Alsop, B. C. and Dowden, D. A. (1954). *J. chim. Phys.* **51**, 678.

Anderson, P. J. and Morgan, P. L. (1964). *Trans. Faraday Soc.* **60**, 930.

Barrett, E. P., Joyner, L. G. and Halenda, P. P. (1951). *J. Am. chem. Soc.* **73**, 373.

de Boer, J. H. (1958). *In* "The Structure and Properties of Porous Materials" (D. H. Everett and F. S. Stone, eds.), Colston Papers, vol. 10, p. 68. Butterworth, London.

de Boer, J. H , ed. (1961). "The Mechanism of Heterogeneous Catalysis."

de Boer, J. H., Fahim, R. B., Linsen, B. G., Visseren, W. J. and de Vleesschauwer, W. F. N. M. (1967). *J. Catalysis*, **7**, 163.

Dell, R. M. and Weller, S. W. (1959). *Trans. Faraday Soc.* **55**, 2203.

de Vleesschauwer, W. F. N. M. (1967). Thesis, Delft University of Technology, The Netherlands.

Goodman, J. F. (1958). *Proc. R. Soc.* A, **247**, 346.

Lippens, B. C. (1961). Thesis, Delft University of Technology, The Netherlands.

Mars, P. (1960). *In* "The Mechanism of Heterogeneous Catalysis" (J. H. de Boer, ed.), pp. 49–65. Elsevier, Amsterdam.

Razouk, R. I. and Mikhail, R. Sh. (1961). *Actes 2e Congr. Int. Catalyse.* Edition Technip, Paris, pp. 2023–2032.

Sabatier, P. and Mailhe, A. (1910). *Ann. Chim. Phys.* **20**, 289.

Schwab, G. M. and Schwab-Agallides, E. (1949). *J. Am. chem. Soc.* **71**, 1806.

Steggerda, J. J. (1955). Thesis, Delft University of Technology, The Netherlands.

Walter-Lévy, L. (1937). *Ann. Chim.* **7**, 216.

Wheeler, A. (1955). *In* "Catalysis" (P. H. Emmett, ed.), vol. 2, pp. 105–165. Reinhold, New York.

Chapter 7

FORMATION, PREPARATION AND PROPERTIES OF HYDROUS ZIRCONIA

H. TH. RIJNTEN*

Department of Chemical Technology, Technological University of Delft, The Netherlands

*Present address: Department of Physical Chemistry III, Faculty of Sciences, Catholic University of Nijmegen, The Netherlands.

I Introduction

The present chapter presents a broad description of the formation, preparation and behaviour of hydrous zirconia.

Investigations on oxides have been carried out since the early period of Professor J. H. de Boer's laboratory in Delft. Interest in this field has increased greatly since the oxides mentioned have been used as catalysts. Extensive studies on alumina, silica, magnesia and uranium oxide by now have been published, including the preparation and its relation to the properties of the oxides. The precipitation of the oxides is an important step in the preparation, since surface area, pore size and resistance against sintering are parameters strongly depending upon precipitation conditions. The extensive studies on alumina and silica greatly influenced the subsequent studies on the well-known silica-alumina catalyst.

A logical extension of these studies on oxides is found in the Group IV elements. This group, starting with SiO_2, is of interest with respect to changes in size of the metalion, coordination and bonding type.

In this chapter we will give an extensive survey of the preparation of zirconia in relation to its porous structure. Apart from the potential use of zirconia as an adsorbent or catalyst, it is hoped that this study will contribute to a better understanding of oxide precipitation in general, this being a central theme in the preparation of "active oxides".

II The General Chemistry of Zirconium

The literature concerned with zirconium chemistry is largely a conglomeration of empirically determined facts. While assuming the basic laws of chemistry and physics to apply to zirconium, relatively little has been done to make the behaviour of zirconium intelligible within this framework, although Blumenthal (1958a) encouraged efforts in this direction. Some general fundamentals of the properties of zirconium given are outlined below.

The electronic configuration of zirconium and its "huge isotope" hafnium are $4d^25s^2$ and $5d^26s^2$ in the outer shells. The remarkable chemical similarity between Zr and Hf is due in part to the analogous arrangements of electrons in the outermost quantum levels and to the near identity of the atomic radii: 1·452 Å and 1·442 Å. It is also pertinent that zirconium and hafnium occur in their compounds almost exclusively with the oxidation number of 4+ and bonding to the maximum extent that is sterically possible. This results in a maximum coordination of 8.

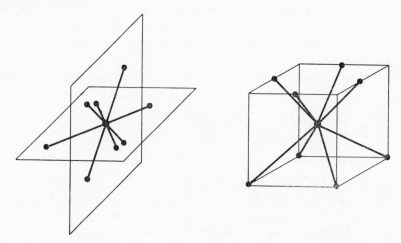

FIG. 1 Configurations in 8-coordination: (left) dodecahedral, (right) square-antiprismatic.

The zirconium ion can use various hybrid orbitals to give strongly directional bonds. For eight-fold coordination the orbitals used are d^4sp^3, leading to a dodecahedral arrangement of bonds, d^5p^3, giving an antiprismatic configuration (Kimball, 1940). These two configurations, which have been found experimentally for various ions, are illustrated in Fig. 1.

The classical example of dodecahedral coordination is given by the $Mo(CN)_8^{4-}$ and $W(CN)_8^{4-}$ complexes (Hoard and Nordsiek, 1939). The square antiprism has been found in TaF_8^{3-} (Hoard et al., 1954) and ReF_8^{2-} (Kozmin, 1964). A similar arrangement of ligands is found in the acetyl acetone complexes of Ce(IV), Th(IV), U(IV) and Zr(IV) (Grdenic and Matković, 1959). The square antiprismatic configuration in zirconium compounds is found in $ZrOCl_2 . 8H_2O$ and $ZrOBr_2 . 8H_2O$

(Clearfield and Vaughan, 1956). In these compounds the Zr ion is coordinated by $4OH^-$ and $4H_2O$ groups. The square antiprismatic coordination indicates $4d$ and $5p$ vacant orbitals of the zirconium ion to form coordinate links with the lone pair of electrons in the ligands present. These coordinate linkages are essentially covalent, since they involve the sharing of two electrons between two atoms or ions. The term coordinate merely signifies that both of the two electrons were provided by one atom or ion. In $ZrOCl_2 . 8H_2O$, in which the zirconium ion is coordinated by $4OH$ and $4H_2O$ groups, the lone pair electrons are provided by the oxygen.

Formula 1 shows the formation of a $Zr—OH_2$ bond. When the bond is strictly a covalent one this results with coordination of 8 for zirconium in a charge of $4-$. The electrostatic approach, which in the case of water would correspond to a dipole bond, leaves the charge of the zirconium ion unchanged. When the final charge on the zirconium ion is adjusted to zero the actual bonding results in a configuration

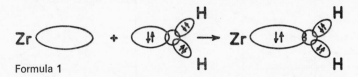

Formula 1

in which the electrons are for the greater part situated at the oxygen ion. When a proton transfer occurs in water solution of a H_2O ligand to a water molecule, the negative charge of the resulting OH^- ligand shifts the electrons in the direction of the zirconium ion.

The general principles that can be given for zirconium include the absence of d-electrons in the zirconium(IV) ion. This limits the possibilities of spectroscopic and magnetic investigations during ligand exchange of the zirconium complexes.

The behaviour of zirconium complexes in water solutions is characterized by hydrolysis and polymerization. In recent years interest in these phenomena have increased. However, the literature on the aqueous chemistry of zirconium frequently contains inconsistencies. In Sections III, IV and V of the present chapter we will give an extended picture of the chemistry of zirconylchloride solutions.

The behaviour of hydrous zirconia has been discussed very poorly in the literature. The composition of hydrous zirconia given varies from $ZrO_2 . xH_2O$, $ZrO(OH)_2 . xH_2O$ and $Zr(OH)_4 . xH_2O$. The behaviour of hydrous zirconia is discussed extensively in Sections VI, VII and VIII in close relation to the picture we gave for the formation of hydrous zirconia.

III   A Literature Survey on the Behaviour of Zirconyl Solutions

A   Introduction

Water solutions of zirconium and zirconyl salts show some character-istic features. In the literature polymerization and hydrolysis are used to describe the behaviour of zirconylchloride solutions. We will define these terms here as they will be used throughout this chapter (Wyatt, 1966).

Hydration. Hydration occurs when a zirconium salt is dissolved in water. The Zr^{4+} ion is 8 coordinated with water molecules, forming a square antiprism.

$$Zr^{4+} + 8H_2O \rightarrow [Zr(H_2O)_8]^{4+}.$$

Hydrolysis. Hydrolysis involves a proton transfer of a Zr—OH_2 linkage in water solution. This results in the liberation of H^+ into the solution.

$$Zr(H_2O)_8^{4+} + H_2O \rightarrow [Zr(H_2O)_7(OH)]^{3+} + H_3O^+.$$

A second hydrolysis step can occur which reduces the charge of the complex $[Zr(H_2O)_7(OH)]^{3+}$ while a second proton is liberated into the solution

$$[Zr(H_2O)_7(OH)]^{3+} + H_2O \rightarrow [Zr(H_2O)_6(OH)_2]^{2+} + H_3O^+.$$

Polymerization. When two complexes have the right charge and composition they can polymerize. The polymerization is achieved by the formation of two OH ligands between two zirconium ions:

$$2[Zr(H_2O)_6(OH)_2]^{2+} \rightarrow [(H_2O)_5(OH)Zr(OH)_2Zr(OH)(H_2O)_5]^{4+} + 2H_2O.$$

B   Zirconylchloride Solutions

Zirconyl solutions frequently are chosen as the starting material for the precipitation of hydrous zirconia. We will limit ourselves to the formation of hydrous zirconia from zirconylchloride solutions.

When a zirconyl salt is dissolved in water and enough base is added a gelatinous precipitate indicated as hydrous zirconia is formed. Zirconylchloride solutions can be obtained when zirconiumdioxide is dissolved in a hot strongly acid HCl solution:

$$ZrO_2 + 2HCl \xrightarrow{H_2O} ZrOCl_2.$$

Another method for preparing zirconyl solutions is the dissolution of a zirconium salt in water. The dissolution is accompanied by a vigorous reaction

$$ZrCl_4 + H_2O \rightarrow ZrOCl_2 + 2HCl.$$

This reaction indicates that a zirconium salt is transferred into a zirconyl salt when the zirconium ion is in aqueous medium.

When a zirconylchloride solution is obtained the solid zirconyl salt can be crystallized out by concentrating the solution, and the amount of solid zirconyl salt obtained can be increased by making a suitable choice of the HCl concentration. The solubility of zirconylchloride in water is shown in Table I (Blumenthal, 1958b), from which it can be concluded that a solubility minimum appears at an HCl concentration of 8·5 mole/l.

TABLE I. Solubility of $ZrOCl_2 . 8H_2O$ in HCl solutions at 20°C

HCl concn. (mole/l)	$ZrOCl_2 . 8H_2O$ concn. (mole/l)
0·2	2·91
1·47	2·14
4·97	0·329
8·72	0·0547
10·14	0·0988
10·94	0·205
11·61	0·334

C The Structure of $ZrOCl_2 . 8H_2O$

The crystalline compound which crystallizes from the concentrated HCl solution has the composition $ZrOCl_2 . 8H_2O$ (Blumenthal, 1958b). This salt can be thought to be built up from the zirconyl ion ZrO^{2+} and two chloride ions held together by eight water molecules. The structure of zirconylchloride octahydrate was clarified by Clearfield and Vaughan (1956). They showed the presence of a tetrameric unit, four zirconium ions lying at the corners of a square each bound to its nearest neighbours through two OH groups, one of which is located above the plane of the zirconium ions and one below. The other four linkages of the zirconium ion to complete the square antiprismatic configuration are formed with water molecules. Figure 2 shows a projection on (001) of the unit cell of $ZrOCl_2 . 8H_2O$, containing eight groups. From this projection it can be seen that the tetrameric complexes are surrounded by the remaining water molecules and chloride ions. The composition of the tetrameric complex in the unit cell was found to be $[Zr_4(OH)_8(H_2O)_{16}]^{8+}$.

Another interesting aspect of the structure of $ZrOCl_2 . 8H_2O$ is the absence of an actual Zr—Cl bond (Clearfield and Vaughan, 1956). When the zirconylchloride octahydrate is dissolved in water, Muha and Vaughan (1960) showed that the same tetrameric complex is present in water solutions as is present in the solid zirconylchloride octahydrate. There were also some indications of the presence of larger species due

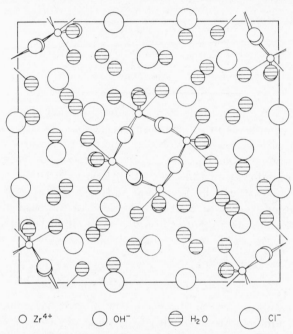

$\bigcirc$ Zr^{4+} $\bigcirc$ OH^- $\ominus$ H_2O $\bigcirc$ Cl^-

FIG. 2 The projection on (001) of the unit cell of $ZrOCl_2 . 8H_2O$. The complex cation $[Zr_4(OH)_8(H_2O)_{16}]^{8+}$ is indicated with solid lines.

to hydrolysis and polymerization. The presence of the tetrameric cations in water solutions indicates that this configuration is obviously stable both in water solutions and in strongly acid solutions.

D   Hydrolysis and Polymerization in ZrOCl₂ Solutions

Water solutions of $ZrOCl_2 . 8H_2O$ show acid properties. Ermakov et al. (1963) studied the acid strength of zirconylchloride solutions. Table II shows the activities of H^+ and HCl in solutions of zirconylchloride kept 24 hours at 25°C.

The activity of HCl in an m-molar solution of $ZrOCl_2 . 8H_2O$ is almost equal to the activity of an m-molar solution of HCl. The formation of the acid solutions is due to hydrolysis.

The presence of tetrameric complexes in water solutions of zirconyl-chloride (Muha and Vaughan, 1960) is widely accepted at this time.

TABLE II. Activities of H^+ and HCl in $ZrOCl_2$ solutions, Ermakov et al. (1963)

$ZrOCl_2$ concn. (mole/l.)	a_{H^+}	$a_{\pm}$
0·00617	0·00595	0·00642
0·01239	0·01127	0·01191
0·02474	0·02171	0·02284
0·2161	0·1737	0·164
0·3868	0·2806	0·273

Many efforts have been made to determine the exact size and composition of the complexes in solution. Investigations on this subject were carried out with diffusion, cryoscopic, distribution and spectrophotometric methods. Table III taken from the article of Ermakov et al. (1963) gives a survey of these investigations with their main results. From this table it can be seen that not only tetrameric complexes with molecular weight of 800 are present. An increase in molecular weight of the species in solution is observed when the acidity of the solution decreases. This increase in molecular weight of the species is indicated as polymerization.

E   The Anions in ZrOCl₂ Solutions

An interesting aspect of the chemistry of zirconyl solutions is the role of the anions. From the investigations of Muha and Vaughan (1960) it followed that in aqueous solutions of $ZrOCl_2 . 8H_2O$ no actual Zr—Cl bond is present. The experiments of Ermakov et al. (1963) indicated that one chloride ion per zirconium ion is free in solution. The other chloride ion is bound in a certain way to the complex. From the thermometric titration curves of Turnbull (1961) it was concluded that no Zr—X bond is present in water solutions of zirconylchloride, zirconylbromide and zirconyljodide. These zirconyl solutions were obtained by dissolving the accessory zirconium salts. Moreover the solutions obtained by dissolving the zirconium salts are very similar to solutions obtained by dissolving zirconyl salts. These inconsistencies will be discussed in greater detail in Section IV.

F   The Charge of the Zirconyl Species in Solutions

A point which is frequently discussed in zirconium literature is the charge of the species in solution. Lister and McDonald (1952) noted

TABLE III. Summary of published information on the formation of polynuclear species in solutions of zirconium salts, Ermakov *et al.* (1963)

Method	Compound	Medium	Main results
Diffusion	Zirconium nitrate	$HClO_4$, HNO_3	Continuous polymerization occurs in nitrate solns. on decreasing the HNO_3 concn., $D_{max} = 2 \cdot 54 \times 10^{-6}$ cm^2 sec^{-1} at 12 moles HNO_3/mole $ZrO(NO_3)_2$ and $D_{min} = 9 \cdot 3 \times 10^{-7}$ cm^2 sec^{-1} at 0·5 mole $NaOH$/mole $ZrO(NO_3)_2$. Perchlorate solns. contain products of low mol. wt; $D = 2 \cdot 08 \times 10^{-6}$ cm^2 sec^{-1} and is almost independent of the $HClO_4$ concn.
Diffusion	Zirconium nitrate	HNO_3	When the acidity is increased from 0·002 to 6 M the self-diffusion coefficient of Zr increases from $3 \cdot 5 \times 10^{-6}$ to $7-8 \times 10^{-6}$ cm^2 sec^{-1}, which corresponds to an approximately six-fold decrease in the weight of the ionic groups
Diffusion	Zirconium nitrate and oxide-chloride solutions	HNO_3, HCl	Nitrate solns. contain species with mol. wts. from 800 to 1500 ($[Zr] = 0 \cdot 08 - 0 \cdot 16$ M, $[HNO_3] = 10-1$ M, $[NH_4NO_3] = 0-8$ M). In HCl solns. the mol. wt. is ~ 2600
Dialysis	Zirconium oxide-chloride solutions of zirconium nitrate and perchlorate	HCl, $HClO_4$, HNO_3	Degree of polymerization (p) depends on the zirconium and acid concn. but is independent of the anion (Cl^-, ClO_4^-, NO_3^-): $P = 1-7$ for $[Zr] = 10^{-3}$ to 10^{-1}, $[H^+] = 2$ M; $p = 2 \cdot 5 - 7$ for $[Zr] = 10^{-3}$ to 10^{-2}, $[H^+] = 0 \cdot 1$ M
Potentiometry, cryoscopy	Zirconium oxide-chloride	Water	Complexes with different compositions exist, for example $[Zr(OH_4)ZrOCl_2 \; ZrO \vdots Cl_2]$ and $[Zr(OH)_4Cl_2 \vdots ZrO]$
Ultra-centrifuge	Zirconium tetra-chloride and oxide-chloride	HCl ($+MCl$)	In 0·08 M HCl the degree of polymerization $N_e \simeq 7-11$ ($[Zr] = 0 \cdot 05$ M, $L = 2$). In 0·2 M HCl, $N_e = 4 \cdot 2$ and 5·5. From 0·2 to 2 M HCl, N_e does not vary and apparently trimers and tetramers predominate
X-ray structural analysis	$MOX_2 . 8H_2O$ ($M = Zr$, Hf; $X = Cl$, Br)	Water	Tetramers predominate in solns. of hafnium oxide-chloride between 0·5 and 2·04 M. In zirconium oxide-chloride solns. the degree of polymerization >4
Distribution	Zirconium perchlorate	$HClO_4$	Continuous polymerization occurs in perchlorate solns.: with increasing zirconium concn. the mol. wt. of the polymeric species increases
Spectro-photometry	Zirconium perchlorate	$HClO_4$	Trimers and tetramers predominate in perchlorate solns., the threshold of polymerization depending on the acidity of the soln.

electromigration of zirconium species in solution towards the cathode.

An elegant method of determining the charge of the species in solution is ion exchange on a cation-exchanger. However, the ion-exchanger is often blocked by the large zirconium species (Lister and McDonald, 1952; Larsen and Wang, 1954; Nabivanits, 1962). A positive charge of the zirconium species could be determined.

Matyević et al. (1962) studied the coagulation of negatively charged AgBr sols with zirconylchloride solutions. From the influence of charge on the coagulation flocculation, the charge of the zirconium species was calculated to be 4+.

G Conclusions from the Literature Survey

From the few literature studies in which the results were given of investigations on the zirconium species in solutions the main conclusions can be given in the following points:

1. Water solutions of $ZrCl_4$ and $ZrOCl_2$. $8H_2O$ behave similarly.
2. The zirconium species in zirconylchloride solutions are present as tetrameric complexes which can further polymerize. The smallest unit in zirconylchloride solutions is the tetrameric complex.
3. The acid strength of an m-molar zirconylchloride solution is equal to the acid strength of an m-molar HCl solution.
4. No actual Zr—Cl bond is present in zirconylchloride solutions.
5. The species in solutions always carry a certain positive charge.

IV Studies on Hydrolysis and Polymerization
A Introduction

Considering the results put forth in the literature (Section III) and the results of some preliminary experiments, the following picture of hydrolysis and polymerization in zirconylchloride solutions can be drawn. This picture is confirmed by the experimental results described in Section V.

B The Formation of Zirconyl Solutions from Zirconium Salts

When $ZrCl_4$ is dissolved in water a zirconylchloride solution is obtained. This solution behaves identically to zirconyl solution obtained from $ZrOCl_2$. $8H_2O$. The reactions which occur can be represented by hydration, hydrolysis and further complex formation:

$$ZrCl_4 + 8H_2O \rightarrow [Zr(H_2O)_8]^{4+} + 4Cl^-.$$
$$[Zr(H_2O)_8]^{4+} + H_2O \rightarrow [Zr(H_2O)_7(OH)]^{3+} + H_3O^+.$$
$$[Zr(H_2O)_7(OH)]^{3+} + H_2O \rightarrow [Zr(H_2O)_6(OH)_2]^{2+} + H_3O.$$

The cation $[Zr(H_2O)_6(OH)_2]^{2+}$ then will give the tetrameric complex $[Zr_4(OH)_8(H_2O)_{16}]^{8+}$.

$$4[Zr(H_2O)_6(OH)_2]^{2+} \rightarrow [Zr_4(OH)_8(H_2O)_{16}]^{8+} + 8H_2O.$$

It is known that $Zr(IV)$ in $ZrOCl_2$ solutions occurs in tetrameric complexes (Section III). From the similar behaviour of $ZrCl_4$ and $ZrOCl_2$ solutions it follows that this scheme also holds for $ZrCl_4$ solutions as given in the above scheme.

C The Hydrolysis of ZrOCl₂ Solutions

When $ZrOCl_2 . 8H_2O$ is dissolved in water the zirconylchloride solution is acid because of hydrolysis of the tetrameric complex:

$$[Zr_4(OH)_8(H_2O)_{16}]^{8+} + 4H_2O \rightarrow [Zr_4(OH)_8(OH)_4(H_2O)_{12}]^{4+} + 4H_3O^+.$$

The hydrolysis reaction is given for one group of the tetrameric complex in Formula 2.

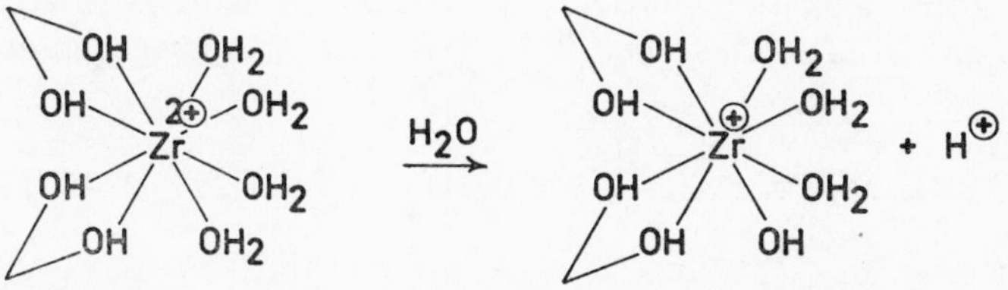

The charge on the complex is reduced to $4+$ in the hydrolysis reaction. We now assume that, dependent on the acid concentration, the charge of the complex $4+$ can be reduced further. The tetrameric complex contains four zirconium ions, which can hydrolyse independently. When one group is involved in a second hydrolysis step the total charge on the tetrameric complex decreases to $3+$.

$$[Zr_4(OH)_8(OH)_4(H_2O)_{12}]^{4+} + H_2O \rightleftharpoons [Zr_4(OH)_8(OH)_5(H_2O)_{11}]^{3+} + H_3O^+.$$

This reaction of one of the groups on the tetrameric complex is shown in greater detail in Formula 3.

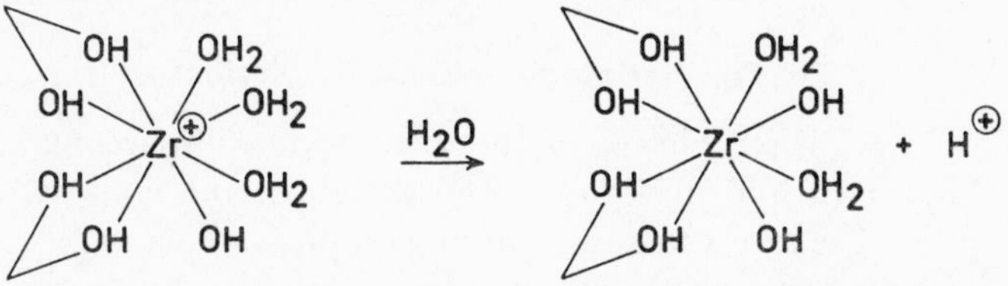

Some experiments were carried out to determine the state of the chloride ion in zirconylchloride solutions to give a complete description of hydrolysis in zirconylchloride solutions. When $ZrOCl_2 . 8H_2O$

(Merck) solutions were titrated potentiometrically with $AgNO_3$ solutions the chloride ions were quantitatively precipitated as AgCl. From the shape of the titration curves no indication of a Zr—Cl bond could be observed. When a m-molar zirconylchloride solution is titrated with a NaOH solution, 2 mmoles NaOH are required to obtain the equivalence point at pH 9. During this neutralization the free chloride ion concentration, as measured potentiometrically, increases. Ermakov et al. (1963) proved that one chloride ion per zirconium ion is free in solution. The second chloride ion, which enters the solution during the neutralization must be bound very weakly to the tetrameric complex. As the positive charge of the complex is firmly established we assume that the chloride ions act as gegenions for the positive charge of the tetrameric complex. When the positive charge of the complex decreases by further hydrolysis, caused by the addition of NaOH, the gegenions enter the solution. When it is assumed that the second hydrolysis step can occur, more than one HCl is liberated per mole zirconium in the solution. The hydrolysis can be described now in greater detail where the Cl^- ion is included as gegenion of the tetrameric complex:

$$[Zr_4(OH)_8(H_2O)_{16}^{8+} \dots . 8Cl^-] \xrightarrow{H_2O} [Zr_4(OH)_{16-n}(H_2O)_{n+8}^{n+} \dots . nCl^-] +$$
$$(8-n)Cl^- + (8-n)H^+.$$

When $n = 4$ the results of Ermakov et al. (1963) are obtained, e.g. the resulting tetrameric complex $[Zr_4(OH)_{12}(H_2O)_{12}^{4+} \dots 4Cl^-]$ and one HCl free in solution per zirconium ion. The second step in the hydrolysis reaction can be represented with values of 3, 2, 1 and 0 for n. When $n = 0$ the tetrameric complex obtained is $Zr_4(OH)_{16}(H_2O)_8$. This represents the fully-hydrolyzed zirconiumhydroxide. When only one group on the tetrameric complex is involved in the second hydrolysis step $n = 3$ giving the complex: $[Zr_4(OH)_{13}(H_2O)_{11}^{3+} \dots 3Cl^-]$. The amount of HCl liberated is 5 mole from 4 mole zirconium. This second hydrolysis reaction on one of the zirconyl groups is given in Formula 3.

D Polymerization in $ZrOCl_2$ Solutions

The reduction of the charge of the tetrameric complex, achieved by the second step of hydrolysis $n = 3$ in the foregoing equation, results in one neutral group on the tetrameric complex. We assume that this electrical neutrality is localized on one of the zirconium sites and is not spread out over the complex, where the three other zirconium sites retain their single positive charge. This neutral site is assumed to be the starting point for the polymerization reaction. The neutral site reacts with a singly-charged site of another tetrameric complex in such a way that the zirconium ions are connected by two OH groups. A similar mechanism is observed for the polymerization of silica (see Chapter V).

The OH groups which connect the zirconium ions have a similar configuration to that present in the tetrameric complex itself. Clearfield and Vaughan (1956) showed that the OH groups are present when $ZrOCl_2 . 8H_2O$ is crystallized from strongly acid solutions. Zaitsev (1966) proposed these OH groups to exist in neutralized $ZrOCl_2$ solutions. We assume here that the OH groups which connect the zirconium ions of two tetrameric complexes are just as resistant to strongly acidic solutions and are fairly stable. The justification for this conclusion is that the amount of neutral sites on tetrameric complexes in zirconylchloride solutions will be very small since they are one of the reactants in the polymerization reaction (Formula 4). The OH groups connecting two tetrameric complexes are called bridging ligands. When zirconium ions are connected by two OH bridging ligands, they are said to be "bridged". When zirconium ions are not connected by bridging ligands, they are said to be "free" or "non-bridged". As the tetrameric complexes are the smallest units in zirconylchloride solutions, we call a solution with only tetrameric complexes unpolymerized. A polymerized solution consists of species in which tetrameric complexes are connected by bridging ligands resulting in bridged zirconium ions which can no longer play a role in the hydrolysis reaction.

From Table III (Ermakov et al., 1963) it was concluded that decreasing acid strength increased the degree of polymerization. When $ZrOCl_2 . 8H_2O$ is dissolved in water, at least one mole HCl is formed per mole salt. Neutralizing this acid by the addition of a NaOH solution causes an increase in the degree of polymerization. When the neutralization is continued to pH 3 a precipitate begins to form. At the equivalence point (pH = 9) the precipitation is complete. The gelatinous precipitate is hydrous zirconia (Zr $(OH)_4$). During the neutralization process of zirconylchloride solutions we assume that continuous polymerization occurs, finally resulting in the formation of hydrous zirconia.

Another method for preparing hydrous zirconia also strongly suggests continuous polymerization in zirconylchloride solutions. Clearfield (1964) obtained hydrous zirconia by refluxing a partly-neutralized zirconylchloride solution at 100°C. We prepared hydrous zirconia in a similar way by refluxing a zirconylchloride solution at 100°C for three weeks without any added base. The acid strength of the solution increased very rapidly, which points to progressive hydrolysis. After one week the solution was coloured light blue. On further refluxing the colour of the solution became progressively whiter and after three weeks the formation of the positively charged sol was complete. The acid strength obtained in the m-molar zirconyl-chloride solution reached a value of almost 2 m-molar. According to the hydrolysis equation given in part C of this section, the n value then is almost zero. Nearly complete hydrolysis was thus achieved at 100°C even without any added base.

The pictures we sketched above for hydrolysis and polymerization in zirconylchloride solutions, based on the literature survey given and on some preliminary experiments, are still rather rough, and need more experimental evidence. In the next section we shall describe our conductivity studies on zirconylchloride solutions and conductivity measurements during the titration of zirconylchloride solutions with NaOH solutions. This method offers a very good opportunity to determine the changes in ion concentrations during titration. When an assumption is made for the mobility of the tetrameric complexes in zirconyl solutions the HCl concentration of zirconylchloride solutions can be calculated. We assumed the conductivity of the big complexes, with a charge which is shielded off by the gegenions, to be zero. The ions which are measured in conductivity experiments are H^+ and Cl^- in equal concentrations. This method of investigation is more reliable than potentiometric measurements, which due to the presence of very small sol particles can give rise to inconsistent measurements (the suspension effect).

V Conductivity Measurements in ZrOCl₂ Solutions

A Experimental

Conductivity measurements were carried out with a conventional cell at a frequency of 1000 Hz and at $25°C \pm 0.05°C$. The ZrOCl₂ solutions were all prepared from de-ionized water and Merck ZrOCl₂ . 8H₂O. The conductivity of de-ionized water is substracted from the conductivities of the ZrOCl₂ solutions.

The conductivity of a m-molar $ZrOCl_2$ solution is often compared with the conductivity of a 2 m-molar HCl solution. The data of the conductivity of HCl and NaCl solutions at 25°C were taken from Conway (1952). From experiments with heated $ZrOCl_2$ solutions it appeared that polymers in $ZrOCl_2$ solutions influence the conductivity measurements. The presence of non-conducting polymers in solutions influences the conductivity in such a way that a lower value for the conductivity is measured than is calculated from the amount of free HCl in solution. The correction depends upon the concentration but it did not exceed 4%. The data of Conway, which are given in different tables, are corrected for this effect as to compare the right values for the conductivity.

When 50 ml portions of $ZrOCl_2$ solutions were titrated conductometrically with NaOH, some dilution of the solution occurred due to the addition of titrant. The conductivity was corrected for this dilution.

B   Influence of Concentration on the Hydrolysis of $ZrOCl_2$ Solutions

Solutions of $ZrOCl_2$ were prepared by dissolving various weights of $ZrOCl_2 . 8H_2O$ in 500 ml de-ionized water. The zirconium concentration of these solutions varied from 0.183×10^{-3} to 13.59×10^{-3} mole/l. The solutions were allowed to stand for one month at 25°C, after which their conductivity was measured. Table IV shows the conductivity and the concentration of these solutions. On complete hydrolysis the

TABLE IV. Influence of concentration on the conductivity of $ZrOCl_2$ solutions

No.	$[Zr] \times 10^3$ (mole/l.)	κ at 25°C $(\Omega^{-1}\,m^{-1})$	$\kappa_{max.}$ at 25°C $(\Omega^{-1}\,m^{-1})$	κ/κ_{max}	% bridged Zr ions
5	0.183	0.0139	0.0154	0.903	80.5
1	0.416	0.0309	0.0350	0.883	76.6
3	1.182	0.0807	0.0986	0.818	63.7
4	2.768	0.161	0.224	0.719	43.8
6	4.673	0.249	0.375	0.664	33.2
10	6.355	0.325	0.503	0.646	29.5
7	13.59	0.650	1.034	0.629	25.7

conductivity of an m-molar $ZrOCl_2$ solution should be equal to the conductivity of a 2 mM HCl solution. Table IV compares the $ZrOCl_2$ solutions to the HCl solutions, indicated by κ_{max}. From Table IV it can be seen that $\kappa_{max} > \kappa > \frac{1}{2}\kappa_{max}$. The ratio κ/κ_{max} increases when the concentration of the $ZrOCl_2$ solution decreases. Obviously the amount of

HCl liberated on hydrolysis of an mM $ZrOCl_2$ solution increases when the concentration of the $ZrOCl_2$ solution decreases. This leads to an acid strength of between m and 2 mmole/l. The conclusions of Ermakov *et al.* (1963) can be extended now for lower concentrations. In the concentration region from 6.17×10^{-3} up to 386.8×10^{-3} mole/l Ermakov *et al.* (1963) found that the acid strength of an mM $ZrOCl_2$ solution and the acid strength of a mM HCl solution are equal. The hydrolysis reaction following from these experiments are given in the equation:

$$[Zr_4(OH)_8(H_2O)_{16}^{8+} \ldots . 8Cl^-] \xrightarrow{H_2O} [Zr_4(OH)_{12}(H_2O)_{12}^{4+} \ldots . 4Cl^-] + 4HCl.$$

The second hydrolysis step, which follows from our measurements, results in a varying amount of HCl being liberated into the solution:

$$[Zr_4(OH)_{12}(H_2O)_{12}^{4+} \ldots 4Cl^-] \underset{}{\overset{H_2O}{\rightleftharpoons}} [Zr_4(OH)_{16}(H_2O)_8] + 4HCl.$$

When one tetrameric complex is considered this reaction can be assumed to occur on the four individual sites of the complex. The foregoing overall equation thus consists of four equations which describe the hydrolysis on the four individual sites of the complex:

$$[Zr_4(OH)_{12}(H_2O)_{12}^{4+} \ldots 4Cl^-] \underset{}{\overset{H_2O}{\rightleftharpoons}} [Zr_4(OH)_{13}(H_2O)_{11}^{3+} \ldots 3Cl^-] + HCl$$

$$[Zr_4(OH)_{13}(H_2O)_{11}^{3+} \ldots 3Cl^-] \underset{}{\overset{H_2O}{\rightleftharpoons}} [Zr_4(OH)_{14}(H_2O)_{10}^{2+} \ldots 2Cl^-] + HCl$$

$$[Zr_4(OH)_{14}(H_2O)_{10}^{2+} \ldots 2Cl^-] \underset{}{\overset{H_2O}{\rightleftharpoons}} [Zr_4(OH)_{15}(H_2O)_9^{+} \ldots Cl^-] + HCl$$

$$[Zr_4(OH)_{15}(H_2O)_9^{+} \ldots Cl^-] \underset{}{\overset{H_2O}{\rightleftharpoons}} [Zr_4(OH)_{16}(H_2O)_8] + HCl.$$

The forward reactions in the above equations lead to the formation of neutral sites on the tetrameric complexes. The amount of such sites is determined by the rate constants in both directions and the HCl concentration in the solution. When an equilibrium solution is obtained the reaction should proceed in the reverse direction to that observed when the equilibrium is disturbed by the addition of HCl. This was done by conductometric titration of the solutions given in Table IV with 0.0303 N HCl. The increase in conductivity of these solutions, plotted against ml HCl added, showed a strictly linear curve with a slope corresponding, within the experimental error, to the slope of the curve which was obtained when similar HCl solutions were titrated with the 0.0303 N HCl solution. The values of κ of the titrated $ZrOCl_2$ solutions remained constant over a period of 24 hours. These experiments show that no acid consumption occurs when the solutions are titrated with 0.0303 N HCl solutions. This result contradicts the assumption of equilibrium reactions given above. In Section V C below the hydrolysis reaction will be shown to be reversible. The obvious conclusion is that neutral sites on the tetrameric complexes are short-lived intermediates. A reaction must be assumed now in which the neutral sites are involved. From Table IV it can be seen that a certain amount of singly-charged zirconium sites is always present in solution. A reaction between these singly-charged sites and neutral sites can explain the irreversibility of the hydrolysis reaction in $ZrOCl_2$ solutions. The reaction which occurs is the polymerization reaction, shown in Formula 4.

If this reaction is irreversible the observed facts can be explained completely. From the experimental data it appears that no acid consumption was observed during the addition of the HCl solution to the $ZrOCl_2$ solution. Obviously no depolymerization occurs and the polymerization reaction is irreversible.

The conclusions given indicate that there is a direct relation between the degree of hydrolysis and polymerization. As shown, one mole HCl is liberated on hydrolysis of one mole $ZrOCl_2$. This means that the charge of the individual zirconium sites on the tetrameric complex is $1+$; only tetrameric complexes with a total charge of $4+$ are present in the $ZrOCl_2$ solution. When hydrolysis proceeds further, neutral sites are formed and the amount of HCl liberated into the solution increases. The amount of HCl formed in the second step of the hydrolysis reaction is equivalent to the number of neutral sites on the tetrameric complexes. While these neutral sites are consumed in the irreversible polymerization reaction the amount of HCl formed in the second step of the hydrolysis reaction is equivalent to the number of bridged zirconium ions. In Table IV the conductivity of m-molar $ZrOCl_2$ solution (κ) was compared with the conductivity of a 2 m-molar HCl solution (κ_{max}). When only the first hydrolysis reaction occurs, $\kappa = \frac{1}{2}\kappa_{max}$ and the amount of bridged zirconium ions is zero since only tetrameric complexes are present in solution. When κ increases, the amount of bridged zirconium ions also increases. Since $\kappa - \frac{1}{2}\kappa_{max}$ stands for the number of zirconium ions, the percentage bridged zirconium ions is given by the expression:

$$\text{percentage bridged zirconium ions} = \frac{\kappa - \frac{1}{2}\kappa_{max}}{\frac{1}{2}\kappa_{max}} \cdot 100\%.$$

Table IV summarizes the percentage bridged zirconium ions for varying $ZrOCl_2$ solutions. Obviously the percentage bridged zirconium ions is related to the degree of polymerization.

In this section we have concluded that zirconylchloride solutions can be hydrolyzed to a higher extent than was found by Ermakov et al.

(1963) and that $ZrOCl_2$ solutions are polymerized to a certain extent depending upon concentration. Section V E below discusses these results in greater detail.

C Influence of Neutralization on Hydrolysis and Polymerization of $ZrOCl_2$ Solutions

In Section III B we suggested that increased polymerization occurs when $ZrOCl_2$ solutions are neutralized to give hydrous zirconia. The possibilities to calculate the percentage of bridged zirconium ions we suggested above will be used here. Conductometric titration curves of $ZrOCl_2$ solutions with NaOH and HCl were recorded. For the experiments described below, 1·0750 g of Merck $ZrOCl_2 . 8H_2O$ was dissolved in 500 ml of de-ionized water. The $6·677 \times 10^{-3}$ molar solution was allowed to stand for one week; 50 ml portions of this stock solution were used for the conductometric titration with 0·0607 N NaOH. 11.00 ml of the NaOH solution were required for complete neutralization of the $ZrOCl_2$ solution. Back-titrations were carried out with 0·0303 N HCl solution when 5, 8 and 11 ml portions of the NaOH solution were added, with 10, 16 and 22 ml of the HCl solution. This results in the formation of NaCl, which amount follows from the added amount of NaOH and HCl. The contribution to the conductivity of this amount of NaCl can be calculated using the data of Conway (1952). Figure 3 shows the conductivity of the $ZrOCl_2$ solutions, only corrected for dilution, as a function of the added volume of 0·0607 N NaOH. The curves with the arrows directed to the right are the forward-titration curves. The curves with the arrows directed to the left are the back-titration curves.

The starting point of the titration curves is point A. When this $ZrOCl_2$ solution is titrated with HCl directly, a straight line is observed with a slope as was discussed in Section V B above. The titration curve with NaOH (ABCDE), shows a part with a negative slope and a part with a positive slope. The equivalence point is obtained in point E of the titration curve. When HCl solutions are titrated with NaOH the conductivity of the solution decreases linearly with the amount of NaOH added, until the equivalence point is reached. This is caused by the decreasing $H^{\oplus}$ concentration, which ion has a higher mobility than the $Na^{\oplus}$ ion. The first part of the titration curve shows such a decrease in conductivity, although this decrease is less than is observed in a HCl–NaOH titration. Moreover, the slope of the curve (ABC) varies during titration, indicating that no distinct change in ion composition can be identified with this curve. The second part of the curve (CDE)

shows a positive slope and from this slope we can calculate that the increase in conductivity is due to the addition of a 0·0607 M NaCl solution.
The solution is titrated however with 0·0607 N NaOH solution. Obviously, in the second part of the titration curve NaCl is formed on the
addition of NaOH. When the titration was stopped after the addition
of 5 ml 0·0607 N NaOH, back-titration was carried out with 10 ml of

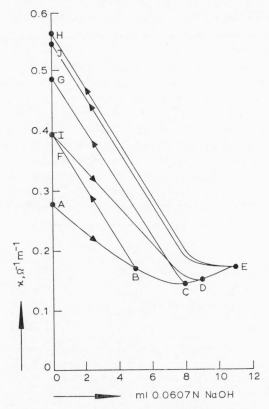

FIG. 3 Titration curves of 50 ml 6·677 × 10⁻³ M ZrOCl₂ solutions against 0·0607
N NaOH.

0·0303 N HCl solution. The back-titration curve is indicated in Fig. 3
by BF. This curve shows a linear increase in conductivity while the
slope of this curve is equal to the slope of the titration curve of a
50 ml HCl solution having a conductivity of about 0·15 $\Omega^{-1}m^{-1}$ with
0·0303 N HCl solution. From this result it can be concluded that the
non-bridged zirconium ions are all singly charged until at least point B
of the titration curve (Section V B, above). This was true for the

starting point of the titration curves with a conductivity of 0·279 $\Omega^{-1}m^{-1}$. The conductivity of the titrated solution point F, corrected for the conductivity of 0·303 mmole NaCl in 50 ml water is calculated to be 0·328 $\Omega^{-1}m^{-1}$. The same procedure was followed when 8 ml and 11 ml of the NaOH solution was added. These back-titration curves are indicated in Fig. 3 with CG and EH respectively. Curve CG shows a slight deviation from linearity at the beginning of the back-titration. Curve EH shows a horizontal part at the beginning of the back-titration while further on a straight line is obtained with a slope equal to BF. The horizontal part of curve EH indicates that the ion concentration of the suspension remains constant despite the addition of HCl.

Table V summarizes the conductivities of the solutions before and after titration. It is clear that the percentage of bridged zirconium ions increases when neutralization is carried on. While the degree of polymerization is related to the percentage of bridged zirconium ions we can conclude that polymerization occurs when these $ZrOCl_2$ solutions are neutralized with NaOH to give $Zr(OH)_4$.

TABLE V. Conductivity of $ZrOCl_2$ solutions after back-titration with HCl, corrected for the amount of NaCl formed during the titrations

	$\kappa(\Omega^{-1}\ m^{-1})$	% Bridged Zr ions
Starting solution, 1 week at 25°C	0·279	5·7
Partly neutralized with 5 ml of NaOH	0·328	24·2
Partly neutralized with 8 ml of NaOH	0·384	45·5
Completely neutralized with 11 ml NaOH	0·414	56·8
Heated for 4 hours at 80°C	0·399	51·1
Heated for 4 hours at 80°C completely neutralized with 11 ml of NaOH	0·402	52·3
Complete hydrolysis (calculated)	0·528	100·0

In the last part of the titration curve (CDE), only a slight increase in the percentage of bridged zirconium ions is calculated. The slope of this curve indicated the formation of NaCl. This can be explained by the neutralization of the non-bridged zirconium ions in this part of the titration curve. The neutralization is accompanied by the liberation of Cl⁻ ions. This fact points to the state of the Cl⁻ ion as being

gegenion for the positive charge of the complexes. We observed in the
middle of CE a coagulation of the sol. We stated in V B above that
the second hydrolysis reaction is reversible. This can be proved by the
following experiment. At point E of the titration curve, all zirconium
ions are neutralized and the formation of $Zr(OH)_4$ is complete. On

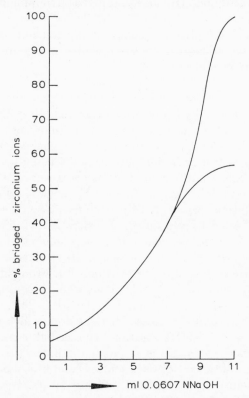

FIG. 4 Percentage of bridged zirconium ions during neutralization with 0·0607 N
NaOH.

back-titration, indicated by the curve EH, these non-bridged zirconium
ions became singly-charged, over the first part of the titration curve,
due to the adsorption of HCl.

The increase in percentage bridged zirconium ions against ml NaOH
added is shown in Fig. 4. The increase in the percentage of bridged
zirconium ions from 5·7 up to 56·8% shows a sigmoid character.
The formation of bridged zirconium ions decreases when the neutralization point at 11 ml NaOH is reached. In this part of the curve the
number of singly-charged zirconium sites decreases. This conclusion

shows that singly-charged zirconium sites are one of the reactants in the polymerization reaction. The upper curve in Fig. 4 shows the percentage neutralized zirconium ions in the complexes. This curve varies from 5·7 up to 100%, while in the first part of the titration curve the percentage neutralized zirconium ions and the percentage bridged zirconium ions are equal. Obviously, bridged zirconium ions are neutralized zirconium ions.

The formation of hydrous zirconia by neutralizing $ZrOCl_2$ solutions involves a polymerization reaction, while the hydrous zirconia is settled down by coagulation.

D   The Neutralization of Heated ZrOCl Solutions

The preparation of hydrous zirconia on refluxing $ZrOCl_2$ solutions was accompanied by an increasing acid strength of the $ZrOCl_2$ solution. The increased hydrolysis was promoted by higher temperatures after which a polymerization reaction occurs, as discussed before. The effect of heating $ZrOCl_2$ solutions on the titration curve was studied by heating 50 ml samples of the $6·677 \times 10^{-3}$ M $ZrOCl_2$ solution described above. The solution was heated for 4 hours at 80°C, after which the solution was allowed to cool down. The titration was carried out with 0·0607 N NaOH solution, while from the equivalence point back-titration was carried out with 0·0303 N HCl solution. The titration curves are shown in Fig. 3, curve IDE and EJ. From the conductivity of the starting solution 0·399 $\Omega^{-1}m^{-1}$, the percentage of bridged zirconium ions could be calculated to be 51·1. The titration curve IDE of the heated solution shows a distinct slope which is almost equal to the slope of a HCl–NaOH titration. The second part of the titration curve DE shows the same slope as was found in the titration curves of the non-heated solutions. Between points D and E of the titration curve of the heated solution, coagulation suddenly occurs. The back-titration curve for this heated solution EJ shows the adsorption of HCl at the beginning of the back-titration accompanied by peptization flocculation of the suspension, as observed above. The conductivity of point J, from which the value for the conductivity of 0·6677 m-mole NaCl in 50 ml water is substracted, is calculated to be $\kappa = 0·402$ $\Omega^{-1}m^{-1}$. Table V summarizes the data of the heated $ZrOCl_2$ solution. The conductivity of the starting solution heated for 4 hours at 80°C is $\kappa = 0·399$ $\Omega^{-1}m^{-1}$. The conductivities of the heated solution before and after neutralization are almost equal. The neutralization of these heated $ZrOCl_2$ solutions leads only to the neutralization of non-bridged zirconium ions. This neutralization occurs in the second part of the titration curve DE.

The polymerization of the species in solution occurs during heating of the solution (Table V). The precipitation of hydrous zirconia from heated solutions involves only a coagulation of the zirconium complexes.

E   The Variation of the Percentage of Bridged Zirconium Ions in Neutralization and Heating Processes

From Table V it can be seen that the percentage of bridged zirconium ions for the completely neutralized non-heated solution is 56·8. The percentage of bridged zirconium ions of the heated solution reaches only

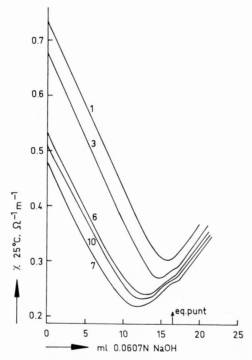

FIG. 5 Titration curves of $ZrOCl_2$ solutions based on 50 ml 0·01 M $ZrOCl_2$ solution against 0·0607 N NaOH: (1) 0·416, (3) 1·812, (6) 4·673, (10) 6·355, (7) 13·59 × 10^{-3} M $ZrOCl_2$.

52·3. Two kinds of experiments were carried out to show that the percentage of bridged zirconium ions can reach higher values, both on neutralization and on heating $ZrOCl_2$ solutions.

The solutions given in V B above were titrated conductometrically. In order to compare the titration curves of $ZrOCl_2$ solutions with different concentrations, the titration curves were based on a 10^{-2} M $ZrOCl_2$

solntion. This was done by multiplying both the actual conductivity and the number of ml NaOH added by the ratio of the concentration of the standard solution, 10^{-2} M $ZrOCl_2$, and the actual concentration of the solution. The equivalence point is at 16·47 ml of 0·0607 N NaOH when 50 ml samples of the solution are titrated. Figure 5 shows the

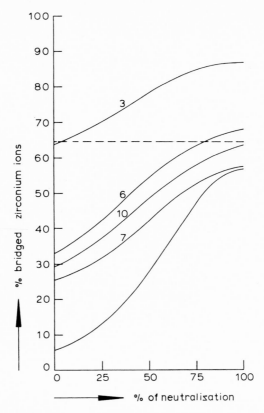

FIG. 6 Percentage of bridged zirconium ions against percentage of neutralization for $ZrOCl_2$ solutions given in Tables IV, V and VI.

titration curves while the numbers in the figure correspond to the numbers given in Table IV. From the titration curve the percentage of bridged zirconium ions formed can be calculated during titration as shown above. A straight line with a slope corresponding to the HCl–NaOH titration indicates that only neutralization of free HCl in the $ZrOCl_2$ solution occurs.

When polymerization occurs during titration a curved line results, since Cl⁻ ions are liberated during the polymerization reaction. The increase in the percentage of bridged zirconium ions during titration is given in Fig. 6 against percentage of neutralization. The numbers correspond to the solutions described in Section V B above. The differences in the percentage of bridged zirconium ions of these aged solutions (1 month 25°C) remain on neutralization. The lower curve in Fig. 6 indicates a solution with a concentration comparable to solution 7 while the time of standing here was only 1 week at 25°C. The difference in the percentages of bridged zirconium ions decreases during the titration of these solutions.

The increase in the percentage of bridged zirconium ions is favoured by neutralization, a long period of standing and heating. From the titration curves of the heated $ZrOCl_2$ solution it was shown that the percentage of bridged zirconium ions did not vary during titration. The dotted line in Fig. 6 indicates a heated solution from Table VI. Heating offers a possibility to prepare hydrous zirconia with a definite amount of bridged zirconium ions. If a variation of the percentage of bridged zirconium ions in the heated solution can be achieved, this difference will remain when the solutions are neutralized. The variation in time of heating can achieve such a difference.

The influence of time of heating was studied. 1·2085 g of Merck $ZrOCl_2 . 8H_2O$ was dissolved in 500 ml de-ionized water. This solution was allowed to stand for one month at 25°C, after which 50 ml samples of this solution were heated at 80°C.

TABLE VI. Measured conductivities κ of $ZrOCl_2$ solutions [Zr] = 0·0075 mole/l, κ max. exptl. = 0·593 Ω^{-1} m^{-1}

Temp. (°C)	Time (days)	κ	% bridged zirconium ions
25	30	0·378	27·7
80	1	0·487	64·5
	2	0·500	68·9
	4	0·504	70·3
	6	0·519	75·3

Table VI summarizes the conductivities of these solutions. From the values of κ and κ_{max} we can calculate the percentage of bridged zirconium ions. The increase in the percentage of bridged zirconium ions on heating is obvious. On prolonged heating only a small increase in the percentage of bridged zirconium ions is observed. At this point we can observe in the neutralized zirconium solutions with moderate concentrations a percentage of bridged zirconium ions varying from 55–75% (Fig. 6). This difference is not very high and it must be

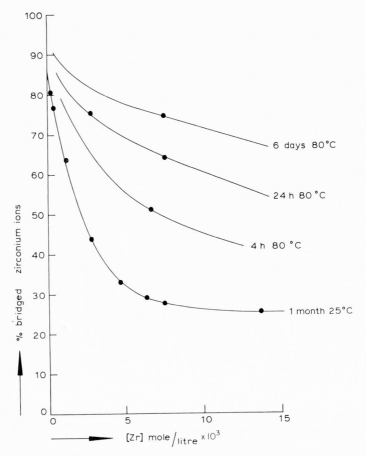

FIG. 7 Percentage of bridged zirconium ions against zirconium concentration.

expected that differences in hydrous zirconia obtained on neutralization will be difficult to detect.

The $ZrOCl_2$ solutions discussed in the different parts of this section are characterized by the percentage of bridged zirconium ions. The data of the $ZrOCl_2$ solutions are represented in Fig. 7. where the percentage of bridged zirconium ions is plotted against concentration.

When solutions are heated, an irreversible increase is observed in the percentage of bridged zirconium ions. It can be expected that prolonged heating for six days will show a further increase in the percentage of bridged zirconium ions, while refluxing $ZrOCl_2$ solutions results in the formation of a hydrous zirconia sol. This is obviously not the most stable form, since a sol can be electrically neutralized when the temperature is raised further. Hydrous zirconia in an acid solution, obtained from the complete hydrolysis of $ZrOCl_2$, will be the most stable condition.

Figure 7 shows one peculiarity. All curves show an increasing percentage of bridged zirconium ions on decreasing the concentration. This follows from the increasing hydrolysis on decreasing concentration. The increased hydrolysis at low concentrations, which can be described by an equilibrium reaction, results in a higher percentage of neutral sites than is present in more concentrated solutions. The percentage of bridged zirconium ions finally obtained will be higher now in more dilute solutions. The rate of formation of polymeric species, which can be calculated from the solutions given in Fig. 7, increases however when the concentration increases. This is to be expected since despite the low rate of formation, all curves must reach a percentage of bridged zirconium ions approaching 100%.

It is necessary that the parameters time and temperature must be indicated when data of hydrolysis of $ZrOCl_2$ solutions are given, since $ZrOCl_2$ solutions are not stable. Kinetic factors merely determine now the actual percentage of bridged zirconium ions of a $ZrOCl_2$ solution.

F   A Three-dimensional Picture of the Polymerization

The formulation we gave for the polymerization reaction in Formula 4 can be extended now with models. The tetrameric complex $Zr_4(OH)_8(H_2O)_{16}^{8+}$ was illustrated in Fig. 2 in a projection on (001) of the unit cell of $ZrOCl_2 \cdot 8H_2O$. When the size of the Zr^{4+} ion and the OH^- ion is taken into account it can be seen that the eight OH^- groups in the tetrameric complex are packed in a way similar to that of the F^- ion in CaF_2. These eight OH^- groups can be enveloped by a cube. We represent the Zr^{4+} ion in Fig. 8b lying in the cavity of four OH groups. Four planes of this cube contain such a Zr^{4+} ion. In Fig. 2 it can be seen that four H_2O groups are linked with the zirconium ion, leading to a square antiprismatic coordination of the Zr^{4+} ion. The four H_2O groups lying in one plane can be represented by a slice while two slices form a cube similar to that already discussed. Every zirconium ion is linked with these four H_2O groups. The way in which the slices are placed on four planes of the cube is indicated by the coordination of the Zr^{4+} ion. Figure 8a shows the complete tetrameric complex

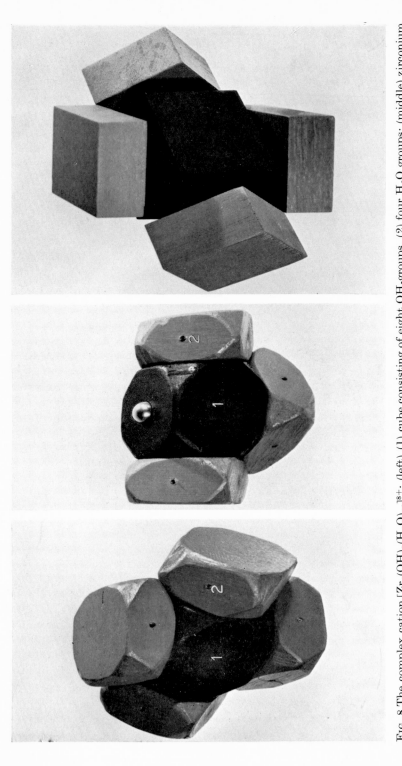

FIG. 8 The complex cation $[Zr_4(OH)_8(H_2O)_{16}]^{8+}$: (left) (1) cube consisting of eight OH-groups, (2) four H_2O groups: (middle) zirconium ion in 8-coordination; (right) representation used in visualizing the polymerization products.

$Zr_4(OH)_8(H_2O)_{16}^{8+}$. The cube is indicated with (1) and the H_2O slices with (2). Figure 8c shows a representation of the tetrameric complexes where the H_2O groups are found at a certain distance from the cube. This representation will be used for the polymerization reaction, as it shows the important parts of the complex more clearly.

The hydrolysis reaction has no influence on the representation of the tetrameric complexes, since the proton is very small compared with the H_2O group. According to Formula 4, polymerization results in the formation of two bridging ligands, while the zirconium ions remain

Fig. 9 The polymeric species formed from two tetrameric complexes.

eight coordinated. The product which is formed in Formula 4 can be represented now by Fig. 9. The two tetrameric complexes are connected by two OH bridging ligands. The configuration which is created now shows that the bridging ligands and the remaining OH^- and H_2O groups form a good point for further polymerization. Figure 10 shows a polymeric species which is formed from four tetrameric complexes. From a comparison of Figs 9 and 10 it is clear that the OH bridging ligands formed between the zirconium ions can be represented in Fig. 10 with a cube. The (0) in the figure indicates where polymerization on the polymer represented in Fig. 9 took place. The bridging ligands

FIG. 10 The polymeric species formed from four tetrameric complexes.

between four tetrameric complexes form a similar arrangement as is present in the stable tetrameric complex itself. This representation of polymerization in $ZrOCl_2$ solutions obviously results in a three-dimensional polymer.

The size of the polymers can be related to the percentage of bridged zirconium ions. When a polymer is built up from the tetrameric complexes represented in Fig. 8c, the number of bridged zirconium ions can be counted. The polymer given in Fig. 9 shows two tetrameric complexes while one zirconium ion is a bridged zirconium ion; 8 zirconium ions are present in this polymer and the percentage of bridged zirconium ions is calculated to be 12·5. The polymer shown in Fig. 10 consists of four tetrameric complexes. Here 16 zirconium ions are present, while 4 zirconium ions are bridged. The percentage of bridged zirconium ions is calculated to be 25. Further increase in the size of the polymers results in an increasing percentage of bridged zirconium ions.

G   The Polymerization of Group IV Elements

The precipitation of oxides and hydroxides can be described by processes such as polymerization and crystallization. Group IV elements exhibit the polymerization processes typical of those which can occur in solutions.

The formation of silica was studied by Okkerse (1961), who showed that polymerization processes occur in silica sols depending on the pH of the solution. Formula 5 illustrates a simplified polymerization

reaction (Okkerse, Chapter V), finally leading to SiO_2. From the kinetics of the polymerization of silica it was indicated that in the case of silica complex formation also plays an important role in the mechanism of the polymerization.

The polymerization of titanyl complexes in solution is the one most difficult to study experimentally in the series of group IV elements. The anion SO_4^{2-} present in titanyl sulphate solutions is strongly bonded to the titanium ion (van den Heuvel and van Doorn, 1966). If this anion is not taken into consideration however, some generalizations can be formulated. The charge of the titanium ion in normal solutions

13*

is 4+, its coordination number is 6. When the polymerization occurs on neutralization of a titanyl solution the formation of $TiO(OH)_2$ must be assumed. The charge of the titanium ion is just compensated for, while the bridging ligands O^{2-} and OH^- account for the coordination number 6. The reaction between a neutral site and a singly-charged site is suggested by the results obtained for silica and zirconia. Formula 6 illustrates one of the possibilities for the polymerization reaction on

titanyl solutions. From a comparison of the polymerization reaction of group IV elements it can be seen that the increase in the coordination number results in the formation of oxide, oxide-hydroxide or hydroxide.

The polymerization of other elements results in similar considerations. Some differences can arise when the metal-anion combination is considered. An anion with a high affinity for the metal ion can act as a bridging ligand in the polymerization reaction as well as O^{2-} or OH^-. This was very clearly shown by Wyatt (1966) and Hermans (1966) for palladium and uranyl solutions.

In the $ZrOCl_2$ solutions studied we showed that the chloride ion acts only as gegenion. The picture we gave for the $ZrOCl_2$ solutions can be extended to other zirconyl solutions where no actual metal-anion bond is present. From the similarity between Zr and Hf (Section II) it can be expected that the chemistry of zirconyl solutions will account for hafnyl solutions too.

VI Preparation of Hydrous Zirconia

A Preparation Method I

The preparation of hydrous zirconia was carried out in various ways. Zirconium hydroxide can be precipitated by neutralizing solutions of zirconium salts with a base. $ZrCl_4$ was first used as the starting material, the base being ammonium hydroxide. In these experiments 250 g of $ZrCl_4$ was dissolved in 25 l. of de-ionized water, and a diluted solution of ammonium hydroxide was added drop-wise to the $ZrCl_4$ solution with vigorous stirring; the precipitation was followed potentiometrically. In this way the precipitation could be stopped at any required pH. Three preparations were done in this way, with the final pH of the solution adjusted to pH 4, 6, and 8. All the suspensions were left for one week at their final pH, after which the gelatinous precipitates were filtered and washed with de-ionized water until a negative reaction for $Cl^{\ominus}$ was obtained in the filtrate. The filtered products were dried for 48 hours at 120°C. On drying the precipitates shrink and form a hard cake. These hard lumps are difficult to handle, but when they are placed in water small particles of about 1 mm separate, which are far more easily manipulated. Filtration and drying again at 120°C yields more or less translucent products similar to splinters of glass. The preparations obtained in this way will be indicated by A-4, A-6, and A-8. This method of preparation will be indicated by I.

B   Preparation Method II

Precipitation of zirconium hydroxide with a dilute solution of ammonium hydroxide is not an ideal procedure. When a drop of the

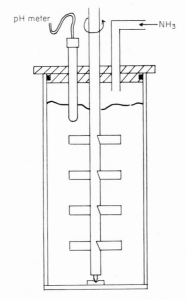

FIG. 11 Reaction vessel for the precipitation of zirconia gel.

ammonia solution falls into the zirconium solution flakes of zirconium hydroxide are formed due to the high hydroxyl concentration around the drop of ammonia. By vigorous stirring these flakes are dispersed in the solution. Homogeneous precipitation would be much better.

For this reason a method of precipitation was applied which avoids

a high local hydroxyl concentration. A precipitation vessel was made
from perspex, as shown in Fig. 11, in which the zirconium hydroxide
could be precipitated by means of gaseous ammonia. The cylindric
vessel can be closed by means of a lid sealed with an O-ring and provided
with openings for a stirrer, the ammonia inlet, and the pH-measuring
cell.

Five litres of de-ionized water were used for every preparation, in whihc
were dissolved 100 g of Merck $ZrOCl_2 . 8H_2O$. The ammonia was purified and its flow was regulated with a needle valve at 9 l./h. The precipitation was complete in $1\frac{1}{2}$ hours. The small air buffer above the solution
led to dilution of the gaseous ammonia. The mixing in this vessel was
very good, as proved by neutralizing HCl solutions in this way with
methyl red as the indicator. After neutralization of the $ZrOCl_2$ solution
easily filtering precipitates were obtained. The gelatinous products
were washed, filtered, and dried at 120°C. The hard lumps were again
immersed in water, where they crumbled into small, easy to handle
particles, and the material was again dried at 120°C. This method of
preparation will be denoted by II.

The hard lumps of zirconium oxide-hydroxide obtained after drying
at 120°C can present some difficulties in catalytic investigations of
ZrO_2 with respect to diffusion problems, even when the particles are
about 1 mm. According to van der Giessen (1966), dehydration of iron
oxide-hydrate gels occurs on freezing at liquid nitrogen temperatures.
When the mass is thawed out at room temperature the gel separates
into a water phase and a brown precipitate. After washing and drying a
finely-divided powder is obtained. This way of dehydrating gels was
adopted therefore also for zirconia gels obtained by preparation
method II. The zirconium oxide-hydroxide gel was frozen at liquid
nitrogen temperature, and after 24 hours separated into a water phase
and a layer of precipitate. Filtration, washing, and drying of this
precipitate at 120°C afforded a finely-divided powder. This preparation
method will be indicated by IIa.

The material can be dried at room temperature over P_2O_5 pellets.
When this is done the water content of the dried product is higher than
when the drying is carried out at 120°C. Table VII gives the data for
some preparations obtained by methods II and IIa. The differences
between frozen and normal preparations are obviously very small, and
DTA results in identical thermograms. From this table it can be seen
that there is a correlation between the water content and the surface
area. When water is liberated the surface area increases, indicating
that at these high water contents water is present in micropores. The
composition of the dried gels will be discussed in greater detail in

Section VII. Preparations obtained by methods I, II, and IIa are designated as A-preparations.

TABLE VII. Characteristics of dried zirconia preparations

Preparation method	Temp. of drying (°C)	Surface area (m²/g)	Loss on ignition (%)	Density (g/cm³)
II	120	308	10·9	4·51
	20 (P₂O₅)	243	16·9	3·63
IIa	120	344	10·5	4·56
	20 (P₂O₅)	177	20·8	3·38

C Preparation Method III

Direct formation of hydrous zirconia from zirconylchloride solutions was described by Clearfield (1964). A 1 M zirconylchloride solution was adjusted to pH 2·5 by the addition of ammonia. The solutions were refluxed and the resulting colloidal sol was coagulated with ammonia or collected by centrifuging. We dissolved 100 g of Merck ZrOCl₂ . 8H₂O in 1 l. of de-ionized water and refluxed the solution for three weeks. After one week the solution was blue, and finally a white colloidal sol was obtained. This sol was coagulated with ammonia, filtered, washed, and dried at 120°C. A finely-divided powder was obtained. DTA showed a crystalline thermogram, and the X-ray diffraction pattern had monoclinic spacings. These preparations are designated as M-preparations.

D Preparation Method IV

As was pointed out by Clearfield (1964), crystalline hydrous zirconia can be obtained by refluxing the gelatinous precipitate from method I. When the precipitates were washed thoroughly no crystallinity was observed during refluxing and the pH of the suspension did not show a decrease. When the precipitates were washed to chlorine content of 0·1–0·4% a decrease in pH was observed during refluxing, and monoclinic zirconia was obtained. When gelatinous precipitates were refluxed in 20% NaOH solution, tetragonal hydrous zirconia was obtained.

We prepared gels according to method II. The gelatinous products were washed thoroughly until $Cl^{\ominus}$ was no longer detectable in the gel. Each preparation from 50 g of $ZrOCl_2 \cdot 8H_2O$ was mixed with 2 l. of de-ionized water, and the resulting slurries were refluxed until no amorphous zirconia could be detected by DTA. The development of crystallinity was followed this way.

Preparation method IVa. The slurry was refluxed in a basic medium. When the crystallinity was complete, the slurry was filtered, washed, and dried at 120°C.

Preparation method IVb. The slurry was refluxed in a neutral medium. When the crystallinity was complete, the slurry was filtered, washed, and dried at 120°C.

Preparation method IVc. The slurry was refluxed in an acid medium. When the crystallinity was complete, the resulting colloidal sol was coagulated with ammonia solution, washed, and dried at 120°C.

VII Characterization of Hydrous Zirconia

A Differential Thermal Analysis

As was pointed out in Section VI, hydrous zirconia can be made in many ways, resulting in various modifications of the product, such as amorphous, tetragonal, and monoclinic zirconia. The DTA curve of amorphous zirconia shows two characteristic parts (Fig. 12).

The endothermic effect caused by dehydration of the amorphous product is followed, when the dehydration is almost complete, by a large exothermic effect. At different points of the analysis, samples were taken for investigation by X-ray diffraction. The diffraction patterns of preparations removed from the furnace before the exothermic effect show an amorphous character. The preparation taken just after the exothermic effect shows a fine tetragonal pattern (Fig. 13), and the preparation taken at the end of the analysis (800°C) evidently contains a mixture of tetragonal and monoclinic ZrO_2 (Fig. 14). From these experiments we concluded that the exothermic effect is due to crystallization of the amorphous ZrO_2 into the tetragonal form. The conversion of tetragonal into monoclinic ZrO_2 on prolonged heating is accompanied by small heat effects, not detectable by DTA. Kommissarova *et al.* (1960) obtained a similar thermogram obtained from amorphous ZrO_2. The exothermic peak at 405°C was due to crystallization into monoclinic ZrO_2. As was shown by our measurements, the exothermic peak is responsible only for the crystallization of amorphous to tetragonal ZrO_2.

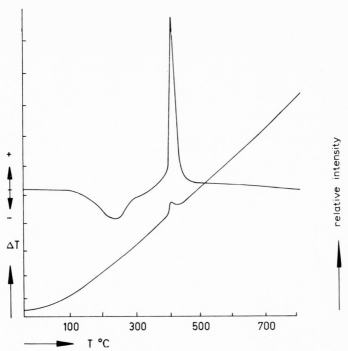

FIG. 12 Differential thermal analysis of amorphous zirconia. Heating rate 10°C/
min.

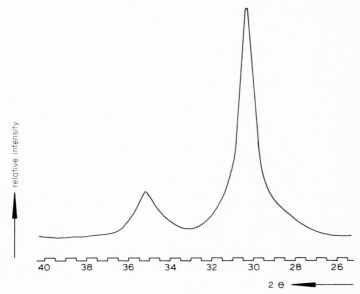

FIG. 13 X-ray diffraction pattern of tetragonal zirconia.

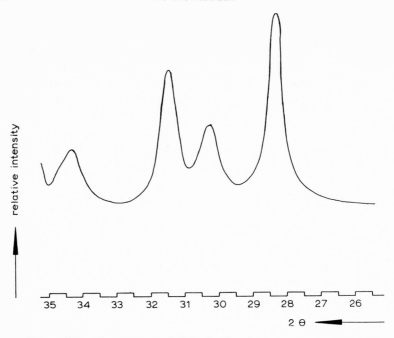

FIG. 14 X-ray diffraction pattern of zirconia, showing tetragonal and monoclinic spacings.

The heat effect at 405°C, the "glow phenomenon" is typical of amorphous zirconia. DTA was used for identification of the products obtained by the various methods outlined in Section VI.

B Density Measurements

Most of the products obtained in this work were dried at 120°C. As indicated by Vleeskens (1959), drying silica gel at this temperature results in the removal of physically adsorbed water, and only chemically bound water remains in the specimen. Steggerda (1955) studied the dehydration of $Al(OH)_3$ by density measurements. He found the volumes of the components of $Al(OH)_3$ to be additive, and the specific volume of OH groups was calculated as 0.70 cm^3/g. As was already mentioned, the composition of hydrous zirconia is unknown. The water content depends on the method of preparation and on the temperature and manner of drying, and variations in the water content lead to formulas such as $Zr(OH)_4 . xH_2O$ (Kommissarova et al., 1960), $ZrO(OH)_2 . xH_2O$ (Zaitsev and Bochkarev, 1962), and $ZrO_2 . xH_2O$ (Blumenthal, 1958c); some authors try to calculate the solubility product of $Zr(OH)_4$ (Kovalenko and Bagdasarov, 1961; Sheka and

Pevzner, 1960). In these formulae x refers to an undefined amount of loosely bound water.

In Section V we proposed a composition $Zr(OH)_4 . xH_2O$ for the gelatinous product. Preparation method III gives rise to crystalline monoclinic ZrO_2, with interatomic spacings same as in the calcined products. The water content of the preparations dried at 120°C can be 7%. As was shown by IR measurements, mainly water bound physically in micropores is present (Rijnten, 1969). From these results it follows that $ZrO_2 . xH_2O$ is the correct representation for this type of zirconia. When this formula is used for amorphous zirconia obtained by methods I and II, the justification must be considered in greater detail. Dehydration isobars show that the aqueous vapour pressure versus the composition falls continuously as the temperature is slowly raised and dehydration progresses, and there are no discontinuities to indicate the presence of hydrates (Simon and Fischer, 1929).

The absence of actual hydrates of zirconia has also been demonstrated by measurements of the magnetic susceptibility during the dehydration process. The magnetic susceptibility is a linear function of the water content (Bourian and Hun, 1928). For this reason amorphous zirconia is called hydrous zirconia, and the adjective "hydrous" implies that the water is loosely bound in non-stoichiometric proportions (Weiser, 1935). Such methods, involving continuous dehydration processes, cannot be successful in determining hydrates of amorphous zirconia. The surface area of zirconia is rather high, and adsorption phenomena, giving rise to continuous changes on the active substance, interfere with the determination of any true hydrates (Broekhoff, 1967, personal communication). Since the gelatinous precipitates are formed on polymerization processes leading to amorphous, undefined preparations, the dehydration of these preparations can be assumed to occur continuously. From the above-mentioned considerations it was thus decided to use density measurements to determine the composition of hydrous zirconia. Water was used as imbibition liquid at 25°C, and the procedure described by Okkerse (1961) was followed. Products from preparation methods I and II were dried and heated to a water content of 2_0 to 3%. As was pointed out previously, the use of density measurements is justified by the additivity of the volumes of the components of the composition. When 1 g of the composition $ZrO_2 . yH_2O$ consists of x grams of ZrO_2 and $1-x$ grams of H_2O, the volumes of the composition and the components can be equated by dividing the amounts by the corresponding densities:

$$\frac{1}{\rho} = \frac{x}{\rho ZrO_2} + \frac{1-x}{\rho H_2O}$$

where ρ is the density of the composition g/cm³, x the residue left by ignition of 1 g of the composition, ρ_{ZrO_2} the density of ZrO_2 present in the composition (g/cm³), and ρ_{H_2O} the density of H_2O present in the composition (g/cm³). Dividing the equation by x we obtain:

$$\frac{1}{\rho x} = \frac{1}{\rho_{ZrO_2}} + \frac{1-x}{x\rho_{H_2O}}.$$

When ρ and x are measured for preparations dried to different extents $1/\rho x$ can be plotted against $(1-x)/x$. The intercept of the curve on the ordinate gives the specific volume of ZrO_2 and the slope of the plot indicates the specific volume of H_2O present in the composition.

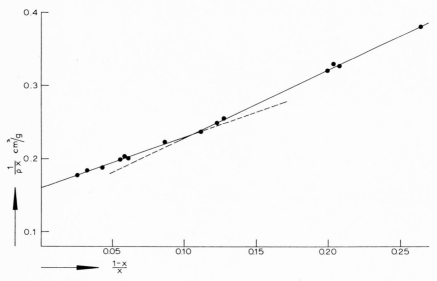

FIG. 15 Specific volume of zirconia preparations against H_2O content.

The results for the different A-preparations, obtained from different starting materials and dried to varying water contents, are shown in Fig. 15. In this figure two straight lines are drawn, although the above relation $(1/\rho x)$ accounts only for the first region of the graph. The slope of the line at high water contents is 1·00, indicating that the H_2O is bound physically. The slope at low water contents was calculated as 0·70 cm³/g, indicating a specific volume that corresponds to water of hydroxylation. This is the same value for the specific volume of the OH groups in $Al(OH)_3$ that was calculated from Steggerda's (1955) results. The break in the curve is situated at 12·0% water. This value is almost obtained when the gels from preparation methods I and II are dried at 120°C. This means that 120°C is a good temperature for drying zirconia gels in order to obtain $ZrO(OH)_2$. Extrapolation of line indicates an intercept of 0·160 cm^3/g for amorphous ZrO_2. The densities of tetragonal and monoclinic ZrO_2 are 6·03 and 5·89 g/cm^3 respectively (Ruff and Ebert, 1929).

C   Dehydration of Zr(OH)₄

From the composition corresponding to the break in the curve of Fig. 15 we obtain the formula $ZrO(OH)_2$. When preparations are treated in such a way that the water content is higher, the formula is $ZrO(OH)_2 . xH_2O$. From the polymerization scheme described in Section IV, the formula of the gelatinous precipitate should be $Zr(OH)_4 . xH_2O$. Zaitsev (1962) showed that in the titration of freshly precipitated zirconia, thoroughly washed with distilled water, four OH groups per zirconium can be exchanged rapidly with fluoride. From these results he concluded that $Zr(OH)_4 . xH_2O$ exists in aqueous suspensions, although its stability is low. When the precipitate was kept under water for several hours or days, it aged and only two OH groups could be exchanged rapidly with fluoride. During the aging the precipitate is dehydrated according to the following reaction:

$$Zr(OH)_4 . xH_2O \rightarrow ZrO(OH)_2 . xH_2O + H_2O.$$

On filtering, washing, and drying the composition $ZrO(OH)_2 . xH_2O$ is obtained, as shown in Fig. 15. Enough information is now available to state that preparation methods I and II first lead to zirconium hydroxide, which is dehydrated already in water suspensions to $ZrO(OH)_2 . xH_2O$. Moreover, we can conclude that zirconium oxide-hydroxide is amorphous. When suspensions of $ZrO(OH)_2 . xH_2O$ are treated in the special ways described in Section VI (method IV), crystalline products are obtained, indicating the formation of $ZrO_2 . xH_2O$ according to the following reaction:

$$ZrO(OH)_2 . xH_2O \rightarrow ZrO_2 . xH_2O + H_2O.$$

The acid-boiled suspensions lead to preparations that are nearly the same as those obtained by method III. The surface area, water content, electron micrographs, and X-ray diffraction patterns are almost identical. As was shown by Clearfield (1964) the X-ray diffraction pattern contained evidence of the presence of tetragonal ZrO_2 during early stages of the formation of the hydrous oxide in method III. Using DTA, we observed an amorphous character of the products in early stages of the formation. We conclude now that in methods III and IVb the formation of the oxides follows the same path. The hydrolysis of the $ZrOCl_2$. $8H_2O$ solution in method III is enhanced when the temperature is raised, leading to complexes which polymerize owing to the increased hydrolysis. $Zr(OH)_4$. xH_2O would result in this way, but due to its instability it is transformed into amorphous $ZrO(OH)_2$. xH_2O. These reactions in the early stages of the formation are followed by further dehydration in the acid suspension where first tetragonal and finally monoclinic ZrO_2 is obtained. In method IVb hydrolysis is favoured by neutralization of the $ZrOCl_2$. $8H_2O$ solution with ammonia. On neutralization $Zr(OH)_4$. xH_2O results, which on aging is dehydrated into $ZrO(OH)_2$. xH_2O. Boiling the acid suspension leads to amorphous ZrO_2 . xH_2O, which is transformed into tetragonal and finally into monoclinic zirconia. The processes described above can be represented in the following scheme where all preparation methods (I, II, etc.) and the modification of the preparations finally obtained are indicated (A, amorphous; T, tetragonal; M, monoclinic).

Transformations in the $ZrOCl_2$–H_2O system

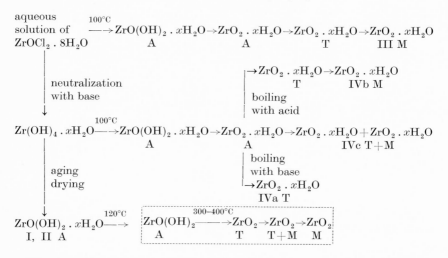

The transformations given in this scheme are carried out in water suspensions and the transformations indicated in the dotted rectangle are carried out in air at higher temperatures. Most of the compounds in this scheme have been identified experimentally, except the amorphous ZrO_2. This compound can be assumed to exist; the only indication for amorphous ZrO_2 can be found in the DTA curve of $ZrO(OH)_2$, where the exothermic effect after dehydration can point to an amorphous-tetragonal transformation.

When the modifications obtained by the various preparation methods are compared, in most cases monoclinic ZrO_2 is obtained. As already known this modification is the stable one in the temperature region up to 1100°C. The scheme provides a survey of the preparative methods leading to different structures; more evidence will be given when the preparations are examined in greater detail with respect to texture.

D Nitrogen Adsorption

The products obtained from all preparation methods after drying can be defined as active, which means they have a large surface area. The measurements for calculating the BET surface areas according to the method of Brunauer *et al.* (1938) were carried out in a macro-BET apparatus described by Meys (1961). Many of the preparations were studied more thoroughly and were also measured in the micro-BET apparatus described by Lippens (1961) to determine their adsorption-desorption isotherm. All the measurements were carried out with highly purified nitrogen; the isotherms were measured at 77·6°K.

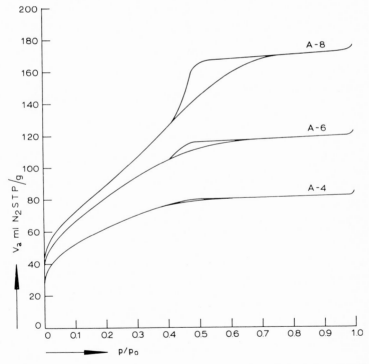

FIG. 16 Nitrogen sorption isotherms of the preparations A-4, A-6 and A-8 from Table VIII.

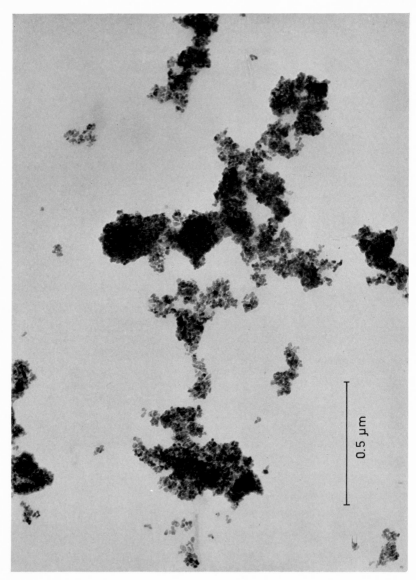

FIG. 17 Electron micrograph of preparation A-8 heated at 450°C.

The sorption isotherms of some preparations obtained by method I are shown in Fig. 16. The symbols A-4, A-6, A-8 denote amorphous zirconia prepared till the pH of the suspensions reached values of 4, 6 and 8.

Table VIII gives the most important characteristics of these preparations, the surface area, pore volume, and loss in weight on ignition. As can be seen from the table and Fig. 16, the surface area increases with increasing pH of precipitation. When electron micrographs of these preparations are examined (Fig. 17), small particles joined into loosely bound conglomerates can be seen.

Good agreement with BET surface is obtained when the surface area of this preparation is calculated from the particle size. Evidently the surface area is only formed from the small individual particles of the preparation. When in Table VIII the surface area increases, the particle size is seen to decrease. The larger particles indicate a further polymerization in preparation A-4 as compared with preparation A-8. This can be understood in the light of the results obtained in Section V, which indicated that polymerization involves a certain charge on the polymers, so that at the isoelectric point (pH 7) the polymerization almost comes to an end. The continuing polymerization in preparation A-4 took place when the gelatinous precipitate was allowed to stand for one week before washing and drying. The surface area of a dried product obtained by neutralizing $ZrOCl_2 \cdot 8H_2O$ solutions with ammonia (pH 9), was measured as 340 m^2/g. This is the highest surface area obtained in our experiments for preparations with a water content of about 10%. When no further polymerization in this higher pH-region of the gelatinous precipitate is assumed on aging, the particle size corresponds to the actual size of the polymers present after neutralization.

TABLE VIII. Influence of neutralization on some characteristics of dried zirconia

Preparation	S_{BET} (m²/g)	V_p (ml/g)	W (%)
A-4	244	0·126	9·96
A-6	308	0·186	9·70
A-8	320	0·268	9·46

E Crystallization of Zirconia Gels

The similarity between the surface area of the monoclinic ZrO_2 formed on hydrolyzing $ZrOCl_2$ solutions and $Zr(OH)_4$ suspensions can be seen in Table IX. The electronmicrographs of these preparations are similar, showing the same texture (Fig. 18).

TABLE IX. Influence of the method of preparation on the surface area and structure of zirconia

Preparation method	S_{BET} (m²/g)	Structure
I	335	Amorphous
II	342	Amorphous
III	157	Monoclinic
IVa	368	Tetragonal
IVb	177	Monoclinic
IVc	160	Tetragonal +monoclinic

The conglomerates in Fig. 18 are built up from small particles of 30 Å. These particles are grown together very firmly leading to conglomerates which have a definite shape and texture.

Another method of formation of the big conglomerates can be found in the solution-condensation mechanism. This explanation will be rejected here since in preparation method IVc a similar preparation is obtained, as is true in method III and IVb; only a difference in structure is noted while both the monoclinic and tetragonal phase are present. The formation of the big conglomerates cannot be explained here with the solution-condensation mechanism, since the crystallization was carried out in a neutral medium. The size of the conglomerates must be explained by the joining of the 30 Å particles which are obtained in the hydrolysis and polymerization processes. The dehydration reactions of $Zr(OH)_4$ which take place at the temperature of preparation produce amorphous ZrO_2. The positively-charged particles undergo a transformation into the tetragonal phase. Hereafter the tetragonal phase is transformed into the monoclinic phase. This transformation starts at the surface of the tetragonal particles and the monoclinic domains grow into the particles. The water boiled suspensions show a difference in the transformation rate since the suspensions in an acid medium show a complete monoclinic diffraction pattern, while the water boiled suspensions show a diffraction pattern with both monoclinic and tetragonal spacings.

The texture of the water boiled suspensions is very similar to that of the acid boiled suspensions. The formation of the big conglomerates

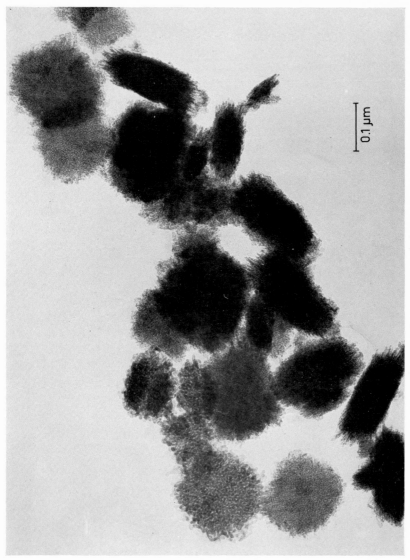

Fig. 18 Electron micrograph of preparation III (Table IX)

can be represented by hydrolysis and polymerization of the sites on the particles. As the surface structure of the water boiled preparations is identical to the surface structure of the acid boiled preparations, the formation of the conglomerates in these methods results in a similar texture.

In the formation of crystalline zirconia in methods III, IVb and IVc the individual particles of 30 Å, obtained in the preparation of $Zr(OH)_4$, are maintained. The transformations in the particles occur without any radical change in particle size, only a slight shrinkage due to dehydration will occur. The polymerization process accounts for the occurrence of the big conglomerates as shown in Fig. 18 and Table X.

TABLE X. Composition, structure, and texture obtained in preparation methods III and IVa-c

Composition	Modification	Preparation method		
		III, IVb	IVc	IVa
$ZrO(OH)_2$	A			
ZrO_2	A			
	T			
	T+M			
	M			

The formation of tetragonal ZrO_2 in a basic medium can be described in a similar way. From Table IX it can be seen that no polymerization reaction takes place during the heating process, while the final structure is tetragonal. A polymerization reaction, in the pH region above the iso-electrical point (pH 7) between a neutral site and a negatively charged site, obviously is not possible. The presence of negatively-charged sites is doubtful since no sol is formed in this preparation method. Moreover in studying positively-charged ZrO_2 sols, from completely hydrolyzed $ZrOCl_2$ solutions, no reversibility of the charge of the sol could be achieved above the iso-electrical point. The tetragonal phase is obviously stabilized in the basic medium since the monoclinic modification is the stable one in the temperature region up to 1100°C.

The reactivity of zirconiumhydroxide gels is shown schematically in Table X. This table shows the texture and modifications obtained during the preparation processes. The small rectangles in Table X denote the elementary particles of about 30 Å and A, T and M indicate the modifications amorphous, tetragonal and monoclinic.

VIII Preparation of $ZrO(OH)_2$ from Decomposition of $ZrOCl_2 . 8H_2O$

A Dehydration of $ZrOCl_2 . 8H_2O$

The formula $ZrOCl_2 . 8H_2O$ suggests a true hydrate. X-ray investigations, however, revealed that the water is bound in three different ways in the $ZrOCl_2 . 8H_2O$ molecule.

Several other hydrates of $ZrOCl_2$ have been suggested in the literature, varying in composition from 10 to 4 water molecules (Castor and Basolo, 1953). No $ZrOCl_2$ remains on dehydration of $ZrOCl_2 . 8H_2O$, which is also found for compounds such as $PtCl_2 . 8H_2O$, $FeCl_3 . 6H_2O$ and $MgCl_2 . 6H_2O$. The oxygen-metal bond is far stronger than the halogen-metal bond. In the case of Zr this provides an opportunity to prepare ZrO_2. The decomposition of $ZrOCl_2 . 8H_2O$ at relatively high temperatures was followed by X-ray diffraction by Clark and Reynolds (1937). The decomposition products obtained at 500°C showed a tetragonal diffraction pattern, while above 600°C a monoclinic diffraction pattern was observed. This behaviour is quite similar to the decomposition of $ZrO(OH)_2 . xH_2O$, written as $ZrO_2 . xH_2O$ by Clark and Reynolds (1937).

The similarity between the decomposition products obtained from $ZrO_2 . xH_2O$ and $ZrOCl_2 . 8H_2O$ observed by Clark and Reynolds (1937) can be explained when the decomposition of $ZrOCl_2 . 8H_2O$ is followed quantitatively at lower temperatures. The decomposition of $ZrOCl_2 . 8H_2O$ was followed by density measurements with CCl_4 as the imbibition liquid, by quantitative analysis, by DTA, and by X-ray diffraction. $ZrOCl_2 . 8H_2O$ was heated for 24 hours at temperatures varying from 20 to 80°C.

The composition of the partly-decomposed products is given in Fig. 19, where the H_2O and HCl contents are given in mg per gram ZrO_2. The most striking point in this figure is the dehydration of $ZrOCl_2 . 8H_2O$ to $ZrOCl_2 . 4H_2O$ in the first part of the decomposition. At 60°C the decomposition changes in character and at higher temperatures both HCl and H_2O are liberated in the same molar ratio. The

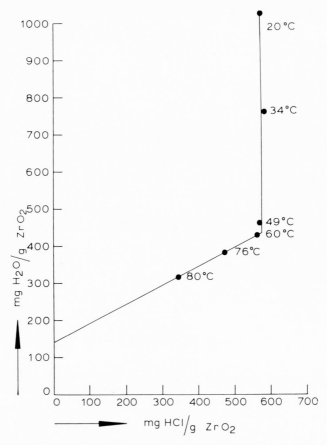

FIG. 19 Composition of partly decomposed $ZrOCl_2 . 8H_2O$.

extrapolated line suggests a composition $ZrO_2 . H_2O$. This composition was found in Section VII during the dehydration of $ZrO(OH)_2 . xH_2O$. In this section the formula $ZrO(OH)_2$ was proposed, and we shall suggest this formula $ZrO(OH)_2$ for the composition $ZrO_2 . H_2O$ obtained by extrapolation in the decomposition of $ZrOCl_2 . 8H_2O$.

From the first stage of the decomposition of $ZrOCl_2 . 8H_2O$ we can derive information on the way the water is bound by density measurements. As might be expected, the water liberated in the first stage is bound very loosely. The formula $ZrOCl_2 . 8H_2O$ can be rewritten as $ZrO_2 . 2HCl . 7H_2O$. The first point in Fig. 19 indicates 7 H_2O molecules

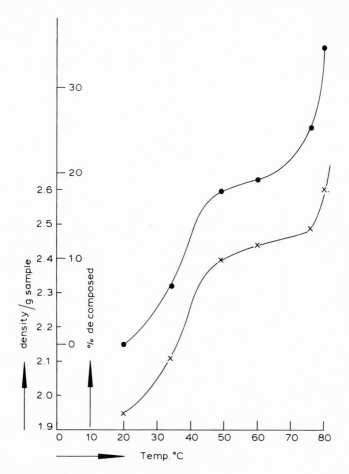

FIG. 20 Percentage decomposed (●) and density (×) of the decomposition products of $ZrOCl_2 . 8H_2O$ against temperature.

and 2 HCl molecules bound to ZrO_2. The break point indicates a composition $ZrO_2 . 2HCl . 3H_2O$. The decomposition products obtained in the dehydration region can be represented by $ZrO_2 . 2HCl . 3H_2O . yH_2O$, where $0 \leqslant y \leqslant 4$. Thus 1 g of this composition consists of y grams of H_2O and $1-y$ grams of $ZrO_2 . 2HCl . 3H_2O$, and, assuming the volumes of the components to be additive, the following expression can be derived:

$$\frac{1}{\rho_c} = \frac{y}{\rho_{H_2O}} + \frac{1-y}{\rho_{ZrO_2 . 2HCl . 3H_2O}}$$

Dividing this expression by $1-y$ results in:

$$\frac{1}{(1-y)\rho_c} = \frac{y}{(1-y)\rho_{H_2O}} + \frac{1}{\rho_{ZrO_2 . 2HCl . 3H_2O}}$$

where y is the water content of the decomposition product, $1-y$ the amount of $ZrO_2 . 2HCl . 3H_2O$ in the decomposition product, ρ_c the density of the decomposition product (g/cm³), ρ_{H_2O} the density of the water indicated by y in the decomposition product (g/cm³), and $\rho_{ZrO_2 . 2HCl . 3H_2O}$ the density of $ZrO_2 . 2HCl . 3H_2O$ (g/cm³).

The density and the degree of decomposition of the various preparations are given in Fig. 20. The similarity between the curves shows that the above-mentioned expression can be valid when the decomposition is continued.

For the preparations the above expression for $1/(1-y)\rho_c$ is obeyed, the straight line having a slope of 0·875 cm³/g and an intercept of 0·414 cm³/g. The density of $ZrO_2 . 2HCl . 3H_2O$ was calculated to be 2·41, and the density of the liberated water 1·14 g/cm³. This result for the density of the escaping water can be interpreted when similar compounds are taken into consideration. In the dehydration of $MgCO_3 . 3H_2O$ a density of 1·14 has been formed for the escaping water (de Vleesschauwer, 1967). This type of water can be interpreted as water of hydration loosely-bound in the molecule. The removal of the three H_2O molecules not bound directly to the Zr ion and one H_2O molecule bound directly to the Zr can account for this. Now two possibilities can be given for the resulting configuration. The first leads to a Zr—Cl bond (Formula 7). This picture does not seem very

likely, because a Zr—Cl bond is improbable in Zr compounds that still contain enough water. A hepta-coordinated Zr ion is shown in Formula 8.

$$
\begin{array}{ccc}
\text{OH} \quad \text{OH}_2 & \text{H}_2\text{O} & \\
\text{OH} \diagdown \diagup \text{OH}_2 & \text{Cl} & \\
\quad \text{Zr} & \text{H}_2\text{O} & \rightarrow \\
\text{OH} \diagup \diagdown \text{OH}_2 & \text{Cl} & \\
\text{OH} \quad \text{OH}_2 & \text{H}_2\text{O} &
\end{array}
\qquad
\begin{array}{cc}
\text{OH} \quad \text{OH}_2 & \text{Cl} \\
\text{OH} \diagdown \diagup & \\
\quad \text{Zr} \!\!-\!\! \text{OH}_2 & \\
\text{OH} \diagup \diagdown & \text{Cl} \\
\text{OH} \quad \text{OH}_2 &
\end{array}
\quad +4\text{H}_2\text{O}
$$

The change in the coordination number from 8 to 7 for Zr is shown in the tetragonal-monoclinic transformation (Grain and Garvie, 1965), and must be regarded as the most probable situation in $ZrOCl_2 \cdot 4H_2O$. Other possibilities, which involve polymerization of the tetramers, will not be taken into account, since these decomposition products are soluble in water.

B   Decomposition of $ZrOCl_2 \cdot 4H_2O$

The products obtained in the second region of the decomposition are insoluble in water. This presents some difficulties in the analysis of the products, as the potentiometric titration curves for the determination of the Cl^- were not reproducible. The preparations were analysed by immersing them in 2 N HNO_3 solution, and heating for 24 hours at 200°C in closed vessels. As was shown in Section VI, for clear $ZrOCl_2 \cdot 8H_2O$ solutions this treatment causes the formation of a stable monoclinic ZrO_2 sol. The Cl^- could then be analyzed reproducibly by titrating the suspension potentiometrically with 0·1 N $AgNO_3$. The water content of the preparations was calculated from the weight loss on ignition at 1200°C, and the Cl^- content as described above.

The X-ray diffraction patterns of the products obtained at 49 and 60°C were examined more thoroughly. These patterns showed lattice spacings corresponding quite well to the spacings obtained for $HfOCl_2 \cdot 4H_2O$ (A.S.T.M. card 15-380).

Figure 21 shows the first part of the X-ray diffraction pattern, obtained with a Philips diffractometer using Cu–K-α-radiation. The structure of the isomorphous compounds $HfOCl_2 \cdot 4H_2O$ and $ZrOCl_2 \cdot 4H_2O$ is unknown, and the A.S.T.M. card 15-380 does not give indices for various spacings. From the calculated density of $ZrOCl_2 \cdot 4H_2O$ (2·41 g/cm³), and assuming eight $ZrOCl_2 \cdot 4H_2O$ groups in the unit cell, as is true for $ZrOCl_2 \cdot 8H_2O$, the volume of the unit cell was calculated as 1389 Å³. When this value was taken into account the diffraction pattern could be indexed using the following cell dimensions, given in Å: $a = 15·54$, $b = 10·33$ and $c = 8·60$. For $ZrOCl_2 \cdot 8H_2O$ the cell dimensions were calculated to be $a = 17·08$, $c = 7·67$ (Clearfield and

Vaughan, 1956). The dehydration causes a change in the cell dimensions. The c-axis in $ZrOCl_2 . 4H_2O$ increased compared with $ZrOCl_2 . 8H_2O$, while the other axes decreased, as could be expected. Decomposition of $ZrOCl_2 . 4H_2O$ leads to products amorphous to X-rays. The second region in the decomposition $ZrOCl_2 . 8H_2O$ shows simultaneous escape of H_2O and HCl in the same molar ratio, finally leading to the composition $ZrO(OH)_2$. In this region the preparations are not soluble

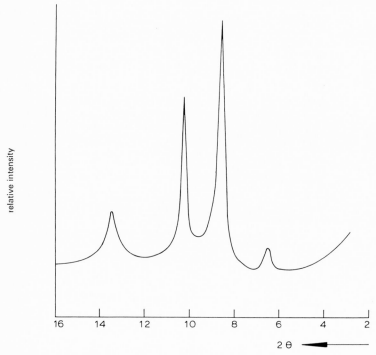

FIG. 21 X-ray diffraction pattern of $ZrOCl_2 . 4H_2O$.

in water, suggesting the formation of zirconium-oxygen bonds. In this region of the decomposition similar expressions can be derived to those used before to correlate density with composition. Another approach is to calculate the difference between the molar volumes of the starting composition and the final product obtained according to the following reaction: $ZrO_2 . 2HCl . 3H_2O \rightarrow ZrO_2 . H_2O + 2HCl + 2H_2O$. The molar volumes of HCl and H_2O can be calculated from the molar volumes of $ZrO_2 . 2HCl . 3H_2O$ (103·3 cm³/mole) and $ZrO(OH)_2$ (32·9 cm³/mole):
$$V(HCl) + V(H_2O) = \tfrac{1}{2}[V(ZrO_2 . 2HCl . 3H_2O) - V(ZrO_2 . H_2O)] = \tfrac{1}{2}(103·3 - 32·9) = 35·2 \text{ cm}^3/\text{mole}.$$

The calculated molar volume of HCl in $MgCl_2 . 6H_2O$ is 21·3 (Weast, 1967a). The molar volume of HCl in aqueous solutions is 21·2 $cm^3/mole$ (Weast, 1967b). From these values the molar volume of H_2O is 14·0 $cm^3/mole$ or 1·29 g/cm^3. For water of hydroxylation a density of 1·42 g/cm^3 was calculated, while the density of water of hydration is 1·14 g/cm^3. The value of 1·29 g/cm^3 thus corresponds to a mixture of the two. As can be seen from the decomposition reaction, two water molecules escape—one is supposed to be water of hydration, and the second water of hydroxylation. With the idea of the formation of zirconium-oxygen bonds, the decomposition of $ZrOCl_2 . 4H_2O$ is represented schematically in Formula 9.

This scheme shows the calculated effects, according to which both water of hydration and water of hydroxylation are liberated. Moreover, polymerization occurs as soon as HCl is liberated.

$ZrO(OH)_2$ is formed in the decomposition of $ZrOCl_2 . 8H_2O$ in a similar way as was proposed in Section IV. The different steps that can be distinguished in the decomposition of $ZrOCl_2 . 8H_2O$ are dehydration (formula 8), hydrolysis and polymerization (Formula 9). The last step in the decomposition indicates increasing coordination of the oxygen atoms. As in the crystalline ZrO_2 each oxygen atom is surrounded by three or four Zr atoms; this value can be finally reached when the zirconium oxide-hydroxide is decomposed further.

C Stability of Zr(OH)₄ and Related Compounds

In Section IV we described the polymerization in aqueous solutions of $ZrOCl_2 . 8H_2O$, where a coordination number of 8 was assumed for the Zr ion. The coordination of the oxygen present in the different compounds was not taken into account. In $ZrOCl_2 . 8H_2O$ oxygen is surrounded by one or two Zr ions, while in $Zr(OH)_4$ the coordination of oxygen, present as OH^- with Zr^{4+} is 2. Dehydration of this compound finally leading to crystalline ZrO_2 increases the coordination of the oxygen from 2 to 3 or 4. The change in the coordination of the oxygen results in considerable rearrangement of the atoms in the

14

particles, and this certainly could produce materials active with respect to sintering. When a high surface area is required for ZrO_2, this way of preparation is unsuitable, as the surface area of crystalline compounds obtained is very low. The hydrous zirconia is very active in sintering. In Section V we discussed the differences between the polymerization of Group IV elements, ending eventually in the corresponding oxide, oxide-hydroxide, or hydroxide. As was shown, the polymerization of Si occurs via oxygen bridges to neutralize the charge of the silicon ion, ending with a tetrahedral arrangement of the oxygens. The coordination number 4 of the Si leads to a coordination number of 2 for the oxygen bridges with Si^{4+}, which is already present in the polymerization process. During dehydration of silica gel no arrangements of the tetrahedral units are necessary. This can perhaps explain the amorphous state and the unique sintering resistance of silica gel. For Ti we discussed an octahedral arrangement which involved polymerization with two oxygen and four hydroxyl bridges. The coordination of these oxygens with Ti^{4+} varies from 2 to 3. When TiO_2 is obtained after dehydration of $TiO(OH)_2$, the coordination of the oxygen with Ti^{4+} finally reaches a value of 3. Strong rearrangements occur in the compounds in the course of the dehydration, which can again lead to very active preparations for sintering. This is true for titania obtained from polymerization processes in solution (de Boer, 1965).

When active solids are prepared in aqueous solutions elementary particles with a size of 30–40 Å are obtained for many substances. This particle size has been found for $Fe(OH)_3$, $Th(OH)_4$, SiO_2, $TiO(OH)_2$, $Zr(OH)_4$ and $Al(OH)_3$; it is obviously a critical dimension, but it is difficult to see why. The boundaries of these particles can be formed in such a way that no further growth is possible sterically. When special methods are used, however, the growth of the particles can be continued.

When active oxides with a large surface area are to be prepared from these hydroxides and oxide-hydroxides, a considerable amount of sintering occurs as a result of rearrangements in the elementary particles. Starting with high surface areas of the hydrous preparations this promising method for preparing active oxides is often unsuccessful. In Section VI we discussed special treatments of the zirconium oxide-hydroxide gel, which in some cases result in stable oxides. The dehydration was carried out in a special way that leaves the elementary particles. unchanged. This method is recommended when active oxides have to be prepared. Special conditions of dehydration and the formation of the right modification of the oxide is a useful approach which can lead to interesting results in this special field.

IX   References

Blumenthal, W. B. (1958a). "The Chemical Behaviour of Zirconium", p. 35. Van Nostrand, Princeton, New Jersey.

Blumenthal, W. B. (1958b). "The Chemical Behaviour of Zirconium", p. 125.

Blumenthal, W. B. (1958c). "The Chemical Behaviour of Zirconium", p. 182.

de Boer, J. H. (1965). *Proc. Brit. ceram. Soc.* **5**, 5.

Bourian, F. and Hun, O. (1928). *C. r. hebd. Séanc. Acad. Sci., Paris.* **187**, 886.

Brunauer, S., Emmett, P. H. and Teller, E. (1938). *J. Am. chem. Soc.* **60**, 309.

Castor, Jr., W. S. and Basolo, F. (1953). *J. Am. chem. Soc.* **75**, 4804.

Clark, G. L. and Reynolds, D. H. (1937). *Ind. Engng Chem.* **29**, 711.

Clearfield, A. (1964). *Inorg. Chem.* **3**, 146.

Clearfield, A. and Vaughan, Ph. A. (1956) *Acta crystallogr.* **9**, 555.

Conway, B. E. (1952). "Electrochemical Data", p. 141. Elsevier, Amsterdam.

de Vleesschauwer, W. F. N. M. (1967). Thesis, Delft University of Technology, The Netherlands.

Ermakov, A. N., Marov, I. N. and Balyaeva, V. K. (1963). *Russ. J. inorg. Chem. (English Transl.)* **8**, 845.

Grain, C. F. and Garvie, C. (1965). *U.S. Bur. Mines, Rept. Invest.* **6619**.

Grdenić, D. and Matković, B. (1959). *Acta crystallogr.* **12**, 817.

Hermans, M. E. A. (1966). *Chem. Weekbl.* **62**, 314.

Hoard, J. L. and Nordsiek, H. H. (1939). *J. Am. chem. Soc.* **61**, 2853.

Hoard, J. L., Martin, W. J., Smith, M. E. and Whitney, J. F. (1954). *J. Am. chem. Soc.* **76**, 3820.

Kimball, G. E. (1940). *J. chem. Phys.* **8**, 188.

Kommissarova, L. N., Simanov, Yu. P. and Vladimirova, Z. A. (1960). *Russ. J. inorg. Chem. (English Transl.)* **5**, 687.

Kovalenko, P. N. and Bagdasarov, K. N. (1961). *Russ. J. inorg. Chem. (English Transl.)* **6**, 272.

Kozmin, P. A. (1964). *Zh. strukt. Khim.* **5**, 70.

Larsen, E. M. and Wang, P. (1954). *J. Am. chem. Soc.* **76**, 6223.

Lippens, B. C. (1961). Thesis, Delft University of Technology, The Netherlands.

Lister, A. J. and McDonald, L. A. (1952). *J. chem. Soc.*, 4315.

Matyeveić, E., Mthai, K. G. and Kerker, M. (1962). *J. phys. Chem.* **66**, 1799.

Meys, W. H. (1961). Thesis, Delft University of Technology, The Netherlands.

Muha, J. M. and Vaughan, Ph. A. (1960). *J. chem. Phys.* **33**, 194.

Nabivanits, B. I. (1962). *Russ. J. inorg. Chem. (English Transl.)* **7**, 609.

Okkerse, C. (1961). Thesis, Delft University of Technology, The Netherlands.

Rijnten, H. Th. (1969). Thesis, Delft University of Technology, The Netherlands.

Ruff, O. and Ebert, F. (1929). *Z. anorg. allg. Chem.* **180**, 19.

Sheka, I. A. and Pevzner, Ts. V. (1960). *Russ. J. inorg. Chem. (English Transl.)*, **5**, 1119.

Simon, A. and Fischer, O. (1929). *Z. anorg. allg. Chem.* **185**, 130.

Steggerda, J. J. (1955). Thesis, Delft University of Technology, The Netherlands.

Turnbull, A. G. (1961). *J. phys. Chem.* **65**, 1652.

van den Heuvel, A. and van Doorn, A. B. C. (1966). *Chem. Weekbl.* **62**, 333.

van der Giessen, A. A. (1966). *J. inorg. nucl. Chem.* **28**, 2155.

Vleeskens, J. M. (1959). Thesis, Delft University of Technology, The Netherlands.

Weast, R. C. (ed.) (1967a). "Handbook of Chemistry and Physics", 48th ed., B-192, The Chemical Rubber Co., Cleveland, Ohio.

Weast, R. C. (ed.) (1967b). " Handbook of Chemistry and Physics ", 48th ed., D-157. The Chemical Rubber Co., Cleveland Ohio.

Weiser, H. B. (1935). "Inorganic Colloid Chemistry", Vol. 2, p. 264. John Wiley and Sons, New York.

Wyatt, R. (1966). *Chem. Weekbl.* **62**, 310.

Zaitsev, L. M. (1962). *Russ. J. inorg. Chem. (English Transl.*), **7**, 409.

Zaitsev, L. M. (1966). *Russ. J. inorg. Chem. (English Transl.*), **11**, 900.

Zaitsev, L. M. and Bochkarev, G. S. (1962). *Russ. J. inorg. Chem. (English Transl.*), **7**, 409.

Chapter 8

HYDROLYTIC PHENOMENA IN U(VI)-PRECIPITATION

M. E. A. Hermans

RCN-KEMA Reactor Development Group
Arnhem, The Netherlands

I Introduction

Uranium oxide is a compound of increasing commercial importance. Still a minor application of UO_2 is its use as a catalyst in the production of certain organics such as acrylonitrile. Far more important, at present, is its potential in the development of a vast nuclear industry.

Obviously, both applications have much in common as far as the chemistry of uranium is concerned. However, the shaping and the texture of the final products must meet rather widely differing specifications.

The studies, reported in this chapter, are mainly of a chemical and physico-chemical character. They were all carried out, however, with the purpose of developing new processes for the production of rather specific nuclear fuels. The work is therefore more aimed at ceramics than at adsorbents or catalysts, which form the scope of this book.

Still there are two firm reasons which seem to justify a more elaborate account of the subject here. First of all, nuclear energy represents an important aspect in the scientific life of Professor J. H. de Boer. From the early years of nuclear studies in The Netherlands, he has played an important role in the development of nuclear energy, both scientifically and as an advisor to The Netherlands government. In this period he stimulated and coached, among others, original studies in the field of nuclear fuels, and part of the work was carried out under his direct supervision.

The work therefore carries the distinguishing mark of his approach and can be presented as a tribute to Professor J. H. de Boer.

Appealing though this argument seems, it is insufficient to justify a discussion of the work in the present book. However, in the past years, the precipitation of hydroxides and hydrated oxides from salt solutions increasingly has been recognized as an important step in the preparation of certain catalysts and their carriers.

Techniques have been introduced to control protolysis, ligand exchange and polymeric phenomena in the hydrolytic sequence of precipitation to ensure certain textural characteristics of the final catalyst. This tendency can be stimulated by a clearer understanding of the underlying mechanisms and by a further increase of the types of hydrolytic processes.

The present work, though carried out with uranyl salt solutions, arrives at conclusions of a rather general validity, which no doubt are applicable to a wide variety of hydroxidic and oxidic systems, as practice has already shown in a number of cases.

It is therefore fortunate that Professor de Boer's nuclear activities can be recorded in a way which may further contribute to the preparation of adsorbents and catalysts.

The basis of the hydroxide precipitation is a more or less alternating sequence of protolysis, anion exchange and polymerization, which finally leads to a precipitate. The only discontinuity in this sequence can be the crystallization of initially amorphous material. The role of anions can be of paramount importance both in the hydrolysis itself and in the crystallization.

Precipitation by hydrolysis can be effected along several rather widely differing routes. The properties of the precipitate may change drastically with the route selected for its preparation.

The present study is an attempt to understand the hydrolytic phenomena more clearly and to correlate the different ways of hydrolysis with the properties of the final products. The uranyl ion in this case has to be considered as a model which stands for a number of other systems.

II The Hydrolysis of Uranyl Ions

A Literature Survey

The behaviour of dioxo-uranium (VI) salts in aqueous solution has been studied in somewhat more detail since about 1950, initially as a consequence of the irreproducibility of the precipitation procedures.

In most cases uranium is obtained in the form of uranyl nitrate, both from the mining and refinery plant, and from the reprocessing plant. From there on, several routes can be followed, one of the more important being to form a precipitate from the aqueous uranyl nitrate solution by the addition of ammonia. The resulting precipitate is generally referred to as ammonium diuranate or ADU, but its composition and structure in most cases suggests that a series of uranium (VI) hydroxide-hydrate-ammoniates is formed (Hermans and Markestein, 1963 and Hermans, 1964).

The hydrolytic phenomena provoked in a uranyl nitrate solution by the addition of ammonia have therefore been studied rather extensively. For this purpose Tridot (1950) used potentiometric and conductometric measurements. According to his experiments, in a stoichiometric solution precipitation starts at 1·5 moles of NH_3 per mole of uranium, the first product being $UO_3 . xH_2O$. At two equivalents the precipitation is complete and at three equivalents the precipitate has been converted into $(NH_4)_2U_2O_7$. The author states that equilibrium has been reached in his experiments, which certainly can not be true in our opinion. His concept of the hydrolytic reactions is still rather simplistic.

Previously MacInnes and Longsworth (1942) had suggested that an ionic species $UO_3 . UO_2^{2+}$ occurred in a hydrolyzed uranyl solution. This opinion was supported by Faucherre (1948) who preferred to nominate the same species $(UO_2OH)_2^{2+}$. The basis of this concept, the occurrence of polymeric ionic species, was further taken up by Sutton (1955).

He applied cryoscopic, conductometric, potentiometric and spectrophotometric techniques to the study of the system uranyl perchlorate—NaOH. He postulated a sequence of hydroxo-polynuclear ions

$$UO_2^{2+} \rightarrow U_2O_5^{2+} \rightarrow U_3O_8^{2+} \rightarrow U_3O_8(OH)^+ \rightarrow U_3O_8(OH)_2 \rightarrow U_3O_8(OH)_3^-$$

which could account for the fact that uranium (VI) is found both in cationic and in anionic form. Valuable though this contribution was for a better understanding of the phenomena, doubt exists concerning the quantitative interpretation of the measuring data. Ahrland (1949) has suggested that apart from the monomeric UO_2^{2+} ion, the UO_2OH^+ would occur also, apart from polymers. The data have been reevaluated since (Ahrland *et al.*, 1954) in the light of Sillén's "core and links" theory. As a result it was concluded that in partially hydrolyzed solutions polynuclear compounds exist of a general formula $[UO_2\{(OH)_2UO_2\}_n]^{2+}$ in which the value of n increases with the degree of hydrolysis. By a technique of curve fitting, titration curves deliver the reaction constants for the successive reactions which finally lead to precipitation.

The basic concept of this theory is widely accepted. The quantitative interpretation in terms of the derived reaction constants sometimes still causes some objections.

Kraus and Nelson (1948) observed that the titration curve in the titration of a uranyl perchlorate solution with alkali hydroxide differed from that in the opposite direction. They wrongly attributed this to a slow depolymerization of the precipitate in the "down scale" titration, suggesting that the "upscale" titration represented the equilibrium states. Later, Kraus (1955) presented a more detailed concept which also covered an abrupt decrease of the pH in the "upscale" branch of the titration curve. He attributed this phenomenon to a sudden change in the structure of the U(VI) polymers, e.g. from chains to sheets.

Brushilovskii (1958) studied the "titration" of uranyl perchlorate solutions with NaOH, varying the time of equilibration of the system from zero to four days. The resulting titration curves show a remarkable time dependency, and the pH decrease in the curve, mentioned already for the work of Kraus (1955), again is evident. The work of Brushilovskii was carried out parallel to and independently from our own work. The observations confirm ours. The conclusions, however, differ in certain respects, mainly because more information was available to the present author.

Finally, Sanderson *et al.* (1959) observed the same decrease of the pH in titration curves of uranyl salt solutions with alkali hydroxides. They also attributed the effect to hydrolytic reactions.

More studies on U(VI) have been reported in the literature, which, however, bear no direct significance for the work presented in this chapter. For other systems mention must be made of certain results, because it will be shown that the aforementioned sudden decrease of the pH in the upscale titration forms an essential clue for the interpretation of the hydrolytic behaviour of the uranyl ion. A similar decrease was for the first time observed by Trombe (1943) during the neutralization of a $Nd(NO_3)_3$ solution with diluted ammonia gas. Trombe suggested that the abrupt decrease is caused by a transition of the precipitate from a colloidal state into a flocculated state or even into a crystal. No clear physical or chemical explanation is presented.

A similar study was made by Hufferman (1952) for a $FeCl_3$ solution and diluted ammonia gas. She attributed the pH decrease to the decomposition of an unstable ionic complex. The essential part of this work has been repeated by us. It is our firm conviction that the decrease of the pH is due to a sudden increase of the rate of hydrolytic reactions.

B   The Basic Concept of Hydrolytic Polymerization

In comparing the monomeric uranyl ion in an acidic solution with the lattice of the precipitate which forms in that solution by hydrolysis, a striking similarity can be observed.

In acidified solutions, e.g. with nitric or perchloric acid the ligands of the monomeric UO_2^{2+} ion are water ligands, which at an increasing pH tend to dissociate. A proton is thereby loosened from the water ligand, which then becomes a hydroxide ligand. In certain systems a further increase of the pH can cause a further dissociation whereby the ligand changes into an oxide ligand. Bridges in the polymeric ions behave in the same way in principle. During this process the charge of the ion changes accordingly. The uranyl ion UO_2^{2+} has a coordination number of 6. It is considered to contain the oxygen of the uranyl group in a short linear O—U—O arrangement, and the six water ligands in hexagonal bipyramidal positions around the U atom. Schematically the ion can be presented as

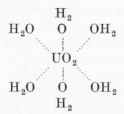

The precipitate which forms from the solution is in principle the so-called $UO_3 . 2H_2O$ (Hermans, 1964; Cordfunke, 1962), of which part of the H_2O may have been replaced by NH_3 with only minor distortions of the lattice. The lattice of $UO_3 . 2H_2O$, which more accurately should be written $UO_2(OH)_2 . H_2O$, is pseudo-hexagonal. It consists of layers of $UO_2(OH)_2$ in which the U is found between the two layers of oxygen which belong to the uranyl ion. Again six OH groups surround each UO_2 ion perpendicular to the O—U—O axis in the hexagonal positions of a puckered ring. The configuration of one $UO_2(OH)_2$ layer is shown in Fig. 1. The H_2O and eventually the NH_3 is found between the hydroxide layers of two subsequent $UO_2(OH)_2$ layers.

It is evident that a close resemblance exists between the monomeric uranyl ion and the crystalline polymeric lattice into which the uranyl ions can be fitted by hydrolysis. It seems therefore justified to use this model for interpreting the phenomena occurring in hydrolytic precipitate formation from the salt solution.

For this concept to be fully valid, the Sutton (1955) sequence

$$UO_2^{2+} \rightarrow U_2O_5^{2+} \rightarrow U_3O_8^{2+}$$

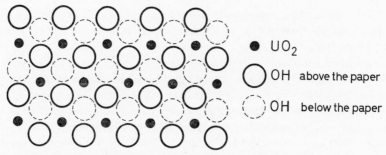

FIG. 1 Configuration of one $UO_2(OH)_2$ layer in the $UO_3 \cdot 2H_2O$ crystal.

should be completed by taking into account the influence of water. The sequence could thus be written

$$\{UO_2(H_2O)_6\}^{2+} \rightarrow \{(UO_2)_2(OH)_2(H_2O)_8\}^{2+} \rightarrow \{(UO_2)_3(OH)_4(H_2O)_{10}\}^{2+}.$$

It might be represented schematically as in Fig. 2. Further polymerization would then lead to the formation of $UO_2(OH)_2$ sheets, which constitute the layers of the $UO_2(OH)_2 \cdot H_2O$ precipitate.

In the sequence of monomeric ion to polymeric precipitate at least two mechanisms must play a role: hydrolysis in a more narrow sense, better indicated as protolysis, and polymerization. Counter ions and such effects are not considered here.

Protolysis is a simple interaction of a hydrated complex cation with the surrounding liquid, which in an equilibrium state determines the OH/H_2O ratio in the ligands. It must be expected that this reaction is a fast one and determined mainly by the pH of the system. Protolysis causes a shift of the OH/H_2O ratio in the ligands towards higher values, and thus decreases the positive charge of the ion. The mutual repulsion between the cations in the solution becomes less and the chance increases that oriented agglomeration occurs, which is called polymerization. This polymerization in principle is a relatively slow reaction, because it requires the meeting of charged species under such conditions of charge, orientation, etc., that they grow together.

Precipitation of $UO_2(OH)_2 \cdot H_2O$ from a uranyl salt solution is therefore composed of a more or less alternating sequence of protolysis and polymerization, of which the polymerization expectedly is the rate-determining step.

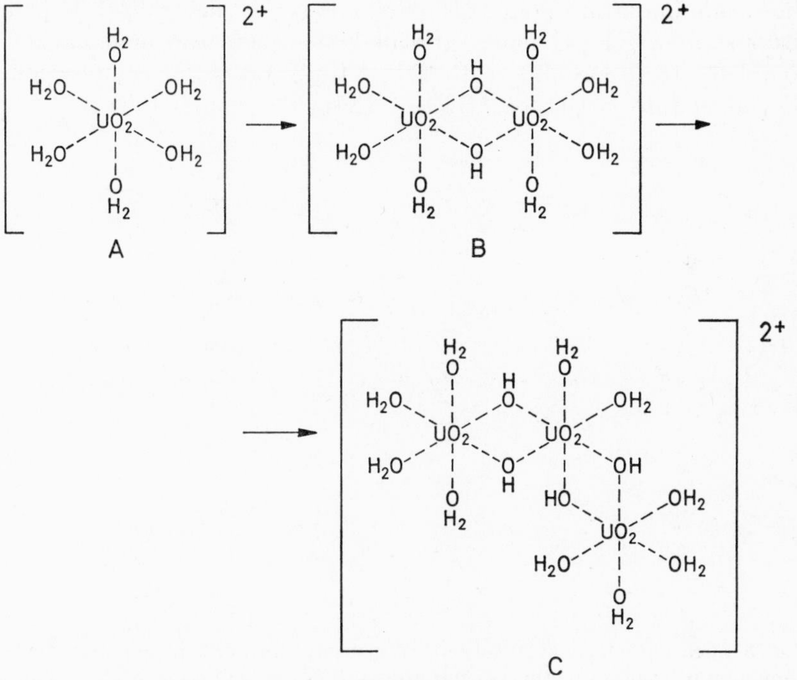

FIG. 2 A monomer, B dimer, C trimer of the uranyl ion.

From the above it will be clear that the cation concentration may exert an influence on the mean size of the polymers for a given pH. It is therefore not at all astonishing that Guitier (1947) arrives at a conclusion different from others, because he achieves his increase of the pH, required for hydrolysis, solely by dilution of the uranyl nitrate solution. Polymerization will therefore take place to a much lesser extent, whereas the protolysis as such follows the change of the pH rather fast.

Phenomenologically, the model seems complete. Experimental results, however, have shown that a few additional mechanisms have to be incorporated into the model before this can explain, still qualitatively, the phenomena observed. The experimental information therefore will be presented first.

C   The Titration Curve

In Fig. 3 a titration curve is given for the titration of a stoichio-metric uranyl nitrate solution with ammonia. A rather high concentra-tion of ammonia was chosen in order to minimize the dilution effect. The presence of carbon dioxide has carefully been avoided. The curve shows two important points. The first one is the "neutralization point" situated at a NH_3/U mole ratio of 2·33, where the precipitation is complete. In accordance with this NH_3/U ratio the composition of the precipitate is $UO_3 . 5/3H_2O . 1/3NH_3$ (Hermans, 1964).

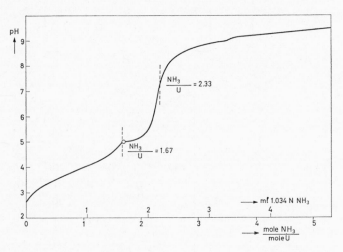

FIG. 3 Titration curve of 20 ml 0·0487 M uranyl nitrate solution with 1·034 N ammonia at a rate of 0·2 ml per minute.

At a ratio of 1·67 a break is observed in the curve. At this point, or shortly before, the precipitation starts. The mean composition of the polymeric uranyl ion at this point is equivalent to $U_3O_8(OH)^+$, which led Sutton (1955) to the conclusion that the highest soluble polymer would be the trimer.

The nature of this break has been studied more carefully because it appeared that the shape of the curve is rather sensitive to the rate of titration.

When ammonia is added to a well-stirred solution of stoichiometric uranyl nitrate, each addition causes the formation of a dark yellow precipitate which, however, dissolves on stirring. The colour of the solution thereby changes gradually from a light yellow to a much darker shade, indicating the change of the ligands and the formation of polymeric uranyl species. Near the breaking point in the curve, not all of the initially-formed precipitate dissolves any longer, but slowly the solution becomes opalescent. As soon as the NH_3/U ratio of 1·67 is reached, the amount of precipitate increases faster and the titration curve levels off.

At the same time the pH meter indicates a tendency of the system to shift its pH towards lower values. A slow but significant drift of the pH is observed. Figure 4 shows a titration curve for which the

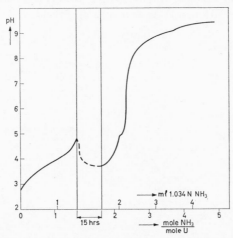

FIG. 4 Interrupted titration of 20 ml 0·0487 M uranyl nitrate solution with 1·034 N ammonia at a rate of 0·05 ml per minute.

ammonia addition was interrupted for 15 hours at $NH_3/U = 1·67$. In this period of 15 hours the pH decreased from 4·88 to 3·70. A considerable amount of precipitate was formed during that period.

The precipitate formed by the addition of ammonia evidently is stable at a higher pH, and therefore is only formed where the ammonia enters the solution. Thereafter it dissolves as the system is homogenized by stirring. However, the precipitate formed at a pH = 4·88 appears not to dissolve when the pH decreases to 3·70. Even more of it is precipitated. This might indicate that part of the titration curve is unstable because for some reason or another, no equilibrium has been reached. This conclusion, of course, is based on the assumption that the decrease of the pH is real.

The decrease was in most cases observed in the presence of an increasing amount of colloidal material or solid precipitate. The sol concentration effect (Overbeek, 1952) might therefore be responsible for an apparent decrease of the pH, although the high electrolyte content of the system would render this supposition unlikely. The sol concentration effect can be detected by a fast inversion of the surface charge of the colloidal particles at a constant pH. In the present case this was done by the addition of a suitable Na-lauryl-sulphate solution. The resulting change of the pH was considerably less than the pH effect observed previously, which leads to the conclusion that the sol concentration effect causes no interferences and that the decrease of the pH is a real one. Consequently it must be supposed, as stated above, that equilibrium is not reached in the titration, and thus that the shape of the titration curve depends on the rate of titration.

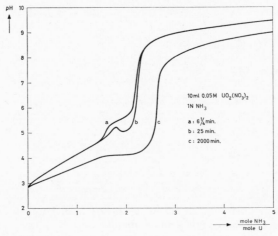

FIG. 5 Influence of the rate of titration of 10 ml 0·0487 M uranyl nitrate with 1·045 N ammonia.

In Fig. 5 three titration curves are presented, for which only the rate of titration differs. Evidently the lowest curve comes nearest to the equilibrium situation. The "neutralization point" now lies at $NH_3/U = 2·64$, which suggests a composition of the precipitate of $UO_3 . 4/3H_2O . 2/3 NH_3$. Such a compound does exist (Hermans, 1964).

It seems that around a mole ratio $NH_3/U = 1·67$ two competing reactions occur, one of which must be rather slow. This one, which then causes a relative decrease of the pH, must have been blocked in earlier stages of the titration. The decrease of the pH suggests that the reaction is a hydrolytic one, and that it competes with the pH increasing effect of the ammonia addition. The hydrolytic reaction must be relatively slow and may show up in comparing the rate of decrease of the pH in such a system with the rate of precipitation.

Figure 6 shows the result of an experiment where the ammonia addition has been stopped near the precipitation point. The pH decreases in two steps, each step being accompanied by an increase of the precipitation rate. During the experiment the pH decreased by one

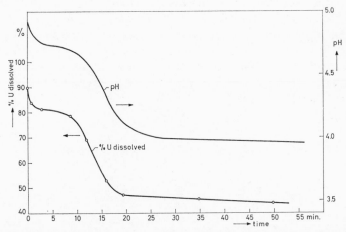

FIG. 6 Rate of precipitation of uranium in a closed system and the simultaneous decrease of the pH (10 ml 0·0487 M uranyl nitrate, 0·778 ml 1·045 N ammonia, NH₃/U = 1·67).

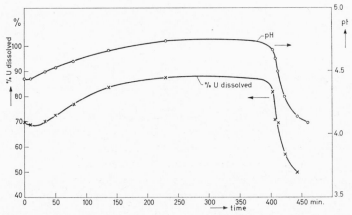

FIG. 7 Changes of the pH and the uranium concentration in a partially hydrolyzed carbonate containing system (200 ml 0·0487 M uranyl nitrate, 12·71 ml 1·1614 N ammonia, NH₃/U = 1·52).

unit and the precipitate increased five-fold. The probability that the pH decreasing reaction is of a hydrolytic nature can be further ascertained by purposely blocking the hydrolytic reaction. An attractive procedure in this case is to coordinate the uranyl ion with carbonate, which in the titration enhances the formation of complexes such as $UO_2(CO_3)_2^{2-}$ and $UO_2(CO_3)_3^{4-}$. (Bullwinkel, 1954). A similar experiment to that of Fig. 6 was therefore carried out with an initial carbon dioxide concen-

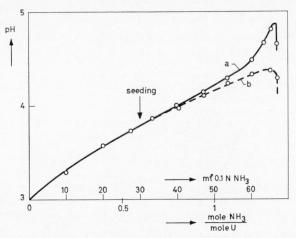

Fig. 8 Influence of seeding on the titration curve of 50 ml 0·1 M uranyl nitrate with 0·1 N ammonia at a rate of 5 ml per minute.

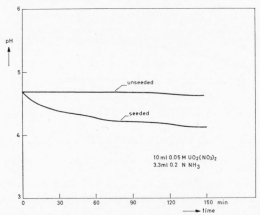

Fig. 9 Influence of seeding on the pH of a partially neutralized uranly nitrate solution (10 ml 0·05 M $UO_2(NO_3)_2$ with 3·3 ml 0·2 N ammonia).

tration in the liquid of 0·192 moles per litre. The result is shown in Fig. 7. Initially the pH rises while part of the precipitate present dissolves. As the system in this case is open to the air, the carbon dioxide content of the liquid decreases slowly and at a certain time is sufficiently l w to give the hydrolytic reaction a chance. The pH decreases, most of the residual carbon dioxide is expelled from the system and precipitation occurs. In the case that the escape of carbon dioxide is prevented, the pH of the system stays high and the precipitation step does not appear. In further experiments it could be shown that for a given NH_3/U ratio, the time before the pH starts to decrease becomes longer with higher CO_2 concentrations. The maximum in the curve becomes

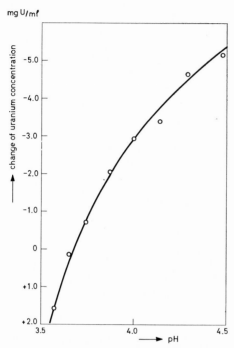

Fig. 10 Changes of the uranium concentration by seeding a 50 ml 0·1 M uranyl nitrate solution, partially neutralized with 0·1 N ammonia.

lower the longer it takes to reach the point of pH decrease. When, for a high CO_2 concentration, the CO_2 is stripped with nitrogen, the point of decrease of the pH is reached faster and the height of the pH maximum is in accordance with that of curves of the same length and thus of lower initial CO_2 concentration. The final pH does not depend on the initial CO_2 content.

The conclusion seems justified that the pH decreasing reaction is a hydrolytic one. However, the question is still open why its influence becomes so strong around the precipitation point. If the system is not in equilibrium before that point—which is evident from Fig. 5—the presence of the precipitate formed during the pH decrease might be important. The colloidal material which causes the opalescence in the system before the precipitation point can in this respect be excluded from consideration, because it evidently shows no influence. To ascertain the influence of the precipitate, experiments were carried out in which systems were seeded with the precipitate of a previous experiment. Seeding a system which is being titrated at some distance before the precipitation point results in a marked lowering of the titration curve from thereon (Fig. 8). Another way is to stop a titration before the precipitation point and to compare its change in pH both with and without seeding (Fig. 9). The pH at which the ammonia containing uranyl nitrate solution is in equilibrium with the true precipitate also has been determined for a certain case. Such solutions of different NH_3/U ratios were seeded with equal amounts of precipitate and after 10 minutes the uranium concentration in the supernatant was determined after centrifugation. In Fig. 10 the change of the uranium concentration has been plotted versus the initial pH of the seeded solution. It appears that at a pH of 3·65 neither dissolution nor growth of the precipitate occurs, whereas for a normal titration the precipitation point is found near 4·8. At the equilibrium point the NH_3/U ratio of the system is very low: it is slightly below 0·5. Such a solution stored at room temperature did not show any sign of precipitation within a few months.

D The Interpretation of the Experimental Results

The following conclusions can be derived directly from the experiments described in Section II C:

(1) in normal titrations of uranyl salt solutions with alkali hydroxide no equilibrium is attained in the lower part of the curve;
(2) apart from the relatively-fast hydrolysis on addition of the alkali hydroxide, a rather slow hydrolytic reaction occurs which counteracts the increase of the pH;
(3) this slow reaction is enhanced by the presence of a specific precipitate, which is formed by the reaction itself;
(4) the precipitate is stable at a remarkably low degree of hydrolysis, but in the titration curve its formation is retarded considerably.

This information now must be understood within one model of the reactions taking place in a hydrolyzing system.

From the experiments it appears that in the titration curves of uranyl nitrate with ammonia, two different precipitates are found near the point of precipitation and only one of those enhances a sequence of hydrolytic reactions leading to a further formation of the precipitate. This precipitate is closely related to the $UO_2(OH)_2 . H_2O$, in both its composition and its crystal lattice. The other precipitate, occurring before the point of enhanced precipitation, must therefore at least crystallographically be different. This would be surprising in the case that the initial polymerization products would fit so well in the $UO_2(OH)_2 . H_2O$ structure, as has been suggested under B.2.

In the simplified model presented there, the hydrolyzing coordinated cation has been taken into account, as well as the presence of H_2O, OH and O as ligands and bridges. Often, however, acidic anions as in the present case the nitrate ion, certainly can not be excluded from competition with the aforementioned groups, both in ligands and in bridges. The extent to which anions are linked to the coordinated cation depends upon a number of factors, such as their relative concentration and their bonding strength to the cation as compared to those of the other groups. It has to be kept in mind that a large difference in bonding strength may be compensated for partly by large differences in concentration of the different ligands in the solution. For example, near the precipitation point, where expectedly the number of OH ligands in the polymers predominates, the concentration of OH^- in the solution is roughly 10^{-10} mole/l as compared to about 10^{-1} for NO_3^- ions and 55 for water. At this pH, another cation might prefer a certain anion over hydroxide, as we will see further on in this chapter, e.g. Pd^{2+} prefers Cl^- over OH^- (Wyatt, 1966).

The important conclusion is that the anion might be an integrated part of the coordinated cation in monomeric or in polymeric form, as ligand or as bridge—and thus of the resulting solid.

This participation of the anions in the ligands and bridges of the cation will be referred to as anion exchange in this chapter. Expectedly, the anion exchange is a rather fast reaction as far as ligands are concerned which are readily accessible for the liquid.

During a titration the equilibrium distribution of ligands in the polymers will adjust itself continuously to the changing composition of the solution. This exchange becomes far more difficult for species which are situated inside a large polymer or which are present in bridges.

Furthermore an anion in a position of the lattice, where a hydroxide should be, may cause certain strains and a certain disorder of the lattice. A further increase of the pH may raise the OH^- concentration of the liquid far enough to initiate an ordering of the polymers or the solid in some places. The ordering and the subsequent growth of these regions must be accompanied by an ejection of anions from the structure or its surface and their replacement by OH. As a consequence the pH must decrease during this process.

In how far is this supposition supported by experimental evidence?

First of all there is the well-known fact that in hydroxide precipitation considerable amounts of anion can be retained, which can not easily be removed by washing. Occlusion or adsorption are insufficient to explain the persistency of the retention nor the selectivity observed. Another argument comes from the colloid chemistry where cases are known for which the presence of anion in the double layer cannot explain sufficiently the colloidal behaviour of certain sols. Some of the anions must be part of the surface and exchangeable with other species such as H_2O, OH and O. In describing the origin of the surface charge of an oxide as a function of the pH, the dissociation sequence $H_2O \underset{\rightarrow}{\overset{\leftarrow}{}} OH^- \underset{\rightarrow}{\overset{\leftarrow}{}} O^=$ of ligands to the metal is frequently applied, similarly to an ion in solution. In many cases wet surface chemistry can be explained in terms of dissolved ions, which however are anchored in the surface. In accordance with this the activation of inert Al_2O_3 for industrial electrophoretic applications by means of a treatment with concentrated hydrochloric acid is interpreted as the local formation of an Al—Cl bond, which on washing with water is replaced by an Al—OH bond.

That a certain fraction of alien ions can prevent the formation of a well ordered phase from a less ordered is known and the fact that those alien ions can be removed from the lattice on crystallization is not new either. Uranium (VI) shows this behaviour clearly. If one tries to precipitate $UO_3 . 2H_2O$ with ammonia in the presence of carbonate, under certain conditions an X-ray amorphous precipitate of a reasonable stability is obtained, provided that about 4% of CO_2 is present in the solid. The carbonate has complexing properties and replaces some of the OH ligands. In the case that in such a precipitate the CO_2 content is carefully decreased at room temperature, a fast crystallization can be observed as soon as the CO_2 content becomes lower than about 3·8%. Then the residual CO_2 is expelled at once.

The ejection of nitrate ions in a uranyl nitrate titration is difficult to demonstrate. A similar experiment, however, is practicable with uranyl chloride, where the Cl^- concentration can be estimated with a chloride electrode. Though the quantitative interpretation is complicated by the presence of the solid, a fast increase of the Cl^- concentration is observed when the pH decreases after the point of precipitation. Wyatt (1966) demonstrated the same phenomenon much more clearly for $PdCl_2$ which retains its Cl^- ion much more strongly. He investigated this system, among others, and contributed greatly to the understanding of the phenomena described in this paragraph. From his work it has also become clear that the phenomenon is not exclusive for the transition of a solid from a less ordered to a well ordered state, but also from one well ordered state to another.

A last question to be answered is why the transition of the uranyl precipitate from a rather amorphous to a well ordered state evidently triggers the hydrolysis of polymers in the solution, thereby increasing the amount of precipitate considerably while the pH decreases further until an equilibrium has been reached. The system behaves as if a certain supersaturation exists in the liquid compared to the composition of the solid. The polymers, still in solution, contain water, hydroxide and anion ligands. When such a polymer comes near the crystalline surface in a good orientation it must be expected that the ordering of the polymer will be enhanced and that the polymer can be incorporated in the surface. A number of water and anion ligands will be removed from the polymer and replaced by OH, and the pH will decrease while the amount of precipitate increases. One could state that the crystalline solid enhances the hydrolysis of nearby polymers, still in the solution on their way to becoming attached to the surface.

The model seems complete now. Expectedly it is in no way restricted to uranyl ions. The different elements of the model have to be applied in a variety of combinations in which the predominating effect depends on the chemical characteristics of the elements. One of the general conclusions is that in a system as described above there is no discontinuity in the sequence from coordinated monomeric ion to the final polymeric precipitate which can not be described with a single model, apart from crystallization. As soon as crystallization occurs, the system suddenly becomes unstable and whereas one might expect that a statistical series of polymer sizes would occur before that point, it is more likely that with a crystalline solid present the distribution becomes limited to only very small polymers and solid.

The above can be summarized by interpreting the curves a, b and c of Fig. 5 with the theory presented. The figure shows clearly two competing processes: first the fast increase of the pH by the addition of ammonia, though buffered by the fast part of the hydrolysis, and second the slow hydrolytic polymerization process which is suddenly enhanced when crystallization occurs. Curve c comes closest to the equilibrium curve. The rate of titration is so slow that the hydrolytic polymerization reaction can reach a point near to the equilibrium throughout the curve. The crystalline solid has sufficient time to be formed in an early stage already.

When a higher titration rate is chosen (curve b), the hydrolytic polymerization stays back, as is evident from the higher pH reached for the same NH_3/U ratio. Time is insufficient for an exchange of the majority of alien groups, both from the polymers and from the double-layer. This results in a somewhat steeper part of the curve where the solid and the polymers "refuse" the OH^- ions. Thereafter crystallization occurs and the rate of hydrolysis predominates over the rate of pH increase by the addition of ammonia. The pH decreases accordingly, but it does not at all reach equilibrium and not even curve c, because the time is too short. In curve a such a rate of titration has been selected that the rate of addition of ammonia is always predominant. The pH decrease present in curve b becomes visible only as a flatter region of the titration curve in a.

It will be evident that the decline in the pH curve is not essential in itself, but that in order to make the phenomenon visible, the right conditions have to be selected carefully.

E   Other Routes to Hydrolysis

In the previous paragraphs the direct addition of alkali hydroxide to a stoichiometric uranyl nitrate solution was used in order to achieve the hydrolysis of the uranyl ion. For some applications, however, this procedure is not sufficiently reproducible, nor does it aim at a specific texture of the resulting solid. Other routes have therefore been explored, such as precipitation from a homogeneous solution, hydrolysis by acid extraction or anion exchange, and reduction induced hydrolysis. Additionally, attention will be paid to controlled hydrolysis such as that applied in the so-called sol-gel processes. As a good understanding of these procedures may help in the preparation of solids with rather strict requirements concerning size, size distribution, shape or texture, a survey of some of these methods will be presented in Section III. Their application will be illustrated with a few examples of processes.

III   The Application of Hydrolytic Processes for Solids Formation

A   Precipitation from a Homogeneous Solution

For certain applications the direct addition of alkali hydroxide has the drawback that inhomogeneities occur in the system during precipitation, which causes a variation in the extent of nucleation throughout the process and thus results in a rather wide and uncontrollable size distribution of the final powder. In cases where a very narrow size distribution or a rather slow growth of the nuclei is required a technique can be used whereby the reagent is added in a masked form, which in itself does not form a precipitate with the salt solution. The reagent can then be set free from the donor, e.g. by increasing the temperature, at a controllable rate. This method ensures only one nucleation step, followed by a very even growth of the nuclei. The method is called precipitation from a homogeneous solution (Gordon *et al*, 1959) and has been applied successfully to the uranium (VI) precipitation with ammonia (Gelin *et al*., 1958: Hermans, 1958, 1964). The method is also applicable for the precipitation of certain insoluble salts in a well controlled way. For some catalytic applications, oxalates may be of importance. In principle they can be precipitated in a homogeneous way with ethyl oxalate as a donor. Another way for a homogeneous precipitation by hydrolysis is to block the hydrolytic reaction when the reagent is added and thereafter to de-blockt he reaction at a controlled rate. Two essentially different ways for stopping or retarding the hydrolytic reactions of the U(VI) are reported here.

The first is to change the coordination of the uranyl ion in the solution temporarily to a more stable complex which prevents precipitation during the subsequent addition of ammonia. An example here is to form very stable soluble aquo-hydroxo-carbonate-uranyl complex ions (Bullwinkel, 1954) from which the carbonate can be removed by stripping carbon dioxide from the solution at a controlled rate. In principle the method works, but it was never developed into a process.

The second way is the retardation of the hydrolysis itself so that ammonia can be added without precipitation. In Section II D it has been argued that particularly the polymerization in the hydrolytic sequence can be a slow process already at room temperature. This polymerization process can be further retarded by cooling the uranyl nitrate solution to a temperature near 0°C. Under those circumstances sufficient ammonia can be added, without direct precipitation, to precipitate the major part of the uranyl ions. The method was developed into a process which required some additional measures to ensure the right shape of the rather equisized precipitate.

A Precipitation with an Ammonia Donor

This process was developed (Hermans, 1958, 1964) with the aim of preparing UO_2 powders of a spherical or near-spherical shape, which could be applied as a nuclear fuel in a suspension reactor. The particles had to be about 10 μm in diameter with a rather narrow size distribution. Swedish investigations (Gelin *et al*., 1958) had led to a process where 100–200 μm ADU spheres could be precipitated from a boiling uranyl nitrate solution containing urea as the ammonia donor. The primary objective of this work was to obtain an easily filterable ADU precipitate of a very reproducible size and composition for further processing into UO_2 pellets.

For 10 μm particles, the process had to be modified. A fully different composition of the precipitate was thereby obtained. As expected, a narrow size distribution can be obtained because the nucleation is limited to a very short period of the process, and because good stirring can assure an equal growth rate for all the nuclei. This consideration made the principle an attractive one for producing a suspension fuel powder.

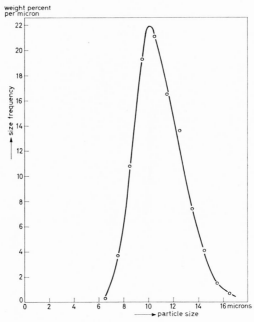

FIG. 11 Particle size distribution of UO_2 prepared with the urea process.

The procedure is as follows: per litre of a 0·40 molar uranyl nitrate solution, containing at the same time 0·52 moles nitric acid, 50 ml 25% ammonia is added to increase the pH to a value of 2·6–3·0. The clear solution is stirred vigorously by a vibrational stirrer and heated to 95°C. At this temperature 500 ml of a warm aqueous solution containing 250 g of urea, is added and the temperature is kept at 95°C under continued stirring. After about 50 minutes the precipitate formation starts. It is complete in another hour. The precipitate is filtered off, washed with cold water and dried with acetone. The yield is in excess of 99·5%. After drying, reduction at 800°C and sintering at

1250°C a powder is obtained with a specific surface area of less than 0·1 m²/g and with a size distribution as shown in Fig. 11. The distribution appears to be a log-normal one with a geometric mean diameter of 10·6 μm and a geometric standard deviation of 1·2. The mean particle diameter depends on the amplitude of the stirrer, the standard deviation on the homogeneity of stirring. The precipitate itself appeared to contain 68% U, 4·6% CO_2, 2·3% NH_3, 1% urea and 9–10% water. The appearance of the particles is gel-like (Fig. 12) and they show a very diffuse X-ray pattern.

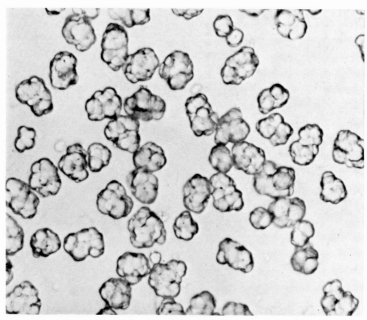

FIG. 12 Amorphous precipitate in the urea process (enlargement 560×).

In our opinion the amorphous precipitate consists of polymers of UO_2^{2+} central ions to which OH^- ions, water molecules, probably some ammonia molecules and carbonate ions are attached. The electrical neutrality can be preserved by exchangeable ammonium ions distributed throughout the structure. A certain minimum ratio of carbonate to uranyl groups is required to block crystallization of the structure to a $UO_3 \cdot 2H_2O$ derivative. Supposedly, the carbonate groups are attached directly to the UO_2^{2+} groups in the same way as in uranyl carbonate complexes. Apart from the high equilibrium constants of formation of such complexes (10^{14} to 10^{18}), there is another indication

15*

for such a bond in the amorphous precipitate. When the ammonium carbonate or the uranyl carbonate is placed in a vacuum desiccator over sulphuric acid and concentrated NaOH, the samples loose ammonia and carbon dioxide rather fast. However, no such loss is observed with ammonium uranyl carbonate or with the amorphous precipitate.

Studying the chemical reactions resulting in the formation of the precipitate, it appeared that the composition of the product is rather sensitive to the urea concentration and the temperature. It could be shown that an intermediate product is formed with the formula

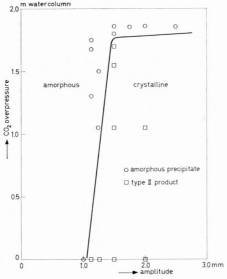

Fig. 13 Carbon dioxide overpressure required to prevent crystallization of the amorphous precipitate at different amplitudes of the stirrer.

$UO_3 . (NH_2 . CO . NH_2)_2 . H_2O$ or $(NH_2 . CO . NH_2)_2 . H_2UO_4$. This compound decomposes ultimately to UO_3, NH_3 and CO_2. This decomposition reaction competes with the growth of the solid particles, determined mainly by the rate of formation of the urea uranate. At low urea concentrations the uranate can decompose and a CO_2 free crystalline product is obtained, which has a composition close to $UO_3 . 5/3H_2O . 1/3NH_3$. On the other hand, at high urea concentrations the urea uranate is obtained. In an intermediate range, where both processes compete, the amorphous precipitate is formed.

With a high nitrate ion concentration a fourth type of precipitate is obtained, which again is crystalline. In this case, the initial precipitate is of the amorphous type, but after a certain time delay it crystallizes, thereby loosing its CO_2 entirely. The time of delay tends to increase with an increasing nitrate ion concentration, and the rate of urea decomposition decreases at the same time.

From the studies it has become evident that the amorphous precipitate derives its relative stability from the presence of sufficient CO_2 in the system. This has been demonstrated in several ways:

(1) a stirrer of such a design that it promotes cavitation and thus bubble nucleation shows also a smaller region of stability for the amorphous product;

(2) the carbon dioxide content of the precipitate decreases with an increasing amplitude of a vibrational stirrer;

(3) stripping the system with an inert gas results in the formation of a crystalline product, whereas CO_2 for the same purpose gives the amorphous product;

(4) by applying a sufficiently high overpressure of CO_2 on the system, the amorphous material can still be produced at high amplitudes of the vibrational stirrer, illustrated in Fig. 13;

(5) although the temperature may exert an additional influence on the system, it certainly will change the CO_2 concentration. Experiments with a rotational stirrer of variable speed have shown that for the preparation of the amorphous precipitate lower rotational speeds have to be used at higher temperatures (Fig. 14).

Apart from the above-mentioned "chemical" aspect of the stirrer, it appeared to exert an important influence on the mechanism of particle formation. The mean size and the size distribution of the precipitate particles is determined by a mechanism which we called "controlled flocculation" (Hermans, 1967, 1964).

On the basis of the principle of precipitation from a homogeneous solution alone, one would expect that the mean particle diameter of the precipitate changes with the number of nuclei, though in a rather moderate way, because for a given uranyl concentration the diameter must be proportional to the cubic root of the number of particles. The number of nuclei, of course, depends on the concentrations and the temperature of the system. No significant influence, however, could be found of any chemical conditions within the region of stability of the amorphous product. On the other hand, the amplitude or the rotational speed of the stirrer showed a strong influence on the mean particle diameter. Furthermore, the shape of the precipitate particles (Fig. 12) suggests that they consist of agglomerates of smaller individual particles intimately grown together. This has been ascertained by following the process under a microscope. At a certain moment in the

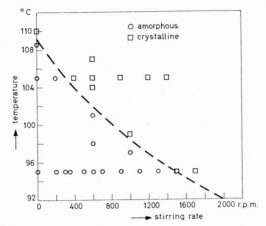

FIG. 14 Critical crystallization temperature of the amorphous precipitate at different rotational speeds of the smaller helical stirrer of Fig. 16.

process a strong tendency towards flocculation of the primary particles is observed.

Quantitative experiments both with a vibrational and with a rotational helical stirrer with draft tube have shown that a simple relation exists between the inverse of the mean particle diameter of the precipitate and the shear rate exerted on the system by the stirrer. Figure 15 demonstrates this for a vibrational stirrer with a 100 Hz frequency. The results for two stirrers of the rotational type (Fig. 16)

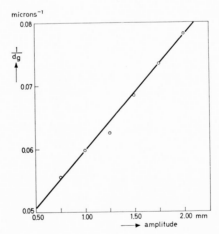

FIG. 15 Correlation between the inverse of the geometric mean diameter d_g of the amorphous precipitate and the amplitude of a vibrational stirrer.

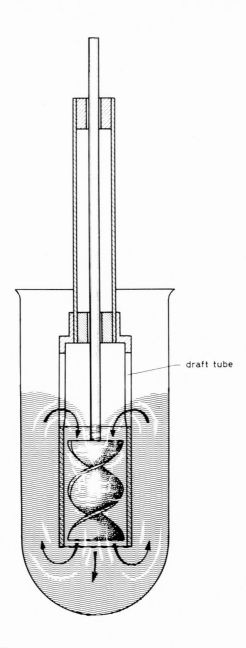

draft tube

FIG. 16 Helical stirrer with draft tube.

are presented in Fig. 17. The crosses are obtained by normalizing the shear rates for curve a to those of curve b.

That flocculation is the basis of this size determining effect can be demonstrated by changing the colloid chemical conditions in the system without effecting the precipitation itself. Flocculating the system purposely right from the beginning by the addition of Separan

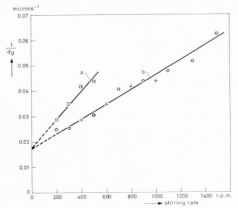

Fig. 17 Correlation between the inverse of the geometric mean diameter d_g of the amorphous precipitate and the rotational speed of two helical stirrers of different size:
  (a) diameter of the stirrer 60 mm.
  (b) diameter of the stirrer 30 mm.
The clearance between stirrer and draft tube was 1 mm in both cases.

2610 (a product from Dow Chemical Company) increased the particle size of the end product only slightly, whereas the addition of gelatine or gum arabic, which keep the system dispersed, yielded a product with a mean particle diameter of well below 2 μm. This is about the diameter of the primary particle constituting the particles of the amorphous precipitate.

Summarizing, the mean particle diameter of the amorphous precipitate is determined by the simultaneous action of three mechanisms:

(1) growth of the individual particles by deposition of uranium from the solution as the pH increases;

(2) agglomeration of the precipitated particles by flocculation under colloid chemically unstable conditions; the deposition of uranium between the particles strengthens the agglomerates;

(3) limitation of the particle size by the shearing forces exerted by the stirrer. The degree of dispersion depends on the bonding strength between the particles, their size and the forces caused by the stirrer. The equilibrium size is determined by balancing the forces

of attraction and disruption. As the basic process is a statistical one, deviations from the equilibrium size will occur, consequently the size distribution presents a curve which may be deduced from the theory of probability.

From the above it appears that the stirrer has a dominating influence on the mean particle diameter. As the stirrer is responsible for the disrupting forces on the agglomerates, it will be evident that the final size distribution will still depend on the frequency with which the system passes along the stirrer and on the homogeneity of the mixing outside the field of the stirrer. As could be expected, experiments revealed that the geometric standard deviation of the particle size distribution decreases with a higher volume ratio of stirrer to system and with more equal times of residence for the system. Furthermore, settling appeared to interfere both with the mean particle diameter and with standard deviation, again as expected.

In principle a system as described above would allow to separate the shearing influence and homogeneity of mixing of a certain stirrer. This is in excess of present characterization techniques for stirrers.

B   Precipitation by Retardation of the Hydrolysis

Part of the hydrolytic sequence is a slow process, as has been demonstrated in Section II D. For this reason it is possible to add ammonia to a uranyl nitrate solution in excess of the amount required to cause precipitation under equilibrium conditions.

This principle can be used to cause a precipitation from a homogeneous solution with the advantages of the latter technique. In fact, the principle is that underlying Fig. 6, where ammonia was added to a uranyl nitrate solution to a pH just below the precipitation point, and where the system was left to itself for nucleation and particle growth until the pH had decreased far enough to the equilibrium state. In the case of Fig. 6 about half of the uranium could thereby be precipitated.

In order to have a higher yield from this reaction, the uranyl nitrate concentration must be increased. This, however, shifts the precipitation point to lower NH_3/U ratios, as can be seen in principle from Fig. 18, where for 20°C and for a certain rate of ammonia addition (0·2 moles NH_3 per mole U per minute) the precipitation points are marked by circles.

During the investigations it appeared that NH_4NO_3 has a favourable effect on the amount of ammonia that can be added, at least under certain conditions.

The shape of the precipitate particles can be controlled somewhat. For the specific purpose for which the process was developed, 10 μm particles were required of a rather spherical shape. It appeared that for this case an acceptable product could be obtained in the presence of sufficient sulphate ions.

A typical example of the process is the following: in 1 l of a well stirred uranyl nitrate solution, containing 0·88 moles of uranium and 1·58 moles of nitrate, 40 g solid ammonium nitrate is dissolved. Thereafter, 680 ml of 1 N ammonia is added at a temperature of 20°C and

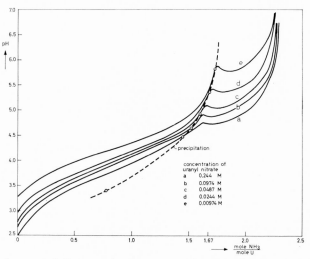

FIG. 18 Influence of the uranium concentration on titrations with 1·045 N ammonia. The ammonia has been added at a constant rate of 0·21 moles NH₃ per mole uranium and per minute.

100 g solid ammonium sulphate. A few seconds after the dissolution of the sulphate, a yellow precipitate starts to form of nearly spherical particles of a very uniform size, while the pH decreases. The process is complete in about one hour. The product is filtered and dried.

It consists of an ammonium uranyl sulphate of a very constant composition (65% U, 14% SO_4^{2-}, 2·7% NH_4^+) and with an X-ray pattern very similar to that of Zippeite (Traill, 1952). Its size distribution is a log normal one with a mean diameter $d_g = 9·8$ μm and a geometric standard deviation $\sigma_g = 1·2$. This size distribution is shown in Fig. 19. An electron micrograph is presented in Fig. 20. The yield of the process is 30–50%.

The residual sulphate in the precipitate is simply removed by leaching with ammonia.

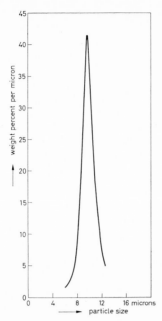

FIG. 19 Particle size distribution of UO_2 prepared with the sulphate process.

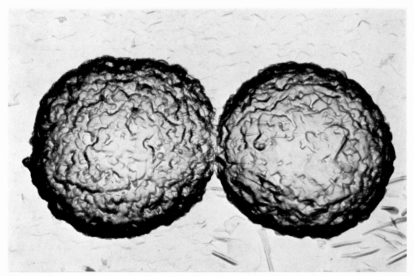

FIG. 20 Electron micrograph of precipitate particles from the sulphate process (Enlargement 6,000 ×).

The role of the ammonium sulphate in the process is solely to control the shape of the particles. It appeared, however, that this is sensitive to the pH, as is the composition of the product. In the case that the pH decreases below a certain critical pH, the shape of the precipitate particles changes and a kind of needles start to grow from the surface. This critical pH depends on the uranium concentration. For the example described above the critical pH is near 2·9.

In order to avoid this critical pH the pH of the system must be as high as possible after the addition of the ammonia. Such a measure also would increase the yield of the process.

For this purpose the rate of hydrolysis must be further suppressed. As expected, decreasing the temperature of the uranyl nitrate solution can be applied. This is shown for a temperature of 0°C in Fig. 21.

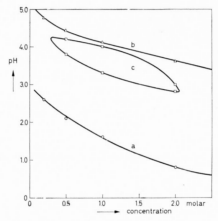

FIG. 21 pH conditions in the sulphate process versus the uranyl concentration at 0°C:

    (a) pH of the initial solution;
    (b) maximum pH attainable in a clear solution by the addition of ammonia;
    (c) region of pH-concentration combinations which yield an acceptable product.

Curve a represents the pH of the initial solution, curve b the upper pH limit which could be attained with ammonia and region c is the region of pHs after the addition of ammonia, which still yield a product of sufficient sphericity for the specific purpose presented above.

In this case sufficient ammonia can be added to avoid a final pH below the critical one, even without the addition of ammonium nitrate. The procedure of this low temperature variant of the sulphate process is the same as that for the example presented above.

Some variation of the particle size is possible by influencing the rate of nucleation. After the addition of ammonia, the higher starting pH yields the smaller particle size of the precipitate.

Yields of 50–80% could be obtained with the process.

B Hydrolysis by Acid Extraction

In 1949 Smith and Page suggested the use of amines for the extraction of acids from aqueous solutions. Jenkins and Robson (1961) applied this method "to extract the acid produced on the hydrolysis of an easily hydrolysable salt, e.g. uranyl nitrate. . . . In addition hydrolytic reactions can be carried out by removal of the acid and without the introduction of significant amounts of reagents into the aqueous phase."

It is especially this last point which makes the method so very attractive for many hydrolytic applications. With primary amines, a sufficiently high efficiency of the extraction can be attained without the extraction of the heavy metal itself by anion complex formation with the amine. Primene JMT (a product of Rohm and Haas Co.) dissolved in kerosene is an often used combination for this type of solvent extraction. The solubility of most amines in water is extremely low (somewhere near 10 p.p.m.) and therefore contamination of the aqueous system with the organic has hardly to be feared.

The extraction is usually carried out at 20–50°C by intimately contacting the aqueous and the organic phases. A stirrer is used for this purpose. Care must be taken to avoid emulsification, as the amines show a certain surface active tendency.

Jenkins and Robson (1961) used the technique for precipitating $UO_2(OH)_2 . H_2O$ from uranyl nitrate solutions and they observed that under certain conditions complex formation occurred between the $UO_2(OH)_2 . H_2O$ and the amine. In recent years there has been a growing interest on the side of nuclear fuel manufacturers to apply a certain type of processes which are now, in their many variants, called "Sol-gel" processes. In those processes a sol is required which after shaping is subsequently solidified by gelation. Both steps are hydrolytic reactions only the total process from solution to solid has been split in order to allow a certain modification of the intermediate product. It appears that acid extraction with a primary amine can be used in both cases, thereby simplifying the sol-gel process considerably and adjusting it better to continuous operation (Cogliati et al., 1968).

For the production of UO_2 no true OU_3 sols have been prepared so far in a concentration of any technical importance. The reason why it is so difficult or even impossible to prepare those sols might be the relatively high solubility of the $UO_2(OH)_2 . H_2O$ in water, especially when anions are present. On the other hand U(IV) sols are rather stable. Consequently, present uranium sol-gel processes unavoidably consist of an electrolytic or a catalytic reduction step with hydrogen and a partial hydrolysis to the required sol. By reducing a suitable substoichiometric uranyl solution, one arrives at a sol at once. The partial hydrolysis of the solution is carried out by extraction of part of the nitric acid with a primary amine, whereas the reduction itself causes a further hydrolysis, as has been mentioned in Section II E.

Similarly the gelation of the sol is effected by an extraction of the residual nitric acid. The amine can be regenerated in a simple way. This type of anion extraction has been used for the preparation of precipitates or sols from Th, U, Pu, Zr and R.A., and some of their combinations.

The information available concerning the mechanism of the reactions involved still is scarce. For example the texture of the resulting sols may deviate considerably from those derived along other routes. Particularly the crystallite growth, required to form a stable sol, may differ from those in sols obtained at higher temperatures.

Recently another important application of the principle of hydrolysis by acid extraction has been found in the field of UO_2 fuel, which might also be of a more general interest (Noothout, 1968).

As mentioned above, UO_3 sols have not been prepared in a concentration which makes them attractive for sol-gel processes. Still there is a growing interest in UO_2 microspheres for a number of nuclear reactor applications. Though sol-gel processes have been developed for UO_2, the reduction of the U(VI) prior to sol formation and the necessity to work in an inert atmosphere thereafter are felt as a drawback. Industrially it would be of great importance when microspheres or other shapes could be prepared in the U(VI) state, and when the required reduction could be combined with the final heat treatment. In the case of microspheres a solution would be to use a concentrated uranyl nitrate solution, which could be dispersed into droplets and solidified by dropping them into a hydroxide solution which would hydrolyze the uranyl ion to its UO_3 state. It appears, however, that the solidified spheres fall apart. Indications were found that a more concentrated solution would be adequate for solving the problem. In order to reach concentrations higher than the solubility of the salt would allow, a partial polymerization could be used, provoked by a limited hydrolysis of the system. When the hydrolysis of the solution starts, the monomeric ions form di- and trimers, which expectedly will have roughly the same ionic charge as the monomeric ion. One might therefore expect that the mean distance between the polymeric cations in the first stages of the hydrolysis is about the same as for the monomers, provided that the electrolyte content is not increased too far. Roughly, by removing nitric acid a dimerization of the cations would mean a maximum concentration which is twice that of the saturated solution. In this case the initial presence of cationic polymers already in a saturated uranyl nitrate solution has been neglected.

On this basis one might expect that, starting from a uranyl nitrate solution the maximum uranium concentration increases with a decreasing NO_3/U ratio by removing nitric acid. On the other hand starting from UO_3 precipitate it is evident that the maximum uranium

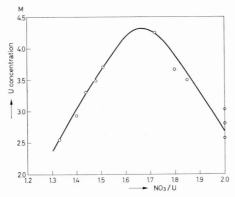

FIG. 22 Maximum concentration of acid deficient uranyl nitrate solutions.

concentration in the supernatant would increase with the addition of nitric acid. Alternatively one could say that starting from a saturated uranyl nitrate solution the extraction of nitric acid must finally lead to precipitation and to a decrease of the maximum uranium concentration thereafter.

A curve which for an acid extraction would show the relationship between the nitrate to uranium ratio and the maximum attainable uranium concentration must then have at least one maximum. Here again, some secondary considerations have been neglected, such as the change in particle or crystallite size throughout the region from monomer to precipitate.

A number of preliminary measurements of this type have been carried out for different uranyl nitrate systems. The results are presented in Fig. 22. Scattering though the values are, they show clearly the predicted tendency. The measurements have been made by successive partial denitration and concentration of the system. In this region and at these concentrations there can hardly be a question in what form the uranium is present. It is a solution in which the uranyl ions are present in a slightly polymerized form, probably not exceeding as a mean, the dimer or trimer state. This, of course, is essentially different from a true sol where the smallest sol particles contain hundreds or thousands or uranyl ions.

The initial uranyl nitrate solution has been modified by controlled hydrolysis to allow a higher uranium concentration than the saturated solution of the stoichiometric salt.

For the specific application envisaged, this modified solution could be used with considerable success. Strictly speaking, the process does not belong to the sol-gel family, though on first sight it shows a striking resemblance.

C   Reduction Induced Hydrolysis of U(VI) and U(IV)

Evidently, though still somewhat surprisingly, oxidation and reduction reactions can lead to hydrolytic reactions. The author is not aware of any application of this technique, but the reaction appeared to interfere with some processes developed for UO_2 production. The relevant example is the catalytic reduction of a uranyl nitrate solution with hydrogen in the presence of palladium. When one starts from a stoichiometric solution of uranyl nitrate, the resulting uranium(IV) nitrate solution is understoichiometric with respect to nitrate. The overall reaction shows the production of hydroxide ions:

$$UO_2^{2+} + H_2 \rightleftharpoons U^{4+} + 2OH^-.$$

The reaction has to be used to enable the application of a sol-gel variant for the production of UO_2. Unless the initial uranyl nitrate solution is diluted or contains extra nitric acid, a partial precipitation of UO_2 is observed in the U(IV) solution.

In exactly the same way the oxidation of a stoichiometric Fe(II) salt solution must yield an understoichiometric Fe(III) solution. In such cases the degree of precipitation depends on the concentration and the substoichiometry of the starting solution.

The reduction or the oxidation can be carried out in several ways, without introducing interfering reagents. Electrochemical reactions could be used, but the use of hydrogen, oxygen, hydrogen peroxide etc., also seems attractive, if necessary in combination with a catalyst.

In order to prepare U(IV) sols, a uranyl nitrate solution is reduced catalytically with hydrogen and Pt or Pd as a catalyst. In doing so at room temperature and under atmospheric pressure, we observed the formation of a crystalline UO_2 precipitate in the system. Under some-what different conditions a yellow UO_3 precipitate could be observed and it appeared also possible to arrive at once at a U(IV) sol (Kanij and Noothout, 1967).

The question about the end product which is obtained depends mainly on the concentration and the stoichiometry of the solution, and sometimes on the degree of reduction. The subject has not been studied systematically. This would in our opinion require, amongst others, that the curve of Fig. 22 for U(VI) should be extended to higher NO_3/U ratios and an additional one should be determined for U(IV). From these two curves optimal conditions could be derived for produc-ing sols or precipitates of a certain type.

In general it can be said that the UO_2 was obtained in cases where the final stoichiometry of the U(IV) solution was too low at the end of the process, but possibly not low enough for sol formation. A yellow precipitate can be formed because the NO_3/U ratio is already too low for the uranyl ion shortly after the beginning of the reduction, due to the unfavourable distribution of nitrate ions across U(IV) and UO_2^{2+}. An additional complication in the system is that in the present case it appeared that towards the end of the reduction nitrate ions are being reduced to ammonia which then gives rise to further hydrolysis (Lane et al., 1968).

D Modification of Precipitates for the Application in Sol-gel Techniques

For a number of reasons, the sol-gel techniques, which have been briefly described above, have gained interest in nuclear fuel produc-tion. In principle the method has been known for years in the industry of catalysts for the preparation of oxidic catalysts or catalyst carriers.

The basis of the process is a controlled hydrolysis in two steps. The first step leads to a nearly complete hydrolysis, whereas in a number of processes in the second step the residual part of the hydrolytic sequence is used to interconnect the separate crystallites into a firm network, enclosing the solution present in the sol. It needs no further explana-tion to understand that the success of the process strongly depends on hydrolytic phenomena.

It is not our intention to present the variants of this process in much detail. A good survey is available in the CNEN proceedings of the Turin Symposium (1968), where especially from Oak Ridge National Laboratory much valuable information has been disclosed.

A few aspects closely connected with hydrolytic reactions have been selected for presentation here.

A   Sol Preparation

Several routes are available, some via a precipitate which is peptized into a colloid chemically stable sol. In a number of cases the crystallites in the sol are rather small (30–50 Å). Peptization of a precipitate does not lead easily to a subdivision of the crystallites, but only to a superficial attack and to growth. Consequently, the precipitate must be obtained in a finely divided form. A normal procedure therefore is to add the uranium, thorium or plutonium salt solution to a concentrated ammonia solution, thereby ensuring a very fast precipitation, and thus a very small crystallite size. The precipitate is then washed free of electrolyte, and peptized. In a few cases, the peptization occurs spontaneously at a somewhat increased temperature (McBride et al., 1968), but generally nitric acid or a suitable nitrate must be added and the system must be boiled for a considerable time before peptization occurs (Kanij et al., 1968). The peptization has been studied in somewhat more detail for ThO_2 (Hermans et al., 1968).

For the investigation a precipitate was used of hydrous thoria, obtained by adding a $Th(NO_3)_4$ solution to concentrated ammonia. The precipitate was washed by decantation with dilute ammonia and water respectively. The resulting solid proved to be X-ray amorphous. Thereafter the peptization rate was studied as a function of the NO_3/Th ratio in the system.

The required NO_3/Th ratios and thus the starting pH were adjusted by the addition of nitric acid, and the peptization was effected by boiling. At intervals samples were taken from which the supernatant was isolated by centrifugation. The Th concentration which could arise both from dissolved and peptized thorium, was measured together with the pH. In the sediment X-ray line broadening was used to determine the mean crystallite size. The results of these measurements are presented in Fig. 23.

On the time axis two points P and A have been marked before the zero of the scale. They represent the period before the boiling point was reached in the system. At P nitric acid was added to the washed precipitate, the pH, the crystallite size and the Th concentration were measured, and the system was homogenized at room temperature for 15 minutes. The measurements in this situation fall on point A. Thereafter the system was heated to boiling and zero hours is the moment at which the boiling point was reached.

The peptization or dissolution—peptization curves show a fast initial increase of the thorium content of the liquid and thereafter for some time they level off in an intermediate region. After this induction period, however, a steep rise is observed again, which then leads to a complete peptization. This steep rise coincides with an increased rate of crystal growth, as is evident from the curves which represent the crystallite size versus time. The close relationship is evident from the comparison of both sets of curves.

Furthermore it is evident that the peptization rate and the rate of crystal growth increase with an increasing NO_3/U ratio.

The significance of the nitric acid in this system is indirect and two-fold:

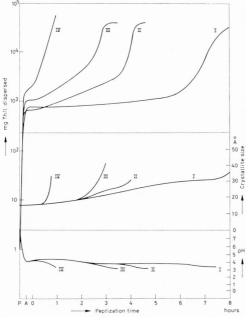

FIG. 23 Peptization of thorium oxide precipitate by boiling with dilute nitric acid of varying concentration. Influence of nitrate to thorium ratio on the rate of peptization, the rate of crystal growth and the change of the pH with time. I = 28·6 mole % NO_3;   II = 35 mole % NO_3;   III = 40 mole % NO_3; IV = 45 mole % NO_3.

1. In the present situation its concentration is a measure of the initial acidity, and therefore bears a certain relation to the colloid chemical stability, which in fact is determined by the hydrogen ion concentration, but which can also be destroyed by too high a nitrate concentration of the liquid. The hydrogen ion concentration controls the degree of dissociation of the water ligands into OH^- or even O^{2-} in the surface of the thorium oxide as described in Section II B. The amount of acid, for which the nitrate ion concentration in the present

case is a measure, required for the stabilization of a sol depends on the solid surface present.

2. The acid determined the amount of dissolved thorium and thus the mobility of thorium containing ions and the rate of crystal growth. In this mechanism the nitrate groups which are still present on the surface of the crystallites must also play a role.

Furthermore, it must be kept in mind that for a given situation there is a minimum distance between the particles in a sol. If this distance is further decreased by some means, flocculation occurs, because the London-van der Waals force becomes predominating.

With these principles, the graphs of Fig. 23 may be understood. Initially, the precipitate is X-ray amorphous, consisting of extremely small primary particles. The addition of acid will peptize at once part of the precipitate and dissolve another part temporarily. The amount of peptized precipitate, however, is limited because local flocculation will correct the situation as soon as the distance between the particles becomes too small in a certain part of the system. Consequently, a dynamic equilibrium exists between the sol and the residue. The acid enhances the growth of the primary particles, which means that more solid can be accommodated in the sol with the same inter-particle distance. At the same time, however, the nitrate ion concentration increases slightly, because of the decrease of the solid surface, and the process proceeds at an increasing rate. At the higher acid concentrations, the process is much faster, as can be expected.

The whole process evidently is a combination of local dissolution and hydrolysis in which H^+, OH^- and NO_3^- take care of dissolution, transport and hydrolysis of the thorium at the crystal surface. The driving force is the more favourable energetic state of the larger crystal.

Doubt still exists whether all the thorium of the system is in a crystalline state or whether the surface still contains less crystalline parts. It is the question whether in the gel the bonding is a London-van der Waals bonding or a chemical bonding. This might even be different for different sols and gels. In our opinion a residual amorphous part still exists at some places of the surface, where bonding between the crystallites takes place preferentially through hydrolytic processes.

The above hypothesis confirms the experimental evidence that with higher acid to thorium ratios the peptization rate is increased, but that at the same time the colloidal stability of the sol decreases. It must be expected that not all anions show this influence to the same extent.

A consequence, of course, would be that in some cases it might be favourable to remove surplus nitric acid from the system as the crystallite growth proceeds, to preserve the stability sufficiently and to shorten the subsequent hydrolytic procedure for gelation. Practical applications of this method have been found.

From this another technically important conclusion can be drawn. It is known that some oxides such as PuO_2 and to a less extent UO_2 do not form crystals readily. Even after they have done so, the growth of the crystallites is extremely slow. Unless measures are taken, this will limit the maximum concentration of the resulting sols. Concentration by evaporation, of course, is hardly possible. In such cases the rate of crystallization, the primary crystal size or the rate of crystal growth must be important. Accordingly, measures could be:

1. increasing the solubility of the oxide by the addition of a suitable anion in the peptization step or by temporarily increasing the acid content;
2. precipitating the (hydrous) oxide under such conditions that less nuclei are formed or that a crystalline precipitate is obtained of not too large a size;
3. applying an aging step in water, if necessary at a temperature above 100°C.

The success of this type of measure has been demonstrated meanwhile. Thorium oxide sols may form a somewhat special case in this respect, because the crystallites of the sol consist of ThO_2, whereas under the prevailing conditions of the pH one would expect that a polymeric thorium hydroxide would be the more stable species. The latter, however, is not known in a crystalline form. The crystal growth then would take place due to a competition between the growth of a hydrolytically less stable component, which, however, has a well-ordered lattice and a non-crystalline, more stable thorium hydroxide. This might explain the relatively low rate of crystal growth in thorium oxide sols.

B Sol Gelation

In the so-called sol-gel processes the sol formation is in effect a controlled modification of the precipitate to a state of incomplete hydrolysis. The subsequent gelation completes the hydrolysis at least in those cases where solidification is effected by an increase of the pH. The latter is done by ammonia penetration into the sol, by the application of an ammonia donor in the sol (e.g. hexamethylenetetramine) or by acid extraction. As a consequence of this procedure the sol droplets which are dispersed in an organic medium solidify into rather rigid gel spheres.

Alternatively, however, the gelation can be effected by a slight dehydration of the sol. By applying a suitable sol concentration the small decrease in the distance between the crystallites seems to be sufficient to link the particles together in a three-dimensional network which encloses most of the water of the sol.

Expectedly, gels from an alkaline gelation and those from a dehydration gelation might show a different texture in a more detailed investigation. No such information is available yet. In both cases the gel is found to exist of very small, equisized crystallites enclosing pores of a similar size. The pore size distribution is narrow. Apart from the favourable shaping properties of the sol into microspheres, this texture of the gel presents a clear cut advantage of the material as such with respect to its thermal reactivity in subsequent stages of production.

IV Texture and Thermal Reactivity of Precipitates and Gels

In considering the thermal reactivity of the different solid products of hydrolysis, their texture appears to be of primary importance. Many of these products are exposed to sintering processes either in the production process itself, such as for ceramics, or during their application, e.g. as catalysts. In both cases, the pore size plays an important role. As the pore size depends on the size of crystallites, granules, etc., it seems justified to discuss briefly how the texture of the final product might be controlled to some extent by the hydrolytic procedure and by subsequent heat treatments. The discussion will be illustrated with a number of technical applications.

It seems very difficult to define quantitatively the thermal reactivity of a system. For the present discussion it might be described as the tendency of the system to change its texture with increasing temperatures in such cases where neither a chemical reaction nor a phase transition occurs.

It then appears experimentally that the pore size of such a system is of paramount importance. In general, the smaller pores disappear first (de Boer, 1958a). In principle Kuczynski (1963) has shown for a simplified model and for a sintering process based on diffusion that pores with the smaller radius will be removed first from the solid. Thus solids with only small pores will show a high sintering rate at relatively low temperatures.

A high thermal reactivity expectedly requires a high mobility in the solid. It will therefore depend on the degree of disturbance of the crystal lattice and on the nature and the size of the defect. The smaller the undisturbed regions and the smaller the defects are, the higher will be the thermal reactivity. Astoichiometry, small crystallite size and, if pores are present, small pores may contribute to rapid sintering, whereas stoichiometry and large pores represent a good thermal stability in a system. Of this principle use can be made to control the porosity of ceramic materials, as will be shown further on.

Powders for ceramic applications, such as "ceramic grade" UO_2, are often characterized by their BET surface area as a measure of sinterability. In this respect, however, the specific surface area must be handled with some reserve. In fact it provides information about a combination of two characteristics of the solid: the total surface area of the crystallites interface and the degree of dispersion of the crystallites. Only in the case of a high degree of dispersion is the specific surface area identical with the total surface area of the crystallites interface and only in this case does the specific surface area provide direct information concerning the mean size of the crystallites, and thus of the thermal history of that specific material. It will be evident that a material consisting of crystallites of a similar size as in the previous case, but without intercrystalline gas-solid interface area can show a similar thermal reactivity. It is therefore not justified to use the specific surface area as a measure of thermal reactivity for materials prepared along different routes, even in a case where the final products are chemically identical. With one preparation method useful information can doubtless be derived from changes in the specific surface area.

A   Textural Considerations of Precipitates and Gels

Because the size of a pore is very important with respect to the sintering behaviour of a material, one might try to envisage several types of textures, all derived from the same equisized crystallites but stacked in different ways within one granule of the material.

First, the crystallites can be grown together so tightly that there is no gas-solid interface, apart from the surface of the granule itself. Both the urea process (Section III A) and the sulphate process (Section III B) in many cases yield such products. Sintering in such a case hardly means densification. For the uranium processes just mentioned a certain porosity is reintroduced by the reduction to UO_2, but the pores normally are of an extremely small size.

A second type of texture consists of randomly stacked crystallites which are only intergrown at the points of contact. The pores are of a size which has the same order of magnitude as the size of the crystals.

The surface of the crystallites is fully accessible for an adsorbent, apart from geometric restrictions. Normal precipitations often show this type of stacking.

A third type consists of stacked agglomerates of crystallites. Within each agglomerate crystallites may be intimately intergrown with a certain loss of specific surface area. The total surface area lies between that of the separate crystallites and that of the outer agglomerate area. The crystallites may show a certain orientation within the agglomerates, but this is not necessary. Certain types of carbon are examples of this texture. The pores are roughly of the size of the agglomerates, but the agglomerates themselves may contain pores in the range of the crystallite size.

The fourth type of stacking is most probably that of many gels, where the crystallites are separate, but show in their way of stacking stringering, sheet formation or a three-dimensional network. The pores can be considerably larger than the crystallite size. The specific surface area is that of the crystallites.

In our opinion these four types are the most essential ones in a grain. In ceramics, however, where compacts are made, the final product is initially built up of granules, which again may arrange in different ways, similar to the crystallites. Whether this occurs and what large pores may result from it depends on the techniques used. Slip casting, extrusion, pelletizing or loose sintering lead to different textural arrangements of the granules. The persistent open pores which hamper the densification in the last percentages below the theoretical density often are residues of intergranular pores. On the other hand, in controlling open porosity, the intergranular pores can be used because of their large size compared to the intercrystalline pores of the starting material.

Much is known about the way crystallites are stacked in solids. Not much, however, is known about procedures to control the type of stacking purposely, although this knowledge could be of profound interest to industrial applications. A few general remarks might be made concerning this problem. The classification of crystallite arrangements proposed above is only a very schematic one. Evidently the shape of the crystallites, their size distribution, and sometimes a variation of their composition may give rise to mixed textures. For example: a compound consisting of long needles in a random packing (type II) may form a gel which in its behaviour is rather similar to a type IV stacking which has stringering. The formation of the particles of a precipitate is controlled by such phenomena as crystal nucleation, crystal growth and by flocculation. Not all of these need to be important in every case, although a certain interrelationship exists. This may be shown by a few examples.

In a case of controlled nucleation, such as precipitation from a homogeneous solution, and a slow crystal growth, dense precipitates generally are obtained of type I. They are virtually non-porous, and they have only a low percentage of impurities. The precipitate obtained from the sulphate process described in Section III B is an example. A similar type is the precipitate from the urea process (Section III A), apart from the fact that it is X-ray amorphous. Its formation, however, is somewhat different. Initially small, dense agglomerates are formed which in a later stage of the process flocculate as a consequence of the decreasing acidity of the system. Thus a type III precipitate must be expected. However, the flocculation occurs at a time when the system still contains a considerable amount of dissolved uranium. Further precipitation then fills the pores between the agglomerates within one granule and a particle without porosity results. If desirable, flocculation can either be prevented or enhanced by the addition of suitable organics. A fast precipitation generally results in smaller sized crystallites with a more random packing.

Finally, for the formation of a type IV material, such as in ThO_2 gels, a rearrangement of crystallites is required if one starts from a precipitate. In that case, the crystallites of the precipitate must be separated and dispersed in the liquid: it must be peptized. The reagents used for this purpose are such that a surface charge is built up, but in many cases they show at the same time a mild etching effect on the precipitate. Gelling the resulting sol in fact means that the surface charge of the individual crystallites is decreased and that flocculation occurs. Under favourable conditions this flocculation is an oriented one which leads to the formation of strings, sheets or complete networks enclosing the liquid phase, and thus to a gel.

As can be envisaged, it is also possible to arrive at a sol, straight from a solution, provided that the crystallites are grown under conditions where the system is colloid chemically stable. An example from the field of uranium fuel chemistry is the reduction of a prepolymerized uranyl solution into a UO_2 sol. The prepolymerization in this case is carried out by a controlled acid extraction.

In cases of spontaneous peptization, the intergrowth between the crystallites of the precipitate is expectedly very loose, and probably a type II precipitate was present. By precipitating $U(OH)_4$ from a suitable uranium (IV) salt solution with ammonia a precipitate is obtained which on washing peptizes spontaneously into a sol which can easily be gelled (McBride, 1966).

Although the available information and experience is still too poor to predict the relationship between the hydrolytic procedure chosen for an oxide system and the texture of the resulting product, it is evident that different routes can lead to different products, even with the same chemical composition. It seems worthwhile to take advantage of this by more systematic studies of hydrolytic phenomena and textures of solids.

B   Thermal Reactivity

In nuclear fuels the initial aim for the application of oxides was to attain a high density of good reproducibility in order to keep the uranium concentration within the reactor core as high as possible. More recently many reactor designers require a controlled porosity of 10–15% in order to provide space for the build-up of fission gases in fuel elements with a high burn-up. This porosity may be an open one or, more specifically for high-temperature reactors, closed. The latter to retain the fission gases within the fuel as far as possible.

Another aspect of thermal reactivity is the chemical reaction which may take place at increased temperatures between two solid components present in the same precipitate or gel. Here also certain hydrolytic routes seem to be more favourable than others, because they provide a higher degree of dispersion of the components.

The above aspects seem to be of sufficient general interest, to discuss them here in somewhat more detail.

A   High Density

According to the above the absence of large pores in the material at the beginning of the sintering procedure is important in order to reach a high density at relatively low temperatures. Although a chemical reaction or a certain heat treatment may create large pores inside precipitate particles, generally the pores between the particles cause most difficulties in sintering.

In some cases it is possible to avoid such pores. In the production of microspheres of high density (size from a few μm to a few mm), the sphere can be made by gelling a single drop of sol, and the pores are those of the material itself. The sintering temperature can be very low, although a considerable shrinkage has to be accepted, which, however, appears to be completely isotropic.

Another way of effectively avoiding intergranular pores is the application of certain extrusion techniques where a dried gel and a wet gel might be mixed so that a rather homogeneous system is obtained (Olsen *et al.*, 1968). In the case that compaction and sintering of powders is required prior to sintering, intergranular pores can hardly be avoided. Their size can, however, be restricted in several ways. As the pore size depends on the particle size to a certain extent, the application of very fine powders can be beneficial. In practice the flow properties of such powders are bad, and they cause excessive dust. Granulation is then applied, e.g. by adding a binder or a lubricant. In that case a favourable size distribution can be chosen in order to avoid large pores, and in certain cases the corresponding sol or gel may be added as lubricant or binder.

Sometimes the more favourable particle size distribution is formed during the compaction step by crushing the particles. Very weak particles are required for this purpose, consisting of small crystallites. An example, here, is the application of certain spray-dried powders for the fabrication of compacts.

Other widely applied techniques for decreasing the size of a powder prior to compaction are wet ball-milling, oxidation-reduction cycles (e.g. with UO_2) or the vigorous removal of volatile constituents at an increased temperature.

Of course, other parameters are important in the sintering itself, such as gas atmosphere, astoichiometry, pressure, and heating programme. These, however, are left out of consideration here.

B Controlled Porosity

A controlled porosity can be of importance both for the final product and for an intermediate material.

Let us first consider the controlled porosity of a highly fired product. As a general consequence of the fact that the larger pores require the higher sintering temperature to remove them, any persistent porosity can be introduced into the unfired material by creating pores of a size several orders of magnitude larger than the pores of the material itself. The procedure followed for many ceramic materials is an empirical one. By selecting a good size distribution of the powder and a reasonable sintering temperature, the required porosity can be assured. A more sophisticated way of working is to use a highly sintered powder material, which on compaction, leaves a certain coarse porosity, and to diminish that porosity by adding controlled amounts of the relating sol or gel. This colloidal material sinters to a very high density and serves at the same time the purpose of a cement between the prefired, non-sintering material. The open porosity of such a sintered compact

16

can easily be controlled by controlling the ratio of sintered to colloidal material in the green compact.

Sometimes a controlled closed porosity is required, such as in microsphere fuel for high temperature reactors. Again cavities must be formed of a size considerably in excess of the intrinsic porosity of the material used. With sol-gel processes this might be accomplished by bubble formation in the still plastic gel material, such as with foam plastics. A method which has been tried with some success for nuclear fuel, however, is to disperse into the sol a solid or liquid material in a suitable size, which can thereafter be removed. Uranium-thorium oxide spheres have been prepared by mixing carbon into the colloidal sol and burning out the carbon in an oxidizing atmosphere (Podo and Horsley, 1966).

Instead of carbon, a low-boiling organic liquid can be selected, which is emulsified in the sol. The droplet size can be controlled by a judicious choice of the type and the amount of surfactant. After gelation and drying, the material has sufficient open porosity to remove the organic from the spherical cavities. Subsequent sintering removes the open porosity of the material itself, but leaves the closed cavities because of their size Netherlands Patent Application nr. 6508991 (1967).

A change of the texture of a precipitate may be desirable in order to apply it in a subsequent step, which, for example, might be impregnation or a ceramic procedure. An interesting example is the precipitate derived from the urea process (Section III A). When washed and dried its specific surface area proved to be as low as $0.26 \text{ m}^2/\text{g}$. After reduction with hydrogen at 800°C this appeared to be near $5 \text{ m}^2/\text{g}$, whereas about $0.1 \text{ m}^2/\text{g}$ would be the accepted maximum for certain experiments in a nuclear suspension reactor. The required decrease was attained by sintering at about 1250°C. The increase of the surface area is caused by the fact that volatile materials such as water (both present in the particle and formed inside the particle by the reduction with hydrogen), ammonia, and carbon dioxide can not escape fast enough by diffusion. Thus pores are created to give way to the gases. It could be shown that a careful reduction and a moderate heating rate of the material produce a powder at 800°C with a specific surface area as low as $0.16 \text{ m}^2/\text{g}$, and of a similar thermal reactivity as the $5 \text{ m}^2/\text{g}$ material. Finally, it appeared to be possible to vary the specific surface area of the UO_2 obtained in the reduction step between 0.16 and about $20 \text{ m}^2/\text{g}$ by varying the rate of heating and reduction. It will be evident that the composition of the precipitate and its residual water content influences this process.

Spray-drying is a technique fully comparable to the case just mentioned. The same holds to some extent for burnable or volatile organic additions often used in the clay industry. A fast process in this case always results in the formation of rather large open pores.

C Mixed Systems

Especially in the case of sol-gel materials, characterized by a small crystallite size and a very open texture, it must be expected that a high chemical reactivity exists, e.g. when a second component is present which can react at an increased temperature.

The second component can be introduced in several ways:

1. It may be added as a salt solution to the initial precipitate in order to peptize this. The method is used to introduce U(VI) in ThO_2 without reduction. The upper limit of the Th/U ratio is near three to four.
2. It may be added to the salt solution prior to precipitation, such that a coprecipitate is formed. Again this can be done with U(VI) in ThO_2. The procedure shifts the upper Th/U ratio to about unity. The extra U(VI) is taken up by the ThO_2 inside the particle (van der Brugghen et al., 1968).
3. It may be adsorbed by impregnation of the still-porous, calcined gel from a salt solution and converted if necessary to the oxide by washing and heating.
4. When "anion extraction" is applied the mixed salt solution can be hydrolyzed.
5. If both components can be prepared as sols, suitable sols can be mixed provided they are so selected as to be compatible.
6. In some cases the solid is just mixed mechanically either into the solution prior to precipitation or into the sol. This technique is used for adding carbon to oxides for subsequently converting to carbides.

The temperature at which new compounds can be formed from such a mixed system is surprisingly low as a consequence of the small crystallite size and the very intimate mixing. The technique is used for nuclear compound fuels such as the oxides or carbides of U–Pu, U–Th, U–Zr, etc.

An example from another field is the spinel $MgAl_2O_4$, which can be formed by mixing Al_2O_3 and MgO and heating. However, by using a coprecipitate of hydroxide for a sol-gel process, the compound was formed at a temperature which is about 300°C lower than usual (Boekschoten, 1968).

A further interesting aspect of mixed systems is the influence of the composition on the pore shape, such as was observed for (U, Th) oxide (Kanij *et al.*, 1968). The phenomenon is not yet understood in detail as the study is not yet finished, but the preliminary results are worth mentioning here.

Under the supervision of J. H. de Boer, Cornelissens (1964), made a study of the sintering of ThO_2 prepared by a sol-gel route. In the precipitate dried at 200°C a crystallite size of about 50 Å and micropores of

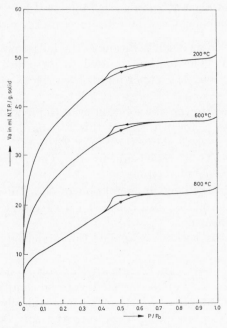

FIG. 24 Nitrogen adsorption and desorption isotherms of sol-gel ThO_2 for different sintering temperatures.

about 14 Å were found. The material was sintered in air at different temperatures. The final product contained some carbonate at the surface as a contaminant. The resulting adsorption-desorption isotherms are presented in Fig. 24. They are of the type E of de Boer's classification (1958b). This type is often found for gels.

With the same method mixed oxides were prepared in which the U(VI) was introduced by peptizing the initial thorium precipitate with uranyl nitrate (Kanij *et al.*, 1968). The resulting 5 μm gel spheres were washed, dried and calcined in air. Samples were prepared with 2, 7, 11 and 14% U based on the heavy metal content. Due to the sintering in air the uranium is present mainly in the six valent state, which renders the mixed oxide astoichiometric with respect to its fcc lattice. The adsorption-desorption isotherms for 800°C sintered material are shown in Fig. 25. The mean crystallite size increases with the uranium content from 90 to 135 Å. At a temperature of 1100°C 600-800 Å is reached and the specific surface area is about 0·2 m²/g.

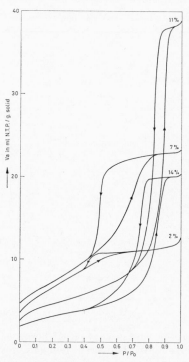

FIG. 25 Nitrogen adsorption and desorption isotherms of 800°C sintered sol-gel (U, Th) oxide of different U/Th ratios.

Apart from a somewhat unexpected variation in the pore volume, the most remarkable fact is that between 7 and 11% U, the type of Th isotherm changes from E to A. This might mean in de Boer's classification that initially present considerably widened parts in the tubular pore system are smoothed out to some extent, so that the variation in pore size becomes less than a factor of two. Although the change in the isotherm is quite significant, the change in the pore system need not be so striking. It is questionable which parameter causes this change. The increasing amount of uranium might affect the texture of the wet gel, because it might influence the way of packing of the sol crystallites. On the other hand, the phenomenon might be caused by the fact that the sinterability changes. Whereas at 7% uranium, a type E isotherm is preserved up to high sintering temperatures, the 11% material shows the transition from type E to type A during its sintering. Figure 26 demonstrates this for temperatures from 600 to 900°C.

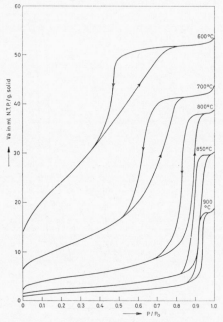

FIG. 26 Nitrogen adsorption and desorption isotherms of sol-gel (U, Th) oxide, containing 11% U, and sintered at different temperatures.

From both these preliminary results and the close resemblance which may exist between pore systems of type A and type E isotherms it seems likely that the observed transition arises from changes in the sinterability of the different systems. However, a more detailed study seems necessary.

The influence of a second component, especially in sol-gel systems, might drastically influence the texture of the resulting gel. In that case it might make a large difference whether the second component is introduced by coprecipitation, by mixing compatible sols, by impregnation with a salt solution or by peptization of the first component with a salt solution of the second.

Also in this respect the knowledge of the relationship between the way of hydrolysis and the texture of the resulting solid is very limited, even for a number of technical applications.

V   References

Ahrland, S. (1959). *Acta chem. scand.* **3**, 374.

Ahrland, S., Hietanen, S. and Sillén, L. G. (1954). *Acta chem. scand.* **8**, 1907.

Boekschoten, H. J. C. (1968). Private communication.

de Boer, J. H. (1958a). *Z. angew. Chem.* **70**, 383.

de Boer, J. H. (1958b). *In* "The Structure and Properties of Porous Materials" (D. H. Everett and F. S. Stone eds), Vol. 10, p. 68. Butterworth, Colston Papers, London.

Brushilovskii, S. A. (1958). *Dokl. Akad. Nauk. SSSR* **120**, 305.

Bullwinkel, E. P. (1954). U.S. Atomic Energy Commission Report RMO-2614.

Cogliati, G., Collenza, F., Lanz, R., Lupparelli, V., Maltzeff, P., Mezi, E. and Recrosio, A. (1968). *In* "I processi sol-gel per la produzione di combustibili ceramici", p. 241. C.N.E.N., Rome.

Comitato Nazionale Energia Nucleare (1968). "I processi sol-gel per la produzione di combustibili ceramici". C.N.E.N., Rome.

Cordfunke, E. H. P. (1962). *J. inorg. nucl. Chem.* **24**, 3032.

Cornelissens, E. G. P. (1964). Unpublished results.

Faucherre, J. (1948). *C. r. hebd. Séanc. Acad. Sci. Paris* **227**, 1367.

Gelin, R., Mogard, H. and Nelson, B. (1958). *Proc. 2nd Conf. Peaceful uses of Atomic Energy.* Geneva **7**, 36.

Gordon, L., Salutsky, M. L. and Willard, H. H. (1959). "Precipitation from Homogeneous Solution", John Wiley and Sons, New York.

Guitier, H. (1947). *Bull. Soc. chim. Fr.* **14 I**, 64.

Hermans, M. E. A. (1958). *Proc. 2nd Conf. Peaceful uses of Atomic Energy.* Geneva **7**, 39.

Hermans, M. E. A. (1964). "The Urea Process for UO₂ Production". Thesis, Delft University of Technology, The Netherlands.

Hermans, M. E. A. (1967). *In* "Science of Ceramics" (G. H. Stewart, ed.), Vol. 3, p. 65, Academic Press, London and New York.

Hermans, M. E. A. and Markestein, T. (1963). *J. inorg. nucl. Chem.* **25**, 461.

Hermans, M. E. A., Kanij, J. B. W., Noothout, A. J. and van der Plas, Th. (1968). *In* " Sol-gel Processes for Ceramic Nuclear Fuels", p. 21. IAEA, Vienna.

Hufferman, L. (1952). *Chem. Weekbl.* **48**, 441.

Jenkins, I. L. and Robson, J. (1961). United Kingdom Atomic Energy Authority. Report AERE-R 3761.

Kanij, J. B. W., Noothout, A. J., van der Plas, Th. and Hermans, M. E. A. (1968). *In* "I processi sol-gel per la produzione di combustibili ceramici", p. 139. C.N.E.N., Rome.

Kraus, K. A. (1955). *Proc. 1st Conf. Peaceful uses of Atomic Energy.* Geneva **8**, 149.

Kraus, K. A. and Nelson, F. (1948). U.S. Atomic Energy Commission. Report AECD-1864.

Kuczynski, G. C. (1963). *Powder Metall.* **12**, 1.

Lane, E. S., Fletcher, J. M., Fox, A. C., Holdoway, M. J., Hyde, K. R., Lyon, C. E. and Woodhead, J. L. (1968). *In* "I processi sol-gel per la produzione di combustibili ceramici", p. 231. C.N.E.N., Rome.

424   M. E. A. HERMANS

MacInnes, D. A. and Longsworth, I. G. (1942). U.S. Atomic Energy Commission. Report MDDC-911.
McBride, J. P. (1966). U.S. Atomic Energy Commission. Report ORNL-3874.
McBride, J. P. et. al. (1968). In "I processi sol-gel per la produzione di combustibili ceramici", p. 161. C.N.E.N., Rome.
Olsen, A. R., Sease, J. D., Fitts, R. B. and Lotts, A. L. (1968). In "I processi sol-gel per la produzione di combustibili ceramici", p. 319. C.N.E.N., Rome.
Overbeek, J. Th. G. (1952). In "Colloid Science" (H. R. Kruyt, ed.), Vol. I, p. 184. Elsevier, Amsterdam.
Podo, L. A. and Horsley, G. W. (1966). In "Dragon Project Report 431" (O.E.C.D. High Temperature Reactor Project.) A.E.E. Winfrith, Dorset.
Sanderson, J. R., Dibben, H. E. and Mason, H. (1959). United Kingdom Atomic Energy Authority. Report CI-R-15 (SCS-R-163).
Sillén, L. G. (1959). Q. Rev. chem. Soc. 13, 146.
Smith, E. L. and Page, J. E. (1949). J. Soc. Chem. Ind. 67, 48.
Sutton, J. J. (1955). J. inorg. nucl. Chem. 1, 68.
Traill, R. J. (1952). Am. Miner. 37, 394.
Tridot, G. (1950). Annls Chim. 12e Serie, 5, 358.
Trombe, M. (1943). C. r. hebd. Séanc. Acad. Sci. Paris 216, 888.
van der Brugghen, F. W., Hermans, M. E. A., Kanij, J. B. W., Noothout, A. J., van der Plas, Th. and Slooten, H. S. G. (1968). In "Thorium Fuel Cycle" (R. G. Wymer, ed.), p. 377. U.S. Atomic Energy Commission/Division of Technical Information, Washington, D.C.
Wyatt, R. (1966). Chem. Weekbl. 62, 310.

Chapter 9

THE TEXTURE AND THE SURFACE CHEMISTRY OF CARBONS

TH. VAN DER PLAS

RCN-KEMA Reactor Development Group, Arnhem, The Netherlands

I General Introduction

A The Types of Carbons

Carbon is a most remarkable substance although this is not always appreciated. Even without considering the hundreds of thousands of organic compounds, there is some reason for the exclamation: "We are dealing with the most exciting element in the whole periodic table" (Cranch, 1962).

There may be two reasons which together, account for this exclamation:

16*

(a) the ease with which carbon is formed from its compounds, especially many cheap and abundant natural products, by heating them in the absence of air, and

(b) the difficulty of crystallization of carbon (which is manifested in the extremely high point of fusion of graphite).

Both points, together, mean that carbon products can be formed whose properties are more determined by the raw materials and the method of preparation than by the properties of graphite. This holds especially for the texture: some of the smallest pores and the highest specific surface areas known are found in certain active carbons. Carbon blacks, on the contrary, are generally spherical particles of relatively high density, practically non-porous but still built-up from very small, disordered graphite crystallites (see, e.g. Heckman and Harling, 1966).

As to the chemistry, in view of their preparation it is not surprising that most carbons are impure. Apart from inorganic constituents, hydrogen, oxygen and sulfur, sometimes nitrogen also, usually are found in carbonaceous products and severe treatments at high temperatures are necessary to free carbons of these impurities.

Especially the requirements of graphite for nuclear reactors have shown the considerable problems that arise if a really pure, but also dense and well-crystallized carbon product is to be manufactured.

One might expect considerable differences in the properties of products as a function of the content of these impurities and their distribution over the "carbon skeleton". Some of these differences can be found in swelling properties, wetting properties, adsorption properties and rates of chemical reaction, e.g. with oxygen. Certain classes of carbons have been characterized by the raw material and the method of preparation. The following review discusses briefly the most important of these classes.

First we should mention the *diamond*, that remarkable form of carbon whose preparation has defied man's attempts for so long a time. The diamond will play no role in the subsequent chapters, although the adsorption of oxygen (Barrer, 1936b) and the surface chemistry have been studied (Sappok and Boehm, 1968).

Specimens of *graphite* from Ceylon and Madagascar have been used for many studies of the mineral. *Artificial graphites* in several forms are produced. They serve as electrodes, materials of construction for special purposes and brushes in electrical motors. Another important use is as a moderator or as fuel cladding in nuclear reactors.

Coal needs no comments here, as it was the foundation of the technical society not so long ago, nor do *charcoals*, prepared from a variety of sources.

Active carbons are prepared from coal, charcoal or other carbonized materials by a process of activation. Nearly always this process amounts to a partial oxidation, conducted in such a way that the desired pore structure is obtained. For adsorption from the liquid phase the pores should be easily accessible for large molecules; these carbons are mostly used in powdered form.

Adsorbents for gases have much smaller pores and, hence, a large specific surface area; granules of different (non-spherical) forms are used.

Carbon blacks are, in principle, soots, prepared under well controlled conditions from natural gas or oils. They form very small, dense spherical particles. Hydrogen is distributed throughout the particles; oxygen is found on the surface only. Their use for the reinforcement of rubbers is extremely important, but they are also used as pigments in paints and inks.

Recently introduced new materials are the *glassy carbons*, prepared from certain polymers, and *carbon fabrics*.

B Carbons as Adsorbents

Active carbon is probably the oldest adsorbent known. In fact, wood charcoal might have been the first "chemical product" made by man, since it would no doubt have been produced with the first artificial fire.

It is well known that the van der Waals forces are responsible for the adsorption on carbon in most of the applications where adsorption from gaseous mixtures is practiced. The adsorption from liquids may be different and will be considered in more detail later on.

The adsorption process as such is, therefore, not very selective as far as the adsorption forces are concerned. This might be influenced if the texture of the carbons could be controlled in such a way that appreciable molecules sieve action occurs.

The main advantage of carbons in adsorption processes seems to be the large surface area they offer at a relatively low price. Especially in the case of adsorption from gases, where narrow pores are effective, the specific surface area of carbons produced for this purpose can be enormous (of the order of 1000 m^2/g). In addition, narrow pores give rise to an increased adsorption energy (de Boer and Custers, 1934). Carbons used for adsorption from gases generally are manufactured in the form of particles with dimensions of the order of several millimetres and of irregular shape.

Carbons used for adsorption from liquids are produced as fine powders for easy suspension. The ideal pore size for this type of application is larger than for use with gases, since the slower diffusion of dissolved products in the liquid phase must be compensated for by larger pores. The extremely fine pores, useful for adsorption from gases, are not desirable in the case of liquids.

Apart from the pore sizes there is the requirement of easy dispersion of the carbon in the liquid to be treated. A surface consisting of carbon only, or carbon plus hydrogen, would be strongly hydrophobic and not at all suited for the treatment of water. The presence of oxygen on the surface tends to make it more hydrophilic and does not influence the adsorption properties adversely. The oxygen can be fixed on the carbon by a mild oxidative treatment; most of the activation processes in common use introduce fixed oxygen together with the porosity produced by the removal of carbon as CO_2 or CO. Some data on oxygen coverage will be given in section III B.

The more polar character of the surface, arising from the partial coverage with oxygen, influences the adsorption properties in the direction of an increased adsorption of polar substances. A clear example of this influence can be found also in section III B. The capacity for the adsorption of non-polar substances is never lost, however.

A special case is the adsorption of electrolytes on carbon that contains oxygen. Depending on the oxidizing treatment, two forms of carbon can be produced, one that assumes a positive charge in water or one that becomes negatively charged. The charge on the solid is, in either case, compensated by the charge of a mobile double layer, in which an excess of ions of a sign opposite to that of the carbon surface is present.

The adsorption of electrolytes such as potassium chloride, etc., can be described as an exchange of ions with the original components of the double layer. Ions of larger molecular weight, such as organic acids or bases, are adsorbed irrespective of the sign of the large ion. Here the influence of the van der Waals forces predominates; the large ions are adsorbed on the carbon surface and do not form a part of the double layer. If the sign of the charge on the large ion is not the same as that of the carbon surface, an apparent reversal of the charge on the solid may be noted.

From the above considerations it would follow that the behaviour of a certain carbon product is determined by:

(a) its texture: specific surface area, pore shape and pore size distribution;

(b) the coverage of the surface with oxygen;

(c) the chemical form assumed by the oxygen attached to the carbon;
(d) the particle size distribution.

In a number of applications the carbon is impregnated with substances in order to improve its capacity and, especially, its selectivity. In most of these applications the carbon seems to function as an inert carrier, giving the possibility of obtaining, for a given mass of impregnant, a much larger active surface area than could be reached with the pure impregnant. Here, of course, the texture of the original and of the impregnated carbon are of importance. They may in fact be significantly different, e.g. because of a blocking of small pores by the impregnant.

It follows, then, that a carbon adsorbent can be characterized by the quantities referred to under *a–d* above. Methods of determining these quantities should, therefore, be available. The following sections deal mainly with these problems.

Another topic of great interest, the preparation of carbons to suit a given application, will not be discussed at all. Here, practical experience has had a great advance on scientific insight and the more refined methods of measurement have served mainly to confirm old ideas.

This does not mean that no progress is possible in tailoring carbons for specific purposes. Numerous studies give insight into the relationships between the properties of final products and the properties of raw materials and the parameters of the activation processes. An example of a study of the activation process will be given in Section II H. A thorough treatment of this subject is outside the scope of the present contribution.

In the following pages, then, only the problems of the texture of carbons and the chemisorbed oxygen will be dealt with. A full coverage of even these limited topics has not been attempted. The emphasis is on the work of pupils of Professor J. H. de Boer. When discussing texture, therefore, the use of the *t*-curve is the main point of interest. The discussion on chemisorbed oxygen deals mainly with the analysis of the functional groups on the carbon surface.

These restrictions necessarily give a somewhat heterogeneous character to this chapter. It is hoped that this is compensated by the use of much recent material.

In the previous discussion the expression "carbons" has been used in a very wide sense, equivalent to that of using the word "steel" when discussing the structural properties of ferrous alloys. Both words indicate a large family of materials, with different properties and different applications.

In what follows, the carbons to be discussed (mostly carbon blacks) have been indicated by their trade names where possible. Since these products are manufactured with good reproducibility, this seems to make sense since a comparison of different batches of these products has been proven to be fully justified. A comparison with literature data is thereby made possible.

At the end of this chapter a list of general references is added to supply the reader with an introduction into the whole field of carbon studies.

II The Texture of Carbons

A Introduction

The introduction to this chapter pointed out the importance of the texture of the carbons, together with the large differences in pore structure shown by different products.

The t-method (Chapter I), if it could be applied to carbons, seems to offer a relatively easy way of interpretation of the adsorption isotherms of nitrogen in terms of pore structure. This section will examine the application of the t-method.

Originally, the t-curve was derived for alumina and related oxide materials. It is certainly not evident that the p/p_0–t relationship found with these materials will hold also for carbonaceous materials, where both the basal planes and the prism faces of the graphite crystallites are very different from the surface of the oxides.

However, for a number of oxidized carbon-blacks it was shown that the p/p_0–t relation as developed gave reasonable results (de Boer et al., 1965b). An apparent deviation, obtained with a fully graphitized carbon (de Boer et al., 1965a) could be explained by taking into consideration the homogeneous character of the surface of this carbon (de Boer et al., 1967).

These results show that it might be worthwhile to study further the application of the t-method to carbons. A serious drawback in this study is the fact that there is no really reliable method for studying the narrow pores specifically. Results based on the Kelvin equation cannot be considered reliable in this region, while investigations on the molecular sieve character give only limited information.

For judging the results, no data are really available for comparison. The plausibility of the results is the only guide line available at present.

The aim, then, of this part of the chapter is three-fold:

(a) to demonstrate the usefulness of the t-method in this field, where texture is so highly important, by showing some examples of application;

(b) to consider some anomalies found;

(c) to discuss the use of gases other than nitrogen.

B The Applicability of the t-Curve to Carbons

The V_a–t plots for the oxidized carbon blacks Carbolac 1, Spheron 6 and Elf 5, all products manufactured by G. L. Cabot Company, Boston, U.S.A. have been given elsewhere (de Boer et al., 1965b).

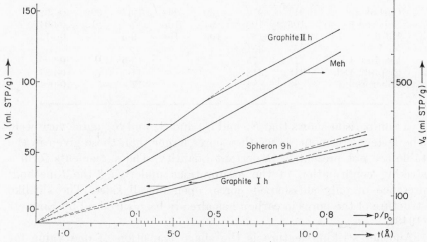

Fig. 1 Examples of V_a–t plots which pass through the origin. (See Table I.)

Van Aken (1969) gives examples of carbons, heated at 1000°C in hydrogen (subsequently exposed to the atmosphere at room temperature). They are: the carbon black Spheron 9 h, an active carbon Me h and two milled graphites I h and II h (h stands for heated in hydrogen). The V_a–t plots are given in Fig. 1. Other examples are given by Abram and Bennett (1968).

In the V_a–t plots of Fig. 1 it can be observed that carbon Me h does not seem to contain any pores, as there is no break in the plot. Graphites I h and II h show porosity; the carbon black Spheron 9 h only a small amount.

The numerical data derived from the measurements are given in Table I. In this table S_B is the BET surface area, S_t the total surface area according to the t-plot, S_w the surface not present in small pores. This is the surface area derived from the slope of the V_a–t plot at high values of p/p_0. S_{em} is the geometrical surface area, calculated from the particle diameter determined with the electron microscope (Cabot Company). The surface area present in micropores is indicated by S_n, $S_n = S_t-S_w$. All values of quantities S in this and subsequent tables are given in m^2/g. V_n, given in ml/g, is the volume of the pores, d_n the corresponding pore width, expressed in Å.

TABLE I. Specific surface area, pore size and pore volume

Carbon	S_B	S_t	S_w	S_{em}	d_n	S_n	V_n
Carbolac	911	972	280	264	7–15	692	0·362
Spheron 6	105	106	94	106	7	12	0·004
Elf 5	124	127	103	104	9·5	24	0·011
Me h	857	851					
graphite I h	75	75			15·5		0·009
graphite II h	218	218			11·5		0·027
Spheron 9 h	83	84			17		0·004

A comparison shows that S_B and S_t, and S_w and S_{em} agree very well. The latter agreement shows that pores larger than those given in the table are not present in important quantity. The agreements form a striking confirmation of the assumptions underlying the t-method: presence of only slit-shaped pores, open on all sides. The slit-like structure of the pores in carbon has already been surmised by Emmett (1948).

Another striking feature is the sharp transition of one value for the slope in the V_a-t plots to another, shown by Spheron 6, Elf 5 and the carbons heated at 1000°C. This shows that the pores in these cases are very uniform in size. This property, however, is not a general one for carbons. Also, it should not be concluded that the pores themselves have a uniform width. It has been shown by van Aken (1969) that similar results are obtained when the pores are wedge-shaped, provided that the entrances of the wedges have the same width.

C The Influence of Submicroporosity on the V_a-t Plots

Together with the three carbon blacks referred to above, another, Mogul A, was investigated. This carbon showed an abnormal behaviour; the V_a-t plot did not extrapolate through the origin (de Boer *et al.*, 1965b). The explanation given was the presence of pores with values of $d = 2t$ so small that the t-curve is not applicable in this region (t smaller than 3·5 Å).

Subsequent investigation has shown that this behaviour is the exception rather than the rule for active carbons. Figure 2 is an example of V_a–t plots for several carbons: the carbon black Mogul A, two sugar carbons ZK 15, verk. O_2 ox and E 1, verk. O_2 ox used by Boehm for investigating their surface chemistry, Spheron 9 and the milled, unheated graphites I and II. The latter graphites are untreated, apart from the milling. (The samples I h, II h and Spheron 9 h, mentioned in the previous section, have been prepared from the graphites I and II, and the carbon black Spheron 9.)

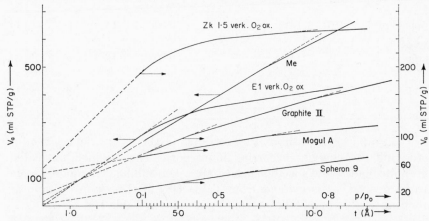

FIG. 2 Examples of V_a–t plots which do not pass through the origin. (See Table II.)

In Table II the data determined for these carbons are given. The notation in the table is the same as that used for Table I, except for the entry under S_t. S_t has been obtained by drawing a straight line through the origin and the first available point (at $t = 3.5$ Å) on the V_a–t plot. In this way a surface can be calculated that is higher than the BET surface; this surface has no real meaning but the difference with S_B shows the inadequacy of the description of the pore structure by the method used.

A consideration of Table II gives rise to a number of remarks. First, it must be noticed that a description of the pore system down to pore widths of 7 Å can be given. The surface of pores down to this width is known.

As an example the full pore size distribution for the two sugar carbons is given in Fig. 3. Sugar carbon has been a favourite object of study throughout the years. Figure 3 is a pore size distribution calculated according to the classical method. Together with the V_a–t plot a reasonable insight into texture is obtained.

TABLE II. Carbons with anomalous t-curves. Specific surface areas (S_n), pore size(d) and pore volume V_n for groups of pores

Carbon	S_B	S_t	d	S_n	V_n	d	S_n	V_n
Mogul A	285	334	<7			10	44	0·044
Mau 1	308	353	<7			10	102	0·102
ZK 15	770	835						
E-1	1048	1083						
Spheron 9	107	107	<7		0·006	14	50	0·013
graphite I	116	119	<7		0·007	12	53	0·010
graphite II	300	316	<7		0·026	11	136	0·030
						17	45	0·025

The graphites furnish another example of the use of the t-curve for studying the changes occurring in carbons. The original, untreated graphite had a low specific surface area. On milling, micropores seem to be opened, as is evident from Table II, but these pores disappear by heat treatment as follows from the results in Table I.

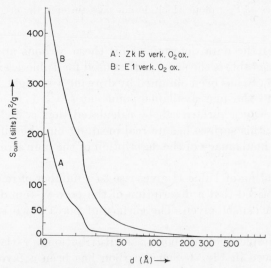

FIG. 3 Cumulative pore size distribution for two sugar carbons:
A: ZK 15, verk. O$_2$ ox.
B: E-1, verk. O$_2$ ox.

These conclusions follow simply from the fact that the V_a–t plot intercepts the V_a-axis above the origin, interpreted as an indication for the presence of pores with widths smaller that 7 Å.

For these pores neither the BET nor the t-method are valid. A strong persorption occurs and the way in which the pores are filled or a layer of adsorbate is formed on the larger of these very small pores is not known.

However, for every experimental point at values for $p/p_0 < 0.08$ a value of the amount of adsorbed gas is known. If this gas volume could be converted into the true volume of the adsorbed fluid as present in the pores (or on the pore surface), at least a range of pore volumes could be obtained. An estimate of the specific volume of the fluid adsorbate is then required and it is by no means certain that this specific volume is equal to that of the liquid adsorbate at the temperature of measurement. It might even differ for pores of different size. In view of this difficulty it has become the custom to use the specific volume of the liquid, at least in the case of nitrogen.

From the pore volumes so obtained it is impossible to derive a value for the surface area corresponding to the pore volumes. For it is easily seen that pores whose width is one, three or four times the diameter of a nitrogen molecule will be filled at the same relative pressure and this may continue for even higher values of the pore width. Hence, even if the pore volumes and the surface area to be attributed to one adsorbate molecule were known with reasonable certainty, the calculation of a surface area would be impossible to within a factor of two. Only if some indication about an average pore width is known, does it make sense to calculate a surface area for the pores smaller than 7 Å.

This brings up a matter of nomenclature. Dubinin (1959) has introduced the division of the pores according to their width (or diameter). Pores between 1000 and 20 Å were called transition pores; pores smaller than 20 Å called micropores. The use of the t-method seems to make it advisable to divide the micropores (at least the slit-like ones) into two classes, those for which a t-curve is known ($d \geq 7$ Å) and smaller pores. The latter could be called submicropores or narrow micropores, while the word micropores could be retained for pores with a width between 7 and 20 Å.

It has already been related that a deviation at the low pressure side of the t-curve, found with a carbon with a homogeneous surface, is due to this homogeneity (de Boer et al., 1967).

Voet and Lamond (1968) have found much smaller anomalies in the same region of pressure when measuring carbon blacks. They suppose that the surface of the small crystals, forming the carbon black particles, is sufficiently homogeneous to cause these anomalies.

D Application: Determination of the Cross-Section Area of Adsorbed Molecules

A number of carbon blacks examined by Abram and Bennett (1968) give rise to V_a-t plots of both the normal and the anomalous types described in Sections B and C above. Again, the sharp breaks in the plots indicate pores of 11 or 15 Å width, while in most cases pores smaller than 7 Å were also found.

The adsorption of two surfactants was studied on the carbons already examined with nitrogen. The surfactants cetyltrimethylammonium bromide (CTAB) and sodium di-2-ethylhexylsulfosuccinate (OT), dissolved in water, gave rise to Langmuir type adsorption isotherms, from which the monolayer capacity of the carbons for these compounds could be derived.

The monolayer capacity can be converted into a surface area per molecule, using the surface areas of the carbons derived from the V_a-t plot or the BET equation. It was shown that the use of S_w, the specific surface area present in wide pores (see B above) allowed the calculation of remarkably constant values for the surface area (occupied) per molecule. The average areas found were 44 and 71 Å^2 (± 3 Å^2) for CTAB and OT respectively.

Further consideration showed that the smallest pore which can be entered by CTAB must have a width between 11 and 15 Å; for OT this value must be larger than 15 Å. The absence of pores wider than 15 Å makes it impossible to define this value better.

Earlier, Bennett and Abram (1967) studied the adsorption of the surfactants, mentioned above, on bone char. Bone char is a composite material, consisting of hydroxyapatite, partially covered with carbon. The authors showed that, most probably, the *total* surface area of the char could be determined by adsorption of OT from water, the *carbon* surface by adsorption of CTAB from water and the *hydroxyapatite* surface by adsorption of OT from benzene.

The results cited above make it possible to put the earlier conclusions on a firmer quantitative basis by correcting them for the more accurate values of the surface area of the adsorbates and the narrow pores that might be present. In this way, the road is opened for a further study of the behaviour of bone char in actual practice.

E   Application: The Adsorption of Water by some Active Carbons

The adsorption of water by active carbons is a matter of great practical interest. Active carbon is used in respirator canisters to adsorb poisonous gases from the inhaled air. The action of the active carbon is nearly always enhanced by inorganic substances that react selectively with certain noxious gases. However, the whole system is useless if the water vapour present in the atmosphere is also adsorbed on the carbon, as it blocks the entrances to the micropores and screens off the reactive impregnants.

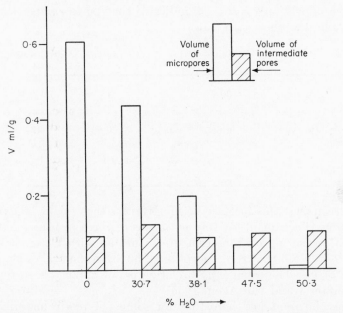

FIG. 4 Change of pore volume, available for the adsorption of nitrogen at 77°K, with increasing amounts of adsorbed water. Contribution of micropores and intermediate pores indicated separately.

A very complete study has been reported by Emmett (1948). The use of the t-method makes it possible to relate the adsorption of water to the texture of the active carbon (van Aken, 1969).

The adsorption isotherm of water on active carbon is a classical example of a type III isotherm. If isotherms are compared, obtained with impregnated active carbon, non-impregnated carbon and the active carbon, heated at 1100°C in hydrogen, the isotherms are shifted towards higher p/p_0 values, as might be expected.

The adsorption of nitrogen at low temperature has been studied on carbons containing increasing amounts of water. With the aid of the V_a–t plot, the total volume of the micropores (width smaller than 20 Å), not yet filled with water, can be determined. The volume of the intermediate pores ($20 < d < 3000$ Å), determined from the desorption isotherm, hardly changes as a function of the amount of adsorbed water.

The results (van Aken, 1969) given in Fig. 4 show clearly that the smallest pores are filled first.

Table III can be used to relate the weight percentage of water, indicated in Fig. 4, to the relative pressure of the water vapour. In this table the indication "pores $<$" indicates that pores smaller than the given value are filled with water.

TABLE III. Water content, relative vapour pressure and pore filling

% H_2O	30·7	38·1	47·5	50·3
rel. pressure	0·68	0·72	0·86	0·92
pores $<$	12	12	14	24

It is seen that the decrease in effectiveness that might be expected can be described quantitatively by means of these measurements.

When measuring carbons that are saturated with water, it should be borne in mind that the adsorption of nitrogen then takes place on a surface of ice. The usual p/p_0–t relation is not applicable to this case (see Chapter 1 and van Aken, 1969).

It may be remarked here that for some polymeric materials this p/p_0–t relation cannot be used either (chapter 1 and van Aken, 1969). However, in some of these cases the BET equation also cannot be applied.

F   The Failure of the t-method with Benzene and Carbon Tetrachloride as Adsorbates

In view of the demonstrated usefulness of the p/p_0–t curve for the adsorption of nitrogen it seems attractive to try to obtain similar relationships for other adsorbates. Of course, from every adsorption isotherm determined with an adsorbent with a freely accessible surface, a p/p_0–t curve can be calculated with the aid of the same assumptions

that were made in the case of nitrogen. An attempt in this direction
has been made by van Aken (1969) for the adsorbates benzene and
carbon tetrachloride.

The four carbons, Me h, Spheron 9 h and graphites I h and II h,
were measured with benzene and, except graphite I h, with carbon
tetrachloride.

A BET surface area has been calculated, using the following values
for the surface area per molecule (σ): $\sigma_b = 30.5$ Å^2 and $\sigma_c = 32.2$ Å^2.
Here σ_b and σ_c refer to the values for benzene and carbon tetrachloride,
calculated in the customary manner from the densities of the pure
liquids. The results are shown in Table IV, where S_b, S_c and S_N are the
BET surface areas determined by means of benzene, carbon tetrachloride and nitrogen respectively.

TABLE IV. Surface area (BET) determined with three adsorbates

Carbon	S_N	S_b	S_c	S_N/S_b	S_N/S_c
Spheron 9 h	83	55	56	1·51	1·48
Meh	857	700	703	1·22	1·22
graphite I h	75	63		1·19	
graphite II h	218	150	139	1·45	1·57

In all cases the nitrogen values prove to be the highest ones. Of
course, the σ values for benzene and CCl$_4$ might be corrected in order
to achieve agreement with the nitrogen values. The last column of
Table IV shows, however, that in every case different correction factors
would have to be applied.

It is found that the values $\sigma_b = 39$–43 Å^2 and $\sigma_c = 41$–49 Å^2 are
necessary to obtain the desired agreement (McClellan and Harnsberger,
1967 give $\sigma_b = 43.0 \pm 6.0$ and $\sigma_c = 39.2 \pm 5.3$ Å^2). Similar discrepancies
are noted, when, instead of S_N, the values of S_w from Table I are used.

In order to obtain p/p_0–t curves, use was made of the BET values
determined with the σ-values derived from the density of the pure
liquids. From the four benzene isotherms and two of the carbon tetrachloride isotherms a single p/p_0–t curve was obtained for every adsorbate. The CCl$_4$ isotherm for Spheron 9 h gave anomalous results and
was not taken into account. This result in itself gives satisfaction,
but it was felt that a closer look at the applicability of the BET theory
to this combination of adsorbates and adsorbents was still necessary.
This can be done by using a theory which seems more firmly based than

the BET theory, and applying this theory to measurements on appropriate adsorbents.

Such a theory is that of the two-dimensional van der Waals gas, extensively discussed in Chapter 2 by Broekhoff and van Dongen. This theory, summarized in the Hill-de Boer equation, allows the calculation of the monolayer volume (V_{uw}) and the degree of occupation, θ_1, of the first adsorbed layer. However, it can only be applied to adsorption on homogeneous surfaces.

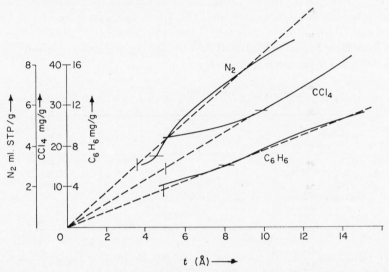

FIG. 5 V_a–t plots for graphitized carbon blacks, with nitrogen, benzene and carbon tetrachloride as adsorbates. Nitrogen at 77°K and benzene at 20°C on Sterling FT 2800, carbon tetrachloride at 20°C on carbon T_1. Note different ordinate scales.

It seems that at present only well graphitized carbons have both a sufficiently homogeneous surface and a specific surface area large enough to allow measurements. The available experimental material consists of the isotherms of the graphitized carbon black Sterling FT (2700), measured with benzene and nitrogen by Isirikyan and Kiselev (1965), and of a similar product, T_1, measured with carbon tetrachloride by Avgul et al. (1962).

Figure 5 shows the V_a–t plots obtained by the application of the just described p/p_0–t relations and the general p/p_0–t relation for nitrogen to these measurements of carbons with a homogeneous surface. In Fig. 5 the values for the unimolecular layer obtained according to the BET method are indicated by vertical dashes, the

V_{uw} values according to the Hill-de Boer equation with horizontal dashes. It is seen that the values are closely together in the case of nitrogen, but differ appreciably in the case of benzene and carbon tetrachloride.

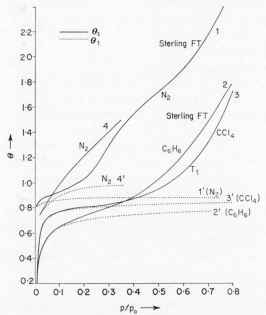

FIG. 6 Degrees of coverage as a function of relative pressure. Drawn lines: total degree of coverage (θ_t); dotted lines: degree of coverage of first adsorbed layer (θ_1). Curves 1, 2, 3 and 1^1, 2^1, 3^1 refer to carbons with a homogeneous surface. Adsorption of nitrogen: 1 and 1^1; of benzene: 2 and 2^1; carbontetrachloride: 3 and 3^1. Curves 4 and 4^1 represent the adsorption of all three adsorbates on carbons with a heterogeneous surface.

Accordingly, for nitrogen, the results of the BET equation are almost equal to those of the Hill-de Boer equation, but the large differences obtained with benzene and carbon tetrachloride indicate failure of the BET equation for these adsorbates (since the Hill-de Boer equation is supposed to give the correct values in these cases).

A further analysis allows a somewhat deeper insight into these relationships. For both cases, the carbons with homogeneous surfaces and the carbons with heterogeneous surfaces, the degree of coverage of the monolayer and the total degree of coverage can be calculated. For the first type of carbons the degree of coverage of the monolayer, θ_1, is found from the Hill-de Boer equation; the total degree of coverage θ_t, is found from $\theta_t = V_{uw}$.

For the second type of carbons, those with a heterogeneous surface, θ_1 is calculated by means of the BET picture. The total degree of coverage, θ_t, is found with the aid of the three p/p_0–t relations obtained for the three adsorbates.

The results are pictured in Fig. 6. In this figure, the drawn curves refer to values of θ_t, the dotted curves to values of θ_1. The curves are indicated by figures, primed figures referring to the θ_1 curves, unprimed figures to the results for θ_t.

The curves marked 1, 2, 3 and 1′, 2′, 3′, refer to the carbons with homogeneous surfaces, giving the results obtained with nitrogen, benzene and carbon tetrachloride respectively. For the carbons with heterogeneous curves two times three curves (one for every adsorbate) might also be expected. However, the results for benzene and carbon tetrachloride are practically the same, while the results for nitrogen are only slightly higher. Accordingly, the results are described by the single curves 4 and 4′.

Consider first nitrogen. The curves 1 and 4 are not very different, which is also the case for 1′ and 4′. The point, where 4 and 4′ start to separate (indicating formation of a second layer) is found at higher pressures than the corresponding point of 1 and 1′.

For benzene, the difference between the corresponding curves (4 and 2, respectively 4′ and 2′) is much larger. Also, the point of separation of 4 and 4′ is now at a lower pressure than that of 2 and 2′. The same conclusion appears on comparison of 4 and 3, respectively 4′ and 3′.

This shows that the adsorption on the heterogeneous carbons (4 and 4′) is appreciably larger than on the homogeneous ones, while the formation of the second layer takes place in a lower range of pressure on the heterogeneous carbons than is found with the homogeneous carbons.

Both results seem unlikely and are, therefore, taken as strong indications of a failure of the BET conception for the combination of carbon adsorbents and the adsorbates benzene and carbon tetrachloride. It follows that a p/p_0–t relation cannot be obtained in the usual way for these adsorbates. Hence, benzene and carbon tetrachloride are not suited to the determination of the specific surface area of carbons, using the BET equation and a molecular surface area, calculated from the density of the bulk liquids.

Although the results described above are obtained with only few experimental data, they do indicate a special, favourable position for nitrogen as an adsorbate.

G On the Use of Carbon Dioxide and other Gases for the Study of the Texture of Carbons

In Section C the inadequacy of the BET equation and the t-method for the study of submicropores was pointed out. Two questions then arise:

(a) how to get more information about these pores, and
(b) are there important quantities of narrow micropores that cannot be penetrated by nitrogen and, hence, are hidden from observation in the usual way of experimentation.

The latter problem has manifested itself very clearly in the case of coal, where the adsorption of nitrogen at low temperature gave low values for the specific surface area, whereas determinations of the heat of wetting with methanol clearly required large specific surface areas. All aspects of this problem have been reviewed by Marsh (1965), who came to the conclusion that the specific surface area of coals is large, even in the absence of any swelling caused by the adsorbate. Moreover, he strongly suggested the use of carbon dioxide as an adsorbate.

Studies by Marsh and Wynne-Jones (1964) in which carbon dioxide was used at 195° and 273°K, have shown the usefulness of this suggestion. Large discrepancies between the CO_2 results and those obtained with nitrogen at 77°K were found, the results with CO_2 always indicating larger specific surface areas.

The principal cause of the advantage of carbon dioxide is the higher temperature at which the measurements are conducted. The rate of diffusion of the adsorbate into the very narrow pores is thereby considerably increased (see Nandi and Walker, 1964). Geometrically speaking, these pores are as accessible to nitrogen as to carbon dioxide.

Continuing this reasoning, the temperature of measurement might be increased to room temperature and some gases other than carbon dioxide used. For example, Kini (1963, 1964) has measured the adsorption of xenon at 0°C on several coals and carbons. In order to reach sufficiently high values of the relative pressure for application of the BET equation, working pressures above one atmosphere had to be used.

Several gases were examined by Walker and Kini (1964) using again a pressurized apparatus and the BET equation for the interpretation. The authors concluded that the use of CO_2 at 298°K was the preferred method.

The use of CO_2 (and other gases) poses two problems:

1. What is the value for p_0 to be used?
2. What is the value for the molecular area?

As to the first problem, p_0 values at the temperatures of interest are generally accurately known. There is, however, doubt as to whether for the adsorbed phase these are the values that should be used. Sometimes, there is reason to suppose that the adsorbate, that should, e.g. be solid at the temperature considered, is more liquid-like in the adsorbed phase. Hence, the use of an extrapolated vapour pressure for the liquid-vapour equilibrium might be more appropriate than the use of the true equilibrium vapour pressure for the solid-vapour equilibrium. For example, the use of a value of p_0 has been recommended, which is 1·84 times the true p_0 at 195°K for carbon dioxide (Lamond and Marsh, 1964b).

For a further discussion of CO_2, see Anderson et al. (1965), Deitz (1967), and Clough and Harris (1968).

The second problem is more or less independent from the first. Several methods for arriving at a molecular diameter exist. All of these are based either on the use of constants measured for the gaseous phase (e.g. viscosity) or on constants for the liquid phase, e.g. the density (coupled with an assumption about the packing of the molecules in the liquid). Therefore, if the adsorbate cannot be considered as a liquid of properties sufficiently similar to those of the pure liquid, the use of the molecular diameter, obtained in the above way, is in serious doubt. An example is krypton, for which various diameters have been used.

The subject of the diameters has been reviewed by McClellan and Harnsberger (1967), who have recommended certain values. However, in principle it should be checked in every case whether these values are indeed the appropriate ones, or whether the particular case studied is an exception.

It is therefore recommended that authors using other gases than nitrogen (and even in this case perhaps) state clearly what constants have been used to convert their measured data to specific surface areas.

Reference has already been made to studies in which the superiority of carbon dioxide over nitrogen became apparent. This point will be taken up later. The use of gases other than nitrogen, and of temperatures in the neighbourhood of room temperature, introduces another problem, that of the validity of the BET equation for the interpretation of the results. Generally, the interval of relative pressures for which the BET equation has been used is 0·05–0·3.

If the use of pressurized measuring apparatus is avoided, in a number of cases the interval of relative pressures that is available for measurement is shifted to much lower values of the relative pressure. Table V gives some examples.

In this table (p/p_0) max. indicates the upper limit of the accessible interval of relative pressure.

TABLE V. Accessible values of relative pressures

Gas	temp. °C	p_0 atm.	(p/p_0) max.	cr. temp. °C
CO_2	−78	1·86	0·60	31
	0	34·4	0·029	
	22	56·6	0·017	
Kr	−78	38·8	0·026	−64
Xe	−78	3·9	0·25	17
	0	41·2	0·025	

It has been suggested (Lamond and Marsh, 1964a) that the equation of Dubinin (e.g. Dubinin, 1967) might fruitfully be used in the case of CO_2 and it seems natural to extend this idea to other gases under similar conditions.

In fact, there are two Dubinin equations, the first reading:

$$K(\text{RT} \log p_0/p)^2 = \log V_0/V \qquad (\text{D1})$$

and the second:

$$K(\text{RT} \log p_0/p) = \log V_0/V \qquad (\text{D2})$$

The first is stated to hold especially for microporous materials, such as active carbons, the second should be used when micropores are absent. A number of constants of adsorbate and adsorbent has been taken together in the constant K. V_0 is the total volume of the pores, V the volume of the gas adsorbed at relative pressure p/p_0.

Kaganer (1957) has interpreted V_0 as being the volume of the adsorbate present in a unimolecular layer; accepting this point of view, a specific surface area can be calculated from V_0 with the aid of a molecular cross-section area, in itself a doubtful quantity, as already mentioned.

Both interpretations, applied to measurements with CO_2, krypton and xenon, can be compared with the results of the application of the BET equation to measurements with nitrogen at 77°K. V_0, the volume of the micropores following from Eq. (D1), can be compared with the value for the micropores, read off from the t-curve. The specific surface area, obtained according to Kaganer's procedure can be compared with the surface area determined with nitrogen.

For such a comparison carbons should be chosen that do not show the large difference between results with nitrogen (at 77°K) and with CO_2 at higher temperatures.

Van der Plas and Zondervan (unpublished) have measured some of the carbon blacks, investigated earlier with nitrogen (de Boer *et al.* 1965b), with carbon dioxide, krypton and xenon.

It was found that, contrary to the expectation, the equilibrium pressure was only slowly approached when using CO_2 and the original carbon blacks after degassing at 120°C. (Practically all of the oxygen chemisorbed on the carbon surface is then retained.) This slow approach

TABLE VI. Standard data

Gas	temp. °C	p_0	ρ_l	σ_l	σ_l
CO_2	−78	1·86	1·28	16·3	21·8
	0	34·4	0·93	20·1	
	22	56·5	0·75	23·1	
Kr	−78	38·8	1·64	21·0	18·4
Xe	−78	3·9	2·88	19·5	30
	0	41·2	1·99	25	30

towards equilibrium was never found with nitrogen (at −196°C!) or the noble gases. It was supposed that there is a special interaction between CO_2 and the chemisorbed oxygen, giving rise to a slower movement of the adsorbed molecules in the pores. Indeed, after degassing at 800°C in a quartz vessel, the carbons Carbolac 1 and Mogul A showed rapid equilibration; in the case of Spheron 6 it remained slow. Perhaps there are pores in this carbon black which are penetrated with difficulty even by CO_2 at −78°C. The temperature of 800°C was chosen in order to drive off most of the oxygen, while reducing the possibility of irreversible changes in the texture that might occur at higher temperatures.

For the evaluation of the isotherms obtained, use has been made of the values for the adsorbates in the liquid condition, extrapolated values have been used for the vapour pressure and density of the liquid where necessary.

Some standard σ values have also been taken from the table of McClellan and Harnsberger (1967).

In the table above the standard data used have been brought

together. The values for p_0 are in atmospheres, the liquid density ρ_l in g/cm^3, the σ values in $Å^2$, σ_l referring to the molecular surface area calculated from the density of the liquid; σ_t has been taken from the table mentioned.

It has already been related that the BET equation might be used for the measurements at $-78°C$ with carbon dioxide and xenon. Table VII allows a comparison with the data obtained with nitrogen, represented with the value of S_t, which can be found in Sections B and C, above. Large deviations are noted, especially between CO_2 and N_2.

TABLE VII. Values, obtained with BET equation, for the specific surface areas (m^2/g)

Carbon gas	Carbolac 1	Spheron 6	Mogul A
CO_2 $(-78°C)$	674	131	241
Xe $(-78°C)$	742	102	229
N_2 $(-196°C)$	972	106	324

All measurements have been used to compare the Dubinin equations (D1) and (D2) by plotting the values of log V versus $RT(\log p_0/p)^2$ respectively $RT(\log p_0/p)$.

In all cases it was found that the plots according to Eq. (D2) fitted a straight line better than the curves obtained for the first equation. However, the numerical values for the specific surface area, derived from Eq. (D2) seem to be much too large; this is especially clear in the case of Carbolac 1. Therefore, the results obtained with Eq. (D2) will not be considered further.

The value of V_0, as obtained by extrapolation, should represent the volume of the micropores, according to one interpretation of the equation. A comparison of the pore volume will therefore be made. However, in order to do so, a value of the density of the adsorbed phase is necessary. The values for the liquid adsorbates have been used to obtain the V_0-values of Table VIII, introducing another element of uncertainty. The micropore volume for N_2 is that established with the aid of the t-curve and the density of liquid nitrogen. (See Tables I and II. In the case of Mogul A the volume of the submicropores has been taken into account.) The unit used in Table VIII is cm^3/g.

In view of the inaccuracies resulting from the extrapolation and the use of log-log plots the agreement does not seem unsatisfactory.

TABLE VIII. Values for the volume of the micropores obtained with the equation
of Dubinin

Gas temp.	CO_2 -78	CO_2 0	CO_2 22	Kr -78	Xe -78	Xe 0	N_2 -196
Carbolac 1	0·37	0·35	0·39	0·39	0·25	0·52	0·36
Spheron 6	0·061	0·065	0·088	0·055	0·079	0·057	0·04
Mogul A	0·11	0·13	0·16	0·13	0·13	0·14	0·15

Now the specific surface areas will be compared. Table IX gives the specific surface areas determined with carbon dioxide at three temperatures, $S(D)$ being obtained with the aid of Dubinin's first equation, $S(B)$ according to the BET equation, $S(N)$ the BET result for adsorption of nitrogen. The unit is m^2/g.

TABLE IX. Specific surface areas determined with carbon dioxide

Carbon	temp. °C	$S(D)$	$S(B)$	$S(N)$
Carbolac 1	-78	1083	674	972
	0	884		
	22	930		
Spheron 6	-78	171	131	106
	0	165		
	22	211		
Mogul A	-78	325	241	324
	0	333		
	22	377		
C(800)*	-78	1091	730	
S(800)	-78	246	188	
M(800)	-78	340	230	

* Carbons marked 800 have been heated *in vacuo* at 800°C.

In Table X one finds the values calculated with Dubinin's first equation from the isotherms of krypton and xenon. The BET values that could be calculated have already been given in Table VII. Two groups of results are given, e.g. one making use of σ_l and one making use of σ_t (see Table VI).

It is seen that the values calculated by means of σ_t seem to be on the large side. They will not be considered further.

As Table VIII has shown, the differences in the micropore volumes are 10–20%. This error contains the experimental error, the error introduced by the extrapolation in the log V_a–$\log^2(p_0/p)$ plots and errors due to the possibly unjustified use of the density of the bulk liquids.

TABLE X. Values obtained from krypton and xenon isotherms with the first equation of Dubinin

	σ_l			σ_t		
Gas temp.	Kr −78	Xe −78	Xe 0	Kr −78	Xe −78	Xe 0
Carbolac 1	955	652	1178	838	1003	1414
Spheron 6	135	203	129	119	312	155
Mogul A	324	335	327	284	516	393

The differences between the values for the specific surface areas of Tables IX and X are somewhat larger, more around 20%. In the case of Spheron 6 it might be that the difference between the BET-nitrogen value and the other results is real.

The fact that the discrepancies are not larger might indicate that both the interpretation of V_0 as a micropore volume and as the volume of a unimolecular layer are equally justified on the basis of the present results. Strictly speaking, this means that the pores are two molecular diameters wide for all of the adsorbates.

There seem to be no systematic differences that could indicate the use of wrong values for the density of the adsorbed layer or the molecular surface area. The use of the standard data of Table VI is therefore supported by the present work.

H Application: a Study of the Activation of Coal

In order to show an application of the contents of the preceding section a study of the activation of coal (Donnet et al., 1968b) will be summarized here.

A French coal (Fosse Ledoux, Valenciennes) has been oxidized by air at low temperature (225–325°C), the oxidation products and the original coal carbonized at 650°C and the resulting cokes progressively activated with water vapour at 900°C.

In view of the preceding section (II G) it might have been guessed that the surface area of the original coal determined with nitrogen is small, while that determined with carbon dioxide should be much larger. This is indeed found to be the case for both the original coal and the three oxidation products. Increasing the temperature of oxidation (the time being kept constant) resulted in higher oxygen content (2·4–9·1%), smaller nitrogen surface areas and constant carbon dioxide surface area (200 m^2/g, by both BET and Dubinin equations). This is explained by the disappearance of superficial irregularities, the surface becomes smoother (but not more homogeneous in the sense of adsorption theories).

Heating at 625°C in a nitrogen atmosphere gives cokes. The remarkable fact is that the nitrogen surface area diminishes somewhat, while the CO_2 surface area increases and the pore volume, determined with the same adsorbate, increases by about 50%.

The differences in oxygen content of the products obtained have decreased, being 2–3% now. It is supposed, and confirmed by electron-microscopy, that crater-like, superficial pores are formed, of the transition type. The craters are larger for higher initial oxygen contents. Also, the diameters of the small pores, that are only found with CO_2, increase somewhat.

The subsequent activations of the cokes with steam at 900°C have removed 50, 60 and 70% of the original material. All of the surface of the resulting samples has become accessible to nitrogen, since the N_2 and CO_2 values agree reasonably. The specific surface areas have been increased by a factor of four to five, the micropore volume about three times. The oxygen content, on the contrary, has decreased to about one per cent.; the surface coverage with oxygen has, therefore, been appreciably decreased.

With increased burn-off, the specific surface area increases, though not rapidly.

The influence of the original oxidation treatment at low temperature is practically lost as far as the micropores are concerned. The transition pores, however, show a dependence on both the initial oxygen content and the percentage of burn-off.

The original publication should be consulted for the numerical data, the results of small-angle scattering and the noteworthy technique used for preparing samples for electron-microscopy.

It is seen from this example how the methods described in the preceding sections can be used to obtain significant results, even though the basis of the methods might not be as firm as might be desired. Especially for work where comparative values rather than absolute ones are desired, the methods might be used with confidence.

I   The Density of Carbons and the Adsorption of Helium

The density of carbons seems mainly to be determined by their degree of graphitization. When carbons are prepared at relatively low temperatures (and this includes temperatures up to 800° or even 1000°C), small graphite layers are formed, which are not yet stacked upon each other in the sequence peculiar to the graphite structure. With increasing degree of graphitization this disorder disappears, while the crystallites grow and point defects are healed out. Finally, the ideal graphite structure is closely approximated.

Large differences in the rate of this crystallization process are found, depending on the type of carbon used. The influence of the raw material used for the production of the carbon is very marked. The technical importance of these phenomena needs no comment. A large number of studies has been devoted to these matters (see, e.g. Kipling et al., 1964; Kipling and Shooter, 1966).

The process of graphitization is best followed by X-ray methods, but the density is a very useful indication; especially the density determined by immersion in gaseous helium has been used as such (Kipling, et al., 1964; Kipling and Shooter, 1966).

However, the measurement of the density with the aid of helium is not without problems, especially when microporous materials such as carbons are investigated.

Steggerda (1955) and de Boer and Steggerda (1958) have pointed out that two corrections have to be made to the experimentally determined specific volumes, both corrections being proportional to the specific surface area.

The first correction is due to the fact that a part of the free volume or "dead space" (that is the volume of the measuring vessel minus that of the solid) is not accessible to the centres of the helium atoms, viz. the volume directly adjacent to the surface of the solid and having a thickness equal to the radius of the helium atom. If this radius is r and the specific surface area S, the volume will be Sr. The specific volume found by measurement should be corrected by subtraction of this amount, since the solid appeared to be larger than it is.

The second correction is the adsorption correction. This correction will balance the first correction, because it means that there are fewer molecules in the gas space than introduced into the measuring vessel.

The first correction can never be made very accurately, because neither the radius of the helium atom, nor the specific surface area are known with the desired precision. The error in the specific volume, due to this cause, may amount to several per cent.

The use of the adsorption correction requires either the measurement of at least a part of the adsorption isotherm or the availability of a formula that describes the adsorption theoretically. In this formula, inevitably, enters the adsorption energy. A rough guess of this energy might be made but, since its value appears in the exponent of an exponential function, a large uncertainty results.

Experimentally, it was observed that the helium densities of coals, determined at several temperatures, were different to an extent that could not be attributed to thermal expansion (Maggs et al., 1960).

Further work has shown that two classes of carbons can be distinguished with respect to their behaviour towards helium (Maggs et al., 1960; Kini and Stacy, 1963; Weber and Bastick, 1968). Kini and Stacy, referring to calculations by de Boer and Kruyer (1958) have suggested that the electric conductivity of the carbon might be the decisive factor, carbons with a high conductivity having the highest energy of adsorption. The influence of the texture, notably the presence of micropores, is a further complicating factor since in the pores the energy of adsorption is higher than on a flat outer surface (de Boer and Custers, 1934). So, even if one could use two values of the energy of adsorption for the two types of carbon, the presence of micropores would obviate this possibility. Further insight in the adsorption of helium clearly is desirable.

The adsorption of helium cannot be denied in view of the above. On the other hand, the adsorption is so small that it cannot be measured accurately in the usual way. Donnet et al. (1967) have shown how information about the isotherm can be obtained and the influence of the texture of the carbon on the adsorption investigated.

The micro-BET apparatus (Chapter 1) is used. A certain number (n) of moles of helium is introduced into the sample bulb and the pressure measured. By means of slight variations in the external pressure the height of the mercury column of the differential manometer is varied, this is effectively a change in the volume of the helium. The resulting variation of pressure is also measured. These variations can be measured accurately by means of a kathetometer. The heights of the mercury column can be recalculated to volume by means of the known diameter (S) of the capillary of the differential manometer.

If one plots n RT/p versus h—the difference between mercury level and indicated reference level—one obtains a straight line in the case the helium behaves as an ideal gas.

From a sufficient number of experimental points, V_0 and S can be calculated. If one plots n RT/p versus V_0–Sh, one obtains a straight line also, the slope K_c of which equals 1 in this case.

If a certain mass of adsorbent is placed in the sample bulb, the volume V_0 is effectively diminished by the volume of the adsorbent, which is known only approximately. The volume now available to the gas molecules for $h = 0$ is indicated by V_d. Again volume and pressure are changed by changing the height of mercury, h. In the present case, however, the adsorption on the sample will cause the measured change in pressure to differ from that expected for the case of no adsorption.

Plotting $n \, \mathrm{RT}/p$ versus V_d-Sh, a slope K_c is found that differs from unity and whose value strongly depends on p. The functions $K_c(p)$, determined for carbons of known texture, show clearly the effects of the presence of pores etc. on the adsorption of helium (Donnet et al., 1967).

More information can be obtained from the functions $K_c(p)$, as shown by Lespinasse (1968). He notices that the measurements performed define the slope of the isotherm of compressibility $(\delta p/\delta V)_T$ for helium, if no sample is present and generalized this to include the case of presence of an adsorbent. Accordingly, a quantity $K(p)$ is defined, being:

$$K(p) = \frac{\delta}{\delta V}(n \, \mathrm{RT}/p)$$

at constant temperature.

Of the total number n_t of moles of helium introduced into the volume V_d, the number n_a is adsorbed, while the number n_g remains in the gas space, exerting a pressure p, for which holds: $p(V_d-Sh) = n_g \, \mathrm{RT}$. The procedure of measurements, in which n_t remains constant and V (and hence p) are varied, amounts to a variation of:

$$n_t = n_a+p(V_d-Sh)/\mathrm{RT} \text{ with } V, \text{ leading to:}$$

$$\left(\frac{\delta p}{\delta V}\right) = -p \Big/ \left[\mathrm{RT}\left(\frac{dn_a}{dp}\right)+ V \right], \text{ giving,}$$

for the slope $K(p)$, calculated at the point $V = V_d(h = 0)$:

$$K(p) = (1+An_a(p))\left(1+A\frac{dn_a}{dp}\right) \tag{1}$$

where $A = \mathrm{RT}/V_d$. Moreover, one has: $K_c = KS$, relating the measured K_c with the K used in the theory.

Since the function K_c and, hence, $K(p)$ is known from experiments, relation 1 is a differential equation for the adsorption isotherm $n_a(p)$. There are now two ways to proceed:

(a) The several well-known types of isotherms can be differentiated, giving the function $K(p)$ corresponding to each type. A comparison with the measured $K(p)$ shows what type of isotherm describes the measured adsorption of helium. For examples see Lespinasse (1968).

(b) Integration of the equation, making use of the experimental $K(p)$. The numerical integration is not difficult to carry out by computer, but one particular value of n_a should be known. At present, unfortunately, this value is not available. Therefore, a more or less arbitrary value has to be used. This procedure is discussed at length by Lespinasse et al. (1968). The arbitrariness is limited by the fact that $n_a(p)$ is a monotonically increasing function.

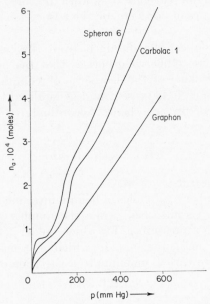

Fig. 7 Adsorption isotherms of helium on three carbons, calculated with arbitrary integration constants.

In Fig. 7 we give as examples of the curves so obtained, the "isotherms" for Graphon, Carbolac 1 and Spheron 6. The curves show clearly the differences in the form of the curves for the different carbons, especially at the lower values of p. It is also observed that the curves show no sign of a saturation of the adsorption, but become straight lines at the higher pressures.

Since the isotherms shown in the figure are not the true isotherms, a true value of the number of adsorbed molecules cannot be calculated. A correction of the helium density as measured is, therefore, not possible. An adsorption energy cannot as yet be derived either. It is hoped that future investigation may solve these problems.

The curves give rise to a number of speculations. Consider first the "isotherm" of Graphon, a carbon with a homogeneous surface. This curve hardly shows the wavy aspect of the other two curves. It might be taken as representing the adsorption of helium on a carbon which is practically pore-free. According to experiment, then, the adsorption is proportional to the pressure on this surface. This region of proportionality is also found with the other carbons but at a higher pressure.

It would seem that the "waves" or "bends" in the isotherms of the porous carbons are due to the pore structure, a conclusion that is in agreement with the results for other carbons (not shown here). The impression is formed that these features of the curves are due to a superposition of one or more Langmuir-type isotherms on the straight-line isotherm due to the carbon surface as a whole.

If true, this means that the adsorption in the pores etc. is limited, while that on the typical carbon surface is not. Quite remarkable in this respect is the fact that pores of several tens of Angströms width still give rise to these phenomena. The de Boer-Custers effect referred to earlier in this section can hardly play an important role here. Should we believe, then, in a kind of "fine structure" of the pores consisting of irregularities, such as steps, in the pore wall? If this were the case, helium would be an adsorbent of choice to investigate these fine details of the texture.

Or are the pores wedge-shaped, so that irrespective of the width indicated by the t-curve, there always is a region of small width?

Finally, it should be remarked that the phenomena described in this section are by no means limited to carbons. An alumina, Bayerite, gave results that are very similar to those obtained with carbon.

III   The Surface Chemistry of Carbon

A   The Chemisorption of Oxygen

The ability to burn is one of the most important properties of carbon and carbonaceous materials. This reaction between carbon and oxygen proceeds rapidly only at high temperatures. It might be guessed that chemisorption of oxygen occurs at lower temperatures and at an early date this had already been found to be the case (Smith, 1863).

In the following sections some of the problems raised by the presence of this chemisorbed oxygen on the surface of the carbon will be related.

If the coverage of the carbon surface with oxygen is so extensive that it might be said that an important fraction of the surface is covered with oxygen, it might be surmised that this part of the surface behaves more like an oxygen or, rather, oxide surface than a carbon surface.

This changes drastically the interaction of the carbon with a number of substances, the most important of which is probably water. While a "normal" carbon surface is hydrophobic, repels water, as has been made evident in Section II E, the carbon that is extensively covered with oxygen assumes a hydrophilic behaviour. Such carbons adsorb water already at low relative pressures and can be easily dispersed in water without the use of surface active agents.

A very clear example of this influence has been presented by Gasser and Kipling (1960). The relative adsorption of benzene and methanol from mixtures, covering the whole range of concentration ratios, was studied. Spheron 6, a carbon black covered with an appreciable quantity of oxygen, was compared with a sample of the same carbon from which the oxygen had been removed by a treatment at high temperature. The oxygen containing sample showed a preferential adsorption of methanol, while the other sample showed a preferential adsorption of benzene. Similar results have been obtained by Puri et al. (1963).

The influence of the surface complex on the rate of the reaction between carbon and oxygen at low temperatures has been extensively studied. (Recent examples: Laine et al., 1963a,b; Vastola et al., 1964; Hart, 1967; see also Bibliography.) The importance of the oxygen for the lubricating properties of carbon is briefly discussed in a review by Smith (1959).

The presence of oxygen on a carbon black used for the reinforcement of rubber retards the vulcanization and, hence, is undesirable.

B   Oxygen Content and Surface Coverage

The chemisorbed oxygen can be determined by the normal methods of organic elemental analysis, e.g. the direct method of Unterzaucher. Care should be taken to remove adsorbed CO_2 and H_2O. Another method that has frequently been used is the complete removal of oxygen by a high-temperature treatment, followed by analysis of the gases produced: H_2O, CO_2, CO (and H_2 at very high temperatures).

The oxygen content and the specific surface area being known, the surface coverage of the carbon with oxygen could be calculated, if the surface area to be attributed to an oxygen atom were known.

Two assumptions can be made:

(a) the van der Waals radius of the oxygen atom is given as $1\cdot4$ Å (Pauling, 1960), hence the surface area is $7\cdot8$ Å^2;

(b) one oxygen atom is bonded to one carbon atom. One C-atom in the hexagonal planes occupies $2\cdot6$ Å^2, but in the prism surfaces one C-atom occupies $4\cdot95$ Å^2. It seems more probable that the oxygen atom is bound to the prism faces, accordingly $5\cdot0$ Å^2 might be used.

The possibility that one C-atom bears two O-atoms has not been taken into consideration. Fortunately, as will be shown later, the amount of COOH groups that might form an example of this type is relatively low.

In Table XI some data have been collected to illustrate the values for the surface coverage arrived at when using 7·8 Å^2 for the surface area of the O-atom and the BET nitrogen values for the specific surface area of the carbon.

TABLE XI. Oxygen content and surface coverage

Carbon	O m.at./g	S m^2/g	cov. %
Carbolac 1	5·7	911	30
Mogul A	4·4	285	73
Spheron 6	1·9	105	85
Elf 5	2·0	124	75
ZK 1, akt., verk.	1·04	870	7*
ZK 1, verk., ox.	3·4	1050	16
ZK 1, akt.	6·7	1170	27
verk ox.			
14	0·66	1025	3†
15	0·60	1180	3
16	0·80	1370	2

* Three values, taken from Boehm and Diehl (1962).
† Three values, taken from Donnet et al. (1968b).

It is seen that the coverage never reaches 100%. Anderson and Emmett (1952), however, describe a carbon called Lampblack T which contains more oxygen than corresponds to a unimolecular layer. This intriguing case will not be discussed here.

It is also seen that highly-oxidized carbons with a large specific surface show a low coverage with oxygen, a fact that has also been noted by Anderson and Emmett (1952). This can be explained by the assumption that the oxidation process removes the smallest crystallites first, exposing more and more the larger graphite crystallites with extended basal planes, which are less easily oxidized.

C The Adsorption of Electrolytes

The van der Waals adsorption on carbons has already been mentioned briefly in Section I B. The adsorption of electrolytes seems to be more complicated and has puzzled many of the older workers. In part this was due to working with impure (that is "ash"-containing) carbons, but the difficulties are real enough, even for materials which are pure in this respect.

De Kadt (1929) and Kruyt and de Kadt (1931) showed that two types of carbon can be prepared from the same original carbon by chemisorption of oxygen at different temperatures. Later on, Steenberg (1944) distinguished these types by calling them H-carbon and L-carbon. The L-carbon is prepared by heating the carbon in air at temperatures of about 400°C. This carbon neutralizes alkali and makes a KCl-solution acidic. Hence it might be classified as acidic and it might be said "to adsorb alkali" from a potassium chloride solution. The oxygen content of this carbon is relatively high.

A carbon heated at high temperature in an oxidizing atmosphere or heated in an inert atmosphere and brought into contact, subsequently, with air or oxygen at room temperature, contains a relatively small amount of oxygen. It "adsorbs acid" and makes a KCl solution alkaline. Steenberg (1944) has shown that the hydrogen ion of the acid is fixed on the carbon, while the anion forms the mobile part of the double layer.

The reader is reminded further of the so called "electro-chemical" theory of the adsorption; see Verwey and de Boer (1936); Kuchinsky et al. (1940); Kellermann and Lange (1940).

The distinction between these types and the recognition that many commercial products are really intermediate types has solved most of the puzzles. There has remained one problem: a fuller description of the chemisorbed oxygen, that explains the properties found in terms of the properties of the common oxygen compounds.

The high oxygen content of the L-carbons makes these products more amenable to chemical analysis than the H-carbons. The following discussion will therefore be concerned exclusively with the former type.

D   Analytical Problems of the L-carbons

A problem has been posed of accounting for all oxygen, found by elemental analysis, in terms of the well-known functional groups. No a priori knowledge is available as to which types are present or absent. So the question really amounts to the separate determination of all oxygen groups in the presence of all others.

Chemists in the fields of coal and humic acids have been working along these lines longer than those interested in active carbons and carbon blacks. Kruyt and de Kadt (1931) postulated the occurrence of carboxyl groups. It was only in 1947, however, that Villars studied the reaction of the carbon surface with the Grignard reagent; earlier work had been mostly limited to a study of the adsorption of alkali, acids, etc.

The analytical problem referred to above was solved for coal by Blom (1960), while Rivin (1962) did the same for carbon blacks, using other methods.

Other workers, notably Studebaker, Garten and Weiss, Boehm, Donnet and their collaborators, have tried out a large number of methods without accounting completely for all of the oxygen present; this arose in part because they did not pose the problem in this way.

In the following a very brief review of the methods applied will be given; there exist several reviews where more details can be found, together with a fuller coverage of the literature (Donnet, 1965; Boehm, 1966; van der Plas, 1968. The somewhat older reviews of Kipling (1956), Smith (1959) and Steenberg (1944) should not be forgotten.

The methods can be divided roughly into exchange methods and derivative methods. The exchange methods are used mainly to study mobile hydrogen. The exchange of an hydrogen ion against an alkali ion, for example, can be used to indicate the number of acid groups. In most cases this reaction is carried out as an "adsorption experiment": a large excess of alkali is added to the carbon and, after equilibration and separation of carbon and solution, the concentration of the alkali is determined and the amount exchanged calculated from the difference with the initial concentration.

A special case of the exchange H^+—Na^+ is the study of "titration curves" (Puri et. al., 1957; de Bruin and van der Plas, 1964).

In the derivative processes a derivative of the functional group is prepared by reaction with the reagent, usually in considerable excess. After isolation of the carbon the introduced groups are determined. The following methods are given as examples:

(a) methylation procedures for the determination of carboxyl and phenolic groups;

(b) the formation of oximes for determination of carbonyl;

(c) the reaction with di-nitrofluorobenzene or p-nitrobenzoyl chloride to determine phenolic groups (Boehm et al., 1964).

If no thorough study has been made of the texture of the carbon, it will always be doubtful whether the reagents used are able to reach all of the groups with which they are supposed to react. This applies especially to the large reagents mentioned above, although they were used successfully by Boehm.

The possible presence of small pores in and between the particles gives rise to long reaction times and long periods of washing. Another cause of concern is the apparent influence of details that superficially would seem of little importance.

It should be borne further in mind that no way of ascertaining the purity of a derivative or the completeness of a reaction is available. The reproducibility of a certain result is merely an indication of a careful reproduction of a given recipe. Therefore a successful analysis can be claimed only if different methods for the determination of one type of group give the same results. The comparison of the sum of the oxygen found by functional group analysis with the total of oxygen found by elemental analysis serves as a welcome check on all of the methods used.

E Some Results of Analytical Work

In this section some of the more recent results of functional group analysis of carbon blacks will be discussed briefly. A discussion of the lactone theory of Garten and Weiss (1957) is omitted for lack of space. It has been adequately reviewed from different points of view (Garten and Weiss, 1957; van der Plas, 1968). First, attention is drawn to the remarkable numerical relations found by Boehm and Diehl (1962).

In the case of fully-oxidized carbons four groups of different acidity can be distinguished by sodium-hydrogen exchange with solutions of different basicity: $NaHCO_3$, Na_2CO_3, $NaOH$ and $NaOEt$, all used at a concentration of 0.05 n (Boehm and Diehl, 1962). The results obtained in this way show the ratio $1:2:3:4$ or, in other words, if a group of different acidity is responsible every time for the increased result on using a solution with increased basicity, equal numbers of these groups are present. Similar results have been obtained by Donnet et al. (1968a).

These numerical relations were verified by Boehm (1968) by the use of other methods, e.g. methylation by diazomethane followed by partial hydrolysis, and reaction with thionylchloride, also followed by partial hydrolysis. Where possible, the H^+—Na^+ exchange was also carried out with the derivatives. The following interpretation has been given: carboxylic acids are neutralized by $NaHCO_3$, the carboxylic acid from a lactone by Na_2CO_3, phenolic groups by $NaOH$. Finally, it is assumed that sodium methylate reacts with a carbonyl group.

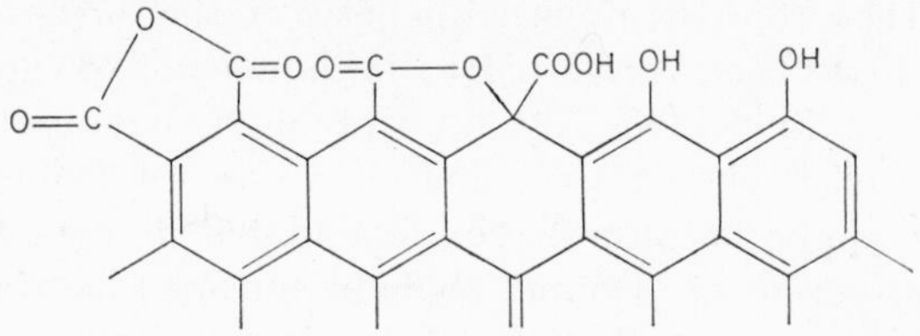

FIG. 8

The structure in Fig. 8 has been proposed to account for the ensemble of results. It should be noticed that these groups do not suffice
to account for all of the oxygen on the carbon studied. The same holds
for the study by Donnet *et al.* (1968a). According to the present author
this is caused by a deficit in the number of quinone groups found.

In order to show to what extent all of the oxygen can be accounted
for, the analysis of one carbon black, Carbolac 1, will be discussed.

Rivin (1962) determined total mobile hydrogen with $LiAlH_4$. The
total of reducible groups were determined by reduction with $LiAlH_4$,
careful isolation and determination of the newly-formed mobile
hydrogen, again with $LiAlH_4$. CO_2 and CO set free on thermal treatment were assumed to be derived from groups containing respectively
two and one oxygen atom. $NaHCO_3$ served to determine carboxylic
acid groups. A combination of all figures results in a partition of the
oxygen among different groups; the total of oxygen found by summation is equal to the amount of oxygen found from the amounts of
H_2O, CO_2 and CO found on thermal treatment of the carbon or from
elemental analysis.

Donnet *et al.* (1968) followed essentially Boehm's method. Van der
Plas (1968) determined total oxygen by Unterzaucher's method, as did
Donnet. Carboxylic acid groups were determined with calcium acetate
and sodium bicarbonate. Total acidity was determined by several
methods, this point is taken up later on. Quinones were determined by
reduction with titanium trichloride according to Blom (1960).

TABLE XII. Comparison of results for Carbolac 1 (meq/g carbon)

	Rivin (1962)	van der Plas (1968)	Donnet (1968)
—COOH	0·45	0·60	0·58
—OH	2·00	1·8*	0·63
—C=O	2·81	3·0	0·56
lactone	0·02	—	0·44

* Total acidity, derived from both carboxylic acids and phenols.

In Table XIII a comparison is made between the three sets of results. These results have been converted to millimoles of oxygen atoms per gram of carbon: m.at. O/g, by multiplying COOH values by two, lactone values of Rivin by two, lactone values of Donnet by three. These factors apply because Rivin formulates in terms of lactones with 2 O-atoms per group; Donnet probably means f-lactones according to Garten and Weiss, contributing 3 O-atoms per group.

For van der Plas the COOH and OH values should be simply added since the COOH groups are included in the "OH-value" under this heading.

TABLE XIII. Oxygen balance for results in Table XII

	Rivin	van der Plas	Donnet
—COOH	0·90	0·60	1·16
—OH	2·00	1·8	0·63
—C=O	2·81	3·0	0·56
lactone	0·04	—	1·32
Total	5·75	5·4	3·67

The totals should be compared with the value 5·7 m.at. O/g found for total oxygen. If Rivin's value for carbonyl groups is added to the values obtained by Donnet, subtracting the 0·56 m.at. O/g, the total for Donnet becomes 5·92 m.at. O/g in agreement with the older values.

In a way, Table XIII is characteristic of the present "state of the art". The present authors' conclusion is that a rough picture of the number of groups can be given by three simple methods: the calcium acetate procedure for carboxyl groups, H^+—Na^+ exchange in 1 N KOH for total acidity and reduction by $TiCl_3$ for quinones. The results, interpreted as shown above for Carbolac 1, will suffice to account for about 90% of the oxygen present.

The use of other methods should be carefully investigated, taking the texture of the carbon into account.

The carbons discussed are relatively rich in surface oxygen, but the simple methods used so far already seem to be approaching the limits of their sensitivity. A further application of the methods to carbons less rich in oxygen would make necessary the development of new methods that might probably make use of radioactive tracers, such as reagents containing ^{14}C.

A first step in this direction has been taken (Papirer and Donnet,

1966) but it seems doubtful at present whether the necessary effort is worthwhile.

F On Graphite Oxide

In the preceding sections the results of the chemisorption of oxygen gas have been discussed. There are, of course, other means of oxidation of carbon, especially graphite.

A number of oxidizing agents, such as air, steam or carbon dioxide at high temperature, or nitric acid at room temperature, convert to carbon dioxide primarily the "amorphous" part of the carbon, or rather the smallest graphite crystallites present in the carbon particle. A study of the X-ray diffraction patterns as a function of the oxidation makes this clear.

The reaction with nitric acid has been studied by Lang et al. (1967) and used to elucidate the internal structure of carbon black particles (Donnet et al., 1963; Donnet and Bouland, 1964).

Surprisingly, there exists also an oxidizing agent that attacks preferentially the larger graphite crystallites. It is a solution of silver bichromate in sulfuric acid (Simon, 1923).

All of these reagents destroy the graphite crystallites by converting them to CO_2. There are also, however, reagents that leave the graphite layers more or less unattacked but insert themselves between the graphite layer planes.

A well-studied example is the formation of the graphite acid sulphate by the reaction of graphite with sulphuric acid and CrO_3, or by elec- trolytic oxidation of a graphite electrode with concentrated sulphuric acid as electrolyte.

If a still stronger oxidizing agent is present, e.g. chlorine dioxide, the carbon layers themselves might be attacked and, while the structure of the carbon layer remains intact, the hexagonal rings lose their aromatic character and oxygen containing groups are attached to the carbon atoms. A compound, graphite oxide, also called graphitic acid, can be prepared as the final product of a prolonged treatment of the kind described. Whether graphitic oxide in fact might be called a compound is in the first instance a matter of definition, but surely, a constant composition is being approached when the treatment described above is carried out repeatedly.

The physical and chemical properties of this remarkable substance cannot be described here at length. Some recent reviews are available: Rüdorff (1959), Croft (1960), Boehm et al. (1961) and Platzer (1965).

Due to the fact that the graphite layers, although modified by the introduction of oxygen, have remained intact, the layer structure of the graphite has been conserved. The insertion of other substances is made much easier; the graphite oxide shows swelling when exposed to polar liquids or the vapours thereof. The adsorption of water especially has been extensively investigated (see Bibliography; van Doorn, 1957; de Boer and van Doorn, 1958; Scholz, 1964).

If the lamellae of the graphite oxide become separated, membranes can be prepared by carefully drying a suspension of the lamellae. These membranes are impermeable to gases, but permeable to water (Clauss and Hofmann, 1956). The membranes can also be used in osmometry (Hellwege et al., 1961).

Graphite oxide, because of its many acidic groups, is a cation exchanger. Membrane electrodes prepared from this material show nearly the theoretically expected membrane potential (Boehm et al., 1961). Technical applications of the membranes have been envisaged (Patents by le Carbone-Lorraine).

The chemical properties of graphitic oxide are characterized by:

(a) constant composition
(b) easy thermal decomposition
(c) acidic character
(d) oxidizing character.

The description of these properties by a kind of "chemical formula" has been the subject of numerous studies that will not be reviewed in detail. Discrepancies between authors remain until this day, however, and the subject cannot be considered to be closed.

Elemental analysis of graphite oxide can be described equally well by either $C_7H_2O_4$ or $C_8H_2O_4$. Carboxylic and phenolic groups can be determined. The general opinion is that the carboxyl groups occur only at the edges of the layers and should not be included in the overall picture of the substance, however important for the physico-chemical properties these groups might be. The phenolic groups are considered to take part in a keto-enol equilibrium (van Doorn, 1957; de Boer and van Doorn, 1958).

The oxidizing properties are attributed to hydroperoxide groups by de Boer and van Doorn (1958). The main argument rests on the production of oxygen from the graphite oxide on heating. This product, however, could not be found by Scholz and Boehm (1964b).

One of the oxygen atoms has replaced a C-atom of the graphite layer, giving rise to a heterocyclic ring system, again according to de Boer and van Doorn, who start their deductions from the formula $C_7H_2O_4$. This point of view cannot be accepted on the basis of the formula $C_8H_2O_4$.

So there is still disagreement on details of the structure of graphite oxide, although authors do agree on many other points. On the other hand, there seems to be a common opinion about the existence of a layer structure, which is not aromatic and not flat, consisting of hexagons with irregular orientation with respect to each other. Microscopically, the hexagonal symmetry of the original graphite layers is lost, but on the average the deviations seem to cancel, since the electron diffraction pattern shows a hexagonal symmetry (Aragon de la Cruz and Cowley, 1962).

For more details, the general literature already given should be consulted, together with the publications by van Doorn (1957), de Boer and van Doorn (1958) and Boehm and collaborators (1965, 1966 and 1967).

IV General Conclusions

We have set ourselves two main tasks in this chapter:

(a) to study the application of the t-method to carbons and
(b) to study the surface chemistry of carbon.

We shall now briefly review the main conclusions regarding these two topics.

It has been shown that the p/p_0–t relation, derived from measurement of the adsorption of nitrogen on selected samples of oxides, can also be applied to carbons with or without an oxidized surface. The use of this t-curve leads to a reasonable description of the pore structure in terms of slit-shaped pores. This description is only possible for pores with a width larger than 7 Å. There is no independent method of control of the results, which, therefore, can be judged only on the basis of plausibility.

Indications have been found that in numerous carbons also pores are present which are accessible to nitrogen, but which are smaller than 7 Å. No information can be found regarding these pores other than their total volume (assuming a value for the density of the adsorbed layer).

Sometimes there are pores present into which nitrogen molecules cannot penetrate within reasonable time at the low temperatures of measurement applied. The use of higher temperatures in that case has as consequence the use of other gases than nitrogen, such as carbon dioxide or the noble gases.

For some combinations of temperature and gas the BET equation can be used. An analysis of some measurements with Dubinin's equation shows a reasonable agreement between the values for the total

18

volumes of the micropores found from the V_a–t plot (absorption of nitrogen at low temperature) and the values from Dubinin's equation applied to measurements with other gases at $-78°C$ and higher temperatures.

Also Kaganer's equation seems to lead to agreement, although by means of this equation it is the specific surface area which is calculated. This contradiction can be resolved by assuming that the pores admit only a layer of nitrogen which is two molecules thick. This seems implausible and moreover is in contradiction with the results obtained from V_a–t plots, showing much larger pores.

A procedure similar to that used for nitrogen to obtain V_a–t plots is not possible for the adsorbates benzene and carbon tetrachloride. A special, favourable position of nitrogen is emphasized by this result.

It would seem that the present methods have reached their limits of applicability. None of them is really able to cope with pores having dimensions of the order of the adsorbate molecules. On that scale of dimensions the concept "pore" as usually applied needs revision.

The occurrence of chemisorbed oxygen on the surface of carbon is not without influence on its adsorption properties. It might be presumed that the oxygen is bound in several ways, similar to the oxygen functional groups studied in organic chemistry. This is indeed found to be the case, since a number of chemical properties of these groups are also found when the oxygen containing carbon is used as a reactant. It is possible to describe the oxygen in terms of quinone, phenolic and carboxylic groups. These groups can be determined by means of relatively simple methods. About 90% of the oxygen present can be accounted for in this way.

The results of the study of the texture and of the surface chemistry show that a plausible description of these important features of carbon adsorbents can be given. A few applications show how the methods may be used in practical problems.

This chapter provides only a brief review of two aspects of the science of carbon. The interested reader will find in Section VI a list of books which deal at more length with more topics. The list is probably not complete.

V Acknowledgements

The author of this chapter is greatly indebted to Professor H. P. Boehm, Heidelberg, Professor J. B. Donnet, Mulhouse, and Dr. J. G. T. van Aken, Rijswijk, for supplying him with, as yet, unpublished material and helpful correspondence.

The Board of the National Defence Research Organization TNO kindly granted permission to publish the results of Dr. J. G. T. van Aken.

VI Bibliography

Bailleul, G., Bratzler, K., Herbert, W. and Vollner, W. (1962). "Aktive Kohle und ihre industrielle Verwendung", 4ᵉ Aufl. Ferdinand Enke Verlag, Stuttgart.
Bond, R. L. (1967). "Porous Carbon Solids". Academic Press, London and New York.
"Les Carbones". Le Groupe Français d'Etude des Carbones (1965). Masson, Paris.
Colloque International de CNRS sur la physico-chimie des noirs de carbone. (1963). Edition du CNRS, Mulhouse, France.
Kirk-Othmer (1964). Encylopedia of Chemical Technology, 2nd edn, Vol. 7, pp. 149–335. Interscience, New York, London, Sidney.
van Krevelen, D. W. (1962). "Coal". Elsevier, Amsterdam.
van Krevelen, D. W. and Schuyer, J. (1957). "Coal Science". Elsevier, Amsterdam.
Mantell, C. L. (1946). "Industrial Carbon", 2nd edn. Van Nostrand, New York.
"Proceedings of the First, Second, Third, Fourth and Fifth Conferences on Carbon" (1956–62). Pergamon Press, New York and London.
Seitz, V. R. (1943–53). "Bibliography of Solid Adsorbents", National Bureau of Standards, Circular 566. Washington, D.C.
Symposium on Carbon (1964). Tokyo.
Walker, P. L., Jr., ed. (1965–68). "Chemistry and Physics of Carbon", Vol. 1, 2, 3. Marcel Dekker, New York.

VII References

Abram, J. C. and Bennett, M. C. (1968). *J. Coll. Interface Sci.* **27**, 1.
Anderson, R. B. and Emmett, P. H. (1952). *J. phys. Chem.* **56**, 753.
Anderson, R. B., Bayer, J. and Hofer, L. J. E. (1965). *Fuel, Lond.* **44**, 443.
Aragon de la Cruz, F. and Cowley, J. M. (1963). *Acta crystallogr.* **16**, 531.
Avgul, N. N., Kiselev, A. V., Lygina, I. A. and Mikhailova, Ye. A. (1962). *Izv. Akad. Nauk. SSSR, Otdel. Khim. Nauk.* 769
Barrer, R. M. (1936a). *J. chem. Soc.* 1256.
Barrer, R. M. (1936b). *J. chem. Soc.* 1261.
Bennett, M. C. and Abram, J. C. (1967). *J. Coll. Interface Sci.* **23**, 513.
Blom, L. (1960). Thesis, University of Delft, The Netherlands.
Boehm, H. P. (1966). *Adv. Catalysis*, **16**, 179.
Boehm, H. P. and Diehl, E. (1962). *Z. Electrochem.* **66**, 642.
Boehm, H. P. and Scholz, W. (1965). *Z. anorg. Chem.* **335**, 74.
Boehm, H. P. and Scholz, W. (1966). *Justus Liebigs Annln Chem.* **691**, 1.
Boehm, H. P., Clauss, A. and Hofmann, U. (1961). *J. Chim. phys.* **58**, 14.
Boehm, H. P., Diehl, E., Heck, W. and Sappock, R. (1964). *Angew. Chem.* **76**, 742.
Boehm, H. P., Eckel, M. and Scholz, W. (1967). *Z. anorg. Chem.* **353**, 236.
de Boer, J. H. and Custers, J. F. H. (1934). *Z. phys. Chem.* **B25**, 225.
de Boer, J. H. and van Doorn, A. B. C. (1958a). *Proc. K. ned. Akad. Wet.* **B61**, 12.
de Boer, J. H. and van Doorn, A. B. C. (1958b). *Ibid.* 17.
de Boer, J. H. and van Doorn, A. B. C. (1958c). *Ibid.* 160.
de Boer, J. H. and van Doorn, A. B. C. (1958d). *Ibid.* 242.

de Boer, J. H. and Kruger, S. (1958). *Trans Faraday Soc.* **54**, 540.

de Boer, J. H., Linsen, B. G. and Osinga, Th. J. (1965a). *J. Catalysis*, **4**, 643.

de Boer, J. H., Linsen, B. G., van der Plas, Th. and Zondervan, G. J. (1965b). *J. Catalysis*, **4**, 649.

de Boer, J. H., Broekhoff, J. C. P., Linsen, B. G. and Meyer, A. L. (1967). *J. Catalysis*, **7**, 135.

de Bruin, W. J. and van der Plas, Th. (1964). *Revue gén. Caoutch.* **41**, 453.

Clough, P. S. and Harris, M. R. (1968). *Chemy Ind.* 343.

Cranch, G. E. (1962). *Proc. 5th Conf. Carb.* **1**, 589.

Croft, R. C. (1960). *Q. Rev. Chem. Soc.* **14**, 1.

de Kadt, G. S. (1929). Thesis, University of Utrecht, The Netherlands.

Deitz, V. R. (1967). *J. phys. Chem.* **71**, 835.

Donnet, J. B. (1965). *In* "Les Carbones" (le Groupe Français d'Etude des Carbones). Vol. 2, pp. 690 ff. Masson, Paris.

Donnet, J. B. and Bouland, J. C. (1964). *Revue gén. Caoutch.* **41**, 407.

Donnet, J. B., Bouland, J. C. and Jaeger, J. (1963). *C. r. hebd. Séanc. Acad. Sci., Paris*, **256**, 5340.

Donnet, J. B., Couderc, P. and Papirer, E. (1967). *J. Chim. phys.* **64**, 1699.

Donnet, J. B., Couderc, P. and Papirer, E. (1968a). *Bull soc. chim.* France, 929.

Donnet, J. B., Courderc, P., Kobel, L. and Papirer, E. (1968b). To be published in *Carbon, Manchr.*

Dubinin, M. M. (1955). *Q. Rev. Chem. Soc.* **9**, 101.

Dubinin, M. M. (1967). *J. Coll. Interface Sci.* **23**, 487.

Emmett, P. H. (1948). *Chem. Rev.* **43**, 69.

Gasser, C. G. and Kipling, J. J. (1960). *Proc. 4th Conf. Carb.* 55.

Garten, V. A. and Weiss, D. E. (1957). *Rev. pure appl. Chem.* **7**, 69.

Garten, V. A. and Weiss, D. E. (1959). *Proc. 3rd Conf. Carb.* 295.

Hart, P. J., Vastola, F. J. and Walker, P. L., Jr. (1967). *Carbon, Manchr.* **5**, 363.

Heckman, F. A. and Harling, D. F. (1966). *Rubb. Chem. Technol.* **39**, 1.

Hellwege, K. H., Knappe, W. and Müh, G. (1961). *Kolloidzeitschrift*, **174**, 146.

Isirikyan, A. A. and Kiselev, A. V. (1956). *J. phys. Chem.* **65**, 601.

Kaganer, M. G. (1957). *Dokl. Akad. Nauk. SSSR*, **116**, 251.

Kellermann, A. and Lange, E. (1940). *Kolloidzeitschrift*, **90**, 89.

Kini, K. A. (1963). *Fuel, Lond.* **42**, 103.

Kini, K. A. (1964). *Fuel, Lond.* **43**, 173.

Kini, K. A. and Stacy, W. O. (1963). *Carbon, Manchr*, **1**, 17.

Kipling, J. J. (1956). *Q. Rev. Chem. Soc.* **10**, 1.

Kipling, J. J. and Shooter, P. V. (1966). *J. Coll. Interface Sci.* **21**, 238.

Kipling, J. J., Sherwood, J. N., Shooter, P. V. and Thompson, N. R. (1964). *Carbon, Manchr.* **1**, 315.

Kruyt, H. R. and de Kadt, G. S. (1931). *Kolloidchem. Beih.* **32**, 249.

Kuchinsky, E., Burstein, R. and Frumkin, A. N. (1940). *Acta phys.–chim. URSS*, **12**, 795.

Laine, N. R., Vastola, F. J. and Walker, P. L., Jr. (1963a). *Proc. 5th Conf. Carb.* **2**, 211.

Laine, N. R., Vastola, F. J. and Walker, P. L., Jr. (1963b). *J. phys. Chem.* **67**, 2030.

Lamond, T. G. and Marsh, H. (1964). *Carbon, Manchr.* **1**, 281, 293.

Lang, F. M., de Noblet, M., Donnet, J. B., Lahaye, J. and Papirer, E. (1967). *Carbon, Manchr.* **5**, 47.

Lespinasse, B. (1968). *C. r. hebd. Séanc., Acad. Sci., Paris*, **C267**, 359.
Lespinasse, B., Otterbein, M., Brousse, M., Donnet, J. B., Couderc, P. and Papirer, E. (1968). *C. r. hebd. Séanc., Acad. Sci., Paris*. **C267**, 1441.
Maggs, F. A. P., Schwabe, P. H. and Williams, J. H. (1960). *Nature, Lond.* **186**, 956.
Marsh, H. (1965). *Fuel, Lond.* **44**, 253.
Marsh, H. and Wynne-Jones, W. F. K. (1964). *Carbon, Manchr.* **1**, 269.
McClellan, A. L. and Harnsberger, H. F. (1967). *J. Coll. Interface Sci.* **23**, 577.
Nandi, S. P. and Walker, P. L., Jr. (1964).
Papirer, E. and Donnet, J. B. (1966). *Bull. Soc. chim. Fr.* 2033.
Pauling, L. (1960). "The Nature of the Chemical Bond", p. 260. Cornell University Press, Ithaca, New York.
Platzer, N. (1965). *In* "Les Carbones" le Groupe Français d'Etude des Carbones. Vol. 12, p. 465. Masson, Paris.
Puri, B. R., Singh, G. and Sharma, L. R. (1957). *J. Indian chem. Soc.* **34**, 357.
Puri, B. R., Kummer, S. and Sandle, N. K. (1963). *Indian J. Chem.* **1**, 418.
Rivin, D. (1962). *Proc. 4th Rubb. Technol. Conf.* 262.
Rüdorff, W. (1959). *In* "Advances in Inorganic Chemistry and Radiochemistry" (H. J. Emeléus and A. G. Sharpe, eds.), Vol. 1, p. 226. Academic Press, New York and London.
Sappok, R. and Boehm, H. P. (1968). *Carbon, Manchr.* **6**, 283.
Scholz, W. (1964). Inaugural Dissertation, University of Heidelberg, Germany.
Scholz, W. and Boehm, H. P. (1964a). *Z. anorg. Chem.* **331**, 129.
Scholz, W. and Boehm, H. P. (1964b). *Naturwissenschaften*, **51**, 160.
Simon, J. (1923). *C. r. hebd. Séauc. Acad. Sci., Paris*, **177**, 122.
Smith, A. (1863). *Proc. R. Soc.* **A12**, 434.
Smith, R. N. (1959). *Q. Rev. Chem. Soc.* **13**, 278.
Steenberg, B. (1944). Thesis, University of Uppsala, Sweden.
Steggerda, J. J. (1955). Thesis, University of Delft, The Netherlands.
Test, R. E. and Hansen, R. S. (1961). United States Atomic Energy Commission. Report IS-341.
van Aken, J. G. T. (1969). Thesis, University of Delft, The Netherlands.
van Doorn, A. B. C. (1957). Thesis, University of Delft, The Netherlands.
van der Plas, Th. (1968). Thesis, University of Delft, The Netherlands.
Vastola, F. J., Hart, P. J. and Walker, P. L., Jr. (1964). *Carbon. Manchr.* **2**, 65.
Verwey, E. J. W. and de Boer, J. H. (1936). *Recl Trav. chim. Pays-Bas Belg.* **55**, 675.
Villars, D. S. (1947). *J. Am. chem. Soc.* **69**, 214.
Voet, A. and Lamond, T. G. (1968). *Carbon, Manchr.* **6**, 707.
Walker, P. L., Jr. and Kini, K. A. (1965). *Fuel, Lond.* **44**, 453.
Weber, J. and Bastick, M. (1968). *Bull. Soc. chim. Fr.* 2702.

Chapter 10

STRUCTURE AND ACTIVITY OF SILICA-SUPPORTED NICKEL CATALYSTS

J. W. E. Coenen

and

B. G. Linsen

Unilever Research Laboratory, Vlaardingen, The Netherlands

I Introduction

Silica-supported nickel catalysts have been used almost since the discovery of hydrogenation of olefins on nickel (Sabatier and Senderens, 1897). One of the first processes to which a nickel on silica catalyst was applied was the hydrogenation of unsaturated fatty oils (Normann, 1903), which is still one of the main applications for this type of catalyst. The catalyst is also used extensively for other processes of technical importance. Moreover, it has been the subject of numerous fundamental studies of catalyst structure and catalytic behaviour. In the latter field the silica-supported nickel catalyst has found its own recognized place alongside evaporated nickel films. Since large nickel areas which are extremely stable at temperatures up to 600°C can be obtained with it, the catalyst affords the possibility of obtaining well-defined and reasonably clean nickel surfaces. In comparison with evaporated films the high area of the supported metal provides a low sensitivity to poisoning, so that use of UHV conditions generally is not needed. Moreover, in recent years it has been found that the structure of evaporated films is far more complicated than was assumed in the past. The thermal stability of the supported catalyst, although obtained by introducing the complexities of the carrier, at the same time affords more possibilities for structural studies.

Ever since Taylor's (1925) postulate of active sites, the specific activity per unit area of heterogeneous catalysts has been a point of great controversy. With respect to nickel catalysts, we may ask whether the activity per unit area of elementary nickel depends on its crystalline state. In numerous studies the hydrogenation activity of nickel catalysts has been found to correlate poorly with the nickel surface area (van Hardeveld and Hartog, 1968; Taylor et al., 1964, 1965, 1967; Carter et al., 1966). In other studies, however, a good correlation between metal surface area and hydrogenation activity has been found (Mars et al., 1960; Aben et al., 1968). These findings have given rise to various hypotheses regarding the state of the nickel in the catalyst. Several investigators have postulated that the presence of the hexagonal close-packed form of nickel is important for catalytic behaviour (Terminasov and Beletskii, 1948; Kefeli and Lel'chuk, 1952; Eucken, 1949). Others suggested the presence of an amorphous form of the elementary nickel (de Lange and Visser, 1946; van Eijk van Voorthuijsen and Franzen, 1951; Ross and McBride, 1960), and still others thought that a certain minimum size of ordered crystalline structure is needed for catalytic activity (Rienäcker, 1955; Taylor, 1957). Dislocation density and other disorder parameters are also sometimes connected with catalytic activity (Bagg *et al.*, 1963; Farnsworth and Woodcock, 1957; Uhara *et al.*, 1962).

In many of the cited cases the structure of the catalyst was inadequately defined, leaving considerable scope for speculation. It is therefore clear that for a thorough understanding of the activity of nickel catalysts a reliable description of the crystalline state of the nickel is of great importance.

It has been known for a long time also that the porous texture of catalyst particles may give rise to considerable concentration gradients when a catalytic reaction takes place on their surfaces, so that the kinetics may be drastically modified by mass transport phenomena. Such effects could mask any simple correlations between surface area and activity. A textural description of the catalyst thus is badly needed for understanding catalytic behaviour.

The structure of silica-supported catalysts has been the subject of numerous studies, but the detailed descriptions evolved by several investigations differ considerably. This obviously is due partly to different preparation techniques. Nevertheless, one may expect that even with different methods of preparation the combination of nickel and silica will provide features common to all types. In the present investigation we shall develop a pictorial description of nickel on silica catalysts prepared by coprecipitation as well as by impregnation, which is based on a number of techniques. It was felt that a combination of structure and texture studies by X-ray diffraction and electron microscopy and by measurements of chemisorption and physisorption of gases, with studies of catalytic activity and selectivity on the same catalyst samples, might provide a more complete picture than has so far been possible. The activity studies were confined to the hydrogenation of unsaturated triglyceride oils and methyl esters of unsaturated fatty acids.

II Structure of the Unreduced Catalyst

The first stage of the investigation was performed on catalysts prepared by precipitating nickel compounds from a nickel sulphate solution with sodium carbonate near pH 10 in the presence of a silica support, and subsequently washing the precipitate with distilled water. For the majority of catalysts kieselguhr was used as the supporting material. No specific effect of nonsiliceous impurities present in the kieselguhr was detected, so for the present purpose we may consider the kieselguhr as a macroporous form of silica.

From the composition of the precipitating ingredients a number of nickel compounds may be expected: hydroxide, carbonate, sulphate, and possibly silicate. With respect to the carbonate there is ample literature evidence that the neutral carbonate $NiCO_3$ can only be prepared under high CO_2 pressures (Bizette and de Saint Léon Langlès, 1950; de Saint Léon Langlès, 1952; François-Rossetti, 1952; Dean, 1952). Basic nickel carbonates, however, can be formed in alkaline solution (Chakravarty and Sen, 1947; Trambouze, 1948, 1950; Perrin, 1948, 1950; Méring and Longuet-Escard, 1953; François-Rossetti and Imelik, 1953). The neutral sulphate may be disregarded because of its solubility, but basic nickel sulphates should be taken into account (Singley and Carriel, 1953). Several investigations have shown that nickel compounds can interact with solid silica in an alkaline medium with the formation of

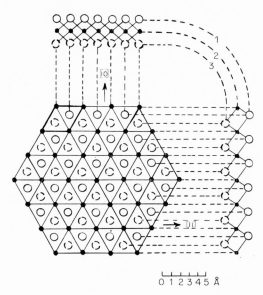

0 1 2 3 4 5 Å

FIG. 1 Projections of the structure of nickel hydroxide, $Ni(OH)_2$. (●) Ni in position 2, (○) OH in position 1, (◌) OH in position 3.

basic silicates (Feitknecht and Berger, 1942; Longuet, 1947; Franzen and van Eijk van Voorthuijsen, 1950). The presence of basic silicates has been repeatedly reported in nickel-silica catalysts (de Lange and Visser, 1946; van Eijk van Voorthuijsen and Franzen, 1951; Perrin, 1950; Trambouze, 1949, 1950; Méring and Longuet-Escard, 1953; François-Rossetti and Imelik, 1953; Singley and Carriel, 1953; König, 1946; Trambouze and Perrin, 1950; Teichner, 1950). Evidently, in strongly alkaline media nickel hydroxide also should be expected, as well as unreacted silica.

From the literature (Feitknecht et al., 1942; Feitknecht, 1954) on

the hydroxide and basic salts of nickel it appears that there is a pronounced structural similarity within this class of compounds. All of
them form layer structures with strong bonding within the layer,
weak interlayer bonding, and often also imperfect stacking of the
layers. Nickel hydroxide crystallizes with the CdI_2 structure (Lotmar
and Feitknecht, 1936), in which a hexagonally packed layer of nickel
ions is enclosed between two hexagonal layers of hydroxide ions. The
latter form a close-packed hydroxyl structure.

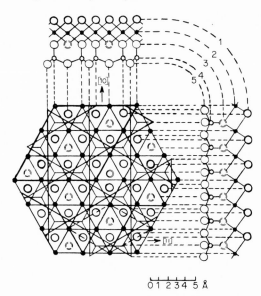

0 1 2 3 4 5 Å

FIG. 2 Projections of the structure of nickel antigorite,$Ni_3(OH)_3(Si_2O_5)OH$.
(●) Ni, (◠) OH in position 3, (o) OH in position 1, (○) O, (◎) O+OH in
position 3, (∘) Si, (△) SiO_4-tetrahedra.

The structures of the basic salts are derived from the hydroxide
structure by partial replacement of hydroxyl ions by other anions.
Distances in the direction of the c-axis, perpendicular to the plane
of the layer lattice, are enlarged by this replacement, whereas distances
in the plane of the layer remain virtually unchanged. This replacement
further reduces the bonding strength between individual layers,
thereby increasing the tendency for disordered stacking, which is of
great importance for obtaining large specific surface areas. This is
one of the reasons for using carbonate as the precipitating agent (Dean,
1952).

A special feature arises when silicate is the replacing anion. Silica
is built up of SiO_4 tetrahedra. One of the oxygen atoms replaces the

hydroxyl ion in the hydroxide structure (Bijvoet *et al.*, 1948). The SiO_4 tetrahedra are linked together by sharing oxygen atoms, thus forming a two-dimensional silica network. This structure is similar to the one found in certain clay minerals, such as dickite, kaolinite, antigorite, serpentine, etc. Again the mutual distances in the plane of the silica network are such that it fits perfectly to the nickel hydroxide structure (de Jong, 1951) with replacement of two out of every three hydroxyl ions. This replacement can either occur on one side or on both, giving

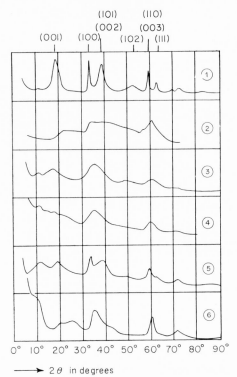

Fig. 3 X-ray diagrams for compounds to be expected in the unreduced catalysts: (1) nickel hydroxide, (2) nickel hydroxide (derived from data given by Feitknecht *et al.* 1942), (3) basic nickel carbonate, (4) basic nickel carbonate/sulphate, (5) basic nickel sulphate, (6) basic nickel silicate.

rise to two types of basic nickel silicate. In the following we shall use for these the terms *nickel morillonite* (two-sided replacement) $Ni_3(OH)_2(Si_2O_5)_2$ and *nickel antigorite* (one-sided replacement) $Ni_3(OH)_3Si_2O_5(OH)$ following van Eijk van Voorthuijsen and Franzen (1951), although "nickel serpentine" would possibly be a more appropriate name for the latter compound (Brindley, 1961).

As already mentioned, these layer structures are characterized by relatively weak bonding between the layers, giving rise to a strong tendency for imperfect stacking (Arnfelt structures; Glemser, 1951). Owing to parallel random displacement of successive layers, (hkl) reflections are weak and broadened, or sometimes totally absent.

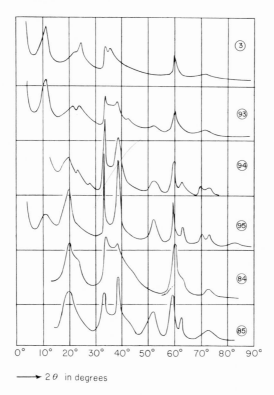

FIG. 4 Diffraction patterns of a number of unreduced catalysts.

Moreover, the distance between adjacent layers is ill-defined. The X-ray powder diagram therefore generally shows only (hk0) reflections, giving distances in the plane of the layer (cross-grating reflections) and (001) reflections, giving distances between the layers.

Figure 3 shows a diagram for well-crystallized $Ni(OH)_2$, as well as diagrams for the basic sulphate, carbonate, and silicate. Figure 4 shows diffraction patterns of a number of unreduced catalysts. The lowest curve in Fig. 4 has a close similarity to well-crystallized nickel hydroxide, whereas the other curves exhibit varying degrees of the described two-dimensional character. Tables I and II give the lattice

Table I. Lattice spacings obtained from the powder diagrams in Fig. 3

| | Nickel hydroxide | | Basic nickel carbonate | Basic nickel carbonate/ sulphate | Basic nickel sulphate | Basic nickel silicate | (hkl) |
	Well crystallized	Laminar dispersed					(hk)
	8·12*		8·45	7·90	7·90	8·85	(001)
	4·72		5·28	5·18	4·70		(001)
						4·39	
						3·52	
	2·70	2·64			2·67		(100)
			2·56	2·55		2·56	(10)
d (in Å)	2·33	2·25			2·34		(101)
	1·76						(102)
	1·56				1·56		(110)
		1·54	1·533	1·540		1·53	(11)
	1·48				1·48		(111)
	1·35						(200)
			1·313	1·33	1·31	1·31	(20)
	1·30						(201)

* Basal reflection of small amount of basic carbonate.

Table II. Lattice spacings in Å obtained from the powder diagrams in Fig. 6; and some comparison patterns

Amorphous silica	Basic nickel silicate	P 3	P 93	P 60	P 94	P 85	P 84	P 21	P 95	$Ni(OH)_2$
	8·9	8·2	8·6	8·1	8·1	8·1	8·2	8·4	8·4	
	(10)	(10)	(10)					(10)	(10)	
	4·4	4·1	4·2	4·6	4·4	4·5	4·4	4·5	4·5	4·7
	(5)	(5)	(12)					(8)	(24)	
3·8	3·5	3·7	3·7	3·8	3·6	3·8	3·8	3·7	3·6	
		(6)	(5)	(6)				(4)	(3)	
2·56	2·56	2·66	2·70	2·70	2·70	2·65	2·70	2·73	2·70	2·70
	2·51	2·35	2·34	2·34	2·34	2·34	2·33	2·33	2·33	2·33
	—	1·76	1·76	1·76	1·76	—	1·76	1·76	1·76	1·76
	(0)	(3)	(8)	(10)	(10)	(1)		(10)	(16)	
1·53	1·54	1·54	1·55	1·55	1·56	1·56	1·56	1·56	1·56	1·56
	—	—	1·48	1·48	1·48	1·48	1·48	1·48	1·48	1·48
1·31	1·32	1·32	1·34	1·34	1·34	1·35	1·34	1·35	1·35	1·35
	—	—	1·30	1·30	1·30	1·30	1·30	1·30	1·30	1·30

Values between brackets given below some of the spacing values are visually estimated relative line intensities.

spacings as obtained from these powder diagrams. Although all catalysts show evidence of three-dimensional nickel hydroxide, the occurrence of a distance of ~ 8 Å in all the unreduced catalysts shows clearly that other anions have been incorporated. Owing to the close similarity between the diagrams of all basic nickel salts involved, it is impossible to arrive at definite conclusions regarding the structure and composition of the unreduced catalysts, since they all contain some carbonate and sulphate (Table III). However, the very fact, that the

TABLE III. Chemical composition of a number of unreduced catalysts

Unreduced catalyst no.	% Ni	SO$_3$		CO$_2$		SiO$_2$	
		%	$100\dfrac{\text{mole}}{\text{mole Ni}}$	%	$100\dfrac{\text{mole}}{\text{mole Ni}}$	%	$100\dfrac{\text{mole}}{\text{mole Ni}}$
P 3	26·5	0·50	1·38	0·45	2·27	48·1	186·2
P 93	35·2	0·50	1·04	1·22	4·63	33·1	96·6
P 60	36·1	0·80	1·78	0·67	2·48	31·4	89·2
P 94	42·5	0·93	1·59	2·13	6·68	21·1	50·9
P 85	43·7	—	—	1·67	5·10	20·1	47·1
P 84	42·2	0·55	0·96	3·28	10·37	18·9	45·9
P 21	43·7	0·90	1·51	1·34	4·10	17·6	41·3
P 95	49·5	1·35	2·00	2·02	5·44	11·2	23·3

tendency for the cross-grating (two-dimensional order) diagram is greater for catalysts with a high silica/nickel ratio indicates that the presence of basic silicate is to be expected. One exception to this tendency, sample P84, contains a high content of carbonate, which in that case gives rise to the basic salt characteristics. Also, confirmation of the occurrence of nickel antigorite was obtained from electron diffraction. Figure 5 shows a selected-area electron diffraction pattern of a minute crystal of nickel antigorite found in one of the catalysts. The greater intensity of the third-order cross-grating reflection confirms the structure.

There is also some chemical evidence for the occurrence of basic silicate (Trambouze and Perrin, 1949). Nickel hydroxide and basic nickel carbonate can be extracted easily with NH_4OH/NH_4Cl solution, leaving the silicate unattacked. It was found that the higher the silica/nickel ratio, the lower the amount of nickel that could be extracted, whereas the diffraction pattern of the extraction residue did not show the presence of three-dimensional hydroxide but showed cross-grating characteristics, analogous to curve 6 of Fig. 3 of basic nickel silicate.

Summarizing, we may conclude that the unreduced catalysts contain amorphous silica and nickel hydroxide as well as basic nickel salts.

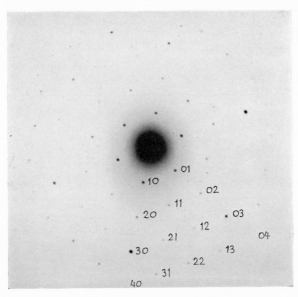

FIG. 5 Selected-area diffraction pattern of a minute crystal of nickel antigorite.

Among the latter the presence of basic silicate is more evident at high silica/nickel ratios. All nickel compounds have imperfectly formed layer lattices, with good order within the layers but imperfect layer stacking.

III   Phase Composition of the Reduced Catalyst

A   Expected Composition

The precipitates described in Section II were reduced at 500°C in a current of hydrogen (30 l h^{-1} g^{-1} during 1 hour). The resulting activated catalysts are highly pyrophoric and thus present considerable difficulties for X-ray investigations. The reduced catalysts were therefore passivated at room temperature by passing over nitrogen to which gradually increasing amounts of air were admixed, in the course of 1$\frac{1}{2}$ hours. The resulting catalysts are reasonably stable in air, although prolonged storage results in gradual oxidation.

It is known (Trambouze, 1948, 1950; Merlin and Teichner, 1953; Sidgwick, 1950; Tsangarakis and Sibut-Pinote, 1954) that nickel hydroxide is easily decomposed even at much lower temperatures than those applied in the reduction process, and the same holds for the basic carbonate (Perrin, 1948; Trambouze, 1950; François, 1950b; François-Rossetti et al., 1957; François-Rossetti and Imelik, 1957). In a hydrogen atmosphere the resulting nickel oxide is easily reduced to metallic (fcc) nickel. The situation with respect to the basic silicate is more complex. Ignition may result in partial decomposition with the formation of nickel oxide. Reduction to elementary nickel is much more difficult than with the hydroxide and carbonate (Schuit and van Reijen, 1958). It has been proposed that part of the nickel atoms formed by reduction of the basic silicate may retain their positions in the original silicate structure (de Lange and Visser, 1946; van Eijk van Voorthuijsen and Franzen, 1951), possibly giving rise to the formation of elementary nickel which is amorphous to X-rays. As mentioned before, a hexagonal form might also play a part.

Summarizing, we must consider the possible occurrence of elementary nickel (fcc, hcp, or amorphous), nickel oxide (due to incomplete reduction or formed in passivation), residual basic silicate and amorphous silica. Sulphate will be reduced to sulphide, but owing to the low S contents any nickel sulphide present will be below the X-ray detection limit.

B Qualitative X-ray Analysis

Owing to extreme line broadening, the back-reflection part of catalyst X-ray patterns does not show any well-defined lines.

Figure 6 shows X-ray powder patterns for the forward reflection half of a number of passivated reduced catalysts. Table IV lists the lattice spacings derived from these graphs, together with some comparison patterns.

To facilitate interpretation, the expected lattice distances for NiO, fcc Ni, and hcp Ni are given in Table V. From this we note that the presence of the line at $d = 1.77$ should constitute evidence for fcc Ni, especially if it occurs in combination with a line at 2·04 Å of about twice the intensity. The patterns of the catalysts thus provide strong evidence for the presence of fcc metallic nickel. From the absence of lines at 2·16, 1·90, and 1·15 Å we may conclude that we have no evidence for the occurrence of appreciable amounts of hcp (Ni). Moreover, Roof (1952) and Kefeli and Lel'chuk (1952) have noted that the diagrams of fcc and hcp nickel (with equal ionic radius) have a number

19

of lines in common, whereas some of the hcp lines coincide with nickel oxide lines, so that conclusions regarding the presence of hexagonal nickel should be treated with reserve.

With respect to the presence of amorphous nickel, no firm conclusions can be obtained from the qualitative analysis. Presence of amorphous

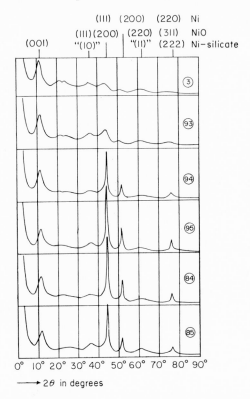

Fig. 6 Diffraction patterns for a number of passivated reduced catalysts.

nickel with liquid-like disorder is highly unlikely in view of the high ignition temperature to which the samples have been subjected. Elementary nickel amorphous to X-rays might still be present in the form of extremely small crystals, which give such tremendous line broadening that the scattered intensity only raises the background. In addition, we cannot yet exclude nickel in an abnormal form (for instance from a memory effect from silicate). Therefore a quantitative X-ray analysis together with a chemical analysis will be used to investigate the possible occurrence of amorphous elementary nickel.

With respect to nickel oxide and nickel silicate, a situation arises

TABLE IV. Lattice spacings of the passivated reduced catalysts

Ni	NiO	Ni silicate	P 3	P 93	P 60	P 94	P 85	P 84	P 21	P 95
		7·25–8·9 (001)	7·63	7·65	7·76	7·63	7·63	7·83	7·83	7·70
		4·56–4·39	4·06	4·07		4·23			4·21	
					3·98			3·88		3·96
		3·63–3·52	3·75	3·56		3·69	3·59			
	2·413 (111)	2·56 "(10)"	2·49	2·48	2·51	2·48	2·50	2·48	2·46	2·46
2·035 (111)	2·089 (200)		2·07	2·05	2·04	2·03	2·04	2·04	2·04	2·04
1·762 (200)			1·768	1·767	1·769	1·761	1·762	1·762	1·761	1·761
	1·477 (220)	1·53 "(11)"	1·52	1·52	1·53	1·50	1·52	1·52	1·51	1·53
		1·32 "(20)"								
	1·260 (311)									
1·246 (220)			1·27	1·27	1·26	1·25	1·25	1·25	1·25	1·25
	1·206 (222)									
		% Nickel	31	43	38	55	62	62	63	70

similar to that discussed for hexagonal nickel: the expected nickel oxide line at 2·19 Å almost coincides with the strongest line of fcc Ni at 2·04 Å. The expected lines at 2·41 and 1·48 Å show coincidence with the

TABLE V. Expected lattice distances for hcp Ni, fcc Ni and nickel oxide

hcp Ni			fcc Ni		NiO		
(hkl)	I	d(Å)	(hkl)	d(Å)	(hkl)	d(Å)	2θ
					(111)	2·41	37·3
(100)	6	2·16					41·9
					(200)	2·09	43·3
(002)		2·04	(111)	2·04			44·5
(101)	36	1·90					47·9
			(200)	1·76			51·9
(102)		1·48			(220)	1·48	62·9
(110)		1·25	(220)	1·25	(311)	1·26	76·0
					(222)	1·21	79·4
(103)	36	1·15					84·2
(112)		1·06	(311)	1·06			93·1
(201)		1·04			(400)	1·04	95·5

extremely broadened silicate cross-grating reflections at 2·56 and 1·53 Å. The presence of NiO therefore cannot be concluded with any degree of certainty from this qualitative analysis, especially as the line at 7·6–7·8 strongly suggests the presence of antigorite-type nickel silicate. Definite proof of the presence of the oxide (and to a lesser extent the silicate) will be derived from accurate intensity analysis.

C Quantitative X-ray Analysis

Quantitative X-ray analysis relies on a comparison of integrated line intensities of the investigated sample with integral intensities for standard substances. Since the comparison is done between separate X-ray diagrams, suitable care should be taken to allow for changes in primary beam intensity. Moreover, corrections must be applied for sample absorption in the two cases.

For a complete description of the method see Coenen (1958). A film method was used, with photometric recording of the film densities and conversion to intensities by means of a calibration curve. Planimetric measurements of the peak areas in this intensity plot were used as the integrated intensities. CuKα radiation was used throughout. A modification of a method described by Goppel (1946) was adopted for measuring the primary beam intensity. In the Debye-Scherrer camera the primary beam traversed successively the centrally-placed catalyst sample—a flat pressed powder plate about 0·1 mm thick—and an MgO reference plate. The reference sample gave rise to a separate powder diagram on a shielded part of the film, which served as a measure of the primary beam intensity and which also eliminated the greater part of the absorption correction. The sample absorption was determined separately to allow calculation of the remaining absorption correction. For this purpose the sample weight was also determined on a microbalance (∼1 mg per sample). An equation for the intensity was derived for the geometry in question, giving an integrated line intensity, standardized on unit sample weight, the primary beam intensity corrected for absorption, and polarization and temperature effects (Coenen, 1958).

The choice of the standard samples for nickel, nickel oxide, and nickel silicate presented some difficulties. For fcc nickel two standard samples were chosen. The first (Ni8) was made by reduction of powdered nickel hydroxide at 300°C and storage after passivation in air for several months to obtain a stable sample. The line intensities of this sample were corrected for its degree of oxidation (metallic nickel content 92%). The second sample (NiV2A) was prepared by electrolytic deposition of nickel on stainless steel, from which the deposited nickel foil was subsequently stripped off.

Nickel oxide can occur with varying degrees of non-stoichiometry. Pure stoichiometric NiO is yellow-green (Brauer, 1954; François, 1950b) and unstable in air. After prolonged exposure to air a composition of approximately $NiO_{1.005}$ (Heikes, 1955; Libowitz and Bauer, 1955) is reached, which is black. The standard line intensities determined for the yellow and the black forms of NiO were found to differ significantly, so that a choice had to be made as to which form of NiO should serve as the reference sample. Since the catalysts were exposed to air, it was expected that the nickel oxide in the catalyst would approach the black form.

For the nickel silicate the choice was even more difficult, since the nickel silicate in the catalysts is ill-defined. The spacing of ~ 8 Å indicates the presence of antigorite-type nickel silicate but the perfection of the crystallization, which can exert an important influence on line intensities, can vary over a wide range. Thus certain arbitrariness could not be avoided. A basic silicate of the badly crystallized type (CLA 8201) was prepared according to van Eijk van Voorthuijsen and Franzen (1951). An X-ray pattern of this preparation was used earlier in the qualitative analysis (Fig. 3, curve 6 and Table II). Since the catalysts during reduction are subjected to high temperature, and in the initial stage to high water vapour pressure, a certain degree of hydrothermal treatment should be reckoned with. Therefore CLA 8201 was subjected to a short hydrothermal treatment, which resulted in some improvement in the crystallization and in a reduction of the interlayer spacing. The resulting sample (NiSil) was used as the standard for the quantitative X-ray analysis. Prolonged hydrothermal treatment of the same silicate sample gave rise to a well-defined nickel antigorite structure, the X-ray data of which were in excellent agreement with the literature (Feitknecht and Berger, 1942; Longuet, 1947; Roy and Roy, 1954; Coenen, 1958).

The standardized integrated line intensities as determined for these standard samples are given in Table VI.

Analysis of the intensity data of the catalysts in terms of their phase composition is rather involved, because several of the considerably broadened lines overlap to such an extent that it is impossible to resolve them. The net effect is that in the catalyst diagrams only four lines occur in the angular range used for the quantitative analysis (1, 2, 3, 4 in Table VI), three of which are combination lines, denoted by brackets at the bottom of the table. The determination of the phase composition of the catalysts is carried out as follows.

From the Ni(200) reflection, the only undisturbed line in the diagram,* the fraction of fcc Ni can be calculated by simple division by 50. From the same line intensity the Ni(111) intensity can be calculated by multiplication by $\frac{111}{50}$. This value is then subtracted from the intensity of the combination line with NiO(200), yielding the line intensity of NiO(200). The NiO fraction is obtained from this residual value by

TABLE VI. Standard line intensities for reference samples (in brackets Miller indices)

Sample θ	17·6	18·7	21·7	22·3	26·0	30·4	31·5
fcc Ni { Ni8				(111)111 } 111	(200)52 } 111		
{ NiV2A				(111)112	(200)48		
Black NiO		(111)46	(200)85				(220)46
NiSil	(10)40					(11)12	

⏜ 3   ⏜ 2   ⏜ 1   ⏜ 4

dividing by 85. The NiO(200) intensity is also used for calculating the NiO(111) and NiO(220) intensities, by multiplication by $\frac{46}{85}$ in both cases. The intensity values thus obtained are then subtracted from the remaining combination lines (3) and (4), yielding the intensity values for the silicate cross-grating reflections NiSil (10) and NiSil (11) respectively. From these figures two values for the silicate fraction are obtained, by division by 40 and 12 respectively. Ideally, these two values should be equal. From the oxide and silicate fractions the percentage of nickel in the catalyst present as oxide and silicate is calculated by simple multiplication by the nickel contents of nickel oxide (79·5%) and nickel silicate (36·5%).

The results of the quantitative analysis are given in Table VII. It should be noted that P84a and P85a were obtained by reduction at 300 instead of 500°C. NiSil 4 hours was obtained by reduction of the standard silicate for 4 hours at 500°C. The poor reducibility of the silicate is clearly demonstrated.

The total nickel content was determined chemically by evaporation

---

* Even for the Ni(200) line at $d = 1\cdot76$ Å it is not self evident that it is completely free of overlap with other lines. The (210) of nickel antigorite would occur at $d = 1\cdot72$ Å. However, this reflection is of very low intensity, even for well-crystallized antigorite (only about 6% of the (11) cross-grating reflection). In badly-crystallized antigorite it may be expected to be even weaker, and no evidence was found in the diagram of the standard silicate NiSil, so that its possible influence may be disregarded.

to dryness with concentrated hydrochloric acid, extraction of the residue with 1:1 hydrochloric acid and filtration. In the filtrate the nickel was determined by precipitation with dimethylglyoxime.

TABLE VII. Results of the quantitative X-ray analysis

			Standardized integral line intensity							
Catalyst no.	Ni (200)	Ni (111) + NiO (200)	NiO (111) + NiSil "(10)"	NiO (220) + NiSil "(11)"	Ni (111)	NiO (200)	NiO (111)	NiO (220)	NiSil "(10)"	NiSil "(11)"
P 60 fresh	10·5	29·4	15·3	6·9	23·3	6·1	3·3	3·3	12·0	3·6
P 62	25·6	66·1	10·5	—	56·9	9·2	4·9	4·9	5·6	—
P 84	23·1	56·9	9·6	—	51·3	5·6	3·0	3·0	3·0	—
P 85	24·4	61·7	9·9	—	54·1	7·6	4·1	4·1	5·8	—
P 84a	7·6	27·2	37·9	16·2	16·9	10·3	6·5	6·5	31·4	9·7
P 85a	7·4	34·7	38·4	19·3	16·4	18·4	9·9	9·9	28·5	9·4
P 93	8·4	29·8	19·1	—	18·6	11·2	6·0	6·0	13·1	—
P 94	11·8	39·5	18·5	—	26·2	13·3	7·1	7·1	11·4	—
P 95	28·1	68·8	11·3	—	62·4	6·4	3·4	3·4	7·9	—
NiSil 4 h	5·6	13·7	26·8	—	12·4	1·3	0·7	0·7	26·1	—
(1)	(2)	(3)	(4)	(5)	(6)	(7)	(8)	(9)	(10)	(11)

X-ray analysis

			Ni as NiSil				Chemical Analysis		
Catalyst no.	Ni_{cryst} (%)	Ni as NiO (%)	%	%	Average %	Ni_{tot} (%)	Ni_{tot} (%)	Ni_{metal} (%)	$Ni_{H_2SO_4}$ (%)
P 60 fresh	21·0	5·7	10·8	10·3	10·6	37·3			
P 62	51·2	8·6	5·1	—	5·1	64·9	68·5	51·5	—
P 84	46·2	5·2	6·0	—	6·0	57·4	62	48	—
P 85	48·8	7·1	5·2	—	5·2	61·1	61·5	45·5	—
P 84a	15·2	9·6	28·4	28·4	28·4	53·2	53	13	—
P 85a	14·8	17·2	25·8	27·6	26·7	58·7	—	10	—
P 93	16·8	19·5	11·8	—	11·8	39·1	—	17·5	42·0
P 94	23·6	12·4	10·3	—	10·3	46·3	—	23·4	54·0
P 95	56·2	6·0	7·1	—	7·1	69·3	—	49·9	69·5
NiSil 4 h	11·2	1·2	23·6	—	23·6	36·0	38·2	10·8	36·5
(1)	(12)	(13)	(14)	(15)	(16)	(17)	(18)	(19)	(20)

The metallic nickel content was determined by dissolving the catalyst in 4 N sulphuric acid in a closed system and measuring the amount of hydrogen evolved. In some cases the total nickel was determined in the resulting sulphuric acid solution ($Ni_{H_2SO_4}$).

The results of the chemical analysis also are given in Table VII. From this table it is evident that despite the very involved method of X-ray analysis there is an unmistakable correlation between metallic nickel and fcc nickel, as well as between the total nickel determined by X-ray and chemical analysis.

In order to assess the results obtained more clearly, the most important data are given in slightly modified form in Table VIII.

TABLE VIII. Quantitative X-ray analysis of Ni/SiO_2 catalysts

				Distribution of nickel		
Catalyst	% Ni chem	$\dfrac{Ni_{cryst}}{Ni_{elem}}$	$\dfrac{x\text{-ray}Ni_{tot}}{chemNi_{tot}}$	$\dfrac{Ni_{cryst}}{Ni_{tot}}$	$\dfrac{Ni\ as\ NiO}{Ni_{tot}}$	$\dfrac{Ni\ as\ NiSil}{Ni_{tot}}$
P 93	42	0·96	0·93	0·43	0·27	0·30
P 60	44	—	0·84	0·56	0·15	0·29
P 94	54	1·01	1·00	0·51	0·27	0·22
P 84	62	0·96	0·92	0·81	0·09	0·10
P 84a	53	1·17	1·00	0·28	0·18	0·54
P 85	62	1·07	1·00	0·79	0·12	0·09
P 85a	53	(1·48)	—	0·25	0·29	0·46
P 62	69	1·00	0·96	0·79	0·13	0·08
P 95	70	1·13	1·00	0·81	0·09	0·10
NiSil 4 h	38	1·04	0·95	0·31	0·03	0·66
Average		1·04 ±0·03	0·96 ±0·02			

One of the principal aims of the present investigation was to detect the presence of amorphous elementary nickel. From the fact that the ratio Ni_{cryst}/Ni_{elem} is very close to unity it is evident that no amorphous nickel need be assumed to be present in the catalysts. Only in one case does a significant deviation occur—in P 84a—but in this catalyst reduced at 300°C the low degree of the reduction leads to an extremely broadened and very weak Ni(200) reflection, so that the experimental error may be expected to be large. This value has therefore been disregarded in averaging. The average values are given with their standard deviation.

It is doubtful whether any real significance may be attached to the fact that the average ratio of Ni_{cryst}/Ni_{elem} is slightly larger than unity. If a significance is attached to this deviation, however, it may be argued that possibly the nickel ions at the Ni—SiO$_2$ interface contribute to the intensity of the nickel reflection, although they behave chemically as non-elementary nickel. This might then be considered as a first indication that the nickel crystallites are grown epitaxially on the silica networks remaining from the silicate, where the nickel ions are in a hexagonal array similar to the (111) plane of nickel, though with extended interionic distances.

If we disregard the samples reduced at 300°C and consider only samples reduced at one temperature—500°C—we see that there is a marked tendency for low nickel/silica ratios to give rise to high silicate contents. The degree of reduction rises in the inverse direction, confirming the findings of other investigators (de Lange and Visser, 1946; van Eijk van Voorthuijsen and Franzen, 1950, 1951; Franzen and van Eijk van Voorthuijsen, 1950) that nickel silicate is more difficult to reduce than the other nickel compounds involved. The low degree of reduction of P 84a and P 85a point in the same direction (compare Ni8).

IV Crystallite Size and Lattice Parameter of fcc Nickel in the Catalysts

From the foregoing investigations it is evident that only one form of elementary nickel occurs in the catalyst samples, i.e. fcc nickel. It is of interest to investigate further whether this nickel is identical with the bulk metal with respect to the lattice parameter. The state of subdivision, characterized by the average crystallite size, is also of interest because it determines the nickel surface area, which is obviously important for catalytic activity.

A Experimental Method

To obtain in the same diffraction diagram reference lines to be used both for elimination of instrumental line width and for standardization in lattice-parameter determinations, all catalyst samples were mixed with 20 wt-% of KCl. The lattice constant of the KCl used was determined separately as 6·921 Å, in agreement with literature data. X-ray diffractometer recordings with CoKα, CuKα, and MoKα were taken of all sample mixtures.

For the lattice constant determination of fcc Ni the θ value of the (200) reflection was read off from the diagrams, as it was for that of the two KCl lines, (222) and (400), located on both sides of the (200)Ni

19*

reflection. The θ value of the nickel line was corrected with the aid of the KCl lines, and from the corrected value the lattice parameter of the fcc nickel was calculated. Clearly the use of only one low-index line is not ideal for lattice parameter determination, but—as explained earlier—no other undisturbed lines were available in the catalyst diagrams. All high-order lines are so excessively broadened that their location cannot be determined with any accuracy.

For the crystallite size determination the widths of the (200) reflections were determined from the same diffractometer recordings. The integral line widths, defined as the integral line intensity divided by the peak height, were used. The KCl line widths were determined in a similar manner. To obtain the pure diffraction broadening of the Ni(200) line the experimental width must be corrected for instrumental broadening effects (beam divergence, $K\alpha$ doublet splitting, etc.). For details of the correction procedure, based on studies by Jones (1938), reference is made to Klug and Alexander (1954), Alexander *et al.* (1948), Alexander (1948, 1950), Alexander and Klug (1950) and Coenen (1958).

For the interpretation of the diffraction broadening thus obtained, it should be noted that, next to small crystallite size, lattice distortion also gives rise to broadening. In the literature (Hall, 1949; Michell and Haig, 1957; Wood and Rachinger, 1949) separation of the two effects is often based on their different wavelength and diffraction angle dependence, and it is for this reason that our investigation was done with three different wavelengths. As was pointed out by Williamson and Hall (1953), this method works only if a number of undisturbed reflections can be utilized. In our case only the (200) reflection can be used. The next undisturbed nickel reflection is the (400), which is so weak and broadened that no accurate line width determination is possible.

For crystallite-size broadening the Scherrer formula applies:

$$\beta_D = \frac{K \cdot \lambda}{D \cos \theta}$$

in which $K =$ a constant, for cubic crystals and integral line width close to unity,

$\lambda =$ wavelength,

$D =$ crystallite size,

$\theta =$ glancing angle.

For lattice distortion, the line broadening is given by:

$$\beta_{\Delta d} = 2\frac{\Delta d}{d} \tan \theta$$

in which $\Delta d/d$ is the relative average deviation of the lattice spacing d from its mean value. This relation can be rewritten, by introduction of the Bragg relation, as

$$\beta_{\Delta d} = \frac{\Delta d}{d^2} \frac{\lambda}{\cos \theta}.$$

Assuming additivity of the two broadening effects, we find for the total broadening

$$\beta = \frac{K \cdot \lambda}{D^* \cos \theta}$$

in which

$$\frac{1}{D^*} = \frac{1}{D} + \frac{\Delta d}{d^2} K.$$

As will be discussed later, there is ample evidence from gas adsorption and electron microscopic data that the nickel in the catalysts is in an extreme state of subdivision, so that the crystallite-size broadening can be expected to be considerable. As will be shown later, the majority of the nickel particles in the catalysts are single crystals, without crystal boundaries. Furthermore, the crystals have been annealed at 500°C, well above the Tamman temperature, so that large distortion effects are very unlikely. Thus D^* may be expected to be close to the actual crystallite size D. In a few of the catalysts a special distortion effect may be present, which will be discussed below.

With the use of the integral line width the crystallite size of cubic crystals is best defined as the cube root of the crystal volume (Klug and Alexander, 1954).

B Results and Discussion

The results obtained are represented in Table IX. The figures are averages of duplicate determinations with three wavelengths, since no systematic differences for the different wavelengths were observed. The standard deviation of the average is also given.

In Table IX the three catalysts above the broken dividing line show a significantly enlarged lattice parameter. These are also the catalysts with the smallest average crystallite size and the highest silica/nickel ratio, as well as the highest fraction of nickel present as silicate. The remaining catalysts have lattice parameters that do not differ significantly from the normal bulk nickel value of 3·524 Å, which value was also obtained for Ni8.

For the interpretation of the lattice parameter and the crystallite size effects the structure of nickel antigorite is of great importance. As discussed above, this structure is derived from the nickel hydroxide structure by one-sided replacement of OH-ions by an interlinked two-dimensional network of SiO_4 tetrahedra. The other side of the structure is unaffected by this replacement, so that nickel hydroxide should fit perfectly to the lattice, an ideal situation for epitaxial growth. We may thus assume for the unreduced catalyst a sandwich structure of silica that has been superficially rearranged to fit the nickel antigorite layer, which in turn is covered with nickel hydroxide.

TABLE IX. Lattice parameter and apparent nickel crystallite size of the catalysts

Catalyst no.	D^* (Å)	Lattice constant (Å)	Fraction of Ni as silicate	$\dfrac{g\ SiO_2}{g\ Ni}$
P 3	$32 \pm 2\cdot3$	$3\cdot536 \pm 0\cdot007$	—	$1\cdot82$
P 93	$38 \pm 1\cdot7$	$3\cdot534 \pm 0\cdot003$	$0\cdot30$	$0\cdot94$
P 60	$40 \pm 2\cdot3$	$3\cdot539 \pm 0\cdot003$	$0\cdot29$	$0\cdot87$
P 1607	$45 \pm 2\cdot1$	$3\cdot526 \pm 0\cdot001$	—	$0\cdot47$
P 94	$59 \pm 2\cdot8$	$3\cdot521 \pm 0\cdot002$	$0\cdot22$	$0\cdot50$
P 84	$63 \pm 2\cdot4$	$3\cdot523 \pm 0\cdot002$	$0\cdot10$	$0\cdot45$
P 85	$68 \pm 4\cdot4$	$3\cdot525 \pm 0\cdot002$	$0\cdot09$	$0\cdot46$
P 21	$57 \pm 1\cdot5$	$3\cdot522 \pm 0\cdot002$	—	$0\cdot40$
P 95	$69 \pm 3\cdot8$	$3\cdot523 \pm 0\cdot002$	$0\cdot10$	$0\cdot23$

In the reduction process the nickel hydroxide is easily reduced. In the antigorite, which is much more difficult to reduce, the hexagonal arrangement of the nickel ions is similar to the (111) plane of fcc nickel, although with a considerably enlarged Ni-Ni-distance. We can thus expect in reduction epitaxial growth of the nickel crystallites with a (111) direction perpendicular to the plane of the silica network. The crystallite size will depend on the thickness of the hydroxide layer. In the case of very small nickel crystallites—presumably derived from a thin hydroxide layer and a high proportion of silicate—one may expect that the poor fit to the silica network will result in an enlargement of the nickel lattice parameter. A similar effect in the reverse direction has been observed by Arkharov and Graevskii (1944) for thin nickel oxide films epitaxially grown on nickel.

Without interaction with the support, the minimum-energy situation for the nickel crystallites probably would be a more or less spherical shape, with a high proportion of the densest crystallographic planes in the surface. For our case of strong interaction the minimum-energy situation would require a combination of a minimum free metal area and a maximal contact area with the support. We were thus led to assume for our catalysts a situation where hemispherical crystallites are attached to the silica with their equatorial planes, for which we

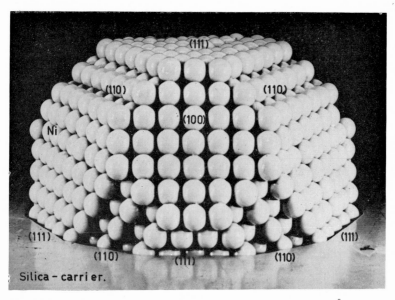

Fig. 7 Model of a hemispherical nickel crystallite ($\sim$35 Å).

expect the best fit with a (111) orientation. Figure 7 shows a model of a hemispherical crystallite measuring about 35 Å, with the three densest crystallographic planes in the surface.

The silicate plays an important role in obtaining a small average crystallite size, since the two-dimensional silica structure will tend to limit sintering of the nickel to a more or less two-dimensional process, where the silica plates act as dividing walls. The relation between the crystallite size and the lattice parameter now can be explained by assuming that less interaction between silica and nickel—less silicate formation—leads to thicker hydroxide layers on the support and possibly even nickel hydroxide completely unattached to the support. Reduction in this case results in considerable sintering—larger average crystallite size—and in a normal lattice parameter.

V   Nickel Surface Area Determination by Adsorption Methods

For catalytic hydrogenation activity the nickel surface area is clearly of predominant importance. It was for this reason that we determined crystallite sizes, which may be expected to show an inverse correlation with the nickel surface area.

A   Hydrogen Adsorption

A more direct method of determining the nickel surface area is measurement of the monolayer capacity for chemisorption of hydrogen. This method has been used by many investigators (Baker et al., 1955; Broeder et al., 1956; Broeder et al., 1957; Gundry and Tompkins, 1956, 1957; Prettre and Goepfert, 1947; Sachtler, 1956; Schuit, 1954; Selwood, 1956; van Itterbeek et al., 1946). For the application of this method one has to decide what adsorption corresponds to a monolayer and what cross-sectional area has to be assigned per adsorbed molecule.

As regards the first problem, considerable differences occur between the details of the methods applied by different investigators with respect to the adsorption temperature, hydrogen pressure, and equilibration time, although the ultimate results generally are not very different. In the present investigation we chose hydrogen adsorption at room temperature. For this determination the passivated form of the catalyst is clearly unsuitable. For hydrogen adsorption a thorough reduction in the adsorption apparatus was performed, after which the sample was evacuated for two hours at 450°C to eliminate the reduction hydrogen.

In the subsequent hydrogen adsorption no great increase in adsorption is observed above 100 torr. For the sake of convenience a pressure of one atmosphere was chosen. Many investigators have observed that most of the hydrogen adsorption is practically instantaneous, but that a small proportion of slow hydrogen adsorption occurs in most cases, ascribed to traces of oxygen left on the nickel surface. Therefore an equilibration time of 16 hours was chosen, although more than 95% of the hydrogen uptake occurred within the first 15 minutes. With the long equilibration time chosen in our method any slow adsorption which might occur is incorporated in the monolayer capacity. A detailed description of the method used is given by Coenen (1958) and Linsen (1964).

With respect to the area corresponding to one molecule of adsorbed hydrogen, there is ample existing evidence that in chemisorption of hydrogen on nickel the adsorption occurs in atomic form, one atom of hydrogen being bound per nickel atom in the surface (Horiuti, 1957; Beeck and Ritchie, 1950; Baker and Rideal, 1955). The problem is thus shifted to the question of what area is taken up by one nickel atom in the surface. This value depends on the crystallographic plane exposed, a question about which no experimental evidence is available. On the basis of the hemispherical model developed earlier, we chose the distribution of (111), (100) and (110) planes as shown in Fig. 7. On the basis of this model an average value of 6·33 Å² is obtained per exposed nickel atom. It is interesting to note that Beeck (1950) derived for evaporated nickel films a value of 6·13 Å from a comparison of low-temerature krypton adsorption and hydrogen adsorption capacity. No definite conclusion can be reached about this problem, and in the present investigation the value of 6·33 Å² will be used, so that the following formula applies for calculating the specific nickel surface area:

$$S_{\text{Ni}} = N_{\text{av}} \times 2 \times (6 \cdot 33) \times 10^{-20} \frac{V_m}{22\,414} \text{m}^2/\text{g} = 3 \cdot 41\, V_m \text{m}^2/\text{g Ni}$$

in which V_m is the hydrogen monolayer capacity (in ml at STP) per gram of nickel in the sample.

B Verification of Hydrogen Adsorption and the Metallic Nickel Content

Since the hydrogen surface area and the metallic nickel content are of primary importance for the present investigation, it was felt that an independent verification of their measurement would be valuable. For one of the investigated catalysts the following series of experiments was performed:

1. Reduction of 500 mg catalyst (about 200 mg Ni) in a current of 60 l H_2/h during 2 hours at 500°C and cooling in hydrogen at 20°C.

2. Dissolution of the catalyst covered with adsorbed hydrogen in acid, as described for the metallic nickel determination (Section III C) $\rightarrow V_1$ ml/g Ni.

3. Reduction as under 1 and subsequent heating in a current of oxygen-free nitrogen for 2 hours and determination of hydrogen entrained in the nitrogen $\rightarrow V_2$ ml/g Ni.

4. Dissolution of hydrogen-free catalyst obtained under 3 and measurement of the volume of evolved hydrogen $\rightarrow V_3$ ml/g Ni.

5. Repetition of the reduction and the nitrogen treatment and subsequent complete oxidation in air, weight increase $\rightarrow \Delta G$ g/g Ni.

The results are presented in the following scheme:

P1607 reduced

$$V_1 = 401 \text{ ml } H_2/g \text{ Ni}_{tot} \qquad V_2 = 23 \text{ ml } H_2/g \text{ Ni}_{tot}$$

$H_2SO_4 \swarrow \qquad \searrow N_2/500°C$

$$\text{air} \swarrow 500°C \qquad \searrow H_2SO_4$$

$$\Delta G = 0.2384 \text{ g} \qquad V_3 = 378.4 \text{ ml } H_2/g \text{ Ni}_{tot}$$
$$\equiv 0.987 \text{ g } \text{Ni}_{met}/g \text{ Ni}_{tot} \equiv 0.992 \text{ g } \text{Ni}_{met}/g \text{ Ni}_{tot}.$$

Adsorbed hydrogen $\leftarrow$ 377.7 ml H_2/g Ni$_{tot}$ $\equiv$ 0.989 Ni$_{met}/g$ Ni$_{tot}$ 23.3 ml/g Ni.

The data found for hydrogen adsorption on this catalyst by three methods are consistent:

Direct adsorption: 25.8 ml H_2/g Ni$_{tot}$
Nitrogen treatment: 23.0 ml H_2/g Ni$_{tot}$
Sulphuric acid treatment: 23.3 ml H_2/g Ni$_{tot}$.

The values for the degree of reduction are also in very good agreement: 0.992 g Ni$_{met}/g$ Ni$_{tot}$ from the sulphuric acid treatment and 0.987 g Ni$_{met}/g$ Ni$_{tot}$ from the weight increase after oxidation.

C Effect of the Presence of Sulphur in the Reduced Catalysts

As explained in Section II, the catalysts were prepared from nickel sulphate, and as a result some sulphate ions that could not be eliminated by washing were incorporated in the precipitate. After reduction this sulphate is reduced to sulphide, which may have an important influence on hydrogen adsorption. We found that no hydrogen adsorption could be measured on a catalyst poisoned with a high amount of sulphur. Roberts and Sykes (1957) have shown that reduction of nickel sulphide at 500°C in hydrogen proceeds easily to metallic nickel, but some sulphur is retained and this remaining sulphur is very difficult to eliminate. After the reduction no hydrogen adsorption could be observed, suggesting that the nickel surface remains covered with chemisorbed sulphur. If we assume that in our samples too all residual sulphur is located at the nickel surface, we can calculate a surface area complementary to the surface area determined by the hydrogen adsorption. For the calculation we assumed that one sulphur atom occupied about two surface nickel atoms, so that a value of 12.66 Å^2 for the cross-sectional area of a sulphur atom can be used. Hence 1 mg S/g Ni is equivalent to a sulphur-poisoned area of 2.38 m^2/g Ni. To check this assumption we proceeded as follows. Three catalysts were used for hydrogenating a triglyceride oil containing sulphur compounds. In the hydrogenation these sulphur compounds are hydrogenolyzed, and the sulphur is deposited on the nickel surface. The hydrogenation was performed with a low catalyst concentration, so that excess sulphur was available in the oil. After hydrogenation the catalyst was filtered off, and the sulphur content was determined by dissolution in acid and determination of H_2S. The increase in the sulphur content may now be compared with the hydrogen adsorption on the same catalyst before poisoning, so that the number of sulphur atoms bound per surface nickel atom can be calculated. The results are shown in Table X. The average value of 0·55 at S/at. Ni is close to our assumed value of 0·5.

TABLE X. Sulphur content before and after hydrogenating a sulphur-containing triglyceride oil

	S-content (mg S/g Ni)				
	Before	After			
Catalyst no.	Hydrogenation	Increase		V_m (ml H_2/g Ni)	$\dfrac{\text{at. S}}{\text{at. Ni}}$
P 93	6	49	43	28·0	0·54
P 1607	1	40	39	25·8	0·53
P 95	11	25	14	8·3	0·59
				Average	0·55

D   Relation between the Nickel Surface Area and the Crystallite Size

Assuming that the hydrogen surface area and the sulphur-poisoned surface area are complementary, we can now calculate the total area of the nickel crystallites. To correlate this area with the crystallite size we shall use the model developed earlier, in which hemispherical crystallites are attached to the support with their equatorial plane.* For this model it can easily be shown that the crystallite size (Coenen, 1958; Linsen, 1964) (defined as the cube root of the volume) can be calculated from the nickel area per gram of nickel using the formula

---

* Other models were tried in this correlation, but the hemisphere model gave the best result.

$$D = \frac{4310}{S_{Ni}}$$

in which D is in Å and S_{Ni} in m^2/g. The results of the surface area determination and the crystallite sizes are given in Table XI.

TABLE XI. Nickel surface area before passivation and the crystallite size of the reduced catalyst after passivation

Catalyst no.	% Ni	$\frac{mg\ S}{g\ Ni}$	Hydrogen adsorption V_m (ml H_2/g Ni)	Surface area (m^2/g Ni)			Crystallite size (Å)		a/b
				Clean nickel	Sulphur-poisoned nickel	Total	From surface area (a)	From X-ray (b)	
P 3	31	8	27·0	92	19	111	39	32	1·22
P 93	43	6	28·0	95	14	109	40	38	1·05
P 1607	60	1	25·8	88	2	90	48	45	1·07
P 60	38	10	16·9	58	24	82	53	40	1·33
P 94	55	9	16·3	56	21	77	57	59	0·97
P 21	63	8	16·0	55	19	74	58	57	1·02
P 85	62	10	12·2	42	24	66	65	68	0·96
P 84	62	5	12·7	43	12	55	78	63	1·24
P 95	70	11	8·3	28	26	54	79	69	1·15

Average a/b 1·12
±0·04

From these results it is evident that the crystallite sizes determined from surface area measurements and from X-ray line broadening are closely correlated. The fact that the ratio of these two values is close to unity may be taken as added support for the assumed structural model. It should be emphasized that a number of uncertainties are attached to both methods of crystallite size determination: for the surface area method: the area per surface nickel atom, the area per sulphur atom adsorbed, and the exact shape of the crystallites; for the X-ray method: uncertainty of the exact value of K in Scherrer's equation (dependent on shape); for both determinations and for the correlation: uncertainty with respect to the size distribution and different types of averaging.

From electron micrographs of the catalysts it appeared that the size distribution is relatively narrow and the crystallite shape is roughly isometric, providing some justification of the shape factor $K = 1$ (Klug and Alexander, 1954) and for disregarding the effect of size distribution.

E   Location of the Nickel Oxide in the Passivated Catalysts

It may be expected that a part of the nickel oxide present in the passivated catalysts is formed on the surface of the nickel crystallites by superficial oxidation in the passivation process. In Table XII the oxide contents in the passivated catalysts, determined by quantitative X-ray analysis, are given together with the clean nickel surface areas in non-passivated catalysts.

TABLE XII. Relation between the nickel surface area and the oxide content

Catalyst no.	$\dfrac{\text{g Ni as NiO}}{\text{g Ni}_{tot}}$ (a)	Clean nickel surface area $(m^2/\text{g Ni}_{tot})$	$\dfrac{\text{g Ni in surface}}{\text{g Ni}_{tot}}$ (b)	n^* $(= a/b)$
P 93	0·27	95	0·144	1·9
P 60	0·15	58	0·087	1·7
P 94	0·27	56	0·084	3·2
P 84	0·09	43	0·066	1·4
P 85	0·11	42	0·063	1·9
P 95	0·09	28	0·043	2·1

* n = number of layers of nickel atoms oxidized in passivation.

In Fig. 8 the relative oxide content is plotted as a function of the clean nickel surface area.

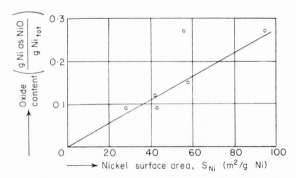

FIG. 8 Relation between the nickel surface area before passivation and the oxide content after passivation.

From these results it is evident that the oxide content and the nickel surface area are closely related. Only in catalyst P 94 is a higher oxide content found than that expected on the basis of this correlation.

This might be explained by assuming that this catalyst was either badly reduced or had suffered further oxidation (owing to badly controlled passivation or during storage). An indication for the former assumption may be found in the fact that the silicate content was also unexpectedly high, indicating inadequate reduction (Coenen, 1958).

From the slope of the line in Fig. 8 or the average value of n (disregarding P 94) we arrive at the conclusion that in passivation about 1.8 nickel layers are oxidized. For one of the catalysts the weight increase during passivation as well as the decrease in metallic nickel content were measured, and these data also indicate that about two nickel layers are oxidized in passivation. A similar conclusion was reached by Dell *et al.* (1956), who found that oxygen adsorption on nickel was not limited to a single chemisorbed layer but proceeded to superficial oxidation of about three statistical nickel layers.

VI Other Types of Nickel on Silica Catalysts

From the preceding sections a structural model for Ni/SiO_2 catalysts has been evolved, which for coprecipitated catalysts with kieselguhr as the source of silica is supported by a considerable volume of substantiating evidence. It is of interest to verify whether the same structural model can be applied to Ni/SiO_2 catalysts prepared with other methods.

A   Preparation of Samples

For all samples in this series pure silica was used as the support material, and nickel chloride or nickel nitrate was used as the nickel source to circumvent the complication of residual sulphur. Details of sample preparation are given in Table XIII.

B   Nickel Surface Areas and Crystallite Sizes

The methods of hydrogen adsorption and crystallite size measurement were the same as before. The same structural model of hemispherical crystallite attached to the support was also used. The results are given in Table XIV.

As in the earlier case of the kieselguhr-supported coprecipitated catalysts, the crystallite sizes determined from surface areas and by X-rays show a close correlation. In the earlier work (Section V D) an average value of $1·12 \pm 0·04$ was obtained for the a/b ratio. We thus find that for nickel on silica catalysts prepared in different ways the same structural model seems to describe our observations.

TABLE XIII. Preparation data for sulphar-free Ni/SiO$_2$ catalysts

Catalyst no.	Support material	Source of Ni	Preparation method	Reduction with H$_2$ at
a Wanig Alnig Enig 1 Enig 2 Niwag Nialg	Wet silica gel freshly prepared at pH 7·5	NiCl$_2$. 6 aq	Various methods of coprecipitation, pH 8·5	500°C‡
b MIG	Silica as under (*c*)	Ni(OH)$_2$	Dry mix	
Cog 1–4	treated hydrothermally			
De01–De06	average pore diameter 1000 Å	Ni(NO$_3$)$_2$. 6 aq		
c De11–De16	Silica prepared at pH 7·5, aged at 80°C, average pore diameter 160 Å		Impregnation at 75°C*	
d De22–De26	Aerosil†			300°C‡

* At 75°C Ni(NO$_3$)$_2$. 6 aq is dissolved in its water of crystallization.
† Non-porous microspheroidal silica ex Degussa. Mean particle size 64 Å (Linsen, 1964).
‡ The reduction was complete for these catalysts under the conditions applied.

If we combine the two series an average a/b value of $1·10 \pm 0·03$ is obtained. The deviation from unity thus probably is significant. This may be due to systematic errors in one or both of the methods of determination (e.g. a value of the Scherrer constant $K = 1·10$ would result in $a/b = 1$). There is, however, a more interesting consideration. The X-ray measurements were performed on passivated catalysts and the hydrogen adsorption on pyrophoric samples. We have seen that passivation results in superficial oxidation of the nickel crystallites. In this process 10–30% of the nickel is oxidized, depending on the nickel surface area. For an assumed average value of 20% oxidation the volume of the fcc nickel crystallite is decreased by 20%. We are thus tempted to correct the X-ray values by a factor of $\sqrt[3]{\dfrac{100}{80}} = 1·08$, which brings the average value of a/b practically to unity.

TABLE XIV. Nickel surface area before passivation and the crystallite size after passivation of the reduced catalysts

| | | | Crystallite size (Å) | | |
% Ni	Catalyst no.	$S_{Ni}(m^2/g\ Ni_{tot})$ from H_2 adsorption	From surface area (a)	From X-ray (b)	a/b
4·9	De 01	60	72	54	1·33
9·4	De 02	57	75	59	1·27
16·1	De 03	47	92	84	1·10
21·7	De 04	39	112	110	1·02
26·7	De 05	38	113	88	1·28
31·7	De 06	48	113	95	1·19
33·1	De 16	69	62	86	0·72
33·4	De 26	56	77	71	1·08
9·2	Cog 1	24	183	175	1·05
16·5	Cog 2	20	219	206	1·06
22·9	Cog 3	16	267	209	1·28
60·7	Niwag	42	79	102	0·77
60·2	Nialg	48	86	90	0·96

Average   1·09
±0·05

VII Relation Between the Total Surface Area and the Nickel Surface Area

For the coprecipitated catalysts made with kieselguhr as the support material, a high total surface area indicates a strong chemical attack of the support, since the area of the kieselguhr is of the order of 20 m^2/g. This high total area will be derived from a high proportion of silicate, and we may then expect small nickel crystallites and a large nickel surface area. For the impregnates a high support area provides good conditions for a fine dispersion of the nickel compounds, again resulting in a large nickel area in the reduced catalyst. For a large number of the catalysts of the two kinds the total surface area was determined by the conventional BET evaluation of low-temperature nitrogen-adsorption isotherms (see Chapter 1). The data are shown in Fig. 9. It should be noted that the scale for the nickel areas is enlarged 20 times compared to the total area scale.

The first gross conclusion is that the nickel and the total surface areas indeed show the expected parallel behaviour, especially within a group of catalysts prepared by a similar technique.

We may further note that the coprecipitates of group 1, prepared under strongly alkaline conditions, have a higher S_{Ni}/S_{tot} ratio than the coprecipitates of group 2, prepared in a less alkaline medium. This must be due to a stronger interaction—more silicate formation—at the higher alkalinity. Comparing groups 2 and 3, both reduced at 500°C, we note that in the impregnates prepared in an acid medium, the nickel surface area development is even smaller. Virtually no silicate is formed, so that the sintering stability is poor. That sintering is indeed the cause of the poor performance in group 3 is demonstrated in group 4, where De 02–05 are duplicates of Cog 1–4 as far as the

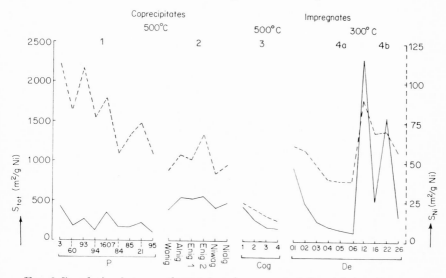

FIG. 9 Correlation between the total surface area and the nickel surface area.

impregnation is concerned. At a lower reduction temperature in group 4a the nickel surface area is considerably larger, since less sintering has occurred. Group 4b gives a further demonstration of the importance of intermediate silicate formation. In this group the silica support had not been hydrothermally treated before impregnation, leaving it with a higher reactivity than the silica of group 4a and group 3.

We have thus further strengthened our conviction that intermediate silicate formation is of great importance.

A further confirmation of our structural model—hemispherical crystallites attached with their equatorial planes to the support—was obtained in the following way. Schuit and de Boer (1954) have described an elegant method of eliminating nickel metal from the reduced catalyst, without inducing changes in the support structure; this involved treatment with carbon monoxide at 80°C, whereby the nickel was carried off as nickel tetracarbonyl.

If our assumed model is correct, there should be a simple relation between the total surface area of the reduced catalyst, the nickel surface area, and the surface area of the catalyst after removal of the nickel:

$$S_{tot} - \tfrac{1}{2}S_{Ni} = S_{Ni\text{-}free}.$$

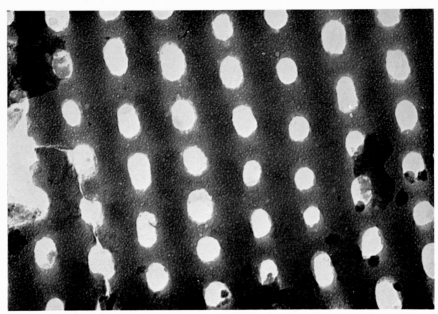

FIG. 10 Structure of kieselguhr ($\times$ 100,000).

For a coprecipitated catalyst on kieselguhr this relation was verified. All areas are expressed per g of SiO_2, since this remains unchanged in the process

$$S_{tot} = 571 \text{ m}^2/\text{g SiO}_2$$
$$S_{Ni} = 246 \text{ m}^2/\text{g SiO}_2$$

Expected: $S_{Ni\text{-}free} = 571 - 123 = 448 \text{ m}^2/\text{g SiO}_2$

Experimental: $S_{Ni\text{-}free} = 446 \text{ m}^2/\text{g SiO}_2$.

These data provide very strong support for the validity of the assumed structural model.

It should be emphasized that this relation will only hold for catalysts in which all the nickel is intimately attached to the support. Quite generally, we may expect $S_{\text{tot}} - \frac{1}{2}S_{\text{Ni}} \geqslant S_{\text{Ni-free}} \geqslant S_{\text{tot}} - S_{\text{Ni}}$. Electron micrographs of kieselguhr before catalyst precipitation and after nickel elimination from the reduced catalyst provide further striking confirmation. Figure 10 shows the structure of the original kieselguhr.

Figure 11 shows the reduced catalyst after nickel extraction with CO. In the later figure we find again the original kieselguhr structure, but modified in a characteristic way. The kieselguhr surface now has a striated appearance: the silica plates remaining from the silicate layer structure are clearly visible, and account for an increase in the surface area from $\sim$20 to 448 m^2/g SiO_2.

FIG. 11 Structure of the catalyst after nickel extraction with CO ($\times$ 100,000).

The nickel-free surface area of 448 m^2/g SiO_2 is equivalent to 1040 m^2/ml SiO_2. If we assume that the silica structure is entirely constructed of plates of uniform thickness, we can calculate this hypothetical thickness. For this catalyst we arrive at a value of 20 Å. This clearly is a maximum value, since no allowance is made for unreacted kieselguhr, so that the actual thickness of the lamellae must be smaller. From the electron micrograph a thickness of 30 Å can be estimated.

These two values are reasonably close, indicating that apparently in this particular catalyst very little of the SiO_2 in the kieselguhr has escaped rearrangement. The thickness of the lamellae indicates that three to four unit layers of silicate are involved in the ultimate construction of the lamellae. A small proportion—about 4%—of the nickel cannot be eliminated from a reduced catalyst with CO. This nickel may be located in the interior of the lamellae. An alternative explanation might be that the nickel atoms in the basal plane of attachment of the crystallites—still present in their original location—are so strongly bound that they cannot be removed with carbon monoxide under the applied conditions. For the catalyst under discussion, with an average crystallite size of 48 Å, it is easily shown that 8% of the nickel atoms in the crystallites are located in these planes of attachment.

VIII　Preliminary Activity Determinations and Correlation with Structure

For the coprecipitated catalysts discussed in the first part of this investigation two activity parameters for fatty oil hydrogenation were determined, which we shall denote by A_s and A_w.

A　Description of the Activity Measurements

For both measurements hydrogenation was performed at 180°C, on 150 g of oil, in a cylindrical stirred vessel. The catalyst was suspended in the oil. A stream of hydrogen (60 l/h) was passed through the oil. The reactor dimensions and the stirring intensity were standardized. The degree of conversion was determined by measuring the refractive index n_D^{65}, the decrease of which is linearly related to the decrease of unsaturation (e.g. the decrease of the iodine value) (Coenen, 1958). In the determination of A_s a vegetable oil of good stability and low sulphur content, sesame oil, and a fixed catalyst concentration of 0·07% Ni/oil were used. The maximum attainable value of Δn_D^{65} for complete hydrogenation of sesame oil is $120 \cdot 10^{-4}$.

To eliminate the influence of quality variation of the sesame oil, the same figure was determined for a standard catalyst under the same conditions. A_s was defined as $(\Delta n_D^{65}/_{st}\Delta n_D^{65}) \times 100\%$. For the standard catalyst Δn_D^{65} is about $80 \cdot 10^{-4}$, so that the maximum value attainable for $A_s = 150$.

Both the unknown and the standard catalysts were freshly reduced under standard conditions before each determination. In the determination of A_w an oil containing a high sulphur content (about 30 p.p.m.), whale oil, was used. This determination involves a series of hydrogenations with different catalyst concentration. The nickel concentration needed to obtain a refractive index drop of $80 \cdot 10^{-4}$ in 30 minutes was determined for the unknown and for a standard catalyst.

$$A_w = \frac{\% \text{Ni}_{\text{standard}}}{\% \text{Ni}_{\text{unknown}}} \times 100\%.$$

B   Results Obtained

The results for the first series of coprecipitated catalysts are given in Table XV.

TABLE XV. Activities of the first series of coprecipitated catalysts

Catalyst no.	$S_{\text{Ni}}(\text{m}^2/\text{g Ni})$ sulphur-free	A_s	A_w	$\bar{L}(\mu)$
P 93	95	111	177	16·5
P 3	92	114	164	14·0
P 1607	88	88	132	19·6
P 60	58	115	—	15·5
P 94	56	110	—	16·6
P 21	55	108	128	15·0
P 84	43	91	81	21·7
P 85	42	112	100	13·7
P 52	37	116	100	13·5
P 95	28	100	70	18·5

It is immediately obvious that A_s does not show any correlation at all with the non-poisoned nickel surface area, whereas A_w does.

The first question to be answered is why A_s does not show any relationship with the nickel surface area. It is logical to assume that mass transport resistances may well play a part in this hydrogenation, in view of the fact that triglycerides have large molecules (molecular weight of the order of 900, molecular diameter $\sim$15 Å). To verify this possibility the samples were therefore subjected to a simple microscopic particle size assessment. The particle size determines the length of the pores and the size of the external surface area. We may thus expect (Wheeler, 1955) that the reciprocal value of the particle size shows a positive correlation with activity. A small amount of the catalyst was suspended in a drop of heptane and three micrographs were taken. The diameters were measured for 100 randomly selected particles, and a volume-average particle diameter was calculated. The results are given in Table XV.

Figure 12 shows that there is indeed a positive correlation. For several reasons such a correlation should only be taken as a qualitative indication that mass transport is indeed important and is probably responsible for the total absence of a correlation between the activity and the nickel surface area. No data on pore width are available for these catalysts, whereas the particle size data should be considered as rough estimates. Finally, the range of activities within the series of catalysts is too narrow to warrant a more quantitative description.

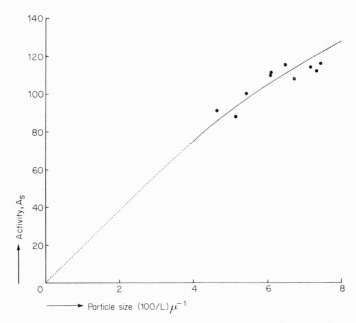

FIG. 12 Relationship between the activity A_s and the reciprocal of the particle size.

Secondly, we may ask why in the case of A_w a correlation with S_{Ni} does appear. This can be understood as follows: the sulphur in the oil, which is deposited on the nickel surface in the course of the hydrogenation, may be expected to deposit preferentially on the most accessible part of the nickel surface, i.e. in the outer shells of the particles. If the catalyst has a high nickel surface area these poisoned shells will be much thinner than in the case of a small area. It may thus be expected that in the hydrogenation of a sulphur-rich oil a large surface area will be a great advantage, i.e. less catalyst will then be needed for a given degree of conversion. Moreover, in this case the particle size will remain of importance. A plot of A_w versus S_{Ni}/L, given in Fig. 13, shows qualitatively the expected behaviour.

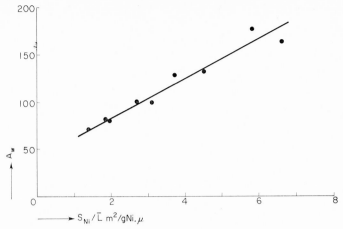

FIG. 13 Relationship between the activity parameter, A_w. and the ratio nickel surface area/particle size, $S_{Ni}/\bar{L}$.

IX Further Characterization of the Catalyst Texture in Connection with Mass Transport

From the provisional investigation in the last section it is evident that mass transport resistance is an important factor in catalyst activity for the hydrogenation of fatty oils. This will also be the case for selectivity. We therefore investigated the texture of a wide range of catalysts, comprising all the catalysts introduced in Section VI as well as four new catalysts of the coprecipitated type discussed in earlier sections.

In connection with the provisional investigation of the last section it was observed that in the course of a hydrogenation with intensive stirring considerable particle fragmentation may occur, so that the average particle size is sensitive to the method of dispersion of particle size analysis. Two methods were found to give reproducible and mutually comparable results, and these were used in the following investigation. It should be stressed that the data obtained here are not directly comparable with the particle size data of Section VIII.

A Particle Size Analysis

Sedimentation in an Andreasen pipette was carried out on reduced catalysts suspended in a 0.002 M solution of $Na_4P_2O_7$ as a peptization agent. Before sedimentation the suspension was stirred for two hours. Microscopic analysis was performed on suspensions in sesame oil, stirred under CO_2 under the same conditions as those used in the activity determinations.

Details of the experimental technique and of the calculations involved are given by Linsen (1964). The reproducibility was excellent, and the surface-average diameter obtained by the two methods showed satisfactory agreement:

$$\text{Wanig } 7\cdot8\mu \text{ and } 8\cdot3\mu$$
$$\text{Nialg } 7\cdot3\mu \text{ and } 7\cdot4\mu$$

so that the results of the two methods can be used indiscriminately.

B   Pore Size Distribution

Information on pore structure was obtained from an analysis of the nitrogen adsorption isotherms on the basis of Kelvin's equation for the vapour pressure of curved liquid surfaces. Several different types of pore structure occurred among the investigated catalysts. The impregnates were characterized by cylindrical pores giving a hysteresis loop of type A (for isotherm classification see de Boer, 1958). For this case analysis of the desorption branch was performed along the lines given by Barrett, Joyner and Halenda (1951) and Linsen (1964). The results are given as pore radii r_p.

The coprecipitates prepared at high alkalinity were characterized by slit-shaped pores (intermediate nickel silicate), giving a hysteresis loop of type B. For this group of catalysts the analysis was performed on the desorption branch, following a method originally given by Innes (1957) and Steggerda (1958) modified according to Linsen (1964). The results are given as pore widths d_p. The coprecipitates prepared at low alkalinity were relatively microporous. For this case analysis of the desorption branch fails, since Kelvin's equation is no longer meaningful, and for these catalysts the adsorption branch was analysed by means of V_a/t-plots (Linsen, 1964; de Boer et al., 1965).

As will be demonstrated later, pore widths may be classified in three ranges with respect to their catalytic behaviour: pores < 20 Å, between 20 and 25 Å, and > 25 Å. Since we are interested in the catalytic activity of the nickel surface, data will be given for the nickel surface area present in these three ranges of pore widths. For the calculation it was assumed that the total nickel surface area was evenly distributed over the total support area, so that the nickel area was divided proportionally to the total area present in the respective pore widths ranges.

C   Catalyst Structure and Activity

For a discussion of the data given in Table XVI we shall first consider groups of catalysts having common structural characteristics. In Fig. 14 the activity A_s of all impregnated catalysts (groups 3 and 4

TABLE XVI. Relationship between sesame activity and some texture characteristics

Catalyst no.	A_s	S_{Ni} (m²/g Ni)	$\bar{r}_p$ or $\bar{d}_p$ (Å)	$S_{Ni}, <20$ Å (m²(g Ni)	$S_{Ni}, 20\text{-}25$ Å (m²/g Ni)	$S_{Ni}>25$ Å (m²/g Ni)	$\bar{L}$ (μ)	$S_{Ni}>25$ Å/$\bar{L}$
Pr 21	118	90	109	0	0	90	5·6	16·1
1 A 1	87	106	66	10	41	55	7·1	7·7
A 2	90	133	34	52	40	41	5·7	7·2
B	53	123	27	45	64	14	6·3	2·3
Wanig	1	44	19	42	1	1	7·8	0·2
Alnig	43	54	30	38	6	10	8·6	1·2
2 Enig 1	42	51	39	36	2	13	9·8	1·3
Enig 2	59	67	40	37	8	22	11·1	2·0
Niwag	2	42	20	41	0	1	6·6	0·2
Nialg	25	48	26	40	1	7	7·3	1·0
Cog 1	45	24	443	0	0	24	17·0	1·4
Cog 2	40	20	371	0	0	20	16·7	1·2
3 Cog 3	18	16	356	0	0	16	20·8	0·8
Cog 4	10	13	319	0	1	12	19·8	0·6
Mig	22	15	270	1	1	13	11·0	1·2
De 01	67	60	—	—	—	—	—	—-
De 02	74	57	457	0	0	57	9·5	6·0
De 03	69	47	—	—	—	—	—	—
De 04	70	39	—	—	—	—	—	—
De 05	54	38	—	—	—	—	—	—-
De 06	53	38	358	0	0	38	27·8	1·4
4 De 11	90	122	—	—	—	—	—	—
De 12	88	90	81	4	3	83	9·8	8·5
De 13	84	71	—	—	—	—	—	—
De 14	76	70	—	—	—	—	—	—
De 15	67	66	—	—	—	—	—	—
De 16	67	69	73	5	5	59	17·3	3·4
De 22	77	70	188	4	3	63	12·9	4·9
De 24	72	60	—	—	—	—	—	—-
De 25	77	52	—	—	—	—	—	—-
De 26	73	56	177	2	4	50	14·7	3·4

of Table XVI) is given as a function of the nickel surface area. All catalysts in these groups are characterized by relatively wide pores, and here we do find a correlation with the surface area. A certain amount of scatter in this figure is due to mass transport effects, as will be seen later.

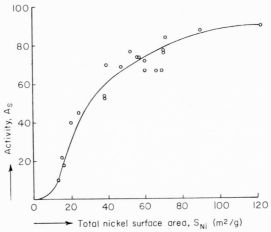

FIG. 14 Activity of impregnates as a function of the total nickel surface area.

For the coprecipitates of groups 1 and 2* again no correlation between A_s and S_{Ni} is found, as can be seen from Table XVI. Taking now the extreme view that with these catalysts mass transport predominates in the performance, we have plotted in Fig. 15 activity versus average pore width $(\bar{d}_p)$. Again we find a positive correlation. Scatter in this case may be due to the fact that the average pore width is only a

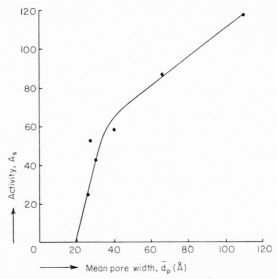

FIG. 15 Activity of coprecipitates as a function of the mean pore width.

* Table XVI.

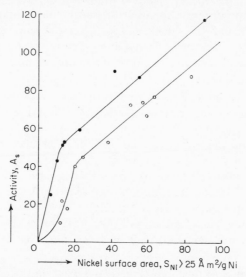

FIG. 16 Activity of the impregnates (○) and coprecipitates (●) as a function of the nickel surface area $S_{Ni} > 25$ Å.

rather crude measure of accessibility, whereas the nickel surface area is completely disregarded. A very significant feature of this figure is that the activity drops practically to zero at an average pore width of 20 Å. This led us to calculate the subdivision in nickel surface area in the pore width ranges, as discussed earlier.

We next plotted in Fig. 16 the activity data against the nickel surface area in pores wider than 25 Å for both groups of catalysts. For

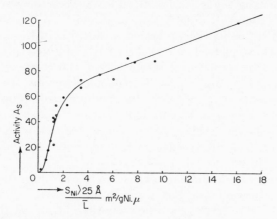

FIG. 17 Activity of the impregnates (○) and coprecipitates (●) as a function of $(S_{Ni} > 25$ Å$)/\bar{L}$.

20

most of the impregnates this area is almost equal to the total nickel surface area so that the curve of Fig. 14 is not changed much. It is obvious, however, that now the coprecipitates too show a correlation, although they do not fit in the curve of the impregnates.

Bearing in mind the expected reciprocal relationship with the particle sizes we then plotted in Fig. 17 all activity data against $(S_{Ni} > 25 \text{ Å})/\bar{L}$, and found that one curve now describes the activity behaviour of all catalysts. Two features of this curve require some discussion. The general shape of the curve can be described as two straight lines of different slope, linked by a transition region.

The first straight line does not pass through the origin—there is a kind of induction period. This may be explained by realizing that sesame oil—although classified as an oil of high purity—still contains small traces of sulphur. These traces will obviously have the greatest effect at very low nickel surface areas or large particle sizes, i.e. at low $(S_{Ni} > 25 \text{ Å})/\bar{L}$.

The marked change in slope is connected with the specific character of the substrate. The fatty acid composition of sesame oil is 42% di-unsaturated (linoleic), 45% mono-unsaturated (oleic) and 13% saturated (stearic and palmitic). It is well known (Coenen, 1960a,b; Coenen et al., 1965) that linoleic acid hydrogenates at a much higher rate than oleic acid. This effect is the cause of an aspect of selectivity that we will discuss in the next Section IX D. Relatively inactive catalysts will in the available time (30 min) hydrogenate almost exclusively linoleic acid, whereas catalysts of high activity (above $A_s = 60$) will have exhausted all available linoleic acid in the first part of the reaction time and will thus work at a handicap in the remaining time. A break in the curve around $A_s = 60$ is thus expected.

This effect is further demonstrated in Fig. 18. In the top section of this figure we have plotted for one of the coprecipitated catalysts (Pr 21) the fatty acid composition of sesame oil in the course of the hydrogenation, as a function of the degree of conversion. In the middle section of the same figure we show the rate of hydrogen uptake against the degree of conversion. We note in this curve that the reaction is of zero order in the initial stage, when a high proportion of linoleic acid is still present. The rate then goes through a transition period, after which again almost zero order is observed. In this latter range only monoenoic acids are hydrogenated, as can be seen from the top section of the figure. In the lower part we have reproduced Fig. 17 in such a way that the activity data are now on the horizontal axis, used for the degree of conversion in the other sections. This is possible because the activity figures correspond to a final refractive index which is directly related to the iodine value of the product. The interrelation between the three sections is obvious. In the range of iodine values where formation of saturated fatty acids commences, linoleic acid

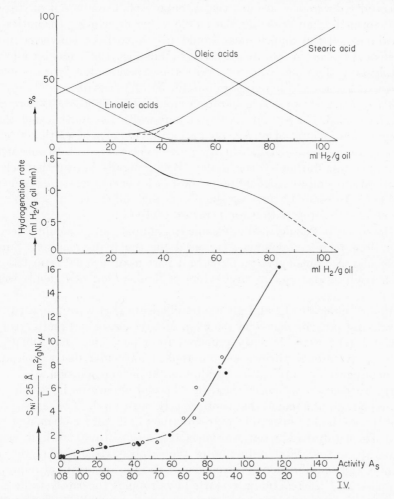

FIG. 18 Relationship between the fatty acid composition, the rate curve, and the catalyst activity.

approaches low values and monoenic acids are near their maximum (top section), the rate drops gradually to the lower level corresponding to monoene hydrogenation (middle section). The break in the activity curve occurs in the range of iodine values where the linoleic acid is exhausted.

D   Catalyst Texture and Selectivity

At the temperature of the activity determinations, 180°C, the selectivity differences are not very pronounced. The amount of stearic acid formed when reaching the iodine value at which—theoretically speaking—all the linoleic acid would just have been converted into oleic acid in case of infinite selectivity (Williams, 1927) was for all the catalysts in the range of 4–8%. With the experimental error involved discussion of these differences would not be very fruitful.

Three catalysts were selected for a more extensive investigation, i.e. A1, A2, and B. These catalysts show a pore width distribution such that a significant amount of surface area is located in pores of width between 20 and 25 Å—a pore range where we may expect important concentration gradients during hydrogenation. It is generally known that selectivity in fatty oil hydrogenation is lower at lower temperature (Coenen, 1960a,b). In order to increase the observable differences in selectivity we chose a hydrogenation temperature of 100°C.

Moreover, it was deemed advisable to eliminate all poisoning effects. Therefore pure compounds were used for the hydrogenation. Since molecular size must play an important part in diffusional retardation, both triglycerides and methyl esters of linoleic and oleic acids were used.

Methyl linoleate (L) and glyceryl trilinoleate (L₃) were prepared by esterifying pure linoleic acid (99·6%). Methyl oleate (O) and glyceryl trioleate (O₃) were similarly prepared from pure oleic acid (99·9%). After conventional purification we applied molecular distillation and chromatographic purification on alumina in hexane solution.

Hydrogenation was performed in a special apparatus in which the hydrogen uptake could be continuously measured. The apparatus and the method of operation were described in detail by Coenen (1960 a,b). The catalyst reduction was effected in a side arm of the hydrogenation apparatus. After reduction of the catalyst, degassing of the oil charge, and equilibration of the oil charge and the apparatus at required temperatures, the reaction was started by dropping the catalyst into the stirred oil. All reaction conditions were closely controlled. The hydrogenations were performed at 100°C and with an amount of catalyst containing 0·2% Ni, calculated on the oil charge. The hydrogen take-up was plotted as a hydrogenation rate curve. At a predetermined degree of saturation the reaction was stopped by sucking out the charge from the reactor and by immediate filtration. All samples were converted into methyl esters and analysed for fatty acid composition by gas chromatography.

The total trans-acid contents were determined by infra-red measurements (American Oil Chemists' Society, 1946). The degree of hydrogenation was obtained from the iodine value, the amount of hydrogen taken up, and the fatty acid composition, all data showing close agreement.

As already mentioned, linoleic acid hydrogenates at a greater rate than oleic acid, giving rise to one selectivity aspect. This selectivity is due to the fact that linoleic acid is adsorbed more strongly than oleic acid. When both are present, the linoleic acid will cover the greater part of the nickel surface. This also explains the initial kinetic zero-order behaviour discussed in Section IX C. The preferential adsorption of linoleic acid was demonstrated in a separate investigation with use of a "labelled" oleic acid (Coenen and Boerma, 1968).

Closer analysis of the reaction scheme reveals several selectivity characteristics, since there are a number of consecutive and parallel reactions.

Owing to the preferential adsorption of linoleic acid, "oleic acid"* may be formed as an intermediate product, which in turn may be saturated to form stearic acid. Hydrogenation of linoleic acid involves then two consecutive reactions. Alternatively, linoleic acid may be supposed to form stearic acid without intermediate desorption of "oleic acid", this reaction competing with the "oleic acid" formation by desorption of this intermediate product. This scheme involves two parallel reactions. The two schemes may be combined into:

The kinetics of this combined scheme were discussed by de Boer and van der Borg (1959, 1960) and van der Borg (1959), who found that it describes adequately several different types of fatty oil hydrogenation. We shall define as selectivity I the ratio $S_I = k_1/(k_2+k_3)$, which is large when high yields of the partially hydrogenated product "O" are obtained.

The fact that the acids in fatty oils are present in triglyceride form must now be considered. It may be felt that the fact that one of the fatty acid chains of a triglyceride is adsorbed and reacts increases the chance of reaction for another chain of this molecule. We therefore define a further selectivity concept, the triglyceride selectivity S_T, this again being large when a high yield of the partially hydrogenated

---

* "Oleic acid" ("O") will be used to denote the group of singly unsaturated fatty acids.

product (i.e. leaving the other chains untouched) is obtained. It should be noted that S_T has meaning also for an oil having only oleic acid (O_3), whereas S_I is only significant for the hydrogenation of oils containing polyunsaturated acids (L_3 and L).

Next to hydrogenation reactions we must consider isomerization. In the raw materials all the double bonds are in the cis configuration in well defined positions in the chain. In an incompletely hydrogenated fatty acid group, desorbing from the catalyst, the residual double bonds may have shifted in the chain and/or may have been converted into the trans configuration. Hydrogenation and isomerization may be considered as a pair of parallel reactions, and we define a further selectivity concept, the specific izomerization S_i, as the ratio of isomerization and hydrogenation rates or rate constants. Two of the mentioned selectivity concepts, namely S_I and S_i, are generally recognized in some form in the literature (Feuge, 1955; Allen, 1962; van den Heuvel, 1956, 1957; Eldib and Albright, 1957).

Table XVII lists five different measures of catalyst activity, four of which are taken from the rate curves of the model compounds at a chosen degree of hydrogenation; the remaining measure, A_s, was defined earlier.

TABLE XVII. Catalyst activities

Catalyst no.	$\dfrac{S_{Ni} > 25 \text{ Å}}{\text{L}}$	A_s	Catalyst activity			
			Rate at 50% saturation		Rate at 25% saturation	
			O	O_3	L	L_3
A_1	7·7	87	4·9	1·6	7·2	2·3
A_2	7·2	90	6·0	1·6	8·0	3·4
B	2·3	53	3·2	1·1	5·5	1·4

A_s as defined before, other activity data in ml H_2/min g oil.

As can be seen from this table, all activity parameters show roughly parallel behaviour: A_1 and A_2 are almost equal and B is clearly inferior. Since mass transport resistance depends on both molecular size and intrinsic rate, no exact correlation between the five activity parameters can be expected. Catalyst B, having the lowest value of ($S_{Ni} >$ 25 Å)/L, has the lowest activity in all five determinations.

In Figs 19 and 20 the fatty acid compositions in the course of the hydrogenations of L_3, L, O_3 and O are shown for two of the catalysts.

It is obvious that the increase in the stearic acid content in the early stages of the hydrogenation is very different for the four cases: we obtain most stearic acid with catalyst B (large area in pores between 20 and 25 Å) and the triglyceride L_3, and least stearic acid with catalyst A_1 and the methyl ester L. We may summarize this by saying that formation of the intermediate product is suppressed by the mass transport resistance.

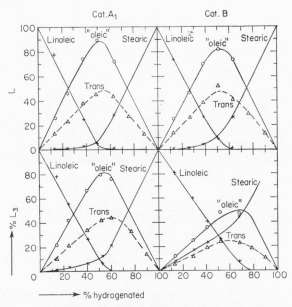

FIG. 19 Fatty acid composition during hydrogenation of methyl linoleate (L) and glyceryl trilinoleate (L_3) with catalysts A_1 and B.

A similar conclusion can be derived from Fig. 20. In oleic acid hydrogenation the trans acid may be considered as an intermediate, and again we find that the lowest trans contents (intermediate product) are found with catalyst B and the triglyceride, and the highest with catalyst A and the methyl ester.

For the L_3 and L hydrogenations we can now apply the kinetic scheme of de Boer and van der Borg and determine k_1, k_2 and k_3. In Table XVIII these rate constants are given in arbitrary units, setting k_2 at unity.

As expected, we find that catalyst B shows the lowest selectivity S_I for L_3 as well as for L; however, the difference with the A catalyst is much larger for L_3 than for L. As a structural parameter describing (in an admittedly rather crude fashion) the selectivity tendency of a catalyst, we defined P_S as the ratio of the nickel area in wide pores (> 25 Å to the nickel area in intermediate pores (20–25 Å)); we find that P_S is much smaller for B than for the A catalysts.

Similar behaviour is observed with respect to the cis-trans isomerization behaviour. For the triglycerides the specific isomerization S_i is considerably depressed for the B catalyst.

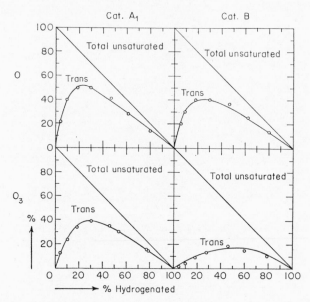

Fig. 20 Fatty acid composition during hydrogenation of methyl oleate (O) and glyceryl trioleate (O_3) with catalysts A_1 and B.

To obtain a measure of the triglyceride selectivity we analyzed the reaction products by thin layer chromatography on $AgNO_3/SiO_2$ (de Vries, 1963). Since the complete triglyceride composition is difficult to connect with the selectivity behaviour, we used only the tristearate contents. From the stearic acid content of a sample we can calculate the tristearate content that would appear if the fatty acids were randomly distributed over the triglycerides. We used the reciprocal value of the excess S_3 formation (above the content for random distribution) as an empirical measure of the triglyceride selectivity S_T. From Table XVIII again catalyst B shows drastically lower S_T values than the A catalysts for L_3 and O_3 hydrogenation.

A further simple demonstration of the influence of triglyceride selectivity can be found in the melting point behaviour of the hydrogenated products. Owing to the fact that the tristearate has a high melting point and is very sparingly soluble in the unsaturated oil, even a relatively low content of tristearate will increase considerably the melting point. For the O_3-hydrogenation products at five per cent

TABLE XVIII. Selectivity data

Catalyst no.	P_s*	L_3			L			S_i				S_T	
		k_1	k_3	S_I	k_1	k_3	S_I	L_3	O_3	L	O	L_3	O_3
A_1	1·2	25	2	8	30	0	30	0·9	2·5	0·9	3·2	0·53	0·23
A_2	1·0	20	0	20	40	0	40	1·1	3·1	1·1	6·3	—	0·17
B	0·2	7·5	4·5	1·4	14	0	14	0·4	0·6	0·9	3·3	0·08	0·04

$$* \ P_s = \frac{S_{N1} > 25 \text{ Å}}{S_{N1} 20\text{–}25\text{Å}}$$

k_1 and k_3 are rate constants in the reaction scheme:

$$\begin{array}{c} \text{``O''} \\ k_1 \nearrow \ \searrow k_2 = 1 \\ L \to S \\ k_3 \end{array}$$

saturation the melting points were found to be 34°C (A_1), 31°C (A_2), and 51°C (B). We should realize at this point that for all three products the stearic content is equal to 5%. If we transesterify the three products randomly we find accordingly a considerable lowering of the melting point to nearly the same low value for all three of about 6°C, showing that we have indeed an excess tristearate content.

The relation between the catalyst texture and the various selectivity aspects can be understood as follows. As we have seen, we can describe the selectivity I to a fair approximation as a case of two consecutive reactions in which the intermediate product is the desired one. We now consider a pore that is sufficiently narrow for mass transport to be partly rate-determining. In this pore significant concentration gradien^{t}s will then arise, since mass transport will have to rely entirely on molecular diffusion. The net transport needed for reaction to occur will require a concentration gradient as the driving force, this gradient being proportional to the rate of reaction and to the transport resistance. As long as the selectivity is high and the intermediate is the main product (zone A), the net transport is directed inward for the raw material, whereas it runs in the reverse direction for the intermediate. It is thus clear that the gradients for raw material and intermediate

20*

will be of opposite sign. For decreasing pore widths these gradients will become progressively greater, since for a given active wall area the transport cross-section will decrease.

In Fig. 21 the situation is illustrated qualitatively for three pore widths at the beginning of the hydrogenation of linoleic ester. From this figure it is clear that the active surface in the inner parts of the catalyst particle is in contact with an oil composition that deviates

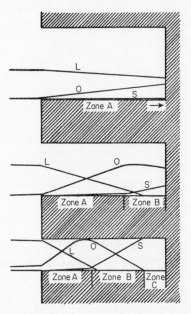

FIG. 21 Influence of pore width on concentration gradients of linoleic (L), oleic (O) and stearic acid (S).

significantly from the composition of the continuous liquid phase outside the particle, this deviation being greater for narrower pores. We may also express this in a different way: the inner surface is in contact with an oil composition that runs ahead of the composition on the outside of the particle. The radius of the particle in the inward direction is then a time axis. The instantaneous hydrogenation product of a narrow pore catalyst can be described with a residence time distribution: it may be considered as a mixture of hydrogenated products.

It follows immediately that in catalysts with very narrow pores (bottom of Fig. 21) there is an inward zone B in which all linoleic acid is exhausted. The sole product is now stearic acid. Again concentration gradients are needed for mass transport, but the oleic acid gradient is now reversed and a stearic acid gradient is set up. With very narrow or long pores there may be even a third zone C in the core of the particle, where only stearic acid is present and no hydrogenation occurs. This part of the catalyst is lost as far as catalytic activity is concerned.

The implication of these phenomena for selectivity is obvious. Hydrogenation proceeds selectively only in zone A. The overall reaction picture is a cumulation of the contributions of zones A and B, resulting in a lowered selectivity I. If we now treat the experimental observations by de Boer and van der Borg's kinetic scheme we need the short-circuit reaction (k_3) to fit the experimental curve. The conclusion is that a non-zero value of k_3 is no proof of the occurrence of a true short-circuit reaction (hydrogenation to stearic acid during one adsorption residence on the nickel surface). This is illustrated by the data of Table XVIII. For catalyst B a k_3 of 4·5 is needed for L_3 hydrogenation, whereas for L hydrogenation (larger diffusion coefficient) k_3 is zero.

Next to the transport of substrate molecules the transport of the other reactant plays an important part in the overall kinetics. Some aspects of this transport have been dealt with elsewhere (Coenen, 1960b; Coenen et al., 1965; Linsen, 1964).

X Conclusions

Summarizing the findings of this investigation, we may formulate the following conclusions regarding the state of the nickel in the reduced catalyst. After incomplete reduction and after passivation the nickel in the catalyst is present in three forms: basic nickel silicate, elementary nickel and nickel oxide. All elementary nickel is present as crystalline face centred cubic nickel. No indication of the presence of amorphous nickel could be found. Especially in samples of high silicate content and small crystallite size the lattice parameter is enlarged, compared with normal nickel metal. The nickel oxide is formed as a result of the passivation process and is all present on the surface of the nickel crystallites. The nickel crystallites are of approximately hemispherical shape and are attached to the silica support with their equatorial plane. These crystallites are grown epitaxially on the silica surface and the partially reduced basic nickel silicate serves as a matrix for the epitaxy and provides the attachment to the silica.

With respect to the catalytic activity of the catalyst on fatty oil hydrogenation the nickel surface area (S_{Ni}), the particle size (L) and the pore distribution in the particle are the determining factors. An empirical correlation between activity and the ratio $S_N{}^i > 25$ Å$/L$ is found. On the selectivity of the hydrogenation the nickel surface area in pores between 20–25 Å has a depressing effect.

XI Acknowledgements

Both authors have carried out their doctoral research under the guidance of Professor de Boer, while employed in industrial research on fatty oil hydrogenation. This chapter is mainly based on the contents of their theses. One of the authors (J. W. E. Coenen) has carried out a major part of his doctoral research—the crystallographic studies of the constituents of the technical catalysts—under the guidance of Professor W. G. Burgers in his laboratory. His helpful and stimulating discussions are gratefully acknowledged.

XII References

Aben, P. C., Platteeuw, J. C. and Stouthamer, B. (1968). *4th Int. Congr. Catal.* Moscow.
Alexander, L. E. (1948). *J. appl. Phys.* **19**, 1068.
Alexander, L. E. (1950). *J. appl. Phys.* **21**, 126.
Alexander, L. E. and Klug, H. P. (1950). *J. appl. Phys.* **21**, 137.
Alexander, L. E., Klug, H. P. and Kummer, E. (1948). *J. appl. Phys.* **19**, 742.
Allen, R. R. (1962). *J. Am. Oil. Chem. Soc.* **39**, 457.
American Oil Chemists' Society (1946). Tentative methods Cd 14-61.
Arkharov, V. J. and Graevskii, K. M. (1944). *Zh. tekh. Fiz.* **14**, 132.
Bagg, J., Jaeger, H. and Sanders, J. V. (1963). *J. Catalysis.* **2**, 449.
Baker, M. McD. and Rideal, E. K. (1955). *Trans Faraday Soc.* **51**, 1597.
Baker, M. McD., Jenkins, G. J. and Rideal, E. K. (1955). *Trans. Faraday Soc.* **51**, 1592.
Barrett, E. P., Joyner, L. G. and Halenda, P. P. (1951). *J. Am. chem. Soc.* **73**, 373.
Beeck, O. (1950). *Adv. Catalysis.* **2**, 151.
Beeck, O. and Ritchie, A. W. (1950). *Discuss. Faraday Soc.* **8**, 159.
Bizette, H. and de Saint Léon Langlès, R. (1950). *Bull. Soc. chim. Fr.* **M**, 1041.
de Boer, J. H. (1958). *In* "The Structure and Properties of Porous Materials" (D. H. Everett and F. S. Stone, eds.), p. 68. Butterworth, London.
de Boer, J. H. and van der Borg, R. J. A. M. (1959). *Proc. K. ned. Akad. Wet.* **B62**, 308.
de Boer, J. H. and van der Borg, R. J. A. M. (1960). *Actes 2e Congr. Int. Catal.* Vol. 1, p. 919. Edition Technip, Paris.
de Boer, J. H., Linsen, B. G., van der Plas, Th. and Zondervan, G. J. (1965). *J. Catalysis.* **4**, 649.
Brauer, G. (1954). "Handbuch der Präparativen Anorganischen Chemie", p. 1156. Enke Verlag, Stuttgart.
Brindley, G. W. (1961). *In* "The X-ray Identification and Crystal Structures of Clay Minerals" (G. Brown, ed.), p. 109. Mineralogical Society, London.
Broeder, J. J., van Reijen, L. L., Sachtler, W. H. M. and Schuit, G. C. A. (1956). *Z. Elektrochem.* **60**, 838.

Broeder, J. J., van Reijen, L. L., and Korswagen, A. R. (1957). *J. chem. Phys.* **54**, 37.

Bijvoet, J. M., Kolkmeijer, N. J. and McGillavry, C. H. (1948). "Röntgenanalyse van Kristallen". Centen, Amsterdam.

Carter, J. L., Cusumano, J. A. and Sinfelt, J. H. (1966). *J. phys. Chem.* **70**, 2257.

Chakravarty, K. M. and Sen, R. (1947). *Nature, Lond.* **160**, 907.

Coenen, J. W. E. (1958). "Onderzoek van Technische Nikkelkatalysatoren op Drager". Thesis, Delft University of Technology, The Netherlands.

Coenen, J. W. E. (1960a). *In* "The Mechanism of Heterogeneous Catalysis" (J. H. de Boer, ed.), p. 126, Elsevier, Amsterdam.

Coenen, J. W. E. (1960b). *Actes 2e Congr. Int. Catal.* Vol. 1a, p. 2705. Edition Technip, Paris.

Coenen, J. W. E. and Boerma, H. (1968). *Fette Seifen Anstrichmittel.* **70**, 8.

Coenen, J. W. E., Boerma, H., Linsen, B. G. and de Vries, B. (1965). *Proc. 3rd Int. Congr. Catal.* p. 1387. North Holland, Amsterdam.

Dean, J. G. (1952). *Ind. Engng Chem. ind. Edn.* **44**, 985.

de Jong, W. F. (1951). "Compendium der Kristalkunde". Oosthoek, Utrecht.

de Lange, J. J. and Visser, G. H. (1946). *Ingenieur, 's-Grav.* **58**, 24.

Dell, R. M., Klemperer, D. F. and Stone, F. S. (1956). *J. phys. Chem.* **60**, 1586.

de Saint Léon Langlès, R. (1952). *Annls Chim.* **7**, 568.

de Vries, B. (1963). *J. Am. Oil Chem. Soc.* **40**, 184.

Eldib, J. A. and Albright, L. F. (1957). *Ind. Engng Chem. ind. Edn.* **49**, 825.

Eucken, A. (1949). *Z. Elektrochem.* **53**, 285.

Farnsworth, H. E. and Woodcock, R. F. (1957). *Adv. Catalysis.* **9**, 123.

Feitknecht, W. (1954). *Kolloid Z.* **136**, 52.

Feitknecht, W. and Berger, A. (1942). *Helv. chim. Acta.* **25**, 1543.

Feitknecht, W. Signer, R. and Berger, A. (1942). *Kolloid Z.* **101**, 12.

Feuge, R. O. (1955). *Catalysis.* **3**, 413.

François, J. (1950a). *C. r. hebd. Séanc. Acad. Sci. Paris.* **230**, 1282.

François, J. (1950b). *C. r. hebd. Séanc. Acad. Sci. Paris.* **230**, 2183.

François-Rossetti, J. (1952). *C. r. hebd. Séanc. Acad. Sci. Paris.* **234**, 840.

François-Rossetti, J. and Imelik, B. (1953). *J. Chim. phys.* **51**, 649.

François-Rossetti, J. and Imelik, B. (1957). *Bull. Soc. chim. Fr.* 1115.

François-Rossetti, J., Charton, M. T. and Imelik, B. (1957). *Bull. Soc. chim. Fr.* 614.

Franzen, P. and van Eijk van Voorthuijsen, J. J. B. (1950). *Trans. 4th Int. Congr. Soil Sci.* Amsterdam. **3**, 34.

Glemser, O. (1951). *Fortschr. chem. Forsch.* **2**, 273.

Goppel, J. M. (1946). "Onderzoek van Kristalliniteit van Natuurrubber". Thesis, Delft University of Technology, The Netherlands.

Gundry, P. M. and Tompkins, F. C. (1956). *Trans. Faraday Soc.* **52**, 1609.

Gundry, P. M. and Tompkins, F. C. (1957). *Trans. Faraday Soc.* **53**, 218.

Hall, W. H. (1949). *Proc. phys. Soc.* **62A**, 741.

Heikes, R. R. (1955). *Phys. Rev.* **98**, 225.

Horiuti, J. (1957). *Proc. 2nd. Int. Congr. Surf. Activ.* London **3**, 71.

Innes, W. B. (1957). *Analyt. Chem.* **29**, 1069.

Jones, F. W. (1938). *Proc. R. Soc.* **A166**, 16.

Kefeli, L. M. and Lel'chuk, S. L. (1952). *Dokl. Akad. Nauk SSSR.* **83**, 697.

Klug, H. P. and Alexander, L. E. (1954). "X-ray Diffraction Procedures". John Wiley and Sons, New York and London.

König, H. (1946). *Naturwissenschaften.* **33**, 71.

Libowitz, G. G. and Bauer, S. H. (1955). *J. phys. Chem.* **59**, 214.

Linsen, B. G. (1964). "The Texture of Nickel-Silica Catalysts". Thesis, Delft University of Technology, The Netherlands.

Longuet, J. (1947). *C. r. hebd. Séanc. Acad. Sci. Paris.* **225**, 869.

Lotmar, W. and Feitknecht, W. (1936). *Z. Kristallogr. Kristallgeom.* **93A**, 368.

Mars, P., Scholten, J. J. F. and Zwietering, P. (1960). *Actes 2e Congr. Int. Catal.*, p. 1245. Edition Technip, Paris.

Méring, J. and Longuet-Escard, J. (1953). *Chim. Ind.* Paris. **69**, 649.

Merlin, A. and Teichner, S. (1953). *C. r. hebd. Séanc. Acad. Sci. Paris.* **236**, 1892.

Michell, D. and Haig, F. D. (1957). *Phil. Mag.* **2**, 15.

Normann, W. (1903). British patent 1515.

Perrin, M. (1948). *C. r. hebd. Séanc. Acad. Sci. Paris.* **227**, 476.

Perrin, M. (1950). *J. Chim. phys.* **47**, 262.

Prettre, M. and Goepfert, O. (1947). *C. r. hebd. Séanc. Acad. Sci. Paris.* **225**, 681.

Rienäcker, G. (1956). *Abh. dt. Akad. Wiss. Berl., Kl. Chem. Geol. Biol.* **3**, 8.

Roberts, M. W. and Sykes, K. W. (1957). *Proc. R. Soc.* **A242**, 539.

Roof, R. B. (1952). *J. chem. Phys.* **20**, 1181.

Ross, R. A. and McBride, G. B. (1960). *Chemy. Ind.* London 1504

Roy, D. M. and Roy, R. (1954). *Am. Miner.* **39**, 957.

Sabatier, P. and Senderens, J. B. (1897). *C. r. hebd. Séanc. Acad. Sci. Paris.* **124**, 1358.

Sachtler, W. H. M. (1956). *J. chem. Phys.* **25**, 751.

Schuit, G. C. A. (1954). *Proc. Int. Symp. React. Solids*, Göthenburg, (1952), 571.

Schuit, G. C. A. and de Boer, J. H. (1954). *J. chem. Phys.* **51**, 482.

Schuit, G. C. A. and van Reijen, L. L. (1958). *Adv. Catalysis.* **10**, 242.

Selwood, P. W. (1956). *J. Am. chem. Soc.* **78**, 3893.

Sidgwick, N. V. (1950). "Chemical Elements and Their Compounds", p. 1449. Clarendon Press, Oxford.

Singley, W. J. and Carriel, J. T. (1953). *J. Am. chem. Soc.* **75**, 778.

Steggerda, J. J. (1955). "De Vorming van Aktief Aluminiumoxide". Thesis, Delft University of Technology, The Netherlands.

Taylor, H. (1957). *Adv. Catalysis* **9**, 1.

Taylor, H. S. (1925). *Proc. R. Soc.* **A108**, 105.

Taylor, W. F. and Staffin, H. K. (1967). *Trans. Faraday Soc.* **63**, 2309.

Taylor, W. F., Yates, D. J. C. and Sinfelt, J. H. (1964). *J. phys. Chem.* **68**, 2962.

Taylor, W. F., Sinfelt, J. H. and Yates, D. J. C. (1965). *J. phys. Chem.* **69**, 3857.

Teichner, S. J. (1950). *J. Chim. phys.* **47**, 244.

Terminasov, Y. S. and Beletskii, M. S. (1948). *Dokl. Akad. Nauk SSSR.* **63**, 411.

Trambouze, Y. (1948). *C. r. hebd. Séanc. Acad. Sci. Paris.* **227**, 971.

Trambouze, Y. (1949). *C. r. hebd. Séanc. Acad. Sci. Paris.* **228**, 1432.

Trambouze, Y. (1950). *C. r. hebd. Séanc. Acad. Sci. Paris.* **230**, 1169.

Trambouze, Y. and Perrin, M. (1949). *C. r. hebd. Séanc.* **228**, 837.

Trambouze, Y. and Perrin, M. (1950). *J. Chim. phys.* **47**, 474.

Tsangarakis, C. and Sibut-Pinote, R. (1954). *J. Chim. phys.* **51**, 446.

Uhara, J., Hikino, T., Numata, Y., Hamada, H. and Kageyama, Y. (1962). *J. phys. Chem.* **66**, 1374.

van den Heuvel, A. (1956). *J. Am. Oil Chem. Soc.* **33**, 347, 531.

van den Heuvel, A. (1957). *J. Am. Oil Chem. Soc.* **34**, 12.

van der Borg, R. J. A. M. (1959). *Proc. K. ned. Akad. Wet.* **B62**, 299.
van Eijk van Voorthuijsen, J. J. B. and Franzen, P. (1950). *Recl. Trav. chim. Pays-Bas Belg.* **69**, 666.
van Eijk van Voorthuijsen, J. J. B. and Franzen, P. (1951). *Recl. Trav. chim. Pays-Bas Belg.* **70**, 793.
van Hardeveld, R. and Hartog, F. (1968). *4th Int. Congr. Catal.* Moscow.
van Itterbeek, A., Mariens, P. and Verpoorten, J. (1946). *Meded. K. vlaam. Acad.* **8**, 8.
Wheeler, A. (1955). *Catalysis.* **2**, 105.
Williams, K. A. (1927). *J. Soc. chem. Ind. Lond.* **46**, 446T.
Williamson, G. K. and Hall, W. H. (1953). *Acta Metall.* **1**, 22.
Wood, W. A. and Rachinger, W. A. (1949). *J. Inst. Metals.* **75**, 571.

Chapter 11

INTERACTION OF OXYGEN WITH TUNGSTEN AND MOLYBDENUM SURFACES

J. W. GEUS

Central Laboratory, Staatsmijnen/DSM, Geleen, Netherlands

I Introduction

Interaction of oxygen with metal surfaces has many important practical applications. Oxidation of metals is one of the most obvious examples. In addition, the physical properties of metal surfaces, e.g. frictional behaviour or thermionic emission, are determined largely by the depth to which the metal has reacted with oxygen. From a theoretical point of view also, interaction of oxygen with metal surfaces is very interesting, since with many metals formation of bulk oxides is thermodynamically possible at low oxygen pressures. That kinetic factors restrict the extent of the interaction is evident from the fact that actually only a limited number of metal atomic layers can react with oxygen, unless high temperatures are used. Understanding the kinetic factors and the characteristics of metal surfaces that have reacted with oxygen requires knowledge of the atomic configuration of the oxygen-covered metal surfaces.

Adsorption of gases has been studied more extensively on tungsten surfaces than on any other metal. Doubtless this is connected with the fact that by heating to elevated temperatures all impurities can be desorbed from the tungsten surface without appreciable evaporation of the metal itself. Consequently, a large body of experimental evidence about surface reactions of this metal is available, including data from which conclusions can be drawn about the atomic configuration of the tungsten surface before and after reaction to varying degrees with gas molecules. This makes it tempting to investigate whether a consistent picture of the structure and reactivity of tungsten surfaces after interaction with oxygen can be developed.

In our opinion the structure and reactivity of surface compounds should be elucidated in the same way as those of bulk compounds. It is characteristic of studies on bulk compounds that not one, but a number of physical and chemical properties are determined. The structure derived from the combined results should account as far as possible for the complete complex of data. For bulk chemical compounds, stoichiometry, heat of formation, structure as evident from X-ray or electron diffraction, optical properties such as infra-red spectra, NMR or ESR results, dipole moments, and magnetic and electrical properties are usually invoked to arrive at a structure consistent with the chemical reactivity.

It is clear that the same procedure should be followed for surface compounds, which possess considerable extension in two directions only. However, a difficulty impedes application of the procedure used for bulk compounds, namely the identification of the surface compounds whose physical and chemical properties have to be determined. Since surface compounds can be obtained only under specific conditions, their properties have to be determined in the measuring cell in which they are prepared. This implies that generally only one property can be measured at a time. Other properties have to be determined on other metal specimens in other measuring cells.

It is therefore difficult to ascertain whether the physical and chemical properties determined in different experiments relate to the same surface species. Nevertheless, recent progress in vacuum technology and experimental techniques permits sufficiently accurate identification of surface compounds in different experiments. This is true especially for tungsten, the surface of which has been extensively investigated. Using experimental results of different origin, we have developed a consistent picture of tungsten surfaces showing different degrees of reaction with oxygen. To this end, results regarding the stoichiometry of the surface compounds, their heats of formation, dipole moments, and electrical properties have been used together with low-energy electron diffraction (LEED) patterns.

Although metals have many properties in common, the chemical reactivities of the metal atoms are widely different. The results for tungsten can be applied to chemically analogous metals only. Since the chemistry of molybdenum is almost identical with that of tungsten, we include results on molybdenum. It is to be expected that other metal surfaces behave quite differently upon reaction with oxygen; some of these are considered in a forthcoming book.

The organization of this chapter reflects the above line of reasoning. The extent of the interaction of oxygen with tungsten and molybdenum surfaces at different temperatures is discussed in Section II. This part provides information about the depth to which the metal is affected in the sorption process; moreover, indications as to the stoichiometry of the surface compounds may be derived from it.

Next, the heats of oxygen sorption are considered (Section III). If the heat is determined as a function of the extent of oxygen sorption (coverage), a distinction can be made regarding the way in which the oxygen species are bonded on or in the surface. Besides, comparison of the heats of sorption with the heat of formation of the corresponding bulk oxides enables us to draw conclusions about the structure of the surface compounds. Data about the nature and the amounts of the species desorbing upon flashing of metal specimens that have interacted to increasing extents with oxygen give additional information about the surface compounds (Section IV). The kinetics of the evolution of atomic oxygen on flashing suggest that the bonding energy to the surface is lower than the value calculated from the heat of adsorption. The origin of differences in bonding energy as found from adsorption and desorption experiments is explained. The effects of oxygen sorption on the work function of tungsten and molybdenum are examined in Section V. The results permit a more accurate description of the surface structure after interaction with oxygen. Field-emission experiments provide data about the mobility of adsorbed oxygen species over the metal surfaces. Detailed studies on the effect of adsorption on the work function of monocrystalline planes reveal the influence of the arrangement of the metal surface atoms. The most accurate indication of the depth to which oxygen sorption influences the metallic structure is derived from the effects of oxygen on the electrical conductance of metal specimens. Results for evaporated molybdenum and tungsten films are discussed in Section VI. It appears that the surface layer of the metals is rendered non-conducting by interaction with oxygen; moreover, it is shown that above 200°K the sub-surface layer of the metal is affected. The data reviewed in Section VI are used to explain the observations on desorption of oxygen by slow-electron impact, which is dealt with in Section VII. Detailed descriptions of the structure of different crystallographic planes after interaction with oxygen are developed by combining the previous data with LEED (low-energy electron diffraction) results. This is done in Section VII. Finally, the main results are summarized in Section IX.

II The Extent of the Oxygen Sorption

In three-dimensional chemistry it is rather easy to establish the composition of the compounds to be investigated. In surface reactions only the adsorbent atoms situated at or near the surface are involved in the process. As both this fraction and the ratio of adsorbate to adsorbent atoms in the chemisorption complex may vary, determination of the composition of surface compounds may be very difficult.

Data about the velocity and the extent of sorption give very useful information about the composition of the chemisorption complex. Adsorption of oxygen on tungsten and molybdenum proceeds rapidly at very low temperatures. Gomer and Hulm (1957) observed chemisorption of oxygen on tungsten at temperatures as low as 20°K. Earlier, Roberts (1935a), working with tungsten wires at 300°K, found oxygen to be adsorbed very rapidly. This was also noted by Trapnell (1953) and Lanyon and Trapnell (1954), who used evaporated films at temperatures from 77°K upwards. Moreover, Roberts as well as Lanyon and Trapnell found that at 300°K the rapid adsorption is followed by a slow take-up. Results for molybdenum are analogous (Lanyon and Trapnell, 1954).

The extent of the sorption process can be determined by measuring the oxygen take-up on metal specimens of known surface area. Two different types of metal specimen are used in this work; wires or ribbons and evaporated metal films. Wires and ribbons used in adsorption studies generally have surfaces of some few cm^2; since it is very difficult to determine the roughness of surfaces of this order of magnitude, one must rely upon the geometric surface area. Evaporated tungsten and molybdenum films with surfaces of some 10^3 cm^2 can easily be prepared. Surface areas of this order of magnitude can be determined rather accurately by measuring the extent of physical adsorption (Brunauer, 1945). Although both the theory to be used for calculating the gas volume adsorbed in a monolayer from the experimental data and the cross-sectional area occupied by a physically adsorbed molecule are still being debated, the results obtained are reliable within about 10% (Gregg and Sing, 1967).

We shall now review the published data concerning the amount of oxygen that is rapidly taken up at temperatures of about 300°K and below. We define this amount of oxygen as either the amount rapidly adsorbed at temperatures above 200°K and at pressures af about 10^{-7} mm Hg, or the amount chemisorbed at 77°K. Chemisorption is detected by the effect on the electrical conductance of the adsorbing metal or by the heat of adsorption.

Singleton (1967) measured the oxygen take-up of tungsten wires and ribbons at 300°K and oxygen pressures of the orders of 10^{-7} mm Hg. He used the decrease in pressure brought about by adsorption on the clean surface of the previously flashed tungsten samples to determine the amount of gas adsorbed. For wires and ribbons previously heated for some hours at 2000–2400°K, this author found a rapid adsorption of $(10\cdot3\pm0\cdot4)\times10^{14}$ oxygen atoms per cm^2 of geometric surface area. Ribbons heated at 2750°K or higher for 30 min displayed a higher adsorption capacity at 300°K, that is $(14\cdot3\pm0\cdot6)\times10^{14}$ atoms per cm^2 of geometric surface area. No explanation is offered by Singleton for the increased adsorption of the ribbons heated above 2700°K. It might be due to thermal roughening of the tungsten surface in this temperature range; this roughening remains during heating for short periods at 2000°K. For the amount of oxygen taken up by tungsten wires "heated well above 2000°K" Roberts (1935a) earlier found values of $10\cdot8\times10^{14}$ to $14\cdot5\times10^{14}$ atoms per cm^2 of geometric surface area.

On evaporated tungsten films at 77°K, Geus, Koks, and Zwietering (1963) measured adsorption of $(9\cdot8\pm0\cdot2)\times10^{14}$ atoms cm^{-2} with a decrease in electrical conductance of the film. These authors determined the surface area of the adsorbing tungsten films by measuring the physical adsorption of xenon at 90°K. The surface area per physically adsorbed xenon atom was taken to be $22\cdot4$ A^2, which value was obtained by comparison of the amounts of nitrogen and xenon physically adsorbed by carbonyl iron.

Finally, Brennan and Graham (1966) determined the oxygen sorption by evaporated tungsten and molybdenum films. They determined the atomic ratio of sorbed oxygen atoms and krypton atoms adsorbed in a monolayer. In Table I, values for the cross-sectional area occupied by a physically-adsorbed krypton molecule as determined by different workers are collected. From these data a value of 21 A^2 appears to be the most reliable.

Brennan and Graham assume strongly-localized physical adsorption of noble gas atoms on metal surfaces. Such adsorption would account for the fact that the surface areas of physically-adsorbed krypton and xenon atoms are larger than the cross-sectional areas calculated from the density of the liquid or solid. Indications of strongly-localized adsorption, however, are found only in some atomically rough regions around the (100) poles in field-emission experiments on tungsten and molybdenum (Ehrlich and Hudda, 1959). Nevertheless, Brennan and

TABLE I. Surface area, σ_{Kr}, occupied by physically adsorbed krypton as determined experimentally (p_0-saturation pressure)

Authors	σ_{Kr} (A^2 atom^{-1})	
	based on p^0 liquid	based on p_0 solid
Beebe et al., 1945	19·5$\pm$2·0	
Davis et al., 1947	21·0$\pm$1·0	22·5$\pm$1·5
Wolock and Harris, 1950	21·6	
Haul, 1956		21·0$\pm$3·0
Knor and Ponec, 1961		21·0

Graham's values for the surface areas occupied by physically-adsorbed krypton and xenon molecules are not markedly different from 21 A^2, the experimentally obtained value. (We leave aside the rather improbable alternative for (110) planes, namely 14 A^2). If the value of 21 A^2 is combined with the atomic ratio of oxygen to krypton, the extent of adsorption can be calculated.

The amount of oxygen adsorbed at 77°K with appreciable heat of adsorption is $9·5 \times 10^{14}$ atoms cm^{-2} both for tungsten and molybdenum. This is, again, in very good accordance with the results given above. We therefore assume that the rapid chemisorption of oxygen on tungsten and molybdenum involves $(9·7\pm0·3) \times 10^{14}$ atoms cm^{-2}.

As mentioned above, Roberts observed slightly higher values for the rapid take-up of oxygen by tungsten wires, namely $(10·8$ to $14·5) \times 10^{14}$ atoms cm^{-2}. It is improbable that this should be due to inclusion in the rapid process of some of the slowly-sorbed oxygen. This can be concluded from a comparison of the extent of hydrogen adsorption on tungsten wires and evaporated films; hydrogen does not display activated sorption on tungsten at room temperature. At this temperature, Roberts (1935b), for his wires, measured a hydrogen adsorption of the same order of magnitude as the fast oxygen adsorption, namely $(11 \cdot 4$ to $15 \cdot 2) \times 10^{14}$ atoms cm^{-2} of geometric surface area. On evaporated tungsten films, Geus et $al.$ (1963) measured at $273°K$ a hydrogen adsorption of $10 \cdot 0 \times 10^{14}$ atoms cm^{-2}, which is also equal to the value for the fast oxygen adsorption. We therefore ascribe the slightly higher values of Roberts to the roughness of his tungsten wires.

It is interesting to compare the number of rapidly-chemisorbed oxygen atoms with the number of metal atoms per unit surface area. In Table II the density of metal surface atoms for the most stable crystallographic planes of the b.c.c. lattice are collected.

TABLE II. Density of metal atoms in b.c.c. crystallographic planes

(110)	$14 \cdot 24 \times 10^{14}$ cm^{-2}
(100)	$10 \cdot 07 \times 10^{14}$ cm^{-2}
(211)	$8 \cdot 24 \times 10^{14}$ cm^{-2}

Since the (110) planes are the most stable, they will be the most abundant on b.c.c. metal specimens, though the fraction of (110) planes presumably will be smaller on evaporated metal films than on well-annealed ribbons or wires. Hence it can be expected that the average density of metal atoms in the surface is between 10 and 14×10^{14} cm^{-2}. This is in accordance with the number of hydrogen atoms adsorbed per cm^2 of tungsten at $77°K$. There is evidence that the number of hydrogen atoms adsorbed at $77°K$ and at pressures around 10^{-2} mm Hg equals the number of metal surface atoms.

For tungsten films the hydrogen adsorption at $77°K$ was determined at $12 \cdot 7 \times 10^{14}$ cm^{-2}; a density of metal surface atoms of this order of magnitude appears to be quite acceptable in view of the data in Table II. The number of metal surface atoms per cm^2 is about 12×10^{14}; this is slightly higher than the number of oxygen atoms rapidly chemisorbed. Evidence from low-energy electron diffraction accounting for this will be dealt with later.

The above data show that with tungsten and molybdenum the chemisorption at $77°K$, or the rapid adsorption at $300°K$, is confined to the surface layer of metal atoms. Oxidation beyond this first layer is not appreciable under the conditions given above.

At temperatures above $195°K$ chemisorption of the above amount of oxygen is followed by a further take-up of oxygen that proceeds more slowly. The most extensive investigations of this slow process on metal films were done by Lanyon and Trapnell (1954). They expressed the amount of oxygen taken up slowly as a multiple of the quantity of rapidly chemisorbed oxygen.

The amount of oxygen slowly taken up by molybdenum was 1·0 to 1·4 times the oxygen adsorbed rapidly, the figure for tungsten being 1·0 to 1·6. If the rapid adsorption is taken equal to $9·7 \times 10^{14}$ oxygen atoms cm^{-2}, the total sorption is $19·4 \times 10^{14}$ to $23·2 \times 10^{14}$ atoms cm^{-2} for molybdenum and $19·4 \times 10^{14}$ to $25·2 \times 10^{14}$ atoms cm^{-2} for tungsten.

The rate of the slow sorption process was proportional to $p_{O_2}^{0·57}$ exp. $(-1/T)$, where p_{O_2} is the oxygen pressure and T the absolute temperature; it decreased strongly with increasing amounts sorbed. Working with tungsten films, Geus et al. (1963) extended their measurements of the slow sorption of oxygen at 273°K until 0·7 of the amount rapidly adsorbed had been taken up, when the total sorption was $16·7 \times 10^{14}$ atoms cm^{-2}. Brennan, Hayward and Trapnell (1960) in their measurements at room temperature found total (rapid and slow) take-up figures of up to $14·5 \times 10^{14}$ oxygen atoms cm^{-2} for tungsten, and $16·3 \times 10^{14}$ atoms cm^{-2} for molybdenum. Brennan and Graham (1966) studied the sorption at 273°K up to an amount of $12·7 \times 10^{14}$ atoms cm^{-2} totally taken up.

In experiments where adsorption on wires or ribbons is investigated, the oxygen pressures generally cannot be increased above 10^{-4} mm Hg owing to experimental difficulties, such as variation among ionization gauges. As can be concluded from the results of Lanyon and Trapnell, the oxygen sorption proceeds slowly at low pressures. Consequently, Roberts (1935a), working with oxygen pressures up to about $7·5 \times 10^{-6}$ mm Hg, found the slow sorption at room temperature to be only 0·25 times the quickly-adsorbed amount. Singleton (1967), who used pressures in the 10^{-7} mm Hg range (measured by means of an ionization gauge), determined the amount of oxygen adsorbed within about 10 minutes. Only at temperatures above 650°K could sorption of oxygen beyond $10·3 \times 10^{14}$ atoms cm^{-2} be established in this experimental set-up. At temperatures above 650°K an additional adsorption of $5-6 \times 10^{14}$ atoms cm^{-2} was observed, which brought the total sorption that he found at about 16×10^{14} atoms cm^{-2}. Singleton could not determine whether the coverage at any given temperature is limited by the rate of adsorption or by an equilibrium coverage increasing with temperature. The above results on evaporated films, obtained with higher oxygen pressures, and the data given by Roberts, who used longer adsorption times with tungsten wires, indicate the coverage to be limited by the rate of adsorption.

From the above consistent data it is apparent that the number of oxygen atoms taken up at room temperature is clearly larger than the number of metal surface atoms. Consequently, either bonding of more than one oxygen atoms to one metal surface atom or penetration of oxygen into the metal surface occurs at room temperature. The oxygen sorbed at these high coverages is not bonded uniformly.

At 77°K and pressures of about 10^{-2} mm Hg some oxygen is bonded physically; this is evident from the fact that during heating to room temperature oxygen is desorbed and slowly taken up again. At higher temperatures non-uniform bonding is evident from the effect on the accommodation coefficient and from the electron-induced desorption. Roberts used the accommodation coefficient of neon with tungsten to investigate the tungsten surface (Morrison and Roberts, 1939). The accommodation coefficient varies with the oxygen pressure, from 0·226 at very low pressures to about 0·27, as indicated in Fig. 1.

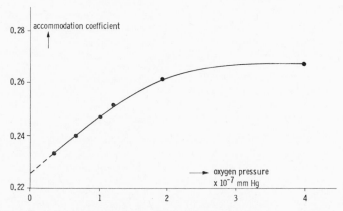

FIG. 1 Accommodation coefficient of neon with tungsten as a function of the oxygen partial pressure (Morrison and Roberts, 1939).

The accommodation coefficient rises steeply from 0·057 for the clean surface to 0·226 at very low partial pressures of oxygen, to increase slowly at higher pressures. Part of the adsorbed oxygen is removed by heating at 1100°K, as is apparent from the decrease in the accommodation coefficient to 0·177; the remaining oxygen is desorbed only at 1700°K, after which the accommodation coefficient for the clean surface is again measured. The amount of oxygen that can be desorbed by electron bombardment shows an analogous gradual increase, as demonstrated by Redhead (1964) for molybdenum and by Madey and Yates (1968) for tungsten. These results will be discussed below.

III   Heats of Oxygen Sorption

Comparison of the heat of formation of surface compounds with the heat of formation of analogous three-dimensional compounds of known structure yields important information about the structure of surface compounds.

The heat of formation of surface compounds can be calculated from the heat of adsorption, the latter being determined either on evaporated metal films or on wires previously cleaned by flashing. Roberts (1935a) determined the heat of adsorption of oxygen on tungsten wires by measuring the increase in the temperature of the wire upon adsorption of a measured amount of oxygen. The temperature of the adsorbing wire was monitored by its resistance. Fig. 2 gives his results; his values

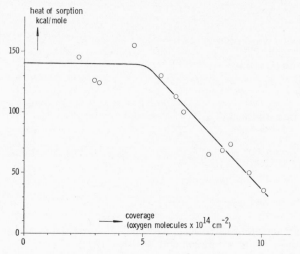

FIG. 2 Heat of oxygen sorption on a tungsten wire. Measurements at room temperature (Roberts, 1935a).

are substantially lower than those measured on evaporated films, which will be discussed later. The heats of hydrogen adsorption, on the other hand, as determined by Roberts on wires and by Beeck and co-workers (Beeck, 1950) on evaporated tungsten films are in good agreement. Hence, the discrepancy is not likely to be due to intrinsic differences in the structure of the surfaces of wires and films. Presumably, Roberts' values are too low owing to a slow transport of oxygen to the adsorbing wire.

The heat of adsorption of oxygen on evaporated tungsten and molybdenum films was determined by Brennan et al. (1960) and later on by

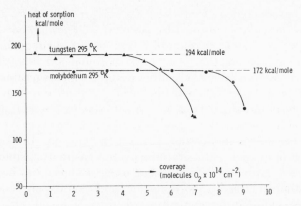

FIG. 3 Heats of oxygen sorption on molybdenum and tungsten (Brennan *et al.*, 1960).

Brennan and Graham (1966). The results obtained by Brennan *et al.*, taking measurements at room temperature, are presented in Fig. 3. Brennan and Graham extended the range of their measurements to 273°K and 77°K, obtaining the results given in Fig. 4.

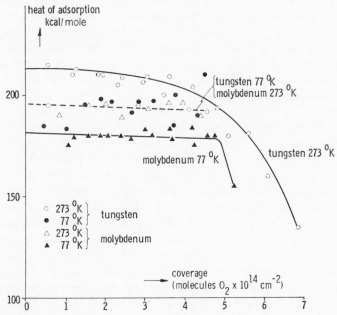

FIG. 4 Heats of oxygen sorption on molybdenum and tungsten (Brennan and Graham, 1966.)

   As can be concluded from these two figures the data are in fair
agreement; the values obtained by Brennan and Graham at 273°K are
markedly higher than those found by Brennan, et al., at room temperature. For molybdenum the latter authors found the heat of sorption
to remain constant at relatively large coverages. This may be due to a
fraction of each oxygen dose being sorbed beyond the monolayer. In
Fig. 4 the heat measured at 273°K is slightly higher than that found
at 77°K.

   As will be shown in Section VI, a large fraction of the internal
surface area of evaporated metal films is not easily accessible from the
gaseous phase. Moreover, chemisorbed oxygen appears to be immobile
over tungsten surfaces at 300°K in field-emission experiments. Consequently, every dose of oxygen admitted to the film converts a fraction
of the surface corresponding to the amount of oxygen in the dose into a
surface compound that remains virtually unchanged until the surface
is completely covered with a monolayer. This is demonstrated by the
fact that the heat of adsorption remains constant till a coverage of
$9 \cdot 5 \times 10^{14}$ oxygen atoms per cm^2 has been reached. At 77°K chemisorption stops, and an amount of oxygen is physisorbed that remains
limited as long as the pressure does not exceed 10^{-1} mm Hg. As argued
earlier, more oxygen is taken up at a measurable rate at temperatures
from about 200°K upwards. As appears from Figs 3 and 4 (Brennan
and Graham did not extend the range of their measurements on
molybdenum far enough) the oxygen sorption at these temperatures
shows a lower thermal effect. Brennan and Graham (1966) also investigated the oxygen sorption at 273°K on tungsten and molybdenum
surfaces previously saturated at 77°K. Molybdenum takes up $10 \cdot 9 \times 10^{14}$
atoms cm^{-2} at 77°K against $14 \cdot 3 \times 10^{14}$ oxygen atoms cm^{-2} at 273°K.
After heating to 273°K a molybdenum surface saturated with oxygen
at 77°K displays an additional up-take of $4 \cdot 3 \times 10^{14}$ oxygen atoms
cm^{-2}, with a heat of sorption of 104 kcal mole^{-1}. The total sorption in
the latter case, that is, $15 \cdot 2 \times 10^{14}$ oxygen atoms cm^{-2}, is about the
same as that found upon saturation at 273°K, namely, $14 \cdot 3 \times 10^{14}$ cm^{-2}.
The findings for tungsten are analogous. On saturation at 77°K,
$10 \cdot 0 \times 10^{14}$ oxygen atoms cm^{-2} were adsorbed, against $15 \cdot 7 \times 10^{14}$ cm^{-2}
at 273°K. After heating of a tungsten surface previously saturated
at 77° to 273°K, an additional up-take of $4 \cdot 8 \times 10^{14}$ oxygen atoms cm^{-2},
with a heat of sorption of about 120 kcal mole^{-1}, was recorded. From
the above it follows that the total sorption is equal within the experimental error if the sorption is carried out completely at 273°K and if
the surface is saturated first at 77°K and subsequently at 273°K. The
heats of sorption after adsorption of about 10×10^{14} atoms cm^{-2} are

also equal. Hence it can be concluded that the structure of the metal surface is not influenced by the way in which the coverage is brought about at temperatures below 300°K.

From the above results it is apparent that two different surface compounds can be distinguished on tungsten and molybdenum that have reacted with molecular oxygen at temperatures up to 300°K. The first structure is formed very rapidly at all temperatures and displays a large heat of formation; in this structure slightly less than one oxygen atom per metal surface atom is present. The second structure is established at a well-measurable rate at temperatures from 200°K onwards. The heat of formation of this structure is appreciably lower.

Values of heat of sorption compared to the heat of formation of analogous bulk compounds are collected in Table III. It appears that

TABLE III. Comparison of heat of oxygen sorption and heat of formation of bulk oxides (Both calculated per mole O_2).

Molybdenum		
Heat of sorption	1st stage	190 ± 10 kcal mole^{-1}
	2nd stage	104 kcal mole^{-1}
Heat of formation	MoO_2	133 kcal mole^{-1}
	MoO_3	123 kcal mole^{-1}
Tungsten		
Heat of sorption	1st stage	205 ± 5 kcal mole^{-1}
	2nd stage	120 kcal mole^{-1}
Heat of formation	WO_2	137 kcal mole^{-1}
	WO_3	134 kcal mole^{-1}

the heat of adsorption on the clean tungsten and molybdenum surfaces is appreciably higher than the heat of formation of bulk oxides.

A difference in heat of formation between surface and bulk oxides may be due to the fact that the two compounds differ in the degree of weakening of their intermetallic bonds and in lattice energy. Converting a metal into a bulk oxide in many cases requires almost complete rupture of the intermetallic bonds. This is not necessarily true in the formation of a surface metal-oxygen compound, where in the first stage of the sorption process metal atoms lacking a number of neighbouring metal atoms react, yielding a heat of adsorption exceeding the heat of formation of the bulk oxides. On the other hand, it is likely that the lattice energy of a two-dimensional compound is lower than that of the corresponding three-dimensional oxide, where the mutual

J. W. GEUS

coordination of metal and oxygen ions is better. If the latter situation dominates, the heat of adsorption is lower than the heat of formation of bulk oxides. Following this reasoning, it is assumed that the two-dimensional compound interacts with the underlying metal *via* the metal atoms only. The adsorption energy of the two-dimensional compound is hence ascribed exclusively to bonding between metal atoms. Section VIII, dealing with the LEED results, will present arguments to justify this assumption. Should the metal surface layer be liable to considerable distortion on interaction with oxygen, inter-action of both the metal and the oxygen atoms of the surface layer with the underlying metal has to be envisaged. Inasmuch as the structure of the distorted surface layer as well as the characteristics of the bonds between the different types of metal atoms and oxygen are yet unknown, not even a rough estimation can be made of the order of magnitude of this adsorption energy.

For clean tungsten and molybdenum surfaces, the heat of adsorption is appreciably higher than the heat of formation of the bulk oxides. This points to domination of the effect connected with reduced weakening of the intermetallic bonds in the formation of the surface compound. Hence, the distortion of the metal surface in the first stage of the adsorption process can only be moderate. This is in accordance with the very low activation energy of the chemisorption process, as well as with the fact that the activation energy for migration of chemisorbed atoms over the tungsten surface is only a small fraction (at most 20%) of the binding energy to the surface (Gomer and Hulm, 1957). A large distortion of the metal surface is likely to require an appreciable activation energy; this activation energy has to be provided upon adsorption from the gas phase, and, at least partly, upon migration of adsorbed oxygen over the metal surface.

After adsorption of about one oxygen atom per metal surface atom, sorption of more oxygen requires an activation energy increasing strongly as more oxygen is taken up. That the sorption process in this stage is activated may be due both to the absence of two neighbouring empty sites and to the need for the surface structure established in the rapid adsorption to reorganize so as to accommodate more oxygen. As argued first by Roberts, adsorption of oxygen as immobile atoms leads to a surface structure containing about eight per cent isolated empty sites. These singletons cannot adsorb *atomic* oxygen without one oxygen atom having to migrate over the surface already covered to another empty single site. Since now only one oxygen atom of an adsorbing molecule is bonded strongly, adsorption is likely to be activated in this stage. (The implications of recent LEED results will be discussed later).

The activated process, however, involves appreciably more than a fraction of about 10% of the amount of rapidly-adsorbed oxygen. Therefore, the second mechanism mentioned above, reorganization of the primarily formed surface structure, has to be operative too. Presumably this reorganization requires a higher activation energy than the above adsorption into singletons. Overlap of the two processes can lead to the experimentally-observed increase in the activation energy with the amount taken up.

The fact that in the later stages of the activated sorption the thermal effect is substantially lower than that for the rapid adsorption points to a considerable weakening of the intermetallic bonds. This is in accordance with the high activation energy for sorption in this range of coverages. As said above the chemisorption complex is stabilized to an unknown extent by interaction with the undisturbed metal, and its lattice energy must be smaller than that of corresponding three-dimensional compounds. We therefore do not want to draw conclusions from the heat effects of the following reactions that are, we believe, in accidental accordance with the heat of sorption at high coverages:

$$2MoO_2 + O_2 \rightarrow 2MoO_3 + 100 \text{ kcal.}$$
$$2WO_2 + O_2 \rightarrow 2WO_3 + 128 \text{ kcal.}$$

From the above data we can conclude that on interaction of clean molybdenum or tungsten surfaces with oxygen at low pressures (10^{-7} mm Hg or less) and at temperatures below 300°K, the metal surface atoms each bind one oxygen atom. In this process the metal surface is not strongly disturbed. At temperatures above 200°K, more oxygen is taken up. The metal surface is distorted more strongly in this process, in which oxygen atoms penetrate into the metal surface, or more than one oxygen atom is bonded to one metal surface atom.

IV Flash-desorption Experiments

Experiments on evaporated films have shown that in the range of coverages up to about 10×10^{14} atoms cm^{-2}, oxygen is rapidly adsorbed, with a constant high heat of adsorption. Since the adsorption proceeds rapidly and adsorbed oxygen is not mobile over the metal surface at the temperatures used, it is not possible by determining the heat of adsorption as a function of coverage to discriminate between different modes of surface bonding. The desorption of gas from a metal surface whose temperature is increased according to a given programme is recorded in flash-filament experiments. If the differently-adsorbed species do not interconvert rapidly during heating, they each desorb in a definite temperature range. In that case, flash-filament experiments in which

544   J. W. GEUS

the pressure of the desorbing gas is measured by a device giving a rapid response permit differentiation among the differently-bonded atoms (Ehrlich, 1963).

At coverages above 10×10^{14} atoms cm^{-2} oxygen is sorbed differently, as is evident from both the kinetics and the heat of the sorption process. The oxygen sorbed in the second stage can be bonded to the surface beside or over the oxygen atoms primarily adsorbed, without markedly affecting the latter. On the other hand, it is also possible that in the process of accommodation of more oxygen on the surface both the oxygen adsorbed first and the oxygen taken up in the second stage are converted into a single, identically-bonded species. Ehrlich (1961a,b)

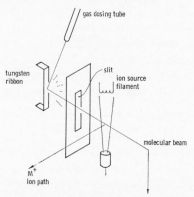

Fig. 5 Schematic diagram of the apparatus for flash-filament experiments, using a time-of-flight mass spectrometer (McCarroll, 1967).

has demonstrated that for carbon monoxide and nitrogen adsorbed on tungsten, the flash-filament method is suitable for discriminating between the above two alternatives. If a mass spectrometer is used to record the desorption, it is moreover possible to determine the nature of the desorbing material.

Flash-filament experiments on oxygen adsorbed on tungsten and molybdenum are difficult to carry out, due to the fact that many species desorbing from oxygen-covered molybdenum or tungsten are captured and trapped by every solid surface which they contact. Consequently, to measure all the desorbing species, a line-of-sight path between the desorbing metal surface and the ion gauge or ion source of the mass spectrometer is required. This condition is satisfied in experiments on tungsten published by Ptushinskii and Chuikov (1967a) and by McCarroll (1967a); in both cases time-of-flight mass spectrometers giving a very fast response were used. A schematic diagram of McCarroll's very carefully-designed apparatus is presented in Fig. 5.

Ptushinskii and Chuikov as well as McCarroll found that atomic oxygen and tungsten oxides only are desorbed from oxygen-covered tungsten. McCarroll did not observe any desorption of molecular oxygen. Ptushinskii and Chuikov demonstrated that molecular oxygen as well as carbon monoxide and carbon dioxide observed during flashing of oxygen-covered tungsten are formed by interaction of desorbing atomic oxygen with atoms adsorbed on the wall of the measuring cell.

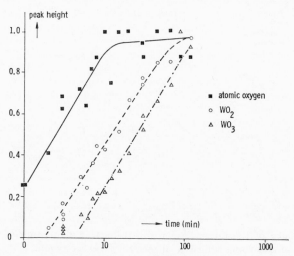

FIG. 6 Normalized peak heights of mass signals as a function of time of exposure of the adsorbing tungsten ribbon to oxygen gas (McCarroll, 1967).

In both sets of experiments it was found that atomic oxygen, WO_2 and WO_3 are desorbed from tungsten reacted at room temperature with oxygen. The desorption of WO_2 and WO_3 starts at about 1700°K, and that of atomic oxygen at a slightly higher temperature. The desorption of atomic oxygen is completed at higher temperatures than that of the tungsten oxides. Ptushinskii and Chuikov (1968) found this behaviour also with monocrystalline surfaces, namely the (100) and (110) planes of tungsten. Desorption of the polymeric tungsten oxides $(WO_3)_2$ and $(WO_3)_3$ is observed only after reaction of tungsten with oxygen at temperatures around 1000°K. Evolution of these oxides is found between about 1400 and 2000°K. Figure 6 gives McCarroll's data, showing the dependence of the signals from atomic oxygen, WO_2 and WO_3 on the time of exposure to an oxygen impingement of about $1 \cdot 7 \times 10^{12}$ molecules cm^{-2} sec^{-1}. It is apparent that oxygen first

21

adsorbs in a form that will desorb as atoms. After about 10 minutes
the surface is clearly saturated with oxygen desorbing atomically;
according to McCarroll about one monolayer then is present. Before
this saturation point has been reached, oxygen desorbing as WO_2, and
slightly later oxygen desorbing as WO_3, is taken up. Whereas the
take-up of atomically desorbing oxygen clearly ceases, the amount of
oxygen desorbing as WO_2 and WO_3 steadily increases with time. This
is seen more clearly in Fig. 7 (Ptushinskii and Chuikov, 1967a). In
contrast with the finding of McCarroll, Ptushinskii and Chuikov

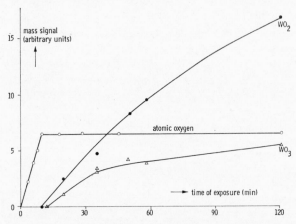

FIG. 7 Intensity of the mass signals (integrated) as a function of the time of
exposure of an adsorbing tungsten surface to gaseous oxygen.

observed the onset of desorption of tungsten oxides only after saturation of the signal due to atomic oxygen.

It is gratifying that the existence of two different stages apparent in
the kinetics and heats of sorption is also reflected in the flash-filament
results. The oxygen desorbing in atomic form is taken up at a high
rate and with a high heat of adsorption. As can be concluded from the
desorption spectra, this oxygen constitutes a single adsorbed phase.
This does not imply that the heat of adsorption should be independent
of the degree of coverage; interaction between uniformly adsorbed
atoms can give rise to a continuous decrease in the heat of adsorption.
This can be demonstrated, for example, with hydrogen adsorbed on
tungsten.

The oxygen desorbing as WO_2 and WO_3 is taken up in an activated
process displaying a lower heat of adsorption. As was apparent in
particular from the results of Lanyon and Trapnell (1954), saturation
of a tungsten surface with oxygen sorbed in this way is approached

slowly. The slow saturation was demonstrated by McCarroll in some separately published experiments (McCarroll, 1967b). This author convincingly showed that exposure of a tungsten surface to an impingement flux of 8.2×10^{13} molecules $cm^{-2} sec^{-1}$ for 14 minutes increases the amount of oxygen desorbing as tungsten oxides to about 1·5 times the amount released after four minutes' sorption. The amount of atomically-desorbing oxygen did not rise when the time of sorption was increased from four to 14 minutes. McCarroll further showed that if the tungsten surface after having sorbed oxygen for four minutes is kept at 5×10^{-10} mm Hg for an additional 10 minutes no change is observed in the amount of tungsten oxides desorbed. This proves that the species desorbing as oxides is formed by interaction with gaseous oxygen, and not by activated interaction between oxygen already adsorbed and tungsten. As said earlier, Singleton noted an increased sorption of oxygen on heating tungsten to about 750°K at pressures of about 10^{-7} mm Hg. This finding is confirmed by Ptushinskii and Chuikov (1967a), working at oxygen pressures of $8-10 \times 10^{-8}$ mm Hg. On increasing the sorption temperature to 750°K, they observed an appreciable increase in the desorption of tungsten oxides, whereas the amount of atomically-desorbing oxygen remained unchanged. Later they investigated the effect of the sorption temperature on the amounts of oxygen desorbing as atoms, WO_2 and WO_3 more extensively on the (110) and (100) planes of tungsten (Ptushinskii and Chuikov, 1968). For both the (110) and the (100) plane, the amount of atomic oxygen desorbing remained constant up to a critical temperature, beyond which it quickly decreased. The latter temperature is distinctly lower for the (110) plane than that for the (100) plane, namely, 1500 and 1700°K.

We shall now consider the relative amount of sorbed oxygen that desorbs as oxides. McCarroll used impingement rates equivalent to oxygen pressures from 5×10^{-9} to 10^{-7} mm Hg, and exposure times up to about 100 minutes. Ptushinskii and Chuikov worked with oxygen pressures of $8-10 \times 10^{-8}$ mm Hg and times up to 60 minutes. With adsorption at room temperature, the results obtained by Lanyon and Trapnell (1954) suggest a limited activated adsorption under the above conditions.

McCarroll plotted the peak heights of the mass-spectrometric signals after normalization (Fig. 6). The proportion of the peak heights in his experiments after exposure for a period about 10 times as long as that needed for reaching saturation with atomically desorbing oxygen was $O:WO_2:WO_3 = 1:0.23:0.23$ (McCarroll, 1967a). Later, using a new tungsten ribbon, he found a proportion of the integrated signals of $O:WO_2:WO_3 = 1:0·071:0·23$, which changed into $O:WO_2$: $WO_3 = 1:0·098:0·37$ when the exposure time was increased by a factor of 3·5 (McCarroll, 1967b). Ptushinskii and Chuikov integrated their signals in all cases. After an exposure time of 1·6 times that needed to saturate the atomic oxygen signal, they observed $O:WO_2$: $WO_3 = 1:0·35:0·32$ for a polycrystalline tungsten wire (Ptushinskii and Chuikov, 1967a) and $1:0·21:0·08$ for a single-crystal specimen with (110) surfaces (Ptushinskii and Chuikov, 1967b). This latter specimen gave $O:WO_2:WO_3 = 1:2·56:0·84$ after an exposure 12·9 times that needed for saturation with atomically-desorbing oxygen. This shows that the proportions found after comparable exposures vary rather widely; Ptushinskii and Chuikov observed a signal for WO_2 that was about a factor of 30 larger than that recorded by McCarroll.

A much larger discrepancy, however, is caused by the difference in the way in which McCarroll on the one hand and Ptushinskii and Chuikov on the other convert the mass spectrometer signals to molecular proportions. McCarroll (1967a) derived the conversion factor theoretically from the mass and the ionization cross-sections of the desorbing species. He arrived at a proportion for the conversion factors of $O:WO_2:WO_3 = 1:0·0128:0·0118$. For a signal proportion of $O:WO_2:WO_3 = 1:0·23:0·23$ this gives a molecular proportion of $1:0·0030:0·0027$, while a signal proportion of $1:0·098:0·037$ corresponds to a molecular proportion of $1:0·0013:0·0004$. If McCarroll's treatment is correct, it follows that in his experiments activated sorption proceeds to a very small extent only. Even the signal proportion as high as $O:WO_2:WO_3 = 1:2·56:0·84$ observed by Ptushinskii and Chuikov leads to a molecular proportion of only $1:0·033:0·010$. In that case the activated sorption is about 10% of the rapid adsorption.

Ptushinskii and Chuikov (1967a) determined the weight of the tungsten oxides desorbing from the tungsten ribbon by means of a quartz crystal plate. This was done in a separate measuring cell. They arrived at a desorption of $1·9 \times 10^{14}$ WO_3-molecules cm^{-2}, and $1·9 \times 10^{14}$ WO_2-molecules cm^{-2} from a tungsten surface having sorbed oxygen at room temperature. The amount of atomic oxygen was calculated from the known ratio of the mass spectrometer signals for the different oxides desorbing from the ribbon upon adsorption at 300° and 1100°K, and from the ratio of the total amounts of oxygen adsorbed at these two temperatures. The latter ratio was determined by measuring with a mass-spectrometer the decrease in oxygen partial pressure caused by adsorption.

In this way Ptushinskii and Chuikov found an adsorption of 12×10^{14} oxygen atoms cm^{-2}; together with the oxygen desorbing as tungsten oxides, this brings the total oxygen sorption at 21.5×10^{14} atoms cm^{-2} at room temperature. These figures give $O:WO_2:WO_3 = 1:0.15:0.15$, which differs by a factor of 50 from the values found by McCarroll at about the same proportion among the mass spectrometer signals for the desorbing species. The results published by Ptushinskii and Chuikov for the monocrystalline specimen (Fig. 7), using their conversion factors, lead to desorption figures as high as 7×10^{14} oxygen atoms cm^{-2}, $8.1 \times 10^{14} WO_2$ cm^{-2}, and $3.2 \times 10^{14} WO_3$ cm^{-2}. The results they obtained for different specimens at different temperatures are collected in Table IV. (Ptushinskii and Chuikov, 1967a,b, 1968.)

TABLE IV. Ratio of oxygen desorbing as different species from tungsten surfaces

Sorption temperature (°K)	Crystallographic plane	Amounts of oxygen desorbing as ($\times 10^{14}$ cm^{-2})			Proportion $O:WO_2:WO_3$
		atoms	WO$_2$	WO$_3$	
300	Polycrystal	12	1·9	1·9	1:0·15:0·15
300	110	7	1·3	0·6	1:0·19:0·09
300[a]	110[a]	7	8·1	3·2	1:1·14:0·46
300	100	9	0·8	1·0	1:0·09:0·11
1200	110	7	2·7	2·1	1:0·39:0·30
1200	100	9	2·1	1·6	1:0·23:0·18

[a] After relatively high exposures.

Ptushinskii and Chuikov did not describe their calibration of the mass spectrometer signals in detail; the reliability of the calibration is therefore difficult to judge. However, the extent of the activated sorption at room temperature and pressures of about 10^{-7} mm Hg found with their calibration seems to be too large compared with other experimental evidence. This holds for the results obtained with the polycrystalline specimen, which would imply the take-up of an amount of oxygen corresponding to 0·8 times the amount rapidly adsorbed. The activated sorption calculated for the monocrystalline specimen, 3·3 times the amount rapidly taken up, brings out this discrepancy even more strongly in that it exceeds the values found by Lanyon and Trapnell at much higher oxygen pressures and longer sorption periods. In view of the number of tungsten surface atoms (Table II), it is moreover difficult to imagine how 8.1×10^{14} WO$_2$ and 3.2×10^{14} WO$_3$ molecules cm^{-2} can be present on the surface without their presence decreasing the amount of atomically-desorbing oxygen. As can be seen from Fig. 7 the amount of atomically-desorbing oxygen remains unchanged within the experimental error, whereas the amount of oxygen desorbing as tungsten oxides increases considerably. For the time being therefore we prefer McCarroll's conversion of the mass spectrometer signal proportions to atomic and molecular proportions; this fits in smoothly with the other experimental evidence and readily explains why the adsorption of oxygen desorbing as oxides, being only approximately 10%, has such a small effect on the amount of oxygen desorbing atomically.

The desorption energies determined by Ptushinskii and Chuikov (1967a) and by McCarroll (1967a) are in very good agreement. Ptushinskii and Chuikov showed the desorption of atomic oxygen to be the first order in oxygen coverage. Making some assumptions, they calculated a heat of desorption of about 138 kcal/atom from their experimental results. McCarroll varied the rate of heating of a wire specimen; from the temperatures of maximum desorption he arrived at a heat of desorption of 128 kcal/atom (Ehrlich, 1963). If the heat of dissociation of molecular oxygen, 118 kcal/mole, is taken into consideration, Ptushinskii and Chuikov's value gives a heat of adsorption equal to 158 kcal/mole, while that of McCarroll leads to 138 kcal/mole. Engelmaier and Stickney (1968) found a value of the same order of magnitude from thermal desorption measurements. These authors determined the change in work function during heating at temperatures from 1900 to 2200°K by monitoring of the electron emission. From the rate of decrease of the work function, measured for various crystallographic planes on a single-crystal tungsten filament, they calculated the activation energy of desorption, assuming a linear dependence of the work function on the coverage. The resulting values for the desorption energy did not vary markedly with the crystallographic plane on which the measurement was done. We will return to this below. The value found for the desorption energy was about 135 kcal/atom; this leads to a heat of adsorption of 153 kcal/mole.

The values obtained from desorption experiments, however, are markedly lower than those found in direct adsorption measurements on evaporated films. For the first stage of the adsorption, these measurements gave a heat of adsorption of (200 ± 10) kcal/mole (Figs 3 and 4; Table III). On wires, Roberts measured values that are lower and in agreement with the desorption results. As argued above, however, his low values can be ascribed to the slow transport of oxygen to the adsorbing tungsten wire.

Inasmuch as the characteristics of the oxygen sorption process are essentially the same on both wires and evaporated films, we do not want to ascribe the above discrepancies to a difference in structure between the two surfaces. We feel that the different values for the binding energy of oxygen are due to an intrinsic difference between the adsorption and the desorption experiments. Adsorption experiments are carried out at a temperature where the *chemisorbed* atoms are not mobile over the surface. In adsorption experiments, consequently, the chemisorbing species cannot very well select the most strongly-bonding sites; this is valid especially for evaporated films of tungsten and molybdenum, where access to a large fraction of the surface is difficult from the gas phase. Hence, the bonding energies in this case represent

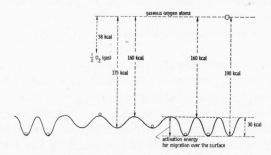

FIG. 8 Energy-level diagram for oxygen atoms adsorbed on a tungsten surface.

averages taken over the most tightly-bonding sites. Since the activation energy for surface migration is about 20% of that for desorption (see Section V), it follows that the adatoms in desorption experiments have a high mobility. Desorption experiments therefore are carried out under conditions where the most weakly-bonding sites can be filled by migration over the surface. Consequently, all the adsorbed oxygen can be removed by desorption from these sites.

Several authors regard the activation energy for desorption as the sum of the energies required for migration and desorption. It will be shown, however, that this is not correct.

Sites with bonding energies of about 190 kcal/atom (from adsorption) and of about 160 kcal/atom (from desorption) are assumed in Fig. 8. From the data of Gomer and Hulm (Section V), the activation energy for migration over the surface is taken to be about 30 kcal/atom (Gomer and Hulm, 1957). At temperatures where desorption proceeds, the oxygen adatoms bonded at more weakly-adsorbing sites are removed; the emptied sites are replenished, however, by oxygen having migrated from more tightly-bonding parts of the surface. Since the activation energy for migration over the surface is about 20%

of that for desorption, thermodynamic equilibrium between oxygen atoms adsorbed on sites with different bonding energies is established quickly at these temperatures. This implies that upon heating of the specimen to the level required for desorption, the more weakly-bonding sites are vacated first. Next, adatoms migrating from more strongly-bonding sites tend to fill the sites just vacated. This will happen to a limited extent only, because the occupation ratio of weakly and strongly-bonding sites is determined by the difference between the bonding energies divided by the thermal energy. Since the latter ratio is about eight at 1800°K, the weakly-bonding sites will be covered sparsely (coverage about 3×10^{-4} of that of the strongly-bonding sites). The desorption process will therefore be characterized by an activation energy corresponding to the lower bonding energy and, owing to the low coverage of the weakly-bonding sites, by a low pre-exponential factor.

In the experiments of Engelmaier and Stickney (1968) the decrease in the work function of a monocrystalline wire was recorded during heating at desorption temperatures. The oxygen adatoms are desorbed from the most weakly-adsorbing planes after migration over the surface. The rate at which the work function of the clean surface is approached is determined by desorption from the planes with the lowest bonding energy. This is why Engelmaier and Stickney measured the same desorption rate on all crystallographic planes of the wire.

The desorption energies for WO_2 and WO_3 were determined too from flash-filament experiments. McCarroll (1967a) found a desorption energy of about 100 kcal/mole for both oxides. Ptushinskii and Chuikov (1967a) from their data calculated a desorption energy of 97 kcal/mole, which fell off to 76 kcal/mole when the coverage was decreased by a factor of two. For a tungsten wire having adsorbed at temperatures above 900°K, these authors found a desorption of tungsten oxides which was proportional to the first power of the sorbed oxygen. Desorption from a tungsten ribbon having reacted with oxygen at room temperature, on the other hand, was proportional to the second power of the sorbed oxygen.

McCarroll does not agree with Ptushinskii and Chuikov about the temperature range in which formation of tungsten oxides is possible. McCarroll maintains that the oxides are formed already at room temperature, though to a very limited extent. Ptushinskii and Chuikov believe that the oxides are formed only when during the flash the temperature rises above 900°K; the oxides originate from the oxygen sorbed beyond the amount desorbing atomically. They base their view on the second order desorption of tungsten oxides after adsorption at room temperature, whereas a first-order desorption, the behaviour expected for oxides, is found after adsorption at temperatures above 900°K. There is other evidence that around 900°K the character of the interaction of oxygen with tungsten changes. Singleton (1967) found that the oxygen coverage at pressures of about 10^{-7} mm Hg reached saturation within 30 minutes or less, provided the temperature was below 800°K. At higher temperatures, continuous removal of oxygen from the gas phase was observed; at 865°K and a pressure of 5×10^{-7} mm Hg no saturation was reached over 100 hours. This points to a limited formation of tungsten oxides that desorb too slowly to be noticeable in flash-filament experiments. A change in the interaction of oxygen with tungsten surface at 700°K is also revealed by field-emission and LEED experiments (see Sections V and VIII).

In view of the above, we believe that after the rapid adsorption, oxygen is capable of penetrating into the metal surface layer. The activation energy required to break the intermetallic bonds to an extent permitting formation of tungsten oxides cannot be provided below about 700°K, however. Formation of tungsten oxides adsorbed onto the tungsten surface sets in above 700°K, where the minute amounts of oxides remain largely adsorbed. This is in keeping with the fact that the bulk oxidation of tungsten also starts at about 700°K. Only above 800°K does desorption of oxides take place, although at so low a rate that it cannot be detected in flash-filament experiments. The desorption of oxides in these experiments does not become noticeable until above approximately 1600°K. Since after sorption below 700°K two or three oxygen atoms taken up in the activated process have to be united with one tungsten atom, the desorption is second-order in the coverage with oxygen taken up through activated sorption.

V   Effects of Oxygen Sorption on the Work Function of Tungsten and Molybdenum

In this section we want to give closer consideration to the structure of the surface layer obtained on interaction of tungsten and molybdenum with oxygen. This will be done by investigating the effect of oxygen sorption on the work function. The sign of the effect on the work function shows if the adatoms are located above or below the metal surface atoms, provided the difference in electronegativity between adatoms and metal atoms is sufficient. Since the electronegativity of oxygen is substantially higher than that of metal atoms, unambiguous information can be gained for oxygen sorption. If the negatively-charged oxygen adatoms are present above the metal surface the work function increases, whereas if these adatoms are below the level of the metal atoms the work function decreases. For halogens, which also are strongly electronegative, Burshtein and Shurmovskaya (1964) demonstrated that the temperature at which halogen atoms penetrate into iron surfaces depends strongly on the size of the atoms. Quinn and Roberts (1964) investigated the penetration of oxygen atoms into different metal surfaces by the same technique, and Delchar and Tompkins (1967) published results on the influence of oxygen sorption on the work function of nickel.

The dipole moment of the adsorbed species cannot be reliably derived from the change in the work function. This is due to the fact that the orientation of the metal-adatom dipoles with respect to the surface is not known (MacRae, 1964).

The effect of oxygen sorption on the work function of tungsten and molybdenum was investigated on polycrystalline and monocrystalline samples. The monocrystalline specimens were of either macroscopic or microscopic dimensions; in the latter case the field-emission technique is used. As shown by Delchar and Ehrlich (1965), the results found for the above two types of monocrystalline samples are mutually consistent.

The studies of the effect of oxygen sorption on the work function of tungsten are much more detailed than those made for molybdenum. We shall now first discuss the results obtained for tungsten; thereafter it will be shown that the behaviour of molybdenum is analogous.

Mignolet (1955) studied the effect of oxygen sorption on the work function of evaporated tungsten films; this survey also includes the earlier literature. In accordance with most of the earlier data, Mignolet observed an increase in work function of 1·91 eV on admitting oxygen at 83°K and heating the film to 293°K at an oxygen pressure of 7×10^{-2} mm Hg. In another experiment an increase of the work function of 1·3 eV was measured on oxygen sorption on a film kept at 77°K. Admission of more oxygen decreased the work function by 0·084 eV. After heating to 293°K and saturation with oxygen, the increase in work function went up again to 1·91 eV. Mignolet's finding—an increase in work function below 100°K markedly lower than at room temperature and a slight decrease on adsorption of more oxygen at 77°K—was confirmed by Gomer and Hulm (1957) by means of the field-emission technique.

Hopkins and Pender (1966) measured the effect of oxygen sorption at room temperature on the work function of monocrystalline tungsten surfaces (Fig. 9). The intermediate decrease in the work function of the (110) plane with rising oxygen coverage as well as the approximate equality of the final work functions for all the planes investigated is remarkable.

Gomer and Hulm (1957) investigated the effects of oxygen sorption on the field-emission characteristics of a tungsten tip. Many details of the interaction of tungsten surfaces with oxygen molecules were elucidated by these workers. They deposited oxygen on the tip surface in two ways: (1) Oxygen was evaporated from a copper oxide source on a discrete part of the surface of the tip, which was cooled at 4·2–40°K, whilst the field-emission tube itself was cooled at 4·2°K. The cooled

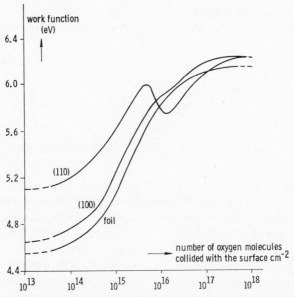

FIG. 9 Work function *versus* arrival rate of oxygen molecules on unit area for monocrystalline and polycrystalline (foil) tungsten surfaces (Hopkins and Pender, 1966).

walls of the tube adsorb every gas molecule hitting them; this prevents adsorption from the gas phase. Next, the oxygen was spread by surface migration over the entire tip surface, which requires temperatures above 27°K. (2) Oxygen was adsorbed from the gas phase onto the entire surface of the tip, which was kept at 300°K.

Procedure (1), in which only a discrete part of the tip surface is covered with oxygen, is suitable for studying the mobility of adsorbed oxygen over the tungsten surface. With the part of the tip surface exposed to the oxygen source having a very low coverage, migration of adsorbed oxygen (as evident from changes in the local emission properties of the tip) is observed only at temperatures above 600°·K The activation energy of this migration was determined to be 30±1.5 kcal/atom. With higher initial coverages, surface diffusion with a rather sharp boundary is observed over parts of the tip surface consisting of slabs of the close-packed (110) and (100) planes at temperatures from 400 to 500°K. The activation energy for this type of surface diffusion is (22·7±1) kcal/atom for slabs of (100) planes, and (24·8±1) kcal/atom for slabs of (110) planes. It is remarkable that on the stepped region with the more closely-packed (110) planes migration requires a higher activation energy than on that with (100) planes. Moreover, Gomer and Hulm observed migration from slabs of (100) orientation to (211) planes to proceed easily, whereas that to slabs of (110) planes did not

FIG. 10 Sites bonding oxygen atoms on the tungsten (100) plane (Gomer and Hulm, 1963).

occur. According to Gomer and Hulm surface diffusion with a sharp boundary is due to a markedly stronger bonding of oxygen atoms at the edges separating two closely packed regions. This causes the atoms migrating over the atomically smooth (110) and (100) planes to be trapped at the edges. The electron emission of the edges, which dominates the electron emission before adsorption, is suppressed by adsorption of oxygen. After saturation of the edge sites, migration of oxygen adatoms across the edges can proceed more easily. If the spacing of the edges is smaller than the resolution of the microscope, a sharp boundary results on migration of oxygen. It follows therefore that migration between trap sites requires an activation energy of 30 kcal/atom, which is markedly higher than that needed for migration over either (100) and (110) tungsten surfaces or the filled edge sites separating these surfaces.

Gomer and Hulm assume that migration over the flat surfaces requires higher activation energies than that across the filled edges. They ascribe the difference between the values for the (110) and (100) planes to the fact that the oxygen on the (100) plane is bonded in different ways, whereas on (110) surfaces the oxygen atoms are bonded uniformly. They maintain that after saturation of the (100) planes with oxygen atoms contacting four or presumably five tungsten atoms, further oxygen is bonded more weakly to two tungsten surface atoms (Fig. 10). They further state that the latter oxygen atoms migrate more easily than oxygen atoms on the (110) plane. This reasoning would imply that below 500°K both the A- and B-sites indicated in Fig. 10 are filled. Consequently, the (100) plane would adsorb a number of oxygen atoms equal to twice the number of metal surface atoms. Since the amount of oxygen that is observed to be taken up is slightly smaller than that corresponding to the number of metal surface atoms, this explanation does not seem likely.

We therefore believe that passage through the filled edges of the slabs of close-packed planes governs the migration process. Edges between (110) planes are similar in character to (211) planes. The LEED

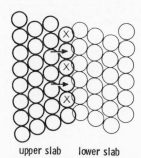

upper slab   lower slab

FIG. 11 Edge between two (110) slabs of a b.c.c. lattice. ⊗ tungsten atoms having adsorbed an oxygen atom. → path of adatoms migrating over the surface.

results discussed in Section VIII suggest that the ridges of metal atoms present on the (211) planes are first covered as indicated in Fig. 11. This structure is ascribed to a repelling action between neighbouring oxygen adatoms, which renders the sites between two covered tungsten atoms energetically less favourable. At room temperature this structure is established in a well-ordered form, pointing to a certain degree of mobility of the adatoms at this temperature. The evidence from LEED experiments leads us to assume that oxygen atoms bonded on the edge between two neighbouring adatoms are able to migrate to the next (110) slab. As the oxygen atoms are bonded rather strongly on these sites, the migration requires an activation energy of 24·8 kcal/atom.

The structure of the edges between (100) slabs normal to the [211] direction and to the [110] direction is represented in Fig. 12. The adatoms bonded on the edge normal to the [110] direction are spaced far enough to prevent strong mutual interaction. Consequently, these atoms will be bonded with a constant, relatively high, energy. Oxygen adatoms migrating towards the (110) plane have to cross over this filled edge, which is energetically very unfavourable. This explains why migration over this edge is not observed at temperatures around 500°K. For adatoms migrating from (100) to (211) planes, the paths indicated in Fig. 12 are the most favourable. While passing through these paths the oxygen atoms are adsorbed momentarily on sites analogous to those present between rows of metal atoms on (211)

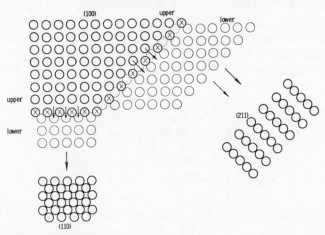

FIG. 12 Edges of (100) slabs normal to the [211] and [110] directions. ⊗ tungsten atoms having adsorbed an oxygen atom. → path of adatoms migrating over the surface.

planes. LEED experiments have shown that oxygen atoms can be bonded also between the rows of metal atoms (see Section VIII). In these experiments it was found that the bonding energy on these sites is lower than that for oxygen bonded on top of the metal atoms of the rows. This difference in bonding energy accounts for the observation that migration through the filled edges of the (100) planes normal to the [211] direction proceeds more easily than that through filled edges of the atomically smoother (110) planes.

At temperatures from 27 to 80°K another type of migration of adsorbed oxygen is found. If at a temperature below 27°K more oxygen is deposited on a discrete part of the tip surface than that which corresponds to a chemisorbed monolayer, this oxygen is physisorbed onto the chemisorbed layer. Heating to temperatures in the above range leads to spreading of the physisorbed oxygen with a sharp boundary. Gomer and Hulm explain this as due to migration of oxygen physically adsorbed on a layer of chemisorbed oxygen atoms. Oxygen reaching the edge of the covered region will be chemisorbed on the clean tungsten surface and be immobilized in the above temperature range. Gomer and Hulm calculated a heat of adsorption of $2 \cdot 2$ kcal/mole from the distance that can be covered by the physically-adsorbed oxygen molecules. They did these spreading experiments at very low oxygen pressures to avoid adsorption from the gas phase. At 80°K, therefore, the amount of physically adsorbed oxygen becomes too small for this type of surface migration to be possible.

We shall now consider the effect on the work function as found from field-emission experiments. Gomer and Hulm (1957) and later on George and Stier (1962) investigated the effect of oxygen sorption on the work function averaged over the tip by means of the Fowler-Nordheim equation. This work function is determined largely by the most strongly-emitting regions of the tip surface. Bell, Swanson and Crouser (1968) investigated the effect of oxygen sorption on definite crystallographic planes on the tip surface.

Gomer and Hulm observed an increase of $1 \cdot 5$–$1 \cdot 6$ eV on spreading from a physisorbed layer over the tip surface at 27–40°K. During heating of the tip at temperatures up to 700°K, the work function went through a slight maximum around 80°K to decrease again at higher temperatures. If the tip was heated at temperatures from 400 to 700°K, redosing of oxygen by spreading from a physisorbed layer at 27°K, would lead to a total increase in work function of $1 \cdot 9$ eV. These results are in accord with Mignolet's. At the very low oxygen pressures used by Gomer and Hulm (their field-emission tube was cooled at $4 \cdot 2$°K) physisorbed oxygen is no longer present on the surface at temperatures above 80°K. Since physisorbed oxygen decreases the work function, as is apparent from Mignolet's experiments, the work function reaches a maximum at about 80°K. Complete coverage apparently cannot be achieved by spreading from a physisorbed layer adsorbed at 20°K; if after spreading the tip is heated to higher temperatures, a rearrangement in the chemisorbed layer takes place; at the same time some oxygen either desorbs or penetrates into the metal. The rearrangement is evident from the fact that redosing of oxygen at 27°K brings the increase in work function to $1 \cdot 9$ eV, which value Mignolet also observed. Evidently, the activation energy needed for establishing the configuration with full coverage cannot be provided at temperatures around 100°K. When the tip is exposed to gaseous oxygen at room temperature, the overall work function increases immediately by $1 \cdot 9$ eV; at this temperature the more stable configuration in the adlayer is quickly established.

George and Stier (1962) studied the effects of oxygen sorption on the overall work function of thermally-annealed and field-evaporated tungsten tips. With the thermally-annealed tips the degree of surface ordering is much lower than with field-evaporated tips; George and Stier determined the degree of ordering by taking field-ion emission pictures of the tip after both treatments. These authors found that the final increase in the work function upon prolonged exposure of the tip to gaseous oxygen at room temperature was about 2·1 eV, which is in accordance with the findings of Gomer and Hulm. The increase was the same for both field-evaporated and thermally-annealed surfaces. The work function found by means of the Fowler-Nordheim equation is determined mainly by atomically rough regions on the tips; these regions are affected in the same way by oxygen adsorption. George and Stier adsorbed oxygen not only at room temperature, but also at 20°K. At the latter temperature, they covered the central portion of the tip surface previously freed from oxygen by field-evaporation both by surface migration from the covered shanks of the tip and by oxygen molecules incident from the gas phase.

The oxygen from the shank is physically adsorbed over a chemisorbed layer. Gomer and Hulm worked with very low oxygen pressures, since they cooled the field-emission tube at 4·2°K. George and Stier, on the other hand, used oxygen pressures of 10^{-8} to 10^{-7} mm Hg, keeping the tip at 20°K. The amount of oxygen physisorbed in their experiments is consequently much larger. This explains why they observed spreading from a physisorbed oxygen layer at 20°K, whereas Gomer and Hulm found the onset of migration at a slightly higher temperature, specifically, 27°K. Since the surface area of the shank of the tip is much larger than the surface area freed from oxygen by field evaporation, the adsorption is dominated by migrating oxygen. It is remarkable that the latter adsorption procedure used by George and Stier increases the work function to the same extent as adsorption from the gas phase at room temperature, that is, by 2·1 eV. Apparently a fully-occupied chemisorbed layer can be obtained in this way. We believe that this difference is due to the difference in trapping of the oxygen molecules reaching the boundary of the chemisorbed layer on the bare tungsten surface. At 20°K the oxygen molecules are trapped by the tungsten surface atoms situated next to the edge of the chemisorbed layer. The chemisorbed layer built up in this way does not contain any vacancies. At 27°K the kinetic energy of the physisorbed molecules is slightly larger; oxygen molecules reaching the edge are now adsorbed also by tungsten surface atoms one or two metal atoms away from the edge. This results in formation of a chemisorbed layer with vacancies. Below about 100°K the vacancies cannot be filled in easily by dissociation of molecular oxygen. We shall return to this point in the discussion of the electron-induced desorption and the LEED results; the data obtained from desorption by electron impact point to weak adsorption of oxygen molecules into these vacancies.

As mentioned in Sections II and III, activated sorption of oxygen displaying a smaller thermal effect follows the rapid adsorption at temperatures above 200°K. This slow sorption is also apparent from the data of Gomer and Hulm. When a tip is exposed to relatively high oxygen pressures (up to 0·18 mm Hg) at 300 °K, the emission slowly decreases, whereas the work function, which owing to the rapid adsorption had increased by 1·9 eV, does not change. The decrease in emission is due to a large decrease in emitting area, which, after an exposure time of about 200 hours, is only about 1/600 of the original value.

George and Stier presented evidence that, after adsorption of a monolayer of oxygen, the emission from the tip is governed by the (110) planes. We believe that the decrease in emitting area is due to sorption beyond a monolayer on these planes. The activated sorption converts the (110) planes patch-wise to a state with a higher work function; the emission is determined by those parts of the (110) planes not yet covered beyond a monolayer.

As mentioned in Section II, Singleton (1967) observed additional take-up of oxygen by tungsten wires at temperatures above 750°K. A change in the interaction of oxygen with tungsten surfaces is apparent also from the results of Gomer and Hulm at temperatures from 600 to 700°K. The effect of heating at or above these temperatures depends strongly on the extent of interaction with oxygen. The latter easily can be evaluated from the above decrease in the emitting surface area.

Heating a tip with a limited oxygen coverage at temperatures above 700°K caused a gradual decrease in the overall work function. In view of the flash-filaments experiments of McCarroll and of Ptushin-skii and Chuikov, it is not to be expected that this decrease is due to desorption of oxygen. Atomic oxygen, which desorbs almost exclusively from tungsten surfaces that have not extensively reacted with oxygen, is found to evolve only at temperatures around 1700°K. Hence, the decrease in work function on heating above 700°K is to be ascribed to a structural change in the covered surface. This is evident also from the fact that Gomer and Hulm could not re-establish the high work function by redosing oxygen at room temperature. The decrease in the work function on heating at temperatures above 700°K points to the onset of mobilization of tungsten surface atoms and adsorbed oxygen atoms to an extent enabling oxygen to penetrate into the tungsten. Penetration of oxygen into the metal lattice causes a decrease in work

22

function. Redosing of oxygen fails to restore the original configuration.

A tip having interacted more strongly with oxygen shows a markedly different behaviour on heating. At temperatures above 600–700°K, bright spots develop in the emission pattern, which are removed by heating to 1000°K. These spots are almost surely due to minute oxide crystallites. At 1000°K the tungsten oxides slowly evaporate, as is evident from Singleton's results.

Thus we again conclude that the surface layer obtained on interaction of tungsten with oxygen is capable of rearranging at these temperatures. Owing to the lack of intermetallic bonds at the tungsten surface, the configuration obtained by adsorption of a monolayer of oxygen

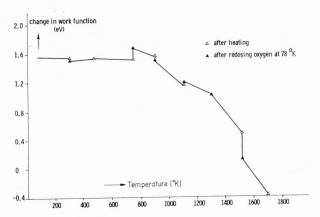

Fig. 13 Effect of oxygen sorption at 78°K on the *average* work function of a tungsten tip. (Bell *et al.*, 1968.)

atoms onto the surface is stable with respect to formation of small tungsten oxide crystallites adsorbed on the metal. After more extensive interaction with oxygen, formation of tungsten oxides, which is thermodynamically favoured, can proceed rapidly. The rearrangement now taking place above 600–700°K, leads to tungsten oxides adsorbed on the metal surface.

Rearrangement of the covered tungsten surface is apparent also from the results of Bell *et al.* (1968) who extended the work of Gomer and Hulm with an investigation of the effect of oxygen sorption on the work function of monocrystalline planes present on a field-emission tip. This was done by projecting the emission of a definite crystallographic plane onto a hole in the fluorescent screen backed by a Faraday cage. The emission characteristics of definite regions of the tip surface could thus be measured separately. These authors always covered the tip surface with oxygen at 78°K; since the sticking coefficient of oxygen incident on the wall of the tube cooled at 78°K is less than unity, this procedure leads to a uniform coverage of the tip surface. Having been covered at this temperature, the tip was kept for 60 seconds at successively higher temperatures and at very low oxygen pressures, after which the work function was determined at 78°K. Bell *et al.*, using the Fowler-Nordheim equation, calculated both the pre-exponential factor and the work function from their experimental data. Attention will be focused here on their work function data, given in Fig. 13. The

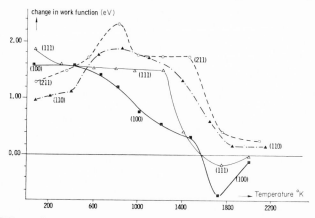

Fig. 14 Effect of oxygen adsorption on the work function of monocrystalline regions on a field-emission tip. (Bell *et al.*, 1968.)

open triangles indicate the change in the work function after heating for 60 seconds at the indicated temperatures; the solid triangles give the change in work function after resaturation of the heated surface with oxygen at 78°K. It can be seen from this figure that the results of Gomer and Hulm are quite well reproduced, although the increase in the work function after heating to 700°K and redosing is slightly smaller; heating above about 900°K leads to a decrease in the overall work function, which cannot be restored by redosing oxygen at 78°K. A decrease of the work function below the value found for the clean surface was also observed by Gomer and Hulm. Heating at still higher temperatures, gave a work function identical to that of the clean surface.

Figure 14 shows the effect of oxygen adsorption on the work function of monocrystalline planes on the tip surface, which was saturated with oxygen at 78°K and heated for 60 seconds at the temperatures indicated.

The maximum work function of the (211) plane might be somewhat exaggerated, since Bell *et al.* published another experiment on the (211) plane in which a much less pronounced maximum was found. (Bell *et al.*, 1968; Fig. 7, where each heating period was followed up with redosage of oxygen to the tip at 78°K). It is remarkable that the increases in work function found by Hopkins and Pender on macroscopic monocrystalline specimens are in very good accordance with the data found on microscopic tips at 300°K by Bell *et al.* (see Table V).

TABLE V. Increase in the work function (eV) of tungsten monocrystalline planes upon reaction with oxygen at low pressures

Plane	Macroscopic specimens[a]	Field-emission tips[b]
(100)	1·6	1·6
(110)	1·0	1·15

[a] Hopkins and Pender, 1966.
[b] Bell *et al.*, 1968.

The work functions of the (100) and (111) planes show a behaviour analogous to that of the average work function upon heating at increasing temperatures; the work function at first remains constant to decrease after a definite temperature has been reached. Eventually, it falls off below the value for the clean surface; this trend is particularly evident on the (100) plane. The work function of the (100) plane starts decreasing at a markedly lower temperature than the overall work function. The strong decrease of the work function of the (111) plane, on the other hand, sets in at an appreciably higher temperature. From another experiment by Bell *et al.*, it appeared that the work function of the (100) plane with a lower degree of coverage decreases only above 800°K. The work functions of the (110) and (211) planes, however, pass through a maximum at about 700°K before decreasing slowly to the value for the clean surface.

We now want to discuss the fact that for the (100) and (111) planes the minima lie below the values for the clean surfaces. The surface atoms in these planes are not in contact with each other, unlike those in the (110) and (211) planes, which contact each other in two directions and in one, respectively. In view of the lower co-ordination of the metal surface atoms, faceting of the more open (100) and (111) planes by evaporation of tungsten atoms in oxide form may be expected. Since a faceted metal surface will display a lower work function, we believe that the minimum in the work function for these planes is due to the establishment of a faceted surface in a definite temperature range. As mentioned in Section IV, Ptushinskii and Chuikov as well as McCarroll showed that evaporation of WO_2 and WO_3 sets in at about 1700°K. This temperature is close to the temperature at which a work function lower than that of the clean surface develops. On evaporation of some of the tungsten surface atoms a faceted surface is likely to form. The oxygen remaining on the surface will leave the protruding tungsten atoms on the facets uncovered; therefore a lower work function can be expected for this surface. The surface area acquiring a faceted structure must be relatively small, seeing that only little oxygen has been found to desorb in oxide form. This is in keeping with the very low value found for the pre-exponential factor in the Fowler-Nordheim equation by Bell, *et al.*, in measurements on the (100) surface after heating at approximately 1700°K.

Evidence from low-energy electron diffraction experiments, to be discussed more extensively below, lends support to this interpretation. One has to keep in mind, however, that a definite surface structure must be established over an appreciably large surface area if this structure is to be observed in LEED experiments. Unlike in the experiments discussed so far, the tungsten surface must, in general, be exposed to relatively high oxygen pressures at high temperatures to induce the LEED patterns now to be discussed. Anderson and Danforth (1965) found formation of (110) facets on a tungsten (100) plane heated at about 1300°K and an oxygen pressure of approximately 10^{-7} mm Hg. Taylor (1964) earlier observed (211) facets on a (111) surface after sorption of oxygen and heating; Germer and May (1966), on the other hand, did not find any faceting on a (110) tungsten surface on heating in oxygen. For the (211) plane the evidence is not entirely unambiguous since, as shown by Chang and Germer (1967), heating of a (211) plane at 1300–1700°K in oxygen leads to formation of (110) facets. Chang and Germer, however, did not observe faceting of the (211) plane on heating to 2200°K in a good vacuum after heavy exposure to oxygen at room temperature. Since Bell *et al.* covered their tips at 80°K and thereafter heated the tip for 60 seconds to the temperatures indicated, faceting is very unlikely in their experiments.

A second remarkable feature of Fig. 14 is that the work functions of the (110) and (211) planes pass through a maximum during heating. We ascribe this to the formation of a surface oxide above approximately 400°K. If oxygen is adsorbed on the above planes at lower temperatures, a configuration with the oxygen atoms disposed on the tungsten atoms develops; the structure of the metal surface is not appreciably distorted by the bonding of oxygen. The negative charge of the oxygen atoms is relatively small for this structure, since the metal atoms still maintain their intermetallic bonds to a marked extent. At higher temperatures, the activation energy needed for a rearrangement of the layer can be provided: a surface is formed in which the bond shows a stronger ionic character. This explanation is supported by LEED evidence obtained by Germer and May, who showed that around 700°K very complicated super-structures are formed on tungsten (110) planes covered with oxygen. Bauer (1967) argued that these structures are due to WO_2 epitaxially present on the tungsten. For the (211) plane both the maximum in the work function and the LEED evidence are more difficult to interpret. The discussion on the results of Bell et al. ends with a consideration of the behaviour of the oxygen-covered (111) and (100) planes during heating: the work functions of both planes first show a decrease, then remain constant for a while, and finally drop below the value for the clean surface. For the (100) plane the constant level is only faintly indicated. We ascribe this to the structure of the (111) and (100) planes being much more open than that of the (110) and (211) planes. In the former planes the metal atoms in the surface layer are not in contact. Owing to the larger distances between the atoms, a configuration in which each metal atom binds one oxygen atom can easily be formed. At higher temperatures, the oxygen atoms penetrate between the metal surface atoms; this leads to a decrease in the work function. For the very open (111) plane, the penetration starts already at 100°K; it is complete at about 500°K. The resulting structure is very stable, since the mutual coordination of oxygen and tungsten is good. The interstices in the (100) plane are markedly smaller. Therefore, a temperature higher than that for the (111) plane —about 600°K—is needed to bring about penetration.

As said in the beginning of this section, quite a number of oxygen-covered metal surfaces display a decrease in work function upon heating above the adsorption temperature. This decrease is due to penetration of the negatively-charged oxygen into the surface. Quinn and Roberts (1964) investigated this point very extensively, in general adsorbing oxygen at 77°K and heating the covered metals to room temperature. For metals like nickel and iron, they found the work function to decrease on heating of the covered surface. The increase in work function observed at 77°K could be reproduced either completely (iron, chromium) or partially (nickel), by exposure to oxygen at room temperature (Delchar and Tompkins, 1967). Molybdenum, which was also examined by Quinn and Roberts, is an exception; after adsorption of oxygen at 77°K, its work function decreases only very slightly upon heating at 300°K. This implies that oxygen does not penetrate into their molybdenum surface at this temperature. The cause is to be sought in the high intermetallic bonding energy of this metal and not in its structure, inasmuch as iron, which is also b.c.c., clearly shows penetration into the surface even at 77°K.

To decrease the work function of nickel below that of the clean surface, a temperature of about 450°K is necessary. For the work function of a nickel surface interacting with gaseous oxygen, Roberts and Wells (1966) observed (Fig. 15) that a certain coverage is needed

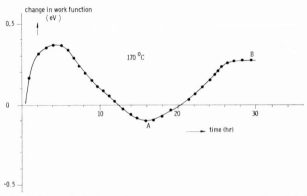

Fig. 15 Effect of slow admission of oxygen to an evaporated nickel film on the work function. (Roberts and Wells, 1966.)

before penetration into the metal surface can proceed at a given temperature. At coverages below this critical value, the oxygen adatoms are situated on top of the metal surface atoms. On the other hand, the oxygen atoms that have penetrated are present below the displaced metal surface atoms; at this point the negatively-charged oxygen atoms cause the work function to decrease below the value for the clean surface. Owing to the sudden penetration, the metal surface cannot be filled up immediately from the gas phase. Gradually, the number of oxygen adatoms on the displaced metal atoms increases, which leads to a second rise of the work function.

In view of the high cohesive energy of tungsten, it is quite conceivable that only the crystallographic planes with a more open structure allow oxygen atoms to penetrate into the surface. For penetration into the (100) plane, which has relatively small interstices between the metal surface atoms, rather a high temperature is needed. Bell *et al.* investigated the effect of heating on the work function of fully and partly-covered (100) planes (Fig. 16).

Unlike Roberts and Wells, Bell *et al.* took their measurements without gradually increasing the coverage. As shown in Fig. 16, the work function of the sparsely-covered surface decreases to below that of the clean surface on heating to about 900°K. Inasmuch as evaporation of tungsten oxides and hence faceting of the surface is very unlikely on heating for 60 seconds at this temperature, this can only be due to

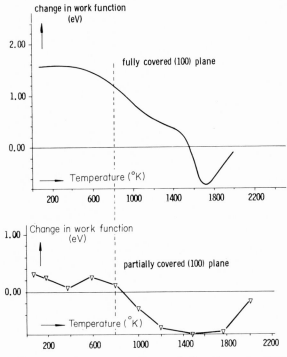

FIG. 16 Effect of oxygen coverage on the work function of a (100) region on a field-emission tip. (Bell *et al.*, 1968.)

penetration of oxygen atoms into the surface. The situation for the partly-covered surface corresponds to that for region A in Fig. 15, which shows the behaviour of nickel. When the temperature is raised, all the oxygen atoms penetrate into the surface, which brings about a decrease of the work function. The large difference in the temperatures at which penetration occurs on nickel and on tungsten is evidence of the influence of the high cohesive energy of tungsten. The anology in the behaviour of the work function of the partly and fully-covered surfaces on heating above 1700°K suggests that evaporation of tungsten oxides and faceting occurs also on the partly-covered (100) surface. The fully-covered surface always remains in a condition corresponding to that of the nickel surface in region B of Fig. 15. The amount of oxygen is too large to be accommodated completely in the surface; a fraction of the oxygen remains bonded above the level of the metal atoms or ions till evaporation of oxides sets in. In Section VIII it will be shown that this reasoning is strongly supported by LEED results obtained by Hayek, Farnsworth and Park (1968) on the molybdenum (100) plane.

It is to be expected that the work function increases again if more oxygen is sorbed after heating at 800°K. In the experiments represented in Fig. 16 the coverage remains limited, since heating is done in a high vacuum. However, another experiment by Bell *et al.* may serve to check the prediction that the work function should increase again if more oxygen is sorbed. In this experiment, the authors saturated the tip surface with oxygen at 78°K after previous heating to increasing temperatures for 60 seconds. Their results are presented in Fig. 17.

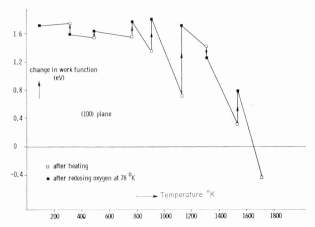

FIG. 17 Effect of adsorption of oxygen on the work function of a (100) region on a field-emission tip. (Bell *et al.*, 1968.)

In complete agreement with our explanation, heating above 800°K causes the work function to decrease, but the original decrease can be reproduced by adsorption of oxygen at 78°K. Only above 1200°K, where minute crystallites of tungsten oxides may be expected to be formed in 60 seconds, can the work function not be restored to its original value. The (110) and (211) planes do not show this variation in work function after this treatment.

The work function of a completely-covered tungsten surface cannot be decreased below that for the clean surface. The minimum in work function for the (100) and (111) planes after saturation at 78°K (Fig.

14) was ascribed to faceting. This interpretation is based on the fact that the minimum is found at high temperatures, where evaporation of tungsten oxides occurs.

Finally, the fact that the configuration of the (111) plane with sorbed oxygen is stable over the considerable temperature range of 400 to 1300°K deserves some attention. We believe that this is due to a relatively small displacement of the metal surface atoms resulting in a stable configuration; moreover, owing to the slight coordination of the surface atoms in this plane, the displacement requires little activation energy. Since the oxygen adatoms can contact the tungsten atoms very closely, the configuration remains stable until formation and evaporation of tungsten oxides set in.

The effect of oxygen on the work function of molybdenum has been studied in less detail. As said above, Quinn and Roberts at 77°K observed an increase in the work function of evaporated films of 1·65 eV. Heating to room temperature had very little effect. This contrasts with the behaviour found for tungsten, the work function of which increased on heating to room temperature and exposure to oxygen. Abon and Teichner (1967) studied the effect of oxygen sorption on the average work function of a molybdenum field-emission tip. They observed an increase of 1·5 eV, which agrees with the findings on evaporated films. After exposure to oxygen at 10^{-5} mm Hg and 300°K for 16 hours, the increase was 2·4 eV. It is difficult to ascertain the origin of this slow increase from the data now available. Hayek et al. combined LEED observations with work function measurements on molybdenum surfaces covered to varying extents with oxygen. Their results will be discussed in Section VIII.

VI   Effects of Oxygen Sorption on the Electrical Conductance of Evaporated Tungsten and Molybdenum Films

A   Introduction

In the preceding section detailed information has been given about the mobility of oxygen adatoms and their penetration into the metal surface. We shall now investigate the effects of the oxygen sorption on the metallic structure. One of the most characteristic properties of metals is the high electrical conductivity decreasing with increasing temperature. It can therefore be expected that the effects of oxygen sorption on the electrical conductance of metals clearly reflect the extent to which the metal structure is affected.

As said in Section II, interaction of molybdenum and tungsten with oxygen at temperatures up to 300°K does not go beyond the first two atomic layers of the metals. Hence, a well-measurable effect of oxygen sorption on the electrical conductance calls for metal specimens with a relatively large surface-to-volume ratio. Metal films evaporated in ultra-high vacuum have both a clean surface and a large surface-to-volume ratio. Two types of evaporated metal films were used to investigate the effect of oxygen sorption on the metal structure: island films and continuous, though highly porous, films.

In order that the influences of oxygen sorption on their conductance can be understood, some aspects of the genesis and structure of evaporated metal films must be discussed first. The energy with which metal

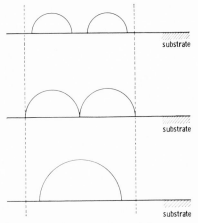

Fig. 18 Coalescence of two growing metal particles on a substrate; denudation of the substrate and increase in dimension normal to the substrate.

atoms are bonded to non-conducting substrates such as glass or sodium chloride is much weaker than the mutual attraction between metal atoms. Benjamin and Weaver (1959, 1961, 1963; Weaver 1963) brought forward evidence that the bond between glass and metal atoms is of the van-der-Waals type, provided reaction of the metal atoms with residual gas molecules like oxygen is prevented. Since van-der-Waals bonding does not lead to adsorption on definite substrate sites, metal atoms are generally mobile over the substrate surface. Hence, evaporation of metal atoms onto a glass substrate at first does not produce a two-dimensional metal layer, but isolated three-dimensional metal crystallites (metal islands) (Mayer, 1955). If the amount of metal deposited per unit surface area of substrate is increased, contacting of two or more metal particles will become more frequent. According to electron-microscope studies done mostly on gold, contact is generally brought about by growth of the metal islands due to trapping of metal atoms incident from the gas phase or migrating over the substrate surface (Pashley, 1965).

Motion of very small metal particles over the substrate surface is also quite conceivable. The behaviour of two contacting metal islands depends on the mobility of the metal atoms over the surface of the metal crystallites. If this surface mobility is high, two small contacting particles displaying liquid-like coalescence can rapidly assume an

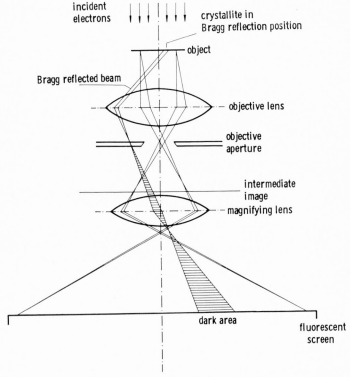

Fig. 19 Origin of crystallites showing as dark spots in transmission electron micrographs of evaporated metal films.

equilibrium shape (Pashley, Stowell, Jacobs, and Law, 1964). Since the interaction with the support is only slight, the newly-formed particles will have an appreciable dimension perpendicular to the substrate. Consequently part of the substrate surface is denuded in this coalescence process (Fig. 18). If the metal islands exceed a critical size, coalescence to a monocrystalline particle with an equilibrium shape can no longer take place. Most obviously this is due to the larger distances that have to be covered by the migrating metal atoms.

Migration of a small number of metal atoms over small distances no longer gives rise to an energetically more favourable configuration. Now a rather stable grain boundary establishes on contact of two metal particles. In this stage of the deposition a continuous film is formed.

The high sublimation energy of tungsten and molybdenum leads to a relatively restricted mobility of the atoms of these metals over their surfaces. It has to be expected, therefore, that the liquid-like coalescence of small crystallites of these metals ceases at a relatively small particle size. This is borne out by the experimental data. Geus, Kiel and Koks

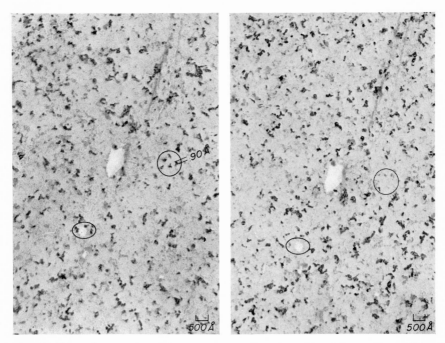

FIG. 20 Two micrographs of the same spot of an iron film taken with a slight difference in orientation (about 10°) with respect to the incident electron beam. Iron film (100A), evaporated on rock salt at room temperature. Enlargement 140,000×. (Micrograph taken by A. M. Kiel, Central Laboratory, Geleen, The Netherlands.)

(unpublished) investigated the size of the monocrystalline regions in evaporated films of the b.c.c. metals iron and tungsten. The Bragg reflection of the electron beam transmitted through the film was used to determine the size of monocrystalline regions. As indicated in Fig. 19, a crystallite exhibiting Bragg reflection deflects the incident electron beam outside the very small aperture of the electron microscope. As a result the crystallite produces a dark spot in the resulting micrograph. Fig. 20 is a micrograph of an iron film.

The dark areas produced by monocrystalline particles can be easily distinguished. That scattering of electrons from these areas is not due to a relatively large thickness (asperites) can be concluded from a comparison of the right-hand and left-hand part of this figure. The

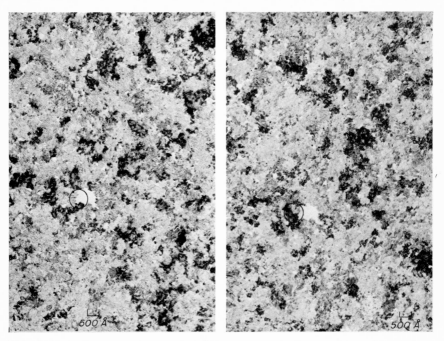

FIG. 21 Two electrons micrographs of the same spot of an evaporated tungsten film taken with a slight difference in orientation (about 10°) with respect to the incident electron beam. Enlargement 128,000 × (Micrograph taken by A. M. Kiel, Central Laboratory, Geleen, The Netherlands.)

two photographs represent the same spot of an iron film specimen, the right-hand one after the specimen was tilted through an angle of about 10°. This relatively small change in orientation changed the conditions for Bragg reflection. Consequently, particles displaying Bragg reflection in the left-hand photograph no longer do so in the right-hand one and the reverse. An evaporated tungsten film specimen with the same 10° change in orientation is photographed in Fig. 21. As in Fig 20, Bragg reflection is evident from the difference in blackening of identical spots in the left and right-hand micrographs. At this film thickness the liquid-like coalescence has stopped; particles with fast-growing planes on top are now growing out over particles less favourably oriented for growth. This gives rise to relatively large thin monocrystalline layers over small particles with random orientation. The small

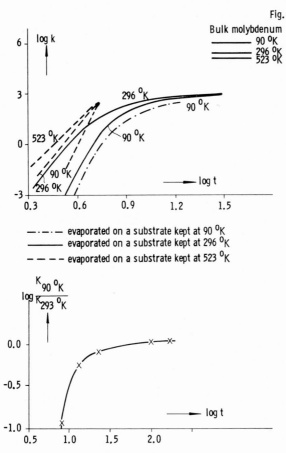

Fig. 22a Conductivity (K) of molybdenum films thrown on glass as a function of nominal film thickness (t-atomic layers). Top: glass kept at different temperatures. The conductivity of bulk molybdenum is included for comparison. Bottom: glass kept at 293°K. The ratio larger than unity, displayed also by bulk metals, is observed at thicknesses above about 1·7 atomic layers. (De Boer and Kraak, 1936.)

particles can be seen in the micrograph with the top layer out of Bragg reflection. It is evident that the monocrystalline regions in the tungsten film are much smaller than in the iron film. This cannot be due to a difference in crystal structure, since both metals are b.c.c.; the smaller

crystallite size of the tungsten clearly results from the much higher
sublimation energy of this metal.

Because the liquid-like coalescence of contacting molybdenum and
tungsten crystallites stops at a very small particle size, formation of
isolated metal particles with a considerable dimension perpendicular
to the substrate accompanied by denudation of the substrate will
occur only as long as the film thickness is very small. As a result the
electrical conductance of films of molybdenum and tungsten gradually
increases with increasing film thickness. On metals with more mobile

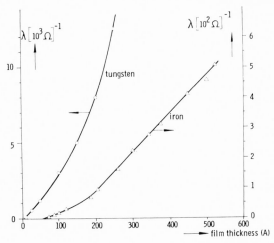

FIG. 22b Conductance (λ) of tungsten and iron films evaporated on glass at 293°
and 283° as a function of film thickness.

surface atoms, the formation of large isolated particles is much more
pronounced. Owing to the denudation of the substrate, the distances
between the metal islands remain large as long as liquid-like coalescence
can take place. In this stage of the deposition process, the electrical
conductance remains very low. Only after the coalescence has stopped
is a continuous film rapidly established. This leads to an abrupt
decrease in electrical resistance. Figures 22a and 22b show the electrical
conductance of evaporated films of some metals as a function of the
film thickness (de Boer and Kraak, 1936; Geus and Koks, unpublished).
The above increase in conductance is very well displayed by the molybdenum and tungsten films, whereas the conductance of iron films
increases at larger thicknesses only. Owing to the extremely small
size of the metal crystallites in the tungsten film, the conductance is
relatively low. (High residual resistivity.) Since liquid-like coalescence

of tungsten films stops at a very low average film thickness, the conductance increases steadily from very low thicknesses on. The conductance of iron films increases only after a thickness of about 60 Å is reached; at this thickness the metal crystallites are too large to give rise to liquid-like coalescence. Figures 22a and 22b illustrate that with molybdenum and tungsten much thinner continuous films can be formed than with iron. (Older work would seem to suggest that such metals as silver can form also very thin continuous films. However, in this work reaction with residual gas molecules strongly decreased the mobility of metal atoms over the substrate and metal surfaces.)

B Island Films

We shall now discuss the electrical conductance of island films and the effect of oxygen sorption on these films. Films composed of isolated metal crystallites on a non-conducting substrate show a decrease in electrical resistance with increasing temperature. This is opposed to the behaviour of bulk metals, whose resistivity increases with temperature owing to the increasing thermal vibration of the metal atoms.

De Boer and Kraak (1936) brought forward a theory for explaining the decrease in the resistance of molybdenum films with increasing temperature. They assumed that the distances between metal atoms in films with an average thickness of the order of one monolayer are slightly larger than the interatomic distances in the bulk metal. Owing to this the overlap of the wave functions on neighbouring atoms is reduced, resulting in a smaller broadening of the atomic energy levels. In very thin evaporated films the broadening is reduced so far that the Fermi level comes to lie below the energies corresponding to wave functions spread out over the whole metal. This gives rise to activated electron transport.

Later, however, evidence was found for the view that metal atoms are mobile over clean substrates. Consequently, the metal atoms will not remain on the spots where they hit the substrate, but will form minute metal crystallites. Recently, two different groups of theories were developed accounting for the negative temperature coefficient of the resistance. One group ascribes the electron transport between the metal particles to thermionic emission. The temperature coefficient of the resistance is easily explained by this assumption. Minn (1960; Minn and Vodar, 1961) assumed the electron transport to proceed through the vacuum separating the metal particles. Van Steensel (1967) provides an even more reasonable explanation of his figures found on gold and platinum films by assuming electron transport to

23

take place through the substrate. In the other group of theories tunnelling is considered responsible for the charge transport. Neugebauer and Webb (1962) assume tunnelling to take place at least partly through the substrate, whereas according to Herman and Rhodin

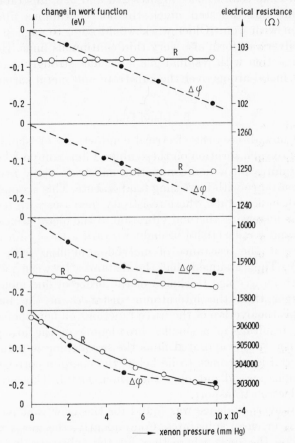

Fig. 23 Effect of xenon adsorption at 77°K on the work function and the electrical resistance of zirconium films of various thicknesses. $\Delta\Phi$: change in work function; R: film resistance. (Hansen and Littmann, 1963.)

(1966) tunnelling through the substrate is the only possibility. Neugebauer and Webb derive the activation energy accounting for the negative temperature coefficient of resistance from the energy required for applying one electronic charge to a very small metal particle (Gorter, 1951). Hartman (1963) ascribes the activation energy to the restricted widths of the electronic energy levels in very small particles.

It is very difficult to judge the validity of the above theories. Island films of different metals, moreover, may differ in properties. Hence, it is perhaps not possible to ascribe the electrical conductance to one and the same mechanism in all cases. In this review we shall consider metal films composed of rather small metal crystallites with a relatively small spacing present on a non-conducting substrate. With these films, which are obtained on evaporation of, e.g. molybdenum, titanium, nickel, and zirconium, electron transport through the substrate alone is very improbable, as will be shown below. Hansen and Littmann (1963) investigated the effect of xenon adsorption at 77°K both on the work function and on the electrical resistance of zirconium films of various thicknesses. Their results are presented in Fig. 23, from which it can be seen that the four films investigated differ widely in resistance and hence in thickness. It is also seen that only for very thin films having an island structure does the resistance decrease on adsorption of xenon. This decrease runs parallel to the decrease in the work function. Continuous thick films show a decrease in the work function, but no effect on the resistance. These results demonstrate unambiguously that at least part of the boundary planes of the metal particles accessible to adsorbing molecules are involved in the conduction process.

This can also be inferred from the extensive work of Fehlner (1966a,b, 1967), who studied the effect of oxygen sorption on the resistance of island films of metals, including titanium, nickel, and zirconium. The films investigated had resistances in the range of two to 500 kΩ, which increased on interaction with oxygen.

Van Steensel (1967), on the other hand, evaporated silicon monoxide onto gold island films; he observed only rather small effects of the overlay of silicon monoxide. As will be demonstrated below, access to small gaps between neighbouring metal islands is difficult from the gas phase. It is quite conceivable that the silicon monoxide cannot penetrate appreciably into the gaps separating the metal particles. Nevertheless, it is still possible that for films composed of widely-separated metal islands which display very high resistances the charge transport is mainly through the substrate.

De Boer and Kraak (1937) were the first to carry out reliable experiments on the effect of oxygen sorption on the electrical conductance of evaporated metal films. They investigated molybdenum films with resistances of the order of 10^{10} to 10^7 Ω; the island structure of the films is evident from the negative temperature coefficient of the resistance. In view of the high cohesive energy of molybdenum, it can be safely assumed that these films are composed of extremely small molybdenum particles separated by small gaps (Fig. 24).

J. W. GEUS

On interaction of gaseous oxygen with these particles, two effects can be expected:

(1) the work function of the metal surface is changed;
(2) the metal is transferred over a certain depth into a non-conducting or poorly-conducting oxide.

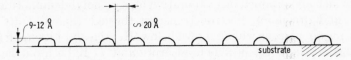

FIG. 24 Model of a molybdenum film with a thickness of three to four atomic layers.

Both the thermionic emission and the tunnelling of electrons from the metal particles are strongly affected by the potential barrier between the metal particles. This barrier is highly dependent on the work function of the particles, which, consequently, affects the electrical resistance of the film. The barrier is determined too by the distances between the still metallic parts of the islands. Oxidation over a certain depth leads to an increase of this distance and hence to an increase of the film resistance.

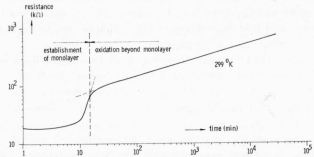

FIG. 25 Effect of continuous sorption of oxygen on the electrical resistance of an island-type titanium film. Above the film a constant oxygen pressure of 6×10^{-8} mm Hg was maintained. (Fehlner, 1966.)

The two effects can be distinguished in Fehlner's (1966a,b, 1967) experiments on titanium, zirconium, and nickel films. Upon exposure to a constant oxygen pressure Fehlner found the film resistance to vary as shown in Fig. 25, provided the heat of adsorption could be dissipated sufficiently fast.

First, the oxygen atoms are adsorbed mainly on top of the metal particles. The surfaces in the gaps separating the metal particles are not affected. The resistance therefore is influenced only slightly during this process. If the outer surface of the film is covered to such an extent that either migration of adatoms over the surface sets in, or the sticking probability is decreased sufficiently, oxygen penetrates into the gaps between the metal islands. As discussed in Section V, the work function strongly increases upon oxygen adsorption. Owing to this, the potential barrier between the metal islands goes up sharply upon adsorption on the surfaces situated in the gaps. Consequently, oxygen penetrating into the gaps produces a sharp rise in the film resistance. Finally, activated oxidation of the metal particles occurs, which gives rise to a continuous increase in the distances between the *metallic* particles and hence also to a continuous increase of the film resistance.

Earlier, evidence was brought forward for the interaction of oxygen with tungsten and molybdenum surfaces below 100°K remaining restricted to the first layer of metal atoms. This is clear from de Boer and Kraak's results (Fig. 26). After admission of oxygen at 90°K to

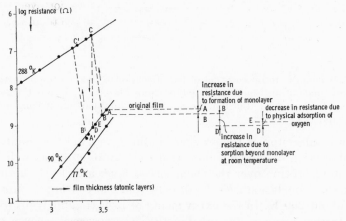

FIG. 26. Effect of interaction with oxygen on the resistance of island-type molybdenum films. (de Boer and Kraak, 1937.)

molybdenum films with resistances A and A', the resistances increased to B and B', respectively. Evidently, this is due to the increase of the work function by adsorption of the first layer of oxygen and the loss of conductivity of the metal surface layer. At the pressures used by de Boer and Kraak, more oxygen is physically adsorbed on the chemisorbed layer, as will be proved. Upon heating to room temperature with simultaneous evacuation, part of the physically-adsorbed oxygen is sorbed by the molybdenum. This is apparent from the strong increase in the resistance upon subsequent cooling to 90°K (point D in Fig. 26). Upon admitting more oxygen at 90°K to the covered molybdenum surface, the resistance decreases to point E in Fig. 26.

As shown in section V, physical adsorption of oxygen over a chemisorbed layer decreases the work function below the value for a surface covered with a chemisorbed layer only. This decrease in the work function lowers the potential barrier between the molybdenum particles and consequently also lowers the resistance. This experiment demonstrates that the oxygen pressures in the experiments of de Boer and Kraak are high enough to produce a marked physical adsorption.

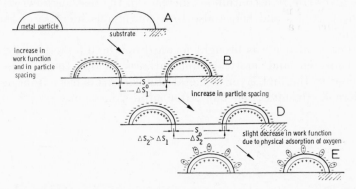

Fig. 27. Schematic representation of the effects of oxygen sorption on the electrical resistance of an island-type molybdenum film. A, B, D and E correspond to the condition indicated in Fig. 26. S_0 is the original particle spacing increased by ΔS_1 and ΔS_2.

Their results support the previous findings very well: the limited, but fast interaction of molybdenum with oxygen at 90°K, as well as the physical adsorption over the chemisorbed layer are clearly noticeable, and further conclusions can be drawn from the continued interaction above about 200°K. In the experiments of Roberts and Wells (Section V) no further increase in work function was observed when a molybdenum film that had adsorbed oxygen at 77°K was heated up to room temperature. Hence, the strong increase in resistance upon heating to room temperature cannot be ascribed to a further increase of the work function; it must be due to an increase of the distances between the metallic particles in the films (Fig. 27). Thus the interaction with oxygen above 200°K is not restricted to the surface layer of the metal; the subsurface layer is involved too.

It is remarkable that admission of oxygen at 90°K to the uncovered film gives a smaller increase in resistance (A B in Fig. 26) than does reaction beyond a monolayer (B D in Fig. 26). Judged by its degree, the fast interaction could have been expected to have a stronger effect than the activated sorption. The fact that it has not might be due to a slight contamination of the molybdenum during previous sintering at 370°C. It is extremely difficult to prevent desorption of impurities from glass kept at temperatures above 200°C. The slight contamination results in an increase of the work function of the molybdenum, which decreases the effect of subsequent oxygen adsorption.

C   Continuous Films

The effects of oxygen sorption on the resistance of continuous tungsten films were investigated by Geus *et al.* (1963). The films had a large specific surface area of $(6 \cdot 5 – 9 \cdot 6) \times 10^6$ cm^2/cm^3. They display a positive

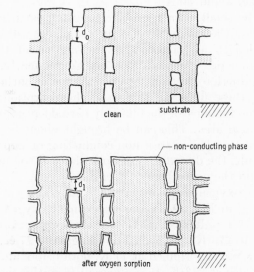

FIG. 28 Model of an evaporated tungsten film.

temperature coefficient of resistance, just as bulk metals do. From this, and from the absence of an appreciable effect of xenon adsorption on the resistance, it appears that neither electron emission nor tunnelling contribute markedly to the electrical conduction in these films. The electron micrographs of Fig. 21 reveal the presence of very small metal crystallites, which account for the very high residual resistivity of the films. (This is the temperature independent part of the resistivity; the residual resistivity is determined by grain boundaries, lattice defects and impurities).

It is difficult to give a good description of the structure of evaporated tungsten films. An older model postulated the presence of clusters of small tungsten particles (diameter about 75 A) intimately grown together and connected by particles of the same order of magnitude. After investigation of the structure of evaporated metal films in the electron microscope, we no longer believe this model to be completely correct. Mainly by using a fracturing technique developed by Nieuwenhuizen and Haanstra, it was possible to ascertain that evaporated iron films are built up of small metal columns, grown together at discrete places (Nieuwenhuizen and Haanstra, 1965, 1966; Geus, 1967). For tungsten films we therefore prefer this model (Fig. 28). Small columns of tungsten (diameter about 50 A) are parallel on the substrate. Enclosing rather narrow crevices, they have grown together over distances of about 30 A.

In view of the small diameter of the tungsten particles in the films, the dimensions of the atomically flat surface planes will be of the order of the wave length associated with the motion of the conduction electrons in the metal, which is about 7 A. Consequently, diffuse reflection of the conduction electrons against the metal surfaces has to be expected with these films. In this case, chemisorption can influence the electrical conductance of the film only *via* a decrease of the conducting cross-sectional area. This can be brought about by conversion of one or more surface layers to a non-conducting or poorly-conducting state. As a result, the dimensions of both the still conducting parts of the columns and the contact areas decrease.

The effect of oxygen sorption on the conductance, λ, of a tungsten film is presented in Fig. 29. In this experiment oxygen was admitted to the film at 77°K; after completion of the sorption process, the film was heated up to 273°K, and cooled down again to 77°K. The conductance of the film was determined at 77°K, both before and after heating to 273°K, and also at 273°K. It is apparent from this figure that up to a coverage of about 5×10^{14} oxygen molecules cm^{-2} equilibrium is reached already at 77°K. Heating up to 273°K and recooling to 77°K does not affect the conductance.

After a coverage of about 5×10^{14} O$_2$-molecules cm^{-2} has been reached, more oxygen can be quickly adsorbed at 77°K, but this does not have an effect on the conductance. Evidently, this oxygen is physically adsorbed, as was also apparent from the decrease of the work function and the increase of the conductance of island films. On heating to 273°K, oxygen is at least partly desorbed and subsequently slowly resorbed. During this sorption process the conductance decreases and remains at this lower level during recooling to 77°K.

Most remarkably, the effect per sorbed oxygen molecule is clearly smaller than in the fast stage of the sorption process.

The fact that the effect on the conductance does not depend on the measuring temperature, provided equilibrium has been attained, demonstrates that the geometry of the metallic conducting phase is affected only by the sorption process. The surface layer of the metal

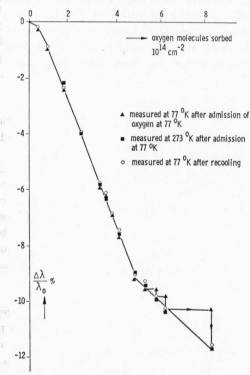

FIG. 29 Effect of oxygen sorption on the conductance (λ) of an evaporated tungsten film. (Geus *et al.*, 1963.)

loses its metallic character on adsorption of oxygen. If the metal atoms of the first layer have reacted, more oxygen can be taken up in an activated process in which metal atoms of the subsurface layers are converted to a non-conducting state. This was apparent also from the results of de Boer and Kraak. Inasmuch as the effect per sorbed oxygen molecule is smaller by more than a factor of two in the activated sorption, it has to be concluded that part of the oxygen is bonded to tungsten atoms already rendered non-conducting. Hence, the oxygen taken up in the slow process is used partly to increase the number of

23*

oxygen atoms bonded per tungsten atom, and partly to convert tungsten atoms not yet involved in the sorption process.

Above it was argued that oxygen can penetrate between the metal particles of an evaporated film only after coverage of that part of the surface which is the more easily accessible from the gas phase. Before oxygen molecules can reach more interior parts of the film surface they have to migrate over, or collide repeatedly with, already-covered surface parts. If oxygen is admitted at 273°K, part of the oxygen taken up is sorbed beyond the extent of a monolayer on its way to more interior parts of the film surface. This leads to a smaller effect on the conductance before the monolayer has been completed, as shown in Fig. 30.

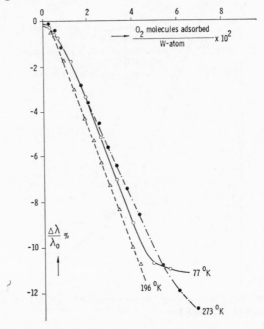

Fig. 30 Effect of oxygen sorption on the electrical conductance (λ) of evaporated tungsten films. Gas admitted and resistance measured at 77, 196, and 273°K. Slope of the experimental curves 2·6 (77°K), 2·7 (196°K), and 2·2 (273°K). (Geus et al., 1963.)

At 77 and 196°K equal and relatively large effects per adsorbed oxygen molecule are observed, since no activated sorption can proceed at these temperatures. At 273°K, the slope of the experimental curve is markedly smaller. Other experiments moreover revealed that the effect of oxygen on the conductance depends on the extent of the dose, a smaller dose having a relatively stronger effect than a larger one. Indeed, this is to be expected, since the concentration of oxygen above the chemisorbed layer increases with the dose.

From the above discussion it can be concluded that data obtained on island and continuous films both point to interaction of metal atoms in the subsurface layers in the slow sorption process. Moreover, it appeared that the intermetallic bonding in molybdenum and tungsten surfaces is strongly affected by interaction between the surface and oxygen.

VII Desorption of Oxygen by Slow Electron Impact

In the foregoing sections we have given a rather detailed picture of the structure of molybdenum and tungsten surfaces that have reacted to varying degrees with oxygen. One of the characteristics of the above metals is the fast formation of a monolayer of oxygen atoms; in the following slow process oxygen atoms penetrate into the metal surface. It is interesting to confront the above picture with data obtained by another technique: desorption induced by impact of electrons of low energy. Study of the interaction of sorbed species with low-energy electrons can shed light on the nature of the bonding between oxygen and metal surface atoms, and the kind of changes in the characteristics of the metal surface upon reaction with oxygen. Some recent detailed investigations of the effects of electron bombardment on molybdenum and tungsten surfaces covered with oxygen (Redhead, 1964; Menzel and Gomer, 1964a,b; Yates, Madey and Payn, 1967; Madey and Yates, 1968; Lichtman and Kirst, 1966) will now be reviewed to examine how the experimental data fit in with the picture developed.

Just as in experiments on the effects of adsorption on the work function, microscopic and macroscopic specimens are used in studying desorption by impact of slow electrons. Field-emission tips are used as microscopic specimens (Menzel and Gomer, 1964a,b). An advantage of this technique is that the structure of the sorbing surface before and after desorption can be easily examined. Desorption is detected by its effect on the work function. Consequently, desorption of neutral particles is included in the determination. In these experiments both the work function and the pre-exponential factor in the Fowler-Nordheim equation are determined as a function of the number of electrons incident on the tip.

Investigation of macroscopic sampler permits detection of charged desorbing particles (Redhead, 1964; Madey and Yates, 1968; Lichtman and Kirst, 1966). The number of desorbing ions per incident electron

as a function of coverage, temperature of the metal, and energy of the
bombarding electrons is determined, as well as the energy distribution
of these ions at a fixed energy of the bombarding electrons. In an
elaborate experimental set-up Lichtman and Kirst (1966) moreover
determined the mass of the desorbing ions by means of a mass spectrometer.

The most extensive experiments on field-emission tips were carried
out by Menzel and Gomer (1964a,b), covering the tip with oxygen at
20°K, and using the spreading process mentioned in Section V. To
remove physically-adsorbed oxygen which gives rise to spurious effects,

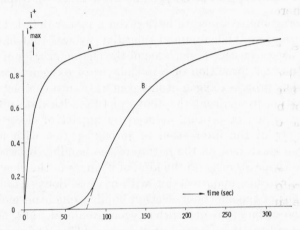

FIG. 31 Relative ion current as a function of time observed on exposure of a
molybdenum ribbon to an oxygen pressure of $1\cdot6\times10^{-7}$ mm Hg at time zero.
(Redhead, 1964.)

the tip was heated to 80°K before the electron bombardment. This
leads to a work function of 6·4 eV, slightly higher than the $6\cdot0\pm0\cdot1$ eV
observed earlier by Gomer and Hulm. Menzel and Gomer generally
did the electron bombardment at 20°K, and observed that the work
function approached a limiting value of 5·7 eV, whereas the pre-exponential factor in the Fowler-Nordheim equation continued to increase.
The time-dependence of these changes leads to cross-sections of about
$4\cdot3\times10^{-19}$ cm². The fact that the decrease in the work function remains
restricted indicates that only a fraction of the adsorbed oxygen can be
desorbed by electron impact. The cross-section for desorption of the
remaining oxygen adatoms is much smaller, less than 2×10^{-21} cm².
The area of the tip hit by electrons showed a considerable increase in
granularity in the electron emission pattern. Redosing of oxygen at

20°K restores the emission pattern and the work function to the pre-bombardment state.

Redhead (1964) investigated the desorption of oxygen from a poly-crystalline molybdenum ribbon by electron bombardment (electron energies 0–300 eV) at 300°K. The presence of two differently-sorbed oxygen species was apparent from a large divergence in cross-section for desorption.

The experimental evidence is given in Fig. 31; on exposure of the ribbon to an oxygen pressure $1 \cdot 6 \times 10^{-7}$ mm Hg, desorption of oxygen ions is observed only after adsorption of a certain minimum amount of oxygen (curve B). The oxygen first adsorbed displays a very low cross-section, whereas the oxygen taken up later can be desorbed by electron impact. The latter oxygen is bonded less strongly. This is demonstrated by heating the ribbon having adsorbed oxygen to 1000°K, which brings about desorption of the loosely-bonded oxygen. If the ribbon is then cooled, electron-induced desorption of oxygen ions is observed as soon as the ribbon is exposed again to oxygen (curve A). The oxygen that cannot be desorbed by electron impact only desorbs at 1700°K.

The time dependence of the desorption induced by electron impact as measured by Redhead, together with the experimental ion/electron ratio, shows that the desorption of oxygen ions is only about two per cent of the amount of oxygen desorbed as neutrals. Electron bombardment therefore brings about desorption of mainly neutral oxygen atoms. The time dependence, moreover, suggests a first-order desorption of both neutral and charged oxygen. From the observed time dependence Redhead calculated a total cross-section of about 10^{-18} cm^2. For oxygen on tungsten, this value is confirmed by Madey and Yates, who found 7×10^{-19} cm^2, which is in fair agreement with the value of $4 \cdot 3 \times 10^{-19}$ cm^2 observed by Menzel and Gomer (1964b). Lichtman and Kirst (1966) also confirmed the findings of Redhead; by mass spectrometry they demonstrated the desorption of oxygen ions. The ratio of desorbed ions to incident electrons depends on the coverage; for about equal conditions of the molybdenum surface, the ratio observed by Redhead—10^{-5} ions/electrons—is slightly lower than that arrived at by Lichtman and Kirst, who found a ratio of about 5×10^{-4} ions/electron. For oxygen on tungsten Madey and Yates found a ratio of about 10^{-6} ions/electron.

Yates et al. (1967), and later Madey and Yates (1968) published extensive studies on the electron-induced desorption of oxygen sorbed on a polycrystalline tungsten ribbon, with results in complete agreement with those mentioned above. In Fig. 32 the increase in ion current due to desorbing oxygen ions is given as a function of the exposure time.

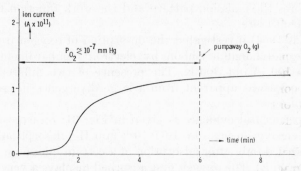

FIG. 32 Ion current *versus* time measured on bombarding a tungsten ribbon exposed to an oxygen pressure of about 1×10^{-7} mm Hg with 20 μA of 100-eV electrons, temperature at 300°K. (Yates *et al.*, 1967.)

The slow onset of the process is clearly observable. These authors also took measurements at temperatures below and above room temperature. Above about 500°K, the amount of oxygen that can be desorbed by electron impact steeply increases, as is apparent from Fig. 33, where the rate of desorption of oxygen ions after an oxygen exposure of 40×10^{-6} mm Hg sec is given as a function of the sorption temperature. Madey and Yates conclude that five per cent of the oxygen sorbed at 300° and 875°K will desorb as ions, which agrees with the result found by Redhead on molybdenum.

The above consistent experimental results, pointing to the presence of two different oxygen species on the surface, the ratio of which

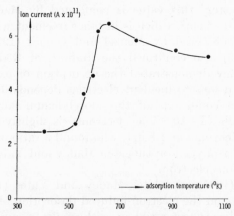

FIG. 33 Effect of adsorption temperature on the amount of adsorbed oxygen desorbable by electron impact. Exposure: 40×10^{-6} mm Hg. Electron current: 40 μA. (Madey & Yates, 1968.)

changes at temperature above about 500°K, agree with the data mentioned earlier. That two differently-sorbed species exist on the surface also appears from

(1) the sequence: fast adsorption-activated sorption;
(2) the rather abrupt decrease of the initially high heat of adsorption upon completion of the monolayer;
(3) the strong increase of the average work function of field-emission tips followed by a change in the pre-exponential factor only;
(4) the abrupt change in the effect per sorbed oxygen molecule on the electrical resistance of evaporated films;
(5) the gradual (McCarroll, 1967a,b,) or abrupt (Ptushinskii and Chuikov, 1967a,b, 1968) onset of desorption of tungsten oxides at increasing coverage in flash-filament experiments.

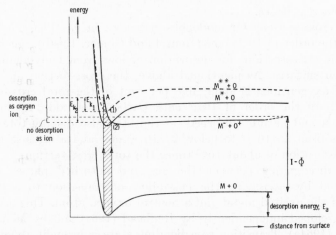

FIG. 34 Energy-level diagram for oxygen adsorbed on a metal surface bombarded by low-energy electrons.

The effect of temperature on the sorption of oxygen by tungsten was apparent from:

(1) Singleton's observations of an increase in the extent of sorption when he raised the temperature of the filament to about 700°K;
(2) the strong increase in the work function of the (110) plane of tungsten on heating above about 500°K, and the decrease in the overall work function of field-emission tips at temperatures above about 700°K.

To explain the results obtained in experiments on electron-induced desorption, we must first consider the mechanism of this desorption, outlined in Fig. 34, which shows a very simplified picture of the process involved. The curve marked M+O gives the energy of an oxygen atom in its ground state adsorbed on the metal. E_a, the bonding energy to the surface, equals $(Q_{ads}+D)/2$, where Q_{ads} is the heat of sorption (per oxygen molecule); D is the dissociation energy of gaseous oxygen. The curve M^-+O^+ represents the energy of an oxygen ion and one electron transferred to the metal. I is the energy required to ionize an oxygen atom $(O \rightarrow O^+ + e)$, and Φ is the work function of the metal. By the incidence of electrons the oxygen atom can be excited from the M+O to the M^-+O^+ state. The transitions which according to the Franck-Condon principle are the most probable are indicated. If the transition is to a state with an energy above that corresponding to an oxygen ion infinitely removed from the metal surface, desorption of an oxygen ion is possible; no desorption occurs upon transition to lower energy states.

The cross-sections for analogous processes in gas phase molecules are of the order of 10^{-16} cm^2 (Menzel and Gomer, 1964b), much larger than the cross-sections for desorption of ions from molybdenum and tungsten surfaces. As mentioned above, the cross-section for desorption of oxygen ions is about five per cent of the total cross-section, which is of the order of 10^{-18} cm^2. Carbon monoxide, nitric oxide, hydrogen and barium adsorbed on tungsten also display total cross-sections from 2×10^{-18} to below 2×10^{-22} cm^2 and a cross-section for ionic desorption of about 10^{-2} times the total cross-section.

The discrepancy between the gas and adsorbed phases can be explained by envisaging the possibility of transition to a bonding state of the excited metal and a neutral oxygen atom. This argument was developed independently by Redhead (1964) and by Menzel and Gomer (1964a). Transition to a bonding state is brought about by an Auger neutralization of the oxygen ion by a tunnelling metal electron. In this transition the adatom retains its kinetic energy acquired during the motion of the ion away from the surface, whilst the remainder of the energy difference between the M^-+O^+ and M+O states is transferred to the conduction electrons of the metal. As indicated in Fig. 34 an oxygen atom neutralized at a distance corresponding to point (1) acquires a kinetic energy E_{k_1}, the corresponding energy for neutralization at point (2) being E_{k_2}. Whether or not a transition leads to desorption of a neutral oxygen atom can be easily seen from Fig. 35, taken from Menzel and Gomer. The curve for the neutral adatom now crosses the ionic curve; the increase in energy is due to the higher energy of the conduction electrons of the metal. As can be seen from this figure, there is a critical distance for neutralization; on neutralization at smaller distances, the kinetic energy is too small to lead to desorption, whereas neutralization at a larger distance brings about desorption of a neutral atom.

The low values of the cross-sections observed for desorption of atoms adsorbed on metals as well as the large fraction of desorbing neutrals can obviously be ascribed to the large probability of Auger transitions. Redhead (1964) maintains that the large difference between the values

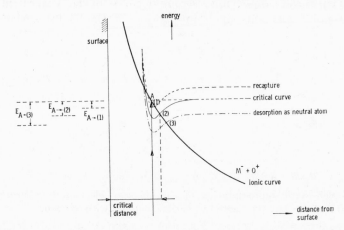

FIG. 35 Energy-level diagram demonstrating Auger neutralization of an oxygen ion moving away from the surface. Transition from the ground state towards A is assumed.

of the cross-sections for desorption of the two adsorbed oxygen species apparent in these experiments is due to a difference in distance from the metal surface between the two types of oxygen adatoms. We believe this should be elaborated, taking into account the effects of oxygen sorption on the electrical conductance of molybdenum and tungsten. It was evident that the surface layer of the metal became non-conducting upon adsorption of the first monolayer of oxygen atoms; hence, the valence electrons of the metal surface atoms and the oxygen adatoms are localized much more strictly than in the unperturbed metal. Consequently the conduction electrons neutralizing the adsorbed ions have to travel a much larger distance after completion of the monolayer. It will now be argued that desorption of oxygen can be appreciable only if the less strongly-bonded oxygen is present on the surface. The effect on the conductance of oxygen taken up in the slow stage of the sorption process may be ascribed to a reaction indicated schematically in Fig. 36. Part of the oxygen penetrates into the metal, affecting the subsurface layer, while the remaining oxygen is bonded to the displaced tungsten atom. After ionization of the oxygen adatoms illustrated on the left, neutralization can proceed effectively *via* the tungsten atom restored to the metallic state to which the ion is bonded. The tungsten atom on the right remains non-metallic after ionization of the oxygen, which impedes the neutralization and causes it to take place at larger distances from the *metallic* electrons. This explanation is substantiated by Hagstrum and his co-workers observing a strong decrease in the Auger neutralization of noble gas ions upon interaction of the metal surface with

FIG. 36 Schematic representation of the effect of electron bombardment on tungsten surfaces having reacted to various extents with oxygen.

residual gas molecules (Hagstrum, 1966; Hagstrum *et al.*, 1964). The divergence in cross-section displayed by differently-adsorbed carbon monoxide and nitric oxide molecules can be explained along the same lines (Menzel and Gomer, 1964b; Degras and Lecante, 1967; Yates *et al.*, 1967; Redhead, 1967).

The above approach can be followed in explaining the further results of electron-induced desorption experiments. The effects of heating above room temperature are shown in Fig. 37, obtained upon electron bombardment at 300°K of a ribbon heated for 30 seconds at the temperatures indicated (Madey and Yates, 1968; Yates *et al.*, 1967).

After high exposures the decrease in desorption by electron impact is observed only after heating at temperatures where desorption of tungsten oxides sets in (a); at lower coverages the electron-induced desorption decreases steadily with rising temperature above approximately 400°K (b). The desorption rate is measured after re-exposure to oxygen at room temperature (c). As can be seen the amount of oxygen that can be desorbed by electron impact increases strongly upon heating to over approximately 700°K. These findings can be explained by assuming that after exposures of about 4000×10^{-6} mm Hg sec oxygen penetrates into some crystallographic planes of the tungsten surface at room temperature. During heating, the surface configuration remains stable until evaporation of tungsten oxides sets in. Electrons incident on those parts of the surface which remain non-metallic

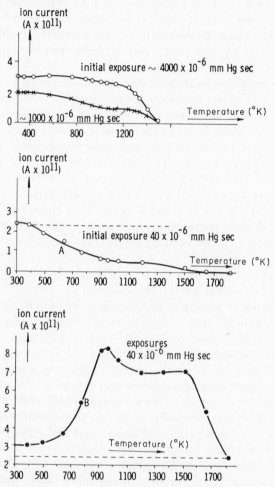

FIG. 37 Effect of heating on ion currents emitted by tungsten surfaces with different oxygen coverages, without redosage of oxygen (top and middle) and with redosage after each heating treatment (bottom).

after ionization of oxygen adatoms owing to penetration of oxygen into the surface give rise to desorption of oxygen. After short s-ures at room temperature, the oxygen adatoms penetrate surface at higher temperatures only. Since heating takes p absence of gaseous oxygen, penetration results in remov from the outer surface. This causes a strong decrease in the amount of oxygen that can be desorbed by electron impact. If oxygen is re-admitted at room temperature, it is adsorbed on top of the non-conducting metal surface, which gives rise to a large increase in the desorbable oxygen. This is also evident from the fact that when the temperature of a tungsten ribbon in oxygen is raised from 300 to 730°K, the desorption of oxygen ions shows a slight decrease followed by a sharp rise.

The above trend is clearly reflected in the effects of heating on the work function of (100) tungsten planes covered to different degrees with oxygen (Bell et al., 1968) (see Section V). But as the surfaces of these tips were covered by oxygen-dosing at low temperatures, the oxygen coverages in the two experiments are difficult to compare. Still, the decrease in the work function below the value of the clean (100) surface was observed at higher temperatures as the initial coverage was higher (see Figs 16 and 37). Further, heating in a high vacuum at temperatures of 800 to 1300°K leads to a decrease in the work function, which disappears again upon re-exposure to oxygen at 78°K (Fig. 17). This, too, is reflected by the electron-impact desorption data of Fig. 37.

It is interesting to compare the above results with the results obtained earlier by Roberts (Section II). He observed an increase in the accommodation coefficient with increasing oxygen pressure at room temperature (Fig. 1) and at very low oxygen pressures an accommodation coefficient of 0·226, caused by fast adsorption of oxygen. The electron-desorption results show that the change of the accommodation coefficient on heating depends on the extent of the previous interaction at room temperature; heating to increasing temperatures after sorption at room temperature to an accommodation coefficient of about 0·34, according to Roberts, gradually decreases the accommodation coefficient to 0·23 at 1100°K. Later, Morrison and Roberts (1939), heating a tungsten wire which had adsorbed oxygen to an accommodation coefficient of 0·226 to 1100°K, found a decrease to 0·177. Only after heating above 1700°K, where desorption takes place, did the accommodation coefficient become equal to that of the clean surface. There is, however, a clear difference in behaviour between the accommodation coefficient and the electron desorption on re-exposure to oxygen; the electron desorption strongly increases, whereas the accommodation coefficient rises only to the value reached after the first sorption at room temperature.

Madey and Yates (1968) demonstrated that the energy distribution of the desorbing oxygen ions and the threshold voltage do not vary with the coverage and the sorption temperature. At 300°K and at 730°K the same characteristics are observed. On the basis of results measured at low temperatures Madey and Yates postulated the presence of molecular oxygen adsorbed in gaps in the atomically adsorbed layer. They considered the molecular oxygen to be responsible for the electron desorption. Previously, Lichtman and Kirst (1966) had made the same assumption for oxygen on molybdenum. This assumption is doubtful for at least three reasons:

(1) Oxygen adatoms are mobile over the tungsten surface above 600°K. A gap-filling mechanism requires an immobile layer of oxygen adatoms, which is certainly not present at 730°K (Gomer and Hulm, 1957) (see Section V).
(2) Electron-induced desorption of oxygen is apparent even above 1400°K; the presence of molecularly-adsorbed oxygen is highly improbable at these temperatures.
(3) Properly conducted flash-filament experiments do not show the least trace of desorption of molecular oxygen.

As said above, Madey and Yates concluded that oxygen is molecularly adsorbed from low-temperature experiments. If a tungsten ribbon is heavily dosed with oxygen at 20°K the ion energy distribution shows a distinct peak, located at the same energy value as that observed for gaseous oxygen. Evidently this is due to dissociation of physically-adsorbed oxygen molecules. On heating to 77°K, the energy distribution gradually changes into that characteristic of electron desorption of chemisorbed oxygen. The distribution is the same as that observed on sorption of oxygen at temperatures from 300 to 730°K; the magnitude of the desorption is, however, more than four times that measured after extensive sorption at room temperature, and twice that found upon interaction at 730°K. After heating to 300°K, this larger desorption of oxygen ions continues.

At temperatures below 80°K, penetration of oxygen into the metal surface is unlikely, in view of the results dealt with in Sections II and III. Madey and Yates, consequently, regard the oxygen atoms that can be desorbed by electron impact as being molecularly adsorbed. Since the oxygen adatoms are immobile below 80°K, adsorption of molecular oxygen into gaps in the atomically-adsorbed layer is to be expected. Desorption of atomic oxygen from adsorbed oxygen molecules by electron impact is obvious since the surface remains electrically non-conducting after dissociation. Thus for this temperature range Madey and Yates' assumption seems to be legitimate.

The energy distribution of the oxygen ions desorbed after sorption at temperatures from 20 to 730°K does not vary. The threshold energies were determined only after interaction with oxygen above 300°K, as far as can be concluded from the description of the experimental results. It may be asked now if the ion energy distribution is a good means for distinguishing between oxygen atoms bonded differently to tungsten surfaces. Data are available for carbon monoxide, nitric oxide and oxygen adsorbed on tungsten; in all these cases desorption of oxygen ions by electron impact is very probable (Degras and Lecante, 1967; Yates et al., 1967). The ion energy distribution for these adsorbed entities is almost the same. (The characteristics for sorbed oxygen given in consecutive papers differ more widely than those for oxygen and for example carbon monoxide). It is therefore questionable that the energy distributions of ions desorbed from oxygen adsorbed in places where penetration into the metal surface has occurred and from molecularly-bonded oxygen differ sufficiently to enable a distinction to be made. In view of this, the oxygen ions desorbing after interaction with oxygen below 80°K can come from adsorbed molecules, whereas the oxygen desorbing after interaction above 200°K, where interaction reached further than a monolayer, originates from regions where oxygen has penetrated into the surface.

This interpretation, however, meets with some difficulties. Only at temperatures above 500°K do the oxygen adatoms become mobile over the surface. Below 500°K therefore, oxygen molecules can be bonded in gaps in the atomic layer. Above 200°K where penetration into the metal surface occurs, the amount of molecularly-adsorbed oxygen should be markedly smaller than at lower temperatures, where no large variations in the amount of adsorbed oxygen molecules can be expected. Experiment has shown that interaction with oxygen as 77° results in desorption of oxygen ions on electron impact at approximately the same rate as that observed after sorption at 300°K. On extensive interaction with oxygen at 20°K, however, the coverage with species releasing oxygen on electron bombardment appears to be larger by about a factor of four than on adsorption above 70°K. This large coverage persists on heating of the adsorbent to 300°K.

It is difficult to explain this behaviour along the lines developed above. For adsorption of immobile oxygen atoms about 10% of gaps have to be expected; an increase by a factor of four upon a decrease of the temperature of the adsorbent from 77 to 20°K can only be accounted for by assuming dissociative adsorption to an appreciably smaller extent at 20°K. There is no experimental evidence supporting this assumption. Moreover, this relatively small amount of atomic adsorption should be maintained on heating up to 300°K, where sorption proceeding beyond the extent of a monolayer has been demonstrated. Therefore, slow attainment of the equilibrium configuration on the surface cannot be the cause of the large electron-induced desorption of ions at room temperature. The adsorbed oxygen molecules will quickly establish the complete atomically-adsorbed layer; the excess of oxygen will either be sorbed beyond the extent of a monolayer or desorb. Finally, the results obtained by Menzel and Gomer (1964a,b) are difficult to account for in the above interpretation. These authors observed a decrease in the work function on bombarding a tungsten tip previously covered at 20°K. If an adsorbed oxygen molecule is dissociated on electron impact, an oxygen adatom results. As stated in Section V, an increase in the number of oxygen adatoms must lead to an increase in work function. Menzel and Gomer also found that redosing of oxygen restored the work function to its pre-bombardment value. Reaction of atomically-adsorbed oxygen with gaseous oxygen molecules to give a large amount of molecularly bound oxygen is highly improbable.

The trend of the work function that is to be expected if the molecularly-adsorbed species is transformed into adsorbed atoms by electron bombardment appears on examination of hydrogen-covered tips. Menzel and Gomer (1964b) succeeded in differentiating the effects of incident electrons on the work function of tips covered with hydrogen at 20°K. They demonstrated that in the first stage of the bombardment mainly desorption, or dissociation of a molecularly-adsorbed species, takes place, accompanied by an increase in the work function. In the second stage, desorption of atomic hydrogen occurs and the work function decreases. Readsorption of hydrogen does not restore the work function to its pre-bombardment value, but to a higher one characteristic of a surface covered mainly with atomic hydrogen.

We believe that the difference between the effects of electron bombardment at 20°K on adsorbed hydrogen and oxygen is due to the fact that oxygen is capable of reacting further with a tungsten surface covered with a monolayer, whereas hydrogen is not. It is well known that atomization of diatomic molecules appreciably raises the extent of sorption. This is demonstrated for hydrogen at temperatures around 100°K on f.c.c. metal surfaces, and for nitrogen on nickel at 300°K (Hayward, Herley, and Tompkins, 1964; Winter, Horne and Donaldson, 1964). It is plausible then that sorption of oxygen *atoms* by a tungsten surface already covered with oxygen may proceed under conditions where molecular oxygen cannot react. Incidence of electrons with energies of about 100 eV will dissociate both oxygen molecularly adsorbed in gaps in the atomic layer and oxygen physically adsorbed over the chemisorbed layer. If some layers of oxygen molecules are physically adsorbed, interaction of released oxygen atoms with the tungsten surface is unlikely. At low coverages with physically-adsorbed molecules, on the other hand, the oxygen atoms may be sorbed by the tungsten surface. This is still more probable upon dissociation of oxygen molecules bonded in gaps in the atomic layer. Hence, a certain fraction of the oxygen atoms released by electron impact penetrates into the surface, giving rise to electron-induced desorption, as after interaction at higher temperatures. The resulting configuration of the surface is maintained on heating at room temperature.

At 20°K the above effects are much stronger than at 77°K and higher. The difference with the situation at 77°K may be due to (a) a larger coverage of physically-adsorbed oxygen, (b) a larger number of gaps capable of binding oxygen molecules, or (c) a larger residence time of the released oxygen atoms on the surface at 20°K. Also at temperatures around 750°K the penetration of oxygen is more limited than at 20°K. This is due to the fact that evaporation of tungsten oxides sets in before the temperature can be raised high enough to bring about appreciable penetration of oxygen into closely-packed crystallographic planes.

Menzel and Gomer's results can be explained along the above lines also. However, two differences between Menzel and Gomer's experiments and those of Madey and Yates deserve attention. Menzel and Gomer bombarded their tips with a number of electrons of the order of 2×10^{18} cm^{-2}, Madey and Yates with a rate of about 4×10^{14} electrons cm^{-2} sec^{-1}. The latter authors would have reached Menzel and Gomer's figures only after bombarding for about two hours. On the other hand, Menzel and Gomer removed excess physisorbed oxygen by heating to 70–80°K before bombardment, whereas Madey and Yates started with a surface heavily covered with physisorbed oxygen. In the experiments of Menzel and Gomer therefore a substantial fraction of the oxygen present on top of tungsten atoms displaced by penetrating oxygen is desorbed. After desorption, protruding tungsten atoms are present on the surface, and these strongly decrease the average work function. These protruding metal atoms give rise to the granularity of the bombarded area. Since excess molecular oxygen is removed before bombarding, a relatively small number of these high-emission centres is formed. By redosing of oxygen, the protruding tungsten atoms are covered again with oxygen, which restores the work function to its high value. This can also be effected by heating to about 300°K, where limited diffusion from other parts of the surface occurs.

VIII   LEED Investigation of Oxygen Sorption on
Tungsten and Molybdenum

Many aspects of the structure and properties of tungsten and molybdenum surfaces covered with oxygen have now been elucidated. So far, however, an important tool of three-dimensional chemistry has not been applied, namely X-ray diffraction. The structure of chemical compounds can be quickly determined by means of modern automatic equipment, provided single crystals are available. The structure of two-dimensional compounds cannot be investigated by X-rays, because the cross-sections for scattering of this radiation are small. X-rays require scattering by many atomic layers before giving a measurable diffraction intensity. The scattering of low-energy electrons (energies up to about 500 eV) is much stronger. Low-energy electrons, consequently, can be used for investigating the surface layer of specimens only. However, inasmuch as the theory of diffraction of low-energy electrons is still poorly developed, LEED offers much less information than X-ray diffraction of three-dimensional compounds; interpretation of diffraction maxima intensities cannot be given. This implies that the dimensions of the two-dimensional unit cell can be derived from LEED results, but the content of the unit cell cannot.

In the sixties the application of LEED for investigating the structure of adsorbents covered to different degrees with simple adatoms, or molecules, has increased enormously. A good introduction to this technique and the main results is given by MacRae (1963) and Lander (1964). A much debated point in the interpretation of LEED patterns of covered adsorbent surfaces is the relative scattering power of adsorbent and adsorbate atoms. Considering the large difference in nuclear charge between tungsten and molybdenum on the one side and oxygen on the other, we consider the scattering of the electrons to be dominated by the metal atoms in these systems.

Although the information that can be obtained from LEED results is limited, it is very interesting to compare it with results of the other experimental techniques. Once again, we must stress the relatively low sensitivity of LEED to differences in the surface configuration. A well-resolved LEED pattern is obtained only if a marked fraction of the surface is converted to an ordered structure. A relatively large extension of the surface structure is a prerequisite for its identification.

LEED experiments were done on the most stable planes of tungsten and to a smaller extent on molybdenum. The effects of oxygen sorption on the LEED patterns of the (110), (100), (211) and (111) planes of tungsten and the (110) and (100) planes of molybdenum have been investigated.

There is a marked difference between the effects of interaction with oxygen at room temperature on the LEED patterns of the (110) and (211) planes and on those of the (100) and (111) planes. The surface atoms in the (110) plane of tungsten and molybdenum are in contact in two directions, those in the (211) plane in one direction only. On the other hand, the metal atoms in the surface of (100) and (111) planes are not in contact. As will be shown below, this strongly influences the effects of oxygen sorption on the surface structure.

The LEED pattern of the more open (100) and (111) planes does not show a marked change upon exposure to oxygen at room temperature, whereas that of the (110) and (211) planes does. For the (111) plane of tungsten Taylor (1964) observed a hazing-over of the pattern, an increase in background intensity, and a general reduction of the intensity of the diffraction maxima displayed by the clean tungsten surface. A modified faceted surface structure was indicated by a faint pattern after extended exposures, which developed more clearly on heating above about 800°K. For the (100) plane of tungsten, Anderson and Danforth (1965) did not find another LEED pattern upon reaction with oxygen at room temperature. In their experiments, too, the background intensity increased. Hayek et al. (1968) more extensively investigated the effects of oxygen sorption on the LEED pattern of the (100) plane of molybdenum, and at the same time studied the work function of this plane. No indication of a change in the geometry of the LEED pattern induced by interaction with oxygen at room temperature was found. However, adsorption was evident from an appreciable change in the intensity distribution; the latter characteristic is obtained by measuring the intensity of a diffraction maximum as a function of the energy, and hence of the wave length of the incident electrons. The work function also showed a rapid rise by about 1·4 eV. Exposures above 6×10^{-3} mm Hg sec produced a uniform decrease of the intensities without any change in intensity distribution. We believe that this is due to local interactions beyond a monolayer giving rise to unordered structures at room temperature.

A structure with symmetry or dimensions parallel to the surface different from those of the clean surface is not formed with a marked extension on the (100) plane. This can be concluded from the absence of any other diffraction pattern during interaction with oxygen. The dimensions perpendicular to the surface are changed, as can be derived from the strongly-modified intensity distribution of the diffraction maxima. If the oxygen adatoms contribute to the diffraction, the latter change can be ascribed to the presence of oxygen atoms with a two-dimensional structure equal to that of the metal atoms in the surface. If, on the other hand, the metal atoms only determine the intensity of the diffraction maxima, the above result would point to a homogeneous displacement of the metal atoms in a direction normal to the surface. In view of the large difference in nuclear charge between oxygen and molybdenum, we prefer the latter interpretation. The effect of oxygen adsorption on the electrical conductance, moreover, suggests a difference in intermetallic bonding and hence a change of the intermetallic distance. Owing to the way in which the adsorbing atoms are co-ordinated with the metal atoms in the subsurface layer, a weakening of the intermetallic bonding will result in an outward displacement of the metal surface atoms normal to the surface (Fig. 38). The explanation of the effect of oxygen sorption on the LEED

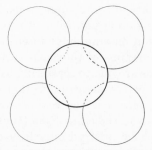

FIG. 38 Arrangement of metal atoms in the (100) plane. The surface atoms have four nearest-neighbouring atoms in the subsurface layer.

pattern is in good accordance with the change in work function of the (100) plane upon interaction with oxygen. No penetration of oxygen into this plane has taken place at 300°K (Bell *et al.*, 1968) (see Section V).

The (111) plane, unlike the (100) plane, is seen on oxygen sorption to have a LEED pattern different from that of the clean surface, although the pattern is faint and diffuse, due to a structure in which the diffraction surface is no longer flat, but built up of very small facets (Taylor, 1964). This was inferred from the movement of the diffraction maxima as the energy of the incident electrons was varied. The faceting of the (111) plane clearly points to penetration of oxygen atoms into the surface; at 300°K evaporation of tungsten oxides, which can also give rise to a faceted surface, is impossible. From the way in which the work function of a (111) plane covered with oxygen at 80°K changes on heating to increasing temperatures, it was concluded that penetration of oxygen into this surface proceeds at temperatures below 300°K

(Section V). At room temperature, the faceted structure cannot be ordered over appreciable distances. Consequently, the new structure is only faintly apparent in the LEED pattern, whilst a large fraction of the incident electrons is scattered randomly, resulting in the strong background intensity accompanying the faint pattern. Since the ordering and hence the crystallinity of the surface layer is small, diffraction from the ordered subsurface layer of the metal remains relatively strong. The crystallinity of the surface layer is increased considerably at higher temperatures. The pattern which can be faintly distinguished at room temperature is the only one observed after heating at 800°K; it is then very intense and obscures the weak pattern of the undistorted subsurface layer.

Already at room temperature the (110) and (211) planes, in which the metal atoms are in contact with each other, show intensive LEED patterns deviating from that of the clean surface on interaction with oxygen. The dimensions of the unit cells corresponding to the diffraction patterns are simple multiples of those of the clean surface. The additional diffraction maxima have intensities of the same magnitude as the diffraction maxima of the clean surfaces; this too suggests that the extra-reflections are due to scattering by metal atoms. Another characteristic of the effect of oxygen sorption on the LEED pattern of the (110) and (211) planes is the reappearance of the patterns of the clean surface. Just as in the case of the (100) plane, the presence of the oxygen adatoms can be inferred only from the different intensity distribution of the diffraction maxima. At room temperature, extensive interaction of the (110) plane with oxygen produces a LEED pattern equal to that of the clean surface, whereas the (211) plane ultimately displays a different pattern.

The effect of oxygen sorption on the LEED pattern of the molybdenum (110) plane has been studied by Haas and Jackson (1966) and Hayek et al. (1968). Germer and May (1966) investigated the (110) plane of tungsten. Figure 39 shows the two-dimensional unit cells as evident from the LEED patterns. Unit cells (2) (4), derived from the same LEED pattern, are equivalent. The sequence of the patterns suggests that (2) corresponds to one quarter and (4) to three quarters of the metal surface atoms being displaced. As indicated, the third diffraction pattern can be derived from two structures with a reflection symmetry. The intensities of the diffraction maxima of this pattern point to the presence of incoherently scattering domains of the two structures on the metal surface. The sequence of these unit cells is given in Table VI, from which we see that the results are quite consistent, but not completely the same. Establishment of pattern (3) was rapid on both molybdenum and tungsten. The change into pattern (1) goes slowly; the sticking probability of oxygen on a surface displaying pattern (3) is considerably lower than that on the clean surface.

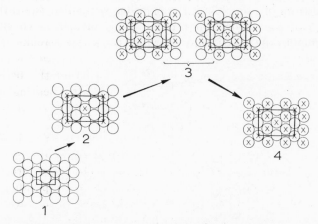

FIG. 39 Two-dimensional unit cells derived from LEED patterns on interaction of oxygen with molybdenum and tungsten (110) planes. Circles: metal surface atoms; crosses: oxygen-covered metal atoms. (See Table VI.)

Hayek *et al.* investigated both the work function of the (110) plane and the LEED pattern during oxygen sorption. The work function of the clean surface was maintained during establishment of pattern (2).

TABLE VI. LEED patterns observed on interaction of oxygen at room temperature with molybdenum and tungsten (110) planes

Metal	LEED pattern as indicated in Fig 39	Authors
Mo	(1)→(2)→(3)→(4)	Haas and Jackson, 1966
Mo	(1)→(2)→(3)– – – →(1)	Hayek *et al.*, 1968
W	(1)– – – →(3)→(4)→(1)	Germer and May, 1966

The change from pattern (2) into (3) was accompanied by a gradual increase of the work function by 1·2 eV. Longer exposure to oxygen led to the pattern of the clean surface, with an appreciable change in the intensity distribution, while the work function reached a constant value of 1·4 eV over that of the clean surface.

The effect of oxygen sorption on the LEED pattern of the (211) plane has been investigated for tungsten only. The two-dimensional unit cells experimentally observed by Chang and Germer (1967) are given in Fig. 40, numbered in the order they appear upon an increase of the oxygen coverage. The LEED pattern corresponding to (2a) (streaks parallel to the [110] direction) indicates a structure well ordered along the rows of atoms and a poor order normal to the rows in the first stage of the adsorption process. With increasing coverage, the order normal to the rows improves, which causes the streaks to coalesce

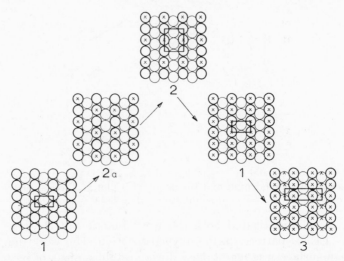

Fig. 40 Two-dimensional unit cells derived from LEED patterns on interaction of oxygen with a tungsten (211) plane. Crosses: metal atoms bonding an oxygen atom. (Chang and Germer, 1967.)

into sharp spots. As mentioned above, the pattern of the clean surface does not persist upon prolonged exposure to oxygen. Finally, oxygen sorption at room temperature leads to pattern (3).

The above experimental data can be explained on the basis of four assumptions.

(1) An oxygen adatom is first bonded upon one single metal atom; some chemical arguments supporting this view will be presented later. From this position the oxygen atom can move to a position between the metal surface atoms. The possibility of this happening depends on the nature of the crystallographic plane and on the temperature.

(2) The metal atom to which the adatom is bonded is pulled slightly out of the metal, as has already been postulated for the (100) plane.

(3) Bonding of an oxygen atom to a metal atom contacting an atom

to which an oxygen atom is already attached is not favoured energetically. This is particularly true for a metal atom surrounded by atoms bonding oxygen.

(4) The mobility of the oxygen atoms over the metal surface is high enough to permit establishment of an energetically favoured configuration at room temperature.

Assumption (2) implies that the diffraction pattern is strongly affected by the geometry of the positions of the oxygen adatoms *via* scattering of the incident electrons by the metal atoms, part of which have been lifted. As indicated in Fig. 41, the conditions leading to constructive

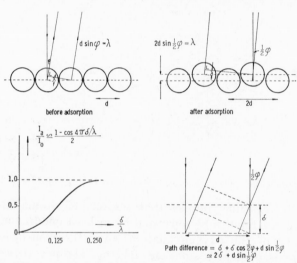

FIG. 41. Effect of a small displacement of an ordered fraction of metal surface atoms on the LEED pattern. Adsorption is assumed to double the spacing, which produces half-order maxima. I_a: intensity of half-order maxima after adsorption; I_0: intensity before adsorption. In LEED experiments the wave length, λ, varied from 2 to 0·5 A; the half-order maxima display at least 50% of the intensities of the maxima of the clean surface at values for δ from 0·5 to 0·06 A.

interference of the radiation scattered from neighbouring atoms are appreciably altered when an ordered fraction of the metal atoms is displaced normal to the surface.

From the change of the LEED pattern upon oxygen sorption, it is apparent that at room temperature the adatoms are sorbed in ordered structures on the (110) and (211) planes, where as on the (100) and (111) planes, they are randomly adsorbed. This is likely to be due to the smaller distance between the metal surface atoms on the (110) and (211) planes. The diameter of an oxygen ion is 2·64 A, whilst the intermetallic distance for molybdenum and tungsten is 2·72 A and 2·74 A, respectively. On the (100) plane, the distance between neighbouring metal atoms is 3·14 A for molybdenum and 3·16 A for tungsten, the figures for the (111) plane being 4·44 A and 4·47 A, respectively. Although the diameter of an oxygen adatom will doubtless be smaller than that of an oxygen ion, repulsion between adatoms spaced 2·72 A apart is quite conceivable. For oxygen atoms present on neighbouring atoms of the (100) and (111) planes, the repulsion will be appreciably smaller. The ordering of oxygen adatoms on these planes will, consequently, be much weaker.

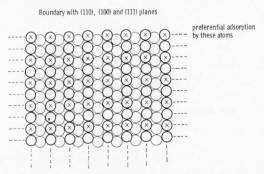

FIG. 42 Edge of (211) plane forming a step with (110), (100), or (111) plane.

The above reasoning implies that the oxygen atoms on the (110) and (211) planes tend to be separated by at least one free metal atom. The mobility of the oxygen adatoms over these surfaces at room temperature is evidently sufficient for the adatoms to establish an ordered configuration. As is clearly evident from LEED pattern (2) in Fig. 40, the partly covered (211) plane has a structure in which alternative metal atoms in the rows bind an oxygen atom. Since the repulsion of an adsorbed oxygen atom only influences the adsorption on neighbouring metal atoms in the same row, the ordering along the rows is very good in contrast with that normal to the rows. For tungsten, the distance between the rows is 4·47 A, which makes the interaction between oxygen atoms on neighbouring rows very weak. At large coverages, the ordering normal to the rows appears to improve appreciably. We believe that this is due to the influence of the ends of the rows. The surfaces of the metal specimens used in LEED experiments are likely to show a large number of steps crossing the rows perpendicularly, as indicated in Fig. 42. Bonding of an oxygen atom to the exposed atoms at the edge is very probable; this determines the sequence of oxygen atoms along the rows. Owing to the equal positions of the atoms at the edge of the rows, the ordering along neighbouring rows is the same. The orienting influence of the end atoms can be effective only at high degrees of coverage, where the domains on the rows have to link up. This explains why the coalescence of the streaks is observed only after a marked adsorption has taken place. The mobility of the adatoms at room temperature is restricted, however: the degree of ordering and consequently the intensity of the diffraction maxima can be considerably increased by heating the covered surface in a good vacuum to temperatures where the mobility is larger (Chang and Germer, 1967). At lower coverages, this increase in intensity on heating is not found; in that case the need for linking up of the domains does not exist.

On the (110) plane, the oxygen atoms are surrounded first by six free metal atoms. Owing to the large sticking coefficient of oxygen on the clean metal surface, this configuration is established over a sufficiently large area to be apparent in the LEED pattern already after relatively low exposures. Hayek et al. (1968) did not observe an increase in the work function of the (110) molybdenum plane exhibiting the second LEED pattern shown in Fig. 39, and Bell et al. (1968) found very little effect of a small oxygen coverage on the work function of the (110) plane of tungsten. The number of oxygen atoms adsorbed at the maximum intensity of the second LEED pattern in Fig. 39 is smaller than that required to cover the surface completely in this way. Hayek et al. observed the maximum intensity after an exposure of 3×10^{-7} mm Hg sec, which corresponds to an incidence of $1 \cdot 2 \times 10^{14}$ oxygen molecules cm^{-2}. If the sticking coefficient equals unity, this gives a coverage of $2 \cdot 4 \times 10^{14}$ oxygen atoms cm^{-2}. The configuration (2) of Fig. 39 corresponds to a coverage of $3 \cdot 6 \times 10^{14}$ oxygen atoms cm^{-2}, provided it extends over the whole surface. Hence, part of the metal is still clean when LEED pattern (2) is at maximum intensity; the apparent work function is determined mainly by this part. The fast appearance of the second LEED pattern points to the formation of patches uniformly covered in the way indicated in the figure, providing evidence that the oxygen atoms have sufficient mobility over the tungsten surface, as inferred earlier from the LEED patterns found for the (211) plane upon oxygen adsorption. Incidence and adsorption of oxygen molecules on a patch results in rearrangement of the oxygen adatoms and, ultimately, in an increase in surface area of the patch. If two meeting patches do not register, a small displacement of the adatoms in one of the patches suffices to produce a large patch of uniform structure.

As can be seen from Fig. 39 arrangement of the oxygen adatoms in rows reduces the repulsive interaction at increasing coverages to a

24

minimum. Since nucleation of rows will be random, two configurations given in Fig. 39 are possible; these two-dimensional structures tend to reorient themselves much less readily than the one-dimensional structures of the rows on the (211) plane and the first structure on the (110) plane. The two configurations persist upon an increase in coverage. The exposures needed on the (110) and (211) planes for establishment of ordered rows of adatoms bonded by neighbouring metal atoms are almost equal. At 300°K, Germer and May observed a maximum intensity of pattern (3) of Fig. 39, corresponding to complete filling of the rows, after an exposure of 1.5×10^{-6} mm Hg sec. At the same temperature, Chang and Germer needed an exposure of 1.9×10^{-6} mm Hg sec to reach a maximum intensity of pattern (1) in Fig. 40 for the (211) plane. As expected, adsorption of oxygen atoms on a (110) surface covered with completely-filled rows of adatoms proceeds slowly. Pattern (4) in Fig. 39 is observed only after an exposure of 1.6×10^{-4} mm Hg sec. Doubtless this is due both to the strong repulsive interaction of the oxygen atoms already adsorbed and to the absence of two neighbouring sites capable of bonding the two atoms of an oxygen molecule. The completely-covered configuration of the (110) plane is found only after an exposure of 3×10^{-4} mm Hg sec (see Sections II and III). This strong decrease in the rate of adsorption before completion of the monolayer explains why the number of rapidly adsorbed oxygen atoms is slightly smaller than the number of metal surface atoms.

One of the most important conclusions that can be drawn from the LEED results on the (110) and (211) planes is that the picture of immobile adsorption has to be modified. Prior to the LEED experiments, the adsorption of oxygen on molybdenum and tungsten was visualized as disclosed e.g. by Roberts (Roberts, 1939). It was assumed that oxygen was dissociatively adsorbed on two neighbouring sites on the metal surface; below approximately 500°K, the oxygen atoms were supposed to remain on the sites nearest to the point where the oxygen molecule had dissociated. This results in random adsorption which, as calculated by Roberts, leaves some 10% of isolated empty sites. The LEED data show that the oxygen adatoms can move over small distances over the surface at room temperature; this can be concluded from the formation of a number of ordered structures noted upon a gradual increase of the coverage. The fourth LEED pattern in Fig. 39 corresponds to a structure with 25% of singletons in the layer of oxygen adatoms. These singletons are relatively slowly filled in with oxygen atoms, showing that single sites isolated by one adatom can be covered (though slowly) by oxygen atoms. Germer and May demonstrated that the rate at which the singletons are filled in increased by a factor of about 10 when the adsorbing plane was kept at 550°K. It may be that an oxygen adatom already adsorbed has to be removed to a singleton before an oxygen molecule can be adsorbed into the two neighbouring empty sites thus generated. This should be an activated process, the rate of which sharply rises with temperature. Adsorption of molecular oxygen into the large fraction of singletons does not appear from the pressure change upon exposition, nor is it evident from the LEED patterns. It would be interesting to investigate how oxygen adsorption below room temperature affects the LEED pattern of the (211) and (110) planes. A restricted mobility of the adatoms giving rise to a different change in the LEED pattern may be expected.

As stated earlier, our interpretation is based on the assumption that the scattering of the incident electrons is due mainly to the metal surface atoms. This assumption is supported by the large difference in nuclear charge between molybdenum and tungsten on the one hand and oxygen on the other, as well as by the strong intensities of the additional diffraction maxima appearing in the LEED patterns. Frequently, a place exchange between metal and oxygen atoms is invoked to account for the LEED patterns, but such an exchange is unlikely: first, because of the nature of the crystallographic planes which display LEED patterns different from those of the clean surface upon interaction with oxygen at room temperature. As said above, the LEED patterns of the closely-packed (110) and (211) planes indicate surface structures with meshes larger than those of the clean surface. If this change in the LEED patterns corresponded to a place exchange between metal and oxygen atoms, the rate of exchange on these closely-packed planes would be at least as high as that on the more open (111) and (100) planes. Since the latter planes do not show a change in LEED pattern, place exchange is unlikely. Second, experimental evidence dealt with in earlier sections argues against place exchange in the early stages of adsorption. As appears from the extent and rate of sorption, penetration of oxygen cannot occur under the conditions of exposure required for the above LEED patterns. If there were a place exchange between oxygen and the metal surface atoms, the displaced and exposed metal atoms should be able to bond oxygen again, and the amount of fastly-bonded oxygen then should be appreciably larger. Absence of place exchange in the first stage is also evident from the effect on the work function. Studies by Roberts and Wells (1966), for example, indicated that penetration of oxygen to below the metal surface reduces the work function appreciably below the pre-penetration value. At room temperature this is

24*

observed on the (111) plane of tungsten only. The interstices between the metal surface atoms in this plane are so large that a slight lifting of part of the metal atoms enables the oxygen atoms to be accommodated between them. A final argument against place exchange is the reappearance of the clean surface pattern upon a sufficient increase in coverage. It is difficult to envisage how a configuration comprising a layer of contacting oxygen atoms covered by a layer of metal atoms, which parallel to the surface shows the same structure as the clean surface, could correspond to a stable state. For metals exhibiting penetration at the exposures used in LEED experiments, the LEED patterns found after penetration are completely different from that of the clean surface. One of the best examples is iron, which

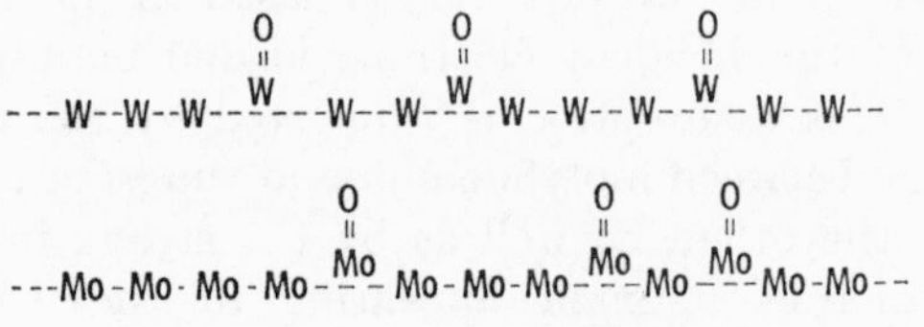

$$
\begin{array}{ccccccc}
& & \underset{\|}{O} & & \underset{\|}{O} & & \underset{\|}{O} \\
---W--W--W-- & \overset{W}{--} & ---W--W-- & \overset{W}{--} & -W--W--W-- & \overset{W}{--} & -W--W--
\end{array}
$$

$$
\begin{array}{ccccccc}
& & \underset{\|}{O} & & \underset{\|}{O} & \underset{\|}{O} & \\
---Mo-Mo-Mo-Mo- & \overset{Mo}{--} & Mo-Mo-Mo- & \overset{Mo}{---} & Mo- & \overset{Mo}{---} & Mo-Mo--
\end{array}
$$

FIG. 43 Bonding of oxygen atoms at low coverages onto tungsten and molybdenum surfaces.

has also a b.c.c. structure. Pignocco and Pelissier (1967) found that upon interaction with oxygen the (110) plane of iron exhibited pattern (3) in Fig. 39. Upon further interaction with oxygen, however, other structures were found and the original pattern did not re-establish.

The total complex of experimental data consequently provides strong evidence that oxygen atoms are bonded on top of the metal atoms. Each metal atom bonding an oxygen atom is lifted slightly out of the surface; thus we assume that the two-dimensional compound formed upon adsorption interacts with the underlying metal via the metal atoms only (see Section III).

Evidence obtained by LEED experiments also indicates penetration of oxygen atoms into the metal surface. At higher temperatures the change of the LEED pattern of the (110) plane covered with oxygen supports the evidence from other experiments. As mentioned in Section V, adatoms at low coverages on a tungsten surface were found to become mobile at 600°K (spreading without a boundary). Germer and May, using a (110) tungsten plane covered with oxygen at room temperature and displaying LEED pattern (3) of Fig. 39, measured the intensity of the diffraction maxima as a function of temperature. From about 600°K the intensity of the fractional-order diffraction maxima decreased much faster than could be accounted for by the thermal vibrations of the surface atoms only. Owing to the mobility of the adatoms the original surface structure is unordered; this increases the incoherent scattering and hence decreases the intensity of the diffraction maxima. Bell *et al.* found that heating of a tungsten (110) surface previously heavily dosed with oxygen at 700°K or higher, brought about a pronounced increase in work function. Germer and May, heating a tungsten (110) surface at low oxygen pressures above 700°K, found three different LEED patterns corresponding to very complicated superstructures. In an interesting paper, Bauer (1967) tried to explain the LEED patterns by assuming a slightly-distorted WO_2 layer to be present on the (110) plane. Though his interpretation

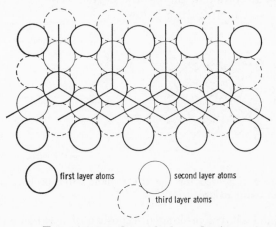

first layer atoms   second layer atoms   third layer atoms

FIG. 44 (111) plane of a b.c.c. lattice.

may have to be modified, we believe it to be basically right; the above experimental evidence suggests the formation of an ionic structure containing both tungsten and oxygen ions.

The (111) and (211) planes of tungsten both have rather open structures. The (111) plane can be visualized as consisting of very small facets of (211) planes; every surface atom is present at the apex of three intersecting (211) planes (Fig. 44). The spacing between the metal surface atoms is large. Moreover, the metal surface atoms have contact with three metal atoms only; this makes lifting of the metal surface atoms from the surface relatively easy. As mentioned above, a structure consisting of (211) facets can be faintly distinguished after interaction with oxygen at room temperature (Taylor, 1964). It is difficult to derive the surface structure from the characteristics of the LEED pattern; nevertheless, it is likely that part of the metal surface atoms are lifted a noticeable distance from the surface, since the LEED pattern indicates the formation of (211) facets larger than those on the clean surface. Evaporation of tungsten oxides is very improbable at room temperature; complete removal of part of the metal surface atoms consequently will not be the cause of the formation of the (211) facets. Slow evaporation can occur on heating above about 800°C, as indicated by Singleton's (1967) data. Taylor (1964) observed three other LEED patterns on heating of oxygen-covered (111) planes and on interaction of clean (111) planes with oxygen at high temperatures. These three patterns also point to a faceted structure; now, part of the metal surface atoms are likely to be removed as tungsten oxides. In all cases the atoms markedly lifted, or the holes left by the metal surface atoms are ordered, though the degree of order of the structure obtained at room temperature is low.

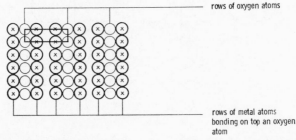

FIG. 45 Structure proposed for the (211) plane after prolonged exposure to oxygen at room temperature.

As mentioned above, prolonged exposure of a tungsten (211) plane to oxygen at room temperature does not give a LEED pattern equal to that of the clean surface (Chang and Germer, 1967). Though the original pattern returns after a pattern with larger dimensions has disappeared a third diffraction pattern finally results. This pattern suggests a structure which parallel to the rows has the same periodicity as the clean surface, whereas normal to the rows, has a mesh twice as large. In view of the above argument with regard to the (111) plane, it is unlikely that every other row of metal atoms should be removed at room temperature. Consequently, we ascribe this pattern to a structure in which the metal atoms of every row are displaced also parallel to the surface, as indicated in Fig. 45. (We assume oxygen atoms present at the positions indicated.) Heating at a temperature above 300°K at very low pressure gradually degrades the structure. Diffraction patterns which normal to the rows show a mesh three or four times that of the clean surface appear before a pattern analogous to that of the clean surface is observed after heating at 2000°K.

However, since heating at 2100°K yields a pattern whose mesh parallel to the rows is twice that of the clean surface (structure (2), Fig. 40)—as was observed also during adsorption at room temperature—the surface must be still strongly covered after heating at 2000°K. Finally, the pattern of the clean surface appears again on heating above 2100°K. It is clear the above sequence of diffraction patterns is due to a gradual evaporation of oxygen atoms. At temperatures above 1300°K, where the adatoms are mobile over the surface, an equilibrium configuration is always established. First, the oxygen atoms between the rows

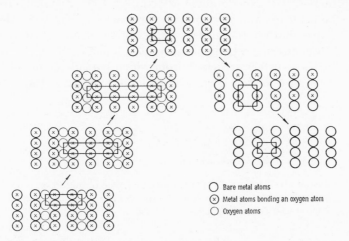

FIG. 46 Surface structures of a tungsten (211) surface, heavily exposed at 300°K, based on LEED patterns displayed on momentary heating to increasing temperatures.

gradually desorb; the remaining adatoms take up such positions that the distance between displaced rows of metal atoms becomes maximum. As a result the mesh normal to the rows should increase from two to three, and from three to four times that of the clean surface, before the configuration can form in which the adatoms are present above the surface atoms only (Fig. 46).

The sequence of diffraction patterns published by Chang and Germer is not in complete agreement with the picture developed above. These authors first found the mesh size to increase from twice to three times that of the clean surface as would be expected. However, before the pattern with the four-fold mesh is observed the two-fold mesh appears once more. It is difficult to account for this sequence; therefore, it might be worthwhile to confirm the experimental results.

The above evidence shows that the oxygen atoms present between the rows of metal atoms are bonded more weakly than those on top of the metal atoms. This difference in bonding energy was used to explain the difference in mobility over stepped regions on field-emission tips (Section V).

When oxygen interacts with a tungsten (211) surface at temperatures from 1300 to 1700°K, faceting analogous to that on the (111) plane above about 700°C is observed (Chang and Germer, 1967). This is evident from the fact that the diffraction maxima do not move to the central region of the pattern if the wave length of the electrons used is increased. The diffraction patterns obtained after interaction with oxygen in the above temperature range point to formation of (110) facets. The intensity distribution (intensity-versus-voltage characteristic) of the reflected electrons suggests the presence of completely clean (110) facets. This indicates a surface structure from which part of the metal surface atoms has been removed (Fig. 47). At large exposures, the extension

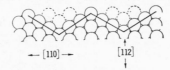

--- [110] ---   [112]

FIG. 47 Faceted structure of a (211) tungsten surface obtained on reaction with low-pressure oxygen at temperatures from 1300 to 1700°K, as suggested by LEED patterns. (Chang and Germer, 1967.)

of the facets varies widely, always above four atomic diameters, whereas at low exposures extensions of four and five atomic diameters usually are found. The intensity distribution implies that at temperatures above 1300°K the (110) surface is not markedly covered with oxygen atoms. As stated in section IV, Ptushinskii and Chuikov (1968) did not find desorption of oxygen from a (110) plane of tungsten after exposure above 1500°K. This shows that above 1500°K no oxygen is adsorbed on this plane, in keeping with the LEED evidence: prolonged heating above 1300°K is not reported to produce LEED patterns deviating from that of the clean (110) surface, neither after previous interaction with oxygen at lower temperatures, nor in the presence of oxygen at low pressures (Germer and May, 1966). Thus the LEED pattern of the (211) plane interacting with oxygen above 1300°K is markedly different from that of a (211) plane previously covered with oxygen at low temperatures and subsequently heated above 1300°K. In the latter case, a series of non-faceted structures is obtained on momentary heating at temperatures above 1300°K, and faceting is not found.

The effects on the LEED pattern of (100) planes were investigated by Anderson and Danforth (1965) for tungsten and by Hayek *et al.* (1968) for molybdenum. Only upon heating to 1250°K at an oxygen pressure of about 10^{-7} mm Hg did Anderson and Danforth observe diffraction patterns deviating from that of the clean surface. Two patterns were found: the first corresponds to a structure composed of two domains, one with a double-sized mesh in the X-direction and another with a double-sized mesh in the Y-direction; the second pattern points to a structure doubly-spaced in both directions. More prolonged exposure at this temperature—which is about the same as that where

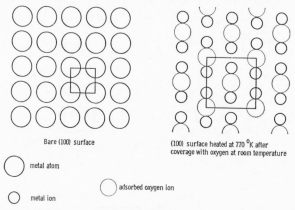

Bare (100) surface

(100) surface heated at 770 °K after coverage with oxygen at room temperature

○ metal atom

○ metal ion

○ adsorbed oxygen ion

FIG. 48 Structure suggested by the LEED pattern of molybdenum and tungsten (100) planes.

faceting of the (211) plane begins (1300°K)—leads to a surface composed of (110) facets. Hayek *et al.* on the other hand, did not find faceting of the molybdenum (100) plane on heating, not even at 1500°K. These authors investigated the effect of heating on the LEED pattern of an oxygen covered (100) plane in more detail. A disordered surface was observed on heating at 620°K for 30 minutes, or for shorter times above this temperature. After this treatment the work function was lower than that of the clean (100) surface. On heating to 770°K, the surface became ordered; the authors did not mention a change in work function, which remains lower than that of the clean surface. The ordering is evident from the appearance of half-order maxima in the diffraction pattern. (Fig. 48). The second pattern of Anderson and Danforth is the same as that found by Hayek *et al.*, shown in Fig. 48. As was observed also for the (211) plane of tungsten, heating at still higher temperatures, 800 to 1300°K, enlarged the mesh-size of the surface structure. A structure compatible with the LEED pattern is shown in Fig. 49. The work function of the surface giving rise to this diffraction pattern is equal to that of the clean (100) surface, and the intensity distribution is the same.

As indicated by the results obtained by Bell *et al.* (1968), the stability of oxygen atoms adsorbed on top of tungsten atoms is much larger for the (211) than for the (100) plane. The work function of the (100) plane covered with oxygen decreased already upon heating above 500°K

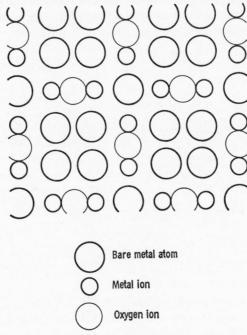

Bare metal atom

Metal ion

Oxygen ion

FIG. 49 Structure of a (100) plane of molybdenum as suggested by the LEED pattern.

for 60 seconds. The work function of the (211) plane on the other hand increased up to about 1000°K, where it maintained a constant level up to 1500°K. This suggests that oxygen adatoms remain present above the tungsten surface atoms for the (211) plane until desorption has proceeded so far that the surface is approximately clean. In view of the fact that we do not accurately know the coverage of the (100) surface prior to heating, the results of Hayek *et al.* are somewhat ambiguous. Another difficulty is that the temperature at which tungsten or molybdenum oxides can be evaporated on prolonged heating cannot be specified with sufficient precision. In flash-filament studies the specimens are fast heated to a final temperature of around 2500°K. Bell *et al.* heated their specimens for 60 seconds and observed a marked evaporation of tungsten oxides only above 1500°K. As mentioned already, the results obtained in these experiments cannot easily be compared with those of the LEED investigations, where the adsorbents are kept at elevated temperatures for periods as long as 30 minutes or more. Singleton's data (Section IV) gives some indication for tungsten. At temperatures above about 800°K, he observed continuous removal of oxygen from the gas phase over extended periods. Though absorption into the interior part of the adsorbent cannot be completely excluded, it is likely that this continuous removal of oxygen is due to the evaporation of tungsten oxides that are condensing on the cold walls of the experimental cell. Analogous data for molybdenum are not available.

In view of the above arguments, the data presented by Hayek *et al.* can be explained in two ways, the first assuming previous partial coverage of the surface and the second full coverage.

First, as observed by Bell *et al.*, the adatoms on a partially-covered tungsten (100) plane penetrate between metal surface atoms. The metal atoms are thus pushed aside as on the (211) plane at high coverage. As a result, every second site is excluded, which can be clearly seen in the LEED pattern. At temperatures of about 620°K, penetration may take place, but the resulting surface structure is still poorly organized. The work function, which is not susceptible to the ordering, decreases below the value of the clean surface, as observed by Bell *et al.* At 770°K the surface structure becomes ordered and a distinct LEED pattern forms. Heating at temperatures from 800°K up brings about desorption of oxygen; as observed for the (211) plane of tungsten, this widens the spacing between the displaced metal atoms. The resulting structure gradually changes into that of the clean surface. It is quite conceivable that diffraction maxima due to this structure are observed, even though a considerable fraction of the surface is already clean. (The parts of the surface between the displaced atoms already have the structure of the clean surface). The work function therefore already equals that of the clean surface. The diffraction maxima of the clean surface, which are also seen in the pattern in Fig. 49, display the intensity distribution of the clean surface, even though some parts still contain oxygen.

Assuming full coverage of the surface, however, part of the oxygen atoms are removed from the surface on heating at about 620°K, either by evaporation as molybdenum oxides, or by penetration into the bulk of the metal specimen. In the latter case the explanation is analogous to that for the partially-covered (100) plane dealt with above.

If desorption of molybdenum oxides proceeds at 620°K, a disordered faceted surface results. This surface has a low work function. Heating at 700°K re-orders the surface; surface diffusion of metal atoms and remaining oxygen adatoms results in the ordered surface structure indicated in Fig. 48.

We shall now consider the sites occupied by the oxygen adatoms on the basis of the preceding LEED results. It appeared that oxygen atoms can penetrate between metal surface atoms of the (111) and the (211) planes already at room temperature. Penetration between the metal atoms of the (100) plane occurs only at higher temperatures. This is understandable when we consider the size of the sites between the metal surface atoms.

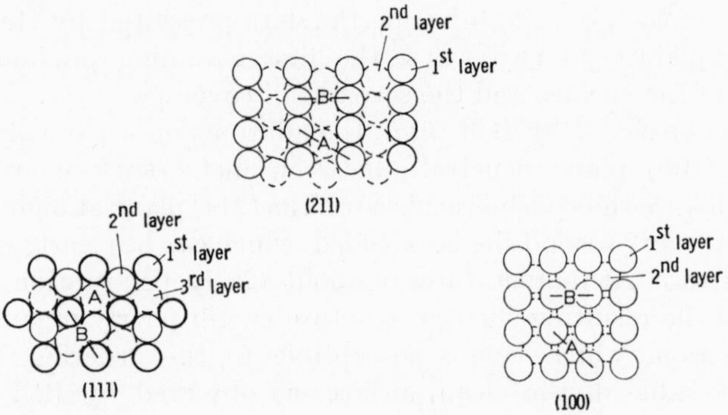

FIG. 50 Dimensions of sites on (111), (211), and (100) planes of the b.c.c. lattice.

Figure 50 shows two types of sites present on the crystallographic planes. On the A-sites, maximum contact of an adatom with metal surface atoms is established, on the B-sites insertion of an oxygen atom between two metal surface atoms is possible. Table VII gives the diameters of the sites. Inasmuch as the ionic character of the oxygen adatoms is likely to be weak, the 2·64 A value of an O^{2-} ion is to be considered an upper limit. In view of the small difference between this value and the diameters of the A-sites on the (111) and (211) planes, a marked displacement of metal surface atoms on accommodation of oxygen atoms into A-sites is not to be expected. Since the LEED patterns clearly indicate a displacement, insertion of oxygen atoms into A-sites has to be rejected. We consequently ascribe the penetration of oxygen atoms into the (111) and (211) surfaces to insertion into B-sites. The penetrated oxygen atom takes up a position on the line connecting the two displaced metal atoms. To realize this configuration, displacement of at least a fraction of the metal surface atoms is re-

quired. The resulting surface structure of the (211) plane has already
been given in Figs 45 and 46. The configuration indicated in Fig. 51
may be compatible with the LEED pattern of the (111) plane after

TABLE VII. Diameters of two types of sites on b.c.c. crystallographic planes

Crystallographic plane	Diameter (Å) A	B
(111)	2·57	1·70
(211)	2·48	1·70
(100)	1·72	0·42

interaction with oxygen. The tungsten atoms indicated by (L) are
lifted slightly out of the surface to accommodate the oxygen atoms.

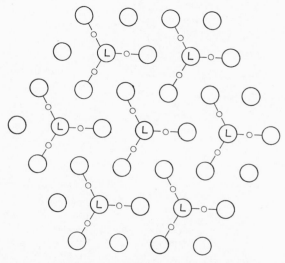

FIG. 51 Structure of a tungsten (111) plane after oxygen exposures higher than
10^{-4} mm Hg sec. At 300°K the LEED pattern is faint only; it can be sharpened
and intensified by heating *in vacuo* up to about 1300°K. Large circles: tungsten
atoms. Small circles: inserted oxygen atoms.

The sizes of both the A- and B-sites on the (100) plane are much
smaller. Hence it is to be expected that insertion of an adatom between
two surface atoms now requires a higher activation energy. This is in
accordance with the experimental data, which point more directly to a
penetration of an oxygen atom between two surface atoms than do the

25

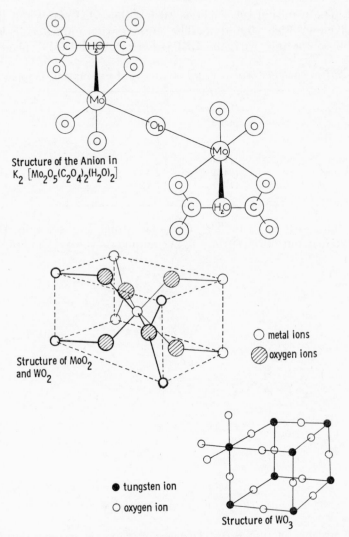

Structure of the Anion in
$K_2 [Mo_2O_5(C_2O_4)_2(H_2O)_2]$

Structure of MoO_2
and WO_2

○ metal ions
⊘ oxygen ions

● tungsten ion
○ oxygen ion

Structure of WO_3

Fig. 52 Structures of some three-dimensional molybdenum and tungsten compounds displaying different oxygen-metal bonds. The structure of MoO_2 and WO_2 actually is less symmetrical than indicated; the intermetallic distances are alternatively larger and smaller.

results for the (111) and (211) planes. Evidently, the metal and oxygen atoms are much too large to be accommodated in the space available. However, the diameters of the tetravalent and hexavalent ions of tungsten and molybdenum are much smaller than those of the corresponding metal atoms, that is, about 1·40 A as against 2·75 A. We therefore believe that the bond between metal and oxygen atoms has a much stronger ionic character when the adatoms have penetrated into the (100) surface. A stronger ionic character implies a lower electron density around the displaced metal surface atoms. This may be the cause of the oxygen present on top of the displaced metal surface atoms in the (100) plane being bonded less strongly than that on the (211) plane.

The LEED results point to the presence of two differently-bonded oxygen adatoms on the surface of molybdenum and tungsten. One oxygen species consists of oxygen atoms bonded to a single metal atom, the other species is bridge-bonded between neighbouring metal surface atoms, which concurs with the normal three-dimensional chemistry of molybdenum and tungsten. There are many compounds in which one or more oxygen atoms are connected by a multiple bond to a tungsten or molybdenum atom; for instance $MoOCl_3$, the $MoOCl_5^{2-}$ ion, $WOCl_4$ and WO_2Cl_2. Besides these multiple-bonded oxygen atoms, there are oxo-atoms forming linear and non-linear bridges between two metal atoms (Mo—O—Mo). A good instance is the oxalato-complex $K_2[Mo_2O_5(C_2O_4)_2(H_2O)_2]$ (Fig. 52), in which besides the four $Mo\!=\!O$ bonds (multible-bonded oxygen), a linear Mo—O—Mo bridge (the bridge-bonded atom is indicated by O_b) is present. Linear oxo-bridges are also indicated in this figure in the structure of the bulk oxide WO_3, and non-linear bridges in the structure of MoO_2 and WO_2.

IX   Conclusions

The very extensive study of the interaction of oxygen with tungsten and molybdenum surfaces has enabled us to give a rather detailed interpretation of the processes involved, in order to demonstrate that the sorption process can be properly visualized only after due consideration of the total body of experimental data.

The most striking conclusion is that sorption of oxygen by tungsten and molybdenum proceeds in two different ways, involving either a weak or a strong effect on the metal surface structure. The fractions of oxygen sorbed in either way is determined by the sorption temperature, the nature of the sorbing crystallographic plane, and the coverage.

At temperatures lower than $100°K$ no penetration of oxygen into the metal surface and consequently no distortion of the metal surface structure occurs. In this temperature range oxygen atoms are bonded on top of the metal surface atoms. The adatom layer contains gaps the amount of which depends on the way in which adsorption is carried out. As argued in Section VII, there is evidence that the gaps contain weakly-bonded molecular oxygen. From the effect on the work function and from electron-induced desorption, physisorption of molecular oxygen over the chemisorbed monolayer is apparent. The electron-induced desorption properties point to the capacity of *atomic oxygen* to penetrate into the surface below 100°K.

In the temperature range from about 200 to 500°K, the coverage determines whether penetration into the surface takes place. On the (111) plane, however, penetration of oxygen between the metal surface atoms probably takes place already at low coverages (section V). Doubtless, this is due to the very open structure of the (111) plane. The other low index crystallographic planes first display adsorption without penetration, after which sorption beyond a monolayer occurs. The two sorption processes can be distinguished by:

(i) the kinetics of sorption; the first monolayer is adsorbed fast, after which more oxygen is taken up in an activated process;

(ii) the heat of sorption, which decreases sharply after completion of the monolayer;

(iii) results of flash-desorption experiments; these show desorption of solely atomic oxygen to occur at low coverages; at higher coverages the desorption of atomic oxygen is accompanied by desorption of tungsten oxides;

(iv) the sharp decrease in the effect of oxygen sorption on the electrical conductance of sorbing metal specimens on completion of the monolayer;

(v) the onset of electron-induced desorption of oxygen only after adsorption of a certain amount of oxygen; the oxygen that can be released by electron bombardment desorbs upon heating of the adsorbent at 1000°K, whereas the oxygen adsorbed first desorbs at 1700°K only.

The mobility of the adatoms over rather large distances is evident from field-emission experiments. At low coverage, the adatoms can migrate over the stepped regions of a field-emission tip at temperatures above about 600°K. At lower temperatures and higher coverages, they are capable of migrating through the covered edges separating slabs of close-packed planes; this type of migration sets in at temperatures from 400 to 500°K. Differences in the mobility over edges with various structures can be explained very well by means of LEED results. Mobility of adatoms over short distances on closely packed planes can also be inferred from LEED experiments. In contrast with the opinion held previously, oxygen adatoms can migrate over short distances on close-packed planes at room temperature. This enables them to establish ordered structures on the close-packed planes. The

LEED experiments further demonstrated that adsorption into single-tons present in an ordered configuration on the surface proceeds slowly.

At temperatures above about 500°K, penetration of oxygen atoms into the metal surface goes faster and at lower coverages. The various crystallographic planes now differ in behaviour. If the metal surface atoms are rather narrowly spaced, penetration is accompanied by the chemisorption bond becoming more ionic. This is displayed less pronouncedly by the (211) plane, where the space between the rows of metal atoms is relatively large. As said above, the large interstices between the metal surface atoms of the (111) plane enable oxygen atoms to be accommodated in the surface already at about 300°K. Both work function and LEED data show the (110) plane to be penetrated only at large coverages. Penetration between the metal surface atoms of the (100) plane, which has larger interstices than the (110) plane, takes place at low coverages already. Both the amount adsorbed at low pressures as well as the electron-induced desorption rapidly increase when the temperature is raised above 500°K; this is also evidence for rapid penetration.

At still higher temperatures, faceting of the metal surfaces due to evaporation of tungsten and molybdenum oxides occurs. For the (111) plane, this is found already at 1000°K; a structure with (211) facets is obtained. The (211) and (100) planes show faceting at higher temperatures, viz. above 1300°K; in both cases (110) facets result. The (110) plane, on the other hand, does not show faceting on heating at high temperatures in oxygen.

To explain the large body of experimental evidence, we associated the oxygen first adsorbed with oxygen atoms multiple-bonded to one tungsten atom. At higher temperatures and higher coverages, where penetration into the surface occurs, the chemisorption bond becomes more ionic. The oxygen atoms are now bridge-bonded between two tungsten atoms. The ionic character is determined by the size of the interstices between the metal surface atoms; a smaller spacing leads to a more strongly ionic bond.

The reaction of molybdenum and tungsten surfaces with oxygen is governed by two factors, viz. the capacity to form multiple bonds with oxygen in a one-to-one ratio and the high intermetallic bonding energy. Multiple bonds with oxygen are also formed by metal atoms like vanadium, niobium, chromium, and iron. It is to be expected therefore that the first stage of the sorption process on these metals is analogous to that on molybdenum and tungsten. As can be concluded from the results of Pignocco and Pelissier (Pignocco and Pelissier,

1967), this has been confirmed for iron. Owing to the lower cohesion energy of the other metals, more drastic changes in the structure of the surface layer are liable to occur upon further interaction with oxygen. It has appeared that no marked growth of oxides on molybdenum and tungsten takes place at oxygen pressures below approximately 10^{-4} mm Hg.

X References

Abon, M. and Teichner, S. J. (1967). *Nuovo Cim.* Suppl. 5, 521.
Anderson, J. and Danforth, W. E. (1965). *J. Franklin Inst.* 279, 160.
Bauer, E. (1967). *Surf. Sci.* 7, 351.
Beebe, R. A., Beckwith, J. B. and Hanig, J. M. (1945). *J. Am. Chem. Soc.* 67, 1554.
Beeck, O. (1950). *Adv. Catalysis* 2, 151.
Bell, A. E., Swanson, L. W. and Crouser, L. C. (1968). *Surf. Sci.* 10, 254.
Benjamin, P., and Weaver, C. (1959). *Proc R. Soc.* A 252, 418.
Benjamin, P. and Weaver, C. (1961). *Proc R. Soc.* A 261, 516.
Benjamin, P. and Weaver, C. (1963). *Proc R. Soc.* A 274, 267.
de Boer, J. H. and Kraak, H. H. (1936). *Recl. Trav. chim. Pays-Bas Belg.* 55, 941.
de Boer, J. H. and Kraak, H. H. (1937). *Recl. Trav. chim. Pays-Bas Belg.* 56, 1103.
Brennan, D. and Graham, M. J. (1966). *Disc. Faraday Soc.* 41, 95.
Brennan, D., Hayward, D. O. and Trapnell, B. M. W. (1960). *Proc. R. Soc.* A 256, 81.
Brunauer, S. (1945). "The Adsorption of Gases and Vapors". Princeton University Press, Princeton, New Jersey.
Burshtein, R. Ch. and Shurmovskaya, N. (1964). *Surf. Sci.* 2, 210.
Chang, C. C. and Germer, L. H. (1967). *Surf. Sci.* 8, 115.
Davis, R. T., Dewitt, T. W. and Emmett, P. H. (1947). *Phys. colloid chem.* 51, 1276.
Degras, D. A. and Lecante, J. (1967). *Nuovo Cim.* Suppl. 5, 598.
Delchar, T. A. and Ehrlich, G. (1965). *J. chem. Phys.* 42, 2686.
Delchar, T. A. and Tompkins, F. C. (1967). *Proc. R. Soc.* A 300, 141.
Ehrlich, G. and Hudda, F. G. (1959). *J. chem. Phys.* 30, 493.
Ehrlich, G. (1961). *J. chem. Phys.* 34, 29.
Ehrlich, G. (1963). *Adv. Catalysis* 14, 225.
Engelmaier, W. and Stickney, R. E. (1968). *Surf. Sci.* 11, 370.
Fehlner, F. P. (1966a). *Nature, Lond.* 210, 1035.
Fehlner, F. P., (1966b). *Trans. 3rd Int. Vacuum Congr.* Vol. 2, p. 692. Pergamon Press, London.
Fehlner, F. P. (1967). *J. appl. Phys.* 38, 2223.
George, T. H. and Stier, P. M. (1962). *J. chem. Phys.* 37, 1935.
Germer, L. H. and May, J. W. (1966). *Surf. Sci.* 4, 452.
Geus, J. W. (1967). *Ingenieur s'Grav.* 79, 41.
Geus, J. W., Koks, H. L. T. and Zwietering, P. (1963). *J. Catalysis* 2, 274.
Gomer, R. and Hulm, J. K. (1957). *J. chem. Phys.* 27, 1363.
Gorter, C. J. (1951). *Physica A'dam* 17, 777.
Gregg, S. J. and Sing, K. S. W. (1967). "Adsorption Surface Area and Porosity". Academic Press, New York and London.
Haas, T. W. and Jackson, A. G. (1966). *J. chem. Phys.* 44, 2921.

Hagstrum, H. D., Takeishi, Y., Becker, G. E. and Pretzer, D. D. (1964). *Surf. Sci.* **2**, 26.

Hagstrum, H. D. (1966). *Phys. Rev.* **150**, 495.

Hansen, N. and Littmann, W. (1963). *Ber. Bunsenges. Physik. Chem.* **67**, 970.

Hartman, T. E. (1963). *J. appl. Phys.* **34**, 4, 943.

Haul, R. A. W. (1956). *Angew. Chem.* **68**, 238.

Hayek, K., Farnsworth, H. E. and Park, R. L. (1968). *Surf. Sci.* **10**, 429.

Hayward, D. O., Herley, P. J. and Tompkins, F. C. (1964). *Surf. Sci.* **2**, 156.

Herman, D. S. and Rhodin, T. N. (1966). *J. appl. Phys.* **37**, 4, 1594.

Hopkins, B. J. and Pender, K. R. (1966). *Surf. Sci.* **5**, 155.

Knor, Z. and Ponec, V. (1961). *Colln Czech. chem. Commun.* **26**, 961.

Lander, J. J. (1964). *Surf. Sci.* **1**, 125.

Lanyon, M. A. H. and Trapnell, B. M. W. (1954). *Proc. R. Soc.* **A 227**, 387.

Lichtman, D. and Kirst, T. R. (1966). *Physics Letters* **20**, 7.

MacRae, A. U. (1963). *Science, N.Y.* **139**, 379.

MacRae, A. U. (1964). *Surf. Sci.* **1**, 319.

Madey, T. E. and Yates, J. T., Jr. (1968). *Surf. Sci.* **11**, 327.

Mayer, H. (1955). "Physik dünner Schichten", Vol. II. Wissenschaftliche Verlagsgesellschaft, Stuttgart.

McCarroll, B. (1967a). *J. chem. Phys.* **46**, 863.

McCarroll, B. (1967b). *Surf. Sci.* **7**, 499.

Menzel, D. and Gomer, R. (1964a). *J. chem. Phys.* **40**, 1164.

Menzel, D. and Gomer, R. (1964b) *J. chem. Phys.* **41**, 3311.

Mignolet, J. C. P. (1955). *Recl. Trav. chim.* **74**, 685.

Minn, S. (1960). *J. Rech. Cent. natn. Rech. scient.* **51**, 131.

Minn, S. and Vodar, B. (1961). *In* "Electric and Magnetic Properties of Thin Metallic Layers" (L. van Gerven, ed.), p. 357. Koninklijke Vlaamse Academie, Brussels.

Morrison, J. L. and Roberts, J. K. (1939). *Proc. R. Soc.* **A 173**, 1.

Neugebauer, C. A. and Webb, M. B. (1962). *J. appl. Phys.* **33**, 174.

Nieuwenhuizen, J. M. and Haanstra, H. B. (1965/66). *Philips tech. Rev.* **27**, 115.

Pashley, D. W. (1965). *Adv. Phys.* **14**, 327.

Pashley, D. W., Stowell, M. J., Jacobs, M. H. and Law, J. T. (1964). *Phil. Mag.* **10**, 127.

Pignocco, A. J. and Pelissier, G. E. (1967). *Surf. Sci.* **7**, 261.

Ptushinskii, Yu. G. and Chuikov, B. A. (1967a). *Surf. Sci.* **6**, 42.

Ptushinskii, Yu. G. and Chuikov, B. A. (1967b). *Surf. Sci.* **7**, 507.

Ptushinskii, Yu. G. and Chuikov, B. A. (1968). *Fizika tverd. Tela* **10**, 795.

Quinn, C. M. and Roberts, M. W. (1964). *Trans. Faraday Soc.* **60**, 899.

Redhead, P. A. (1964). *Can. J. Phys.* **42**, 886.

Redhead, P. A. (1967). *Nuovo Cim.* Suppl. **5**, 586.

Roberts, J. K. (1935a). *Proc. R. Soc.* **A 152**, 464.

Roberts, J. K. (1935b). *Proc. R. Soc.* **A 152**, 445.

Roberts, J. K. (1939). "Some Problems on Adsorption". Cambridge University Press, Cambridge.

Roberts, M. W. and Wells, B. R. (1966). *Trans. Faraday Soc.* **62**, 1608.

Singleton, J. H. (1967). *J. chem. Phys.* **47**, 73.

van Steensel, K. (1967). *Philips Res. Rep.* **22**, 246.

Taylor, N. J. (1964). *Surf. Sci.* **2**, 544.

Trapnell, B. M. W. (1953). *Proc. R. Soc.* **A 218**, 566.

Weaver, C. (1965). *Chemy Ind.* 370.

Winter, H. F., Horne, D. E. and Donaldson, E. E. (1964). *J. chem. Phys.* **41**, 2766.

Wolock, J. and Harris, B. L. (1950). *Ind. Engng Chem.* **42**, 1347.

Yates, J. T., Jr., Madey, T. E. and Payn, J. K. (1967). *Nuovo Cim.* Suppl. **5**, 558.

AUTHOR INDEX

A

Aben, P. C., 472, *524*
Abon, M., 570, *626*
Abram, J. C., 431, 436, *467*
Adam, N. K., 36, *59*
Adams, C. R., 182, *209*, 240, 248, *262*, *264*
Adamson, A. W., 29, *59*, 137, *143*
Ahrland, S., 375, 376, *423*
Akshinskaya, N. V., 246, 248, *262*
Albright, L. F., 518, *525*
Aldcroft, D., 178, 195, *208*
Alder, B. J., 65, 68, 80, 95, 97, 104, *143*
Alexander, G. B., 219, 242, *263*
Alexander, L. E., 490, 491, 498, *524*, *525*
Allen, R. R., 518, *524*
Alsop, B. C., 313, *314*
American Oil Chemists' Society, 517, *524*
Anderson, J., 565, 602, 617, *626*
Anderson, P. J., 301, *314*
Anderson, R. B., 444, 457, *467*
Andreev, A. A., 158, *168*
Aragon de la Cruz, F., 465, *467*
Aristov, B. G., 113, *143*
Arkharov, V. J., 492, *524*
Avgul, N. N., 120, 123, 127, 140, *143*, 440, *467*

B

Bagdasarov, K. N., 352, *371*
Bagg, J., 473, *524*
Baker, M. McD., 494, 495, *524*
Balyaeva, V. K., 321, 322, 323, 326, 327, 330, 331, *371*
Bangham, D. H., 64, *143*
Baraké, N., 248, *263*
Barker, J. A., 80, 87, 92, 102, 136, 140, *143*
Barrer, R. M., 15, *59*, 426, *467*
Barrett, E. P., 14, 15, 28, *59*, 276, *314*, 510, *524*

25*

Bartell, F. E., 213, *263*
Basolo, F., 363, *371*
Bastick, J., 251, 252, *263*
Bastick, M., 452, *469*
Bauer, E., 566, 613, *626*
Bauer, O. J., 195, *210*
Bauer, S. H., 485, *526*
Baumann, H., 219, *263*
Bavarez, M., 251, 252, *263*
Bayer, J., 444, *467*
Beard, E. H., 178, *211*
Bearman, R. J., 80, *145*
Becker, G. E., 594, *627*
Beckwith, J. B., 534, *626*
Beebe, R. A., 534, *626*
Beeck, O., 153, *168*, 495, *524*, 538, *626*
Beletskii, M. S., 472, *526*
Bell, A. E., 559, 562, 563, 564, 568, 569, 596, 603, 609, 618, *626*
Bellemans, A., 35, *60*
Benes, L., 178, *208*
Benesi, H. A., 204, *208*
Benjamin, P., 571, *626*
Bennett, M. C., 431, 436, *467*
Benson, S. W., 153, *168*
Beretka, J., 188, 195, *208*
Berger, A., 474, 485, *525*
Beyer, H., 233, *264*
Bezjak, A., 177, 182, *208*
Beznogova, V. E., 246, 248, *262*
Bijvoet, J. M., 476, *525*
Bird, R. B., 80, 87, 92, 102, *145*
Bizette, H., 474, *524*
Blom, L., 459, 461, *467*
Blue, R. W., 166, *168*
Blumenthal, W. B., 316, 320, 352, *371*
Bochkarev, G. S., 352, *372*
Bodor, E. E., 12, *60*
Boehm, H. P., 426, 457, 459, 460, 463, 464, 465, *467*, *469*
Boekschoten, H. J. C., 419, *423*
Boerma, H., 34, *60*, 514, 517, 523, *525*
Bohra, J. N., 15, *61*

SUBJECT INDEX

A

Acceleration factor, 150
Accessible area, 131
Accommodation coefficient, mean, on tungsten, 537, 596
Activated sorption of oxygen by tungsten and molybdenum, 535, 536, 582, 585
Active magnesia
  active sites, 309
  activity, 302
  catalytic activity in isopropanol decomposition, 305
  dehydration activity, 311
  dehydrogenation activity, 307
  density of solid material, 270
  generators, 267
  mean pore radius, 276, 294
  prepared from magnesite, 268
  prepared from nesquehonite, 284
  pore shape, 298
  pore size distribution, 298
  pore volume, 271
    distribution, 276
    intercrystalline, 271
    intracrystalline, 271
  selectivity in isopropanol decomposition, 305, 307
  surface areas, 274
    maximum, 274
  test reaction for, 305
  texture, 271, 300, 302
  X-ray diffraction, 269
Active solids
  preparation by calcination, 267
  preparation of, 266
  pore genesis in, 271
Adsorbed layer
  density, 23
  equilibrium thickness, 49, 50, 56
  formal thickness, 49, 57
  on spheroidal particles, 44, 45, 46, 49
  stability of, 11, 45

  statistical thickness, 23, 31
  thickness, 50
  thickness on curved surfaces, 44, 49
Adsorbents
  pore systems in, 1–62
  silica, 214
Adsorption
  endothermic, xviii
  entropy of, 155
  equations, 71
  heat of, see Heat of adsorption
  immobile, 65, 149, 152
  immobile dissociative, of nitrogen, 159
  in spheroidal cavities, 37–39
  localized, 65, 73, 99, 127
  mobile, xvii, 65, 127, 152, 155, 159
  multilayer, 12, 32
  multimolecular, 21, 23, 34
    thickness of, 33
  of ammonia on alumina, 205
  of electrolytes on carbon, 428, 457
  of helium on carbon, 452
  of hydrogen on alumina, 203
  of hydrogen on nickel, 494–496, 498, 500, 501
  of krypton on inorganic halides, 129
  of lauric acid in active alumina, 201, 202
  of N_2O_4 on silica, 150
  of nitrogen on alumina, 195
  of nitrogen on nickel, 153
  of surfactants on carbon, 436
  of water by carbons, 437
  of xenon on coals and carbons, 443
  on active carbon, 148
  physical, 153, see also Physisorption
  Polanyi's potential theory of, 9
  pre-dissociative, 159
  thermodynamic analysis, 148
  time of, 21
  van der Waals, xix
Adsorption data, interpretation, 112